MATH 1100
Teacher's Guide

D1085926

Author:

Alpha Omega Publications

Editor:

Alan Christopherson, M.S.

804 N. 2nd Ave. E.
Rock Rapids, IA 51246-1759

© MM by Alpha Omega Publications, Inc. All rights reserved.
LIFEPAC is a registered trademark of Alpha Omega Publications, Inc.

All trademarks and/or service marks referenced in this material are the property of their respective owners.
Alpha Omega Publications, Inc. makes no claim of ownership to any trademarks and/or service marks other
than their own and their affiliates, and makes no claim of affiliation to any companies whose trademarks
may be listed in this material, other than their own.

MATH 1100

LIFEPAC® Overview

MATH SCOPE & SEQUENCE

KINDERGARTEN

Lessons 1–40	Lessons 41–80	Lessons 81–120	Lessons 121–160
Directions – right, left, high, low, etc.	**Directions** – right, left, high, low, etc.	**Directions** – right, left, high, low, etc.	**Directions** – right, left, high, low, etc.
Comparisons – big, little, alike, different	**Comparisons** – big, little, alike, different	**Comparisons** – big, little, alike, different	**Comparisons** – big, little, alike, different
Matching	**Matching**	**Matching**	**Matching**
Cardinal Numbers – to 9	**Cardinal Numbers** – to 12	**Cardinal Numbers** – to 19	**Cardinal Numbers** – to 100
Colors – red, blue, green, yellow, brown, purple	**Colors** – orange	**Colors** – black, white	**Colors** – pink
Shapes – circle, square, rectangle, triangle	**Shapes** – circle, square, rectangle, triangle	**Shapes** – circle, square, rectangle, triangle	**Shapes** – circle, square, rectangle, triangle
Number Order	**Number Order**	**Number Order**	**Number Order**
Before and After	**Before and After**	**Before and After**	**Before and After**
Ordinal Numbers – to 9th	**Ordinal Numbers** – to 9th	**Ordinal Numbers** – to 9th	**Ordinal Numbers** – to 9th
Problem Solving	**Problem Solving**	**Problem Solving**	**Problem Solving**
	Number Words – to nine	**Number Words** – to nine	**Number Words** – to nine
	Addition – to 9	**Addition** – multiples of 10	**Addition** – to 10 and multiples of 10
		Subtraction – to 9	**Subtraction** – to 10
		Place Value	**Place Value**
		Time/Calendar	**Time/Calendar**
			Money
			Skip Counting – 2s, 5s, 10s
			Greater/Less Than

MATH SCOPE & SEQUENCE

	Grade 1	Grade 2	Grade 3
UNIT 1	**NUMBER ORDER, ADD/SUBTRACT** • Number order, skip count • Add, subtract to 9 • Story problems • Measurements • Shapes	**NUMBERS AND WORDS TO 100** • Numbers and words to 100 • Operation symbols: +, –, =, >, < • Add and subtract • Place value and fact families • Story problems	**ADD/SUB TO 18 AND PLACE VALUE** • Digits, place value to 999 • Add and subtract • Linear measurements • Operation symbols: +, –, =, ≠, >, < • Time
UNIT 2	**ADD/SUBTRACT TO 10, SHAPES** • Add, subtract to 10 • Number words • Place value • Patterns, sequencing, estimation • Shapes	**ADD/SUBTRACT AND EVEN/ODD** • Numbers and words to 200 • Add, subtract, even and odd • Skip count 2s, 5s, and 10s • Ordinal numbers, fractions, and money • Shapes	**CARRYING AND BORROWING** • Fact families, patterns, and fractions • Add and subtract with carrying and borrowing • Skip count 2s, 5s, 10s • Money, shapes, lines • Even and odd
UNIT 3	**FRACTIONS, TIME, AND SYMBOLS** • Number sentences • Fractions • Story problems • Time and the = symbol • Oral directions	**ADD WITH CARRYING TO THE 10'S PLACE** • Add with carrying to the 10's place • Subtract • Flat shapes, money, A.M./P.M. • Rounding to the 10's place • Standard measurements	**FACTS OF ADD/SUB AND FRACTIONS** • Add 3 numbers w/ carrying • Coins, weight, volume, A.M./P.M. • Fractions • Skip count 3s, subtract w/ borrowing • Oral instructions
UNIT 4	**ADD TO 18, MONEY, MEASUREMENT** • Add to 18 • Skip count, even and odd • Money • Shapes and measurement • Place value	**NUMBERS/WORDS TO 999, AND GRAPHS** • Numbers and words to 999 • Addition, subtraction, and place value • Calendar • Measurements and solid shapes • Making change	**ROUND, ESTIMATE, STORY PROBLEMS** • Place value to 9,999 • Rounding to the 10's and estimating • Add and subtract fractions • Roman numerals • 1/4 inch
UNIT 5	**COLUMN ADDITION AND ESTIMATION** • Add three 1-digit numbers • Ordinal numbers • Time and number lines • Estimation and charts • Fractions	**ADD/SUBTRACT TO THE 100'S PLACE** • Data and bar graphs and shapes • Add and subtract to the 100's place • Skip count 3s and place value to the 100's • Add fractions • Temperature	**PLANE SHAPES AND SYMMETRY** • Number sentences • Rounding to the 100's and estimation • Perimeter and square inch • Bar graph, symmetry, and even/odd rules • Temperature
UNIT 6	**NUMBER WORDS TO 99** • Number words to 99 • Add two 2-digit numbers • Symbols: > and < • Fractions • Shapes	**SUBTRACT WITH BORROWING FROM 10'S** • Measurements • Time and money • Subtract w/ borrowing from the 10's place • Add and subtract fractions • Perimeter	**MULTIPLICATION, LINES, AND ANGLES** • Add and subtract to 9,999 • Multiples and multiplication facts for 2 • Area and equivalent fractions • Line graphs, segments, and angles • Money
UNIT 7	**COUNT TO 200, SUBTRACT TO 12** • Number order and place value • Subtract to 12 • Operation signs • Estimation and time • Graphs	**ADD WITH CARRYING TO THE 100'S PLACE** • Add with carrying to the 100's place • Fractions as words • Number order in books • Rounding and estimation	**ADD/SUB MIXED NUMBERS, PROBABILITY** • Multiplication facts for 5 and missing numbers • Add and subtract mixed numbers • Subtract with 0s in the minuend • Circle graphs • Probability
UNIT 8	**ADD/SUBTRACT TO 18** • Addition, subtract to 18 • Group counting • Fractions • Time and measurements • Shapes	**VOLUME AND COIN CONVERSION** • Addition, subtraction, and measurements • Group counting and "thinking" answers • Convert coins • Directions – North, South, East, and West • Length and width	**MEASUREMENTS AND MULTIPLICATION** • Multiplication facts for 3 & 10, multiples of 4 • Convert units of measurement • Decimals and directions • Picture graphs and missing addends • Length and width
UNIT 9	**SENSIBLE ANSWERS** • Fact families • Sensible answers • Subtract 2-digit numbers • Add three 2-digit numbers	**AREA AND SQUARE MEASUREMENT** • Area and square measurement • Add three 2-digit numbers with carrying • Add coins and convert to cents • Fractions and quarter-inches	**MULT, METRICS, AND PERIMETER** • Add and subtract whole numbers, fractions, and mixed numbers • Standard measurements and metrics • Operation symbols • Multiplication facts for 4
UNIT 10	**REVIEW** • Addition, subtraction, and place value • Directions – North, South, East, and West • Fractions • Patterns	**REVIEW** • Rules for even and odd numbers • Round numbers to the 100's place • Digital clocks and sensible answers • Add three 3-digit numbers	**PROBABILITY, UNITS, AND SHAPES** • Addition and subtraction • Rounding to the 1,000's place and estimating • Probability, equations, and parentheses • Perimeter and area • Multiplication facts for 2, 3, 4, 5, and 10

MATH SCOPE & SEQUENCE

Grade 4	Grade 5	Grade 6	
WHOLE NUMBERS AND FRACTIONS • Naming whole numbers • Naming fractions • Sequencing patterns • Numbers to 1,000	**PLACE VALUE, ADDITION, AND SUBTRACTION** • Place value • Rounding and estimating • Addition • Subtraction	**WHOLE NUMBERS AND ALGEBRA** • Whole numbers and their properties • Operations and number patterns • Algebra	UNIT 1
MULTIPLYING WHOLE NUMBERS • Operation symbols • Multiplication — 1-digit multipliers • Addition and subtraction of fractions • Numbers to 10,000	**MULTIPLYING WHOLE NUMBERS AND DECIMALS** • Multiplying whole numbers • Powers • Multiplying decimals	**DATA ANALYSIS** • Collecting and describing data • Organizing data • Displaying and interpreting data	UNIT 2
SEQUENCING AND ROUNDING • Multiplication with carrying • Rounding and estimation • Sequencing fractions • Numbers to 100,000	**DIVIDING WHOLE NUMBERS AND DECIMALS** • One-digit divisors • Two-digit divisors • Decimal division	**DECIMALS** • Decimal numbers • Multiplying and dividing decimal numbers • The metric system	UNIT 3
LINES AND SHAPES • Plane and solid shapes • Lines and line segments • Addition and subtraction • Multiplication with carrying	**ALGEBRA AND GRAPHING** • Expressions • Functions • Equations • Graphing	**FRACTIONS** • Factors and fractions • The LCM and fractions • Decimals and fractions	UNIT 4
DIVISION AND MEASUREMENTS • Division – 1-digit divisor • Families of facts • Standard measurements • Number grouping	**MEASUREMENT** • The metric system • The customary system • Time • Temperature	**FRACTION OPERATIONS** • Adding and subtracting fractions • Multiplying and dividing fractions • The customary system	UNIT 5
DIVISION, FACTORS, AND FRACTIONS • Division — 1-digit divisors with remainders • Factors and multiples • Improper and mixed fractions • Equivalent fractions	**FACTORS AND FRACTIONS** • Factors • Equivalent fractions • Fractions	**RATIO, PROPORTION, AND PERCENT** • Ratios • Proportions • Percent	UNIT 6
WHOLE NUMBERS AND FRACTIONS • Multiplication — 2-digit multipliers • Simplifying fractions • Averages • Decimals in money problems • Equations	**FRACTION OPERATIONS** • Like denominators • Unlike denominators • Multiplying fractions • Dividing fractions	**PROBABILITY AND GEOMETRY** • Probability • Geometry: Angles • Geometry: Polygons	UNIT 7
WHOLE NUMBERS AND FRACTIONS • Division — 1-digit divisors • Fractions and unlike denominators • Metric units • Whole numbers: +, −, x, ÷	**DATA ANALYSIS AND PROBABILITY** • Collecting data • Analyzing data • Displaying data • Probability	**GEOMETRY AND MEASUREMENT** • Plane figures • Solid figures	UNIT 8
DECIMALS AND FRACTIONS • Reading and writing decimals • Adding and subtracting mixed numbers • Cross multiplication • Estimation	**GEOMETRY** • Geometry • Classifying plane figures • Classifying solid figures • Transformations • Symmetry	**INTEGERS AND TRANSFORMATIONS** • Integers • Integer operations • Transformations	UNIT 9
ESTIMATION, CHARTS, AND GRAPHS • Estimation and data gathering • Charts and graphs • Review numbers to 100,000 • Whole numbers: +, −, x, ÷	**PERIMETER, AREA, AND VOLUME** • Perimeter • Area • Surface area • Volume	**EQUATIONS AND FUNCTIONS** • Equations • More equations and inequalities • Functions	UNIT 10

MATH SCOPE & SEQUENCE

	Grade 7	Grade 8	Grade 9
UNIT 1	**INTEGERS** • Adding and Subtracting Integers • Multiplying and Dividing Integers • The Real Number System	**THE REAL NUMBER SYSTEM** • Relationships • Other Forms • Simplifying	**VARIABLES AND NUMBERS** • Variables • Distributive Property • Definition of signed numbers • Signed number operations
UNIT 2	**FRACTIONS** • Working with Fractions • Adding and Subtracting Fractions • Multiplying and Dividing Fractions	**MODELING PROBLEMS IN INTEGERS** • Equations with Real Numbers • Functions • Integers • Modeling with Integers	**SOLVING EQUATIONS** • Sentences and formulas • Properties • Solving equations • Solving inequalities
UNIT 3	**DECIMALS** • Decimals and Their Operations • Applying Decimals • Scientific Notation • The Metric System	**MODELING PROBLEMS WITH RATIONAL NUMBERS** • Number Theory • Solving Problems with Rational Numbers • Solving Equations and Inequalities	**PROBLEM ANALYSIS AND SOLUTION** • Words and symbols • Simple verbal problems • Medium verbal problems • Challenging verbal problems
UNIT 4	**PATTERNS AND EQUATIONS** • Variable Expressions • Patterns and Functions • Solving Equations • Equations and Inequalities	**PROPORTIONAL REASONING** • Proportions • Percents • Measurement/Similar Figures	**POLYNOMIALS** • Addition of polynomials • Subtraction of polynomials • Multiplication of polynomials • Division of polynomials
UNIT 5	**RATIOS AND PROPORTIONS** • Ratios, Rates, and Proportions • Using Proportions • Fractions, Decimals, and Percents	**MORE WITH FUNCTIONS** • Solving Equations • Families of Functions • Patterns	**ALGEBRAIC FACTORS** • Greatest common factor • Binomial factors • Complete factorization • Word problems
UNIT 6	**PROBABILITY AND GRAPHING** • Probability • Functions • Graphing Linear Equations • Direct Variation	**MEASUREMENT** • Angle Measures and Circles • Polygons • Indirect Measure	**ALGEBRAIC FRACTIONS** • Operations with fractions • Solving equations • Solving inequalities • Solving word problems
UNIT 7	**DATA ANALYSIS** • Describing Data • Organizing Data • Graphing Data and Making Predictions	**PLANE GEOMETRY** • Perimeter and Area • Symmetry and Reflections • Other Transformations	**RADICAL EXPRESSIONS** • Rational and irrational numbers • Operations with radicals • Irrational roots • Radical equations
UNIT 8	**GEOMETRY** • Basic Geometry • Classifying Polygons • Transformations	**MEASURE OF SOLID FIGURES** • Surface Area • Solid Figures • Volume • Volume of Composite Figures	**GRAPHING** • Equations of two variables • Graphing lines • Graphing inequalities • Equations of lines
UNIT 9	**MEASUREMENT AND AREA** • Perimeter • Area • The Pythagorean Theorem	**DATA ANALYSIS** • Collecting and Representing Data • Central Tendency and Dispersion • Frequency and Histograms • Box–and–Whisker Plots • Scatter Plots	**SYSTEMS** • Graphical solution • Algebraic solutions • Determinants • Word problems
UNIT 10	**SURFACE AREA AND VOLUME** • Solids • Prisms • Cylinders	**PROBABILITY** • Outcomes • Permutations and Combinations • Probability and Odds • Independent and Dependent Events	**QUADRATIC EQUATIONS AND REVIEW** • Solving quadratic equations • Equations and inequalities • Polynomials and factors • Radicals and graphing

MATH SCOPE & SEQUENCE

Grade 10	Grade 11	Grade 12	
A MATHEMATICAL SYSTEM • Points, lines, and planes • Definition of definitions • Geometric terms • Postulates and theorems	**SETS, STRUCTURE, AND FUNCTION** • Properties and operations of sets • Axioms and applications • Relations and functions • Algebraic expressions	**RELATIONS AND FUNCTIONS** • Relations and functions • Rules of correspondence • Notation of functions • Types of functions	UNIT 1
PROOFS • Logic • Reasoning • Two-column proof • Paragraph proof	**NUMBERS, SENTENCES, & PROBLEMS** • Order and absolute value • Sums and products • Algebraic sentences • Number and motion problems	**SPECIAL FUNCTIONS** • Linear functions • Second-degree functions • Polynomial functions • Other functions	UNIT 2
ANGLES AND PARALLELS • Definitions and measurement • Relationships and theorems • Properties of parallels • Parallels and polygons	**LINEAR EQUATIONS & INEQUALITIES** • Graphs • Equations • Systems of equations • Inequalities	**TRIGONOMETRIC FUNCTIONS** • Definition • Equation of functions • Trigonometric tables • Special angles	UNIT 3
CONGRUENCY • Congruent triangles • Corresponding parts • Inequalities • Quadrilaterals	**POLYNOMIALS** • Multiplying polynomials • Factoring • Operations with polynomials • Variations	**CIRCULAR FUNCTIONS & GRAPHS** • Circular functions & special angles • Graphs of sine and cosine • Amplitude and period • Phase shifts	UNIT 4
SIMILAR POLYGONS • Ratios and proportions • Definition of similarity • Similar polygons and triangles • Right triangle geometry	**RADICAL EXPRESSIONS** • Multiplying and dividing fractions • Adding and subtracting fractions • Equations with fractions • Applications of fractions	**IDENTITIES AND FUNCTIONS** • Reciprocal relations • Pythagorean relations • Trigonometric identities • Sum and difference formulas	UNIT 5
CIRCLES • Circles and spheres • Tangents, arcs, and chords • Special angles in circles • Special segments in circles	**REAL NUMBERS** • Rational and irrational numbers • Laws of Radicals • Quadratic equations • Quadratic formula	**TRIGONOMETRIC FUNCTIONS** • Trigonometric functions • Law of cosines • Law of sines • Applied problems	UNIT 6
CONSTRUCTION AND LOCUS • Basic constructions • Triangles and circles • Polygons • Locus meaning and use	**QUADRATIC RELATIONS & SYSTEMS** • Distance formulas • Conic sections • Systems of equations • Application of conic sections	**INVERSE TRIGONOMETRIC FUNCTIONS** • Inverse functions • Graphing polar coordinates • Converting polar coordinates • Graphing polar equations	UNIT 7
AREA AND VOLUME • Area of polygons • Area of circles • Surface area of solids • Volume of solids	**EXPONENTIAL FUNCTIONS** • Exponents • Exponential equations • Logarithmic functions • Matrices	**QUADRATIC EQUATIONS** • Conic sections • Circle and ellipse • Parabola and hyperbola • Transformations	UNIT 8
COORDINATE GEOMETRY • Ordered pairs • Distance • Lines • Coordinate proofs	**COUNTING PRINCIPLES** • Progressions • Permutations • Combinations • Probability	**PROBABILITY** • Random experiments & probability • Permutations • Combinations • Applied problems	UNIT 9
REVIEW • Proof and angles • Polygons and circles • Construction and measurement • Coordinate geometry	**REVIEW** • Integers and open sentences • Graphs and polynomials • Fractions and quadratics • Exponential functions	**CALCULUS** • Mathematical induction • Functions and limits • Slopes of functions • Review	UNIT 10

STRUCTURE OF THE LIFEPAC CURRICULUM

The LIFEPAC curriculum is conveniently structured to provide one Teacher's Guide containing teacher support material with answer keys and ten student worktexts for each subject at grade levels two through twelve. The worktext format of the LIFEPACs allows the student to read the textual information and complete workbook activities all in the same booklet. The easy-to-follow LIFEPAC numbering system lists the grade as the first number(s) and the last two digits as the number of the series. For example, the Language Arts LIFEPAC at the 6th grade level, 5th book in the series would be LAN0605.

Each LIFEPAC is divided into three to five sections and begins with an introduction or overview of the booklet as well as a series of specific learning objectives to give a purpose to the study of the LIFEPAC. The introduction and objectives are followed by a vocabulary section which may be found at the beginning of each section at the lower levels, at the beginning of the LIFEPAC in the middle grades, or in the glossary at the high school level. Vocabulary words are used to develop word recognition and should not be confused with the spelling words introduced later in the LIFEPAC. The student should learn all vocabulary words before working the LIFEPAC sections to improve comprehension, retention, and reading skills.

Each activity or written assignment in grades 2 through 12 has a number for easy identification, such as 1.1. The first number corresponds to the LIFEPAC section and the number to the right of the decimal is the number of the activity.

Teacher checkpoints, which are essential to maintain quality learning, are found at various locations throughout the LIFEPAC. The teacher should check 1) neatness of work and penmanship, 2) quality of understanding (tested with a short oral quiz), 3) thoroughness of answers (complete sentences and paragraphs, correct spelling, etc.), 4) completion of activities (no blank spaces), and 5) accuracy of answers as compared to the answer key (all answers correct).

The self test questions in grades 2 through 12 are also number-coded for easy reference. For example, 2.015 means that this is the 15th question in the self test of Section 2. The first number corresponds to the LIFEPAC section, the zero indicates that it is a self test question, and the number to the right of the zero the question number.

The LIFEPAC test is packaged at the center of each LIFEPAC. It should be removed and put aside before giving the booklet to the student for study.

Answer and test keys in grades 2 through 12 have the same numbering system as the LIFEPACs. The student may be given access to the answer keys (not the test keys) under teacher supervision so that he can score his own work.

A thorough study of the Scope & Sequence by the teacher before instruction begins is essential to the success of the student. The teacher should become familiar with expected skill mastery and understand how these grade level skills fit into the overall skill development of the curriculum. The teacher should also preview the objectives that appear at the beginning of each LIFEPAC for additional preparation and planning.

TEST SCORING AND GRADING

Answer keys and test keys give examples of correct answers. They convey the idea, but the student may use many ways to express a correct answer. The teacher should check for the essence of the answer, not for the exact wording. Many questions are high level and require thinking and creativity on the part of the student. Each answer should be scored based on whether or not the main idea written by the student matches the model example. "Any Order" or "Either Order" in a key indicates that no particular order is necessary to be correct.

Most self tests and LIFEPAC tests at the lower elementary levels are scored at 1 point per answer; however, the upper levels may have a point system awarding 2 to 5 points for various answers or questions. Further, the total test points will vary; they may not always equal 100 points. They may be 78, 85, 100, 105, etc.

Example 1

Example 2

A score box similar to ex. 1 above is located at the end of each self test and on the front of the LIFEPAC test. The bottom score, 72, represents the total number of points possible on the test. The upper score, 58, represents the number of points your student will need to receive an 80% or passing grade. If you wish to establish the exact percentage that your student has achieved, find the total points of his correct answers and divide it by the bottom number (in this case 72). For example, if your student has a point total of 65, divide 65 by 72 for a grade of 90%. Referring to ex. 2, on a test with a total of 105 possible points, the student would have to receive a minimum of 84 correct points for an 80% or passing grade. If your student has received 93 points, simply divide the 93 by 105 for a percentage grade of 89%. Students who receive a score below 80% should review the LIFEPAC and retest using the appropriate Alternate Test found in the Teacher's Guide.

The following is a guideline to assign letter grades for completed LIFEPACs based on a maximum total score of 100 points.

Example:

LIFEPAC Test	=	60% of the Total Score (or percent grade)
Self Test	=	25% of the Total Score (average percent of self tests)
Reports	=	10% or 10* points per LIFEPAC
Oral Work	=	5% or 5* points per LIFEPAC

*Determined by the teacher's subjective evaluation of the student's daily work.

Example:

LIFEPAC Test Score	=	92%	92 × .60	=	55 points
Self Test Average	=	90%	90 × .25	=	23 points
Reports				=	8 points
Oral Work				=	4 points
TOTAL POINTS				=	90 points

Grade Scale based on point system:

100 – 94	=	A
93 – 86	=	B
85 – 77	=	C
76 – 70	=	D
Below 70	=	F

TEACHER HINTS AND STUDYING TECHNIQUES

LIFEPAC activities are written to check the level of understanding of the preceding text. The student may look back to the text as necessary to complete these activities; however, a student should never attempt to do the activities without reading (studying) the text first. Self tests and LIFEPAC tests are never open book tests.

Language arts activities (skill integration) often appear within other subject curriculum. The purpose is to give the student an opportunity to test his skill mastery outside of the context in which it was presented.

Writing complete answers (paragraphs) to some questions is an integral part of the LIFEPAC curriculum in all subjects. This builds communication and organization skills, increases understanding and retention of ideas, and helps enforce good penmanship. Complete sentences should be encouraged for this type of activity. Obviously, single words or phrases do not meet the intent of the activity, since multiple lines are given for the response.

Review is essential to student success. Time invested in review where review is suggested will be time saved in correcting errors later. Self tests, unlike the section activities, are closed book. This procedure helps to identify weaknesses before they become too great to overcome. Certain objectives from self tests are cumulative and test previous sections; therefore, good preparation for a self test must include all material studied up to that testing point.

The following procedure checklist has been found to be successful in developing good study habits in the LIFEPAC curriculum.

1. Read the introduction and Table of Contents.
2. Read the objectives.
3. Recite and study the entire vocabulary (glossary) list.
4. Study each section as follows:
   a. Read the introduction and study the section objectives.
   b. Read all the text for the entire section, but answer none of the activities.
   c. Return to the beginning of the section and memorize each vocabulary word and definition.
   d. Reread the section, complete the activities, check the answers with the answer key, correct all errors, and have the teacher check.
   e. Read the self test but do not answer the questions.
   f. Go to the beginning of the first section and reread the text and answers to the activities up to the self test you have not yet done.
   g. Answer the questions to the self test without looking back.
   h. Have the self test checked by the teacher.
   i. Correct the self test and have the teacher check the corrections.
   j. Repeat steps a–i for each section.
5. Use the **SQ3R** method to prepare for the LIFEPAC test.
   > **S**can the whole LIFEPAC.
   > **Q**uestion yourself on the objectives.
   > **R**ead the whole LIFEPAC again.
   > **R**ecite through an oral examination.
   > **R**eview weak areas.
6. Take the LIFEPAC test as a closed book test.
7. LIFEPAC tests are administered and scored under direct teacher supervision. Students who receive scores below 80% should review the LIFEPAC using the **SQ3R** study method and take the Alternate Test located in the Teacher's Guide. The final test grade may be the grade on the Alternate Test or an average of the grades from the original LIFEPAC test and the Alternate Test.

GOAL SETTING AND SCHEDULES

Each school must develop its own schedule, because no single set of procedures will fit every situation. The following is an example of a daily schedule that includes the five LIFE-PAC subjects as well as time slotted for special activities.

Possible Daily Schedule

8:15 – 8:25	Pledges, prayer, songs, devotions, etc.
8:25 – 9:10	Bible
9:10 – 9:55	Language Arts
9:55 – 10:15	Recess (juice break)
10:15 – 11:00	Math
11:00 – 11:45	History & Geography
11:45 – 12:30	Lunch, recess, quiet time
12:30 – 1:15	Science
1:15 –	Drill, remedial work, enrichment*

*Enrichment: Computer time, physical education, field trips, fun reading, games and puzzles, family business, hobbies, resource persons, guests, crafts, creative work, electives, music appreciation, projects.

Basically, two factors need to be considered when assigning work to a student in the LIFE-PAC curriculum.

The first is time. An average of 45 minutes should be devoted to each subject, each day. Remember, this is only an average. Because of extenuating circumstances a student may spend only 15 minutes on a subject one day and the next day spend 90 minutes on the same subject.

The second factor is the number of pages to be worked in each subject. A single LIFEPAC is designed to take three to four weeks to complete. Allowing about three to four days for LIFEPAC introduction, review, and tests, the student has approximately 15 days to complete the LIFEPAC pages. Simply take the number of pages in the LIFEPAC, divide it by 15 and you will have the number of pages that must be completed on a daily basis to keep the student on schedule. For example, a LIFEPAC containing 45 pages will require three completed pages per day. Again, this is only an average. While working a 45-page LIFEPAC, the student may complete only one page the first day if the text has a lot of activities or reports, but go on to complete five pages the next day.

Long-range planning requires some organization. Because the traditional school year originates in the early fall of one year and continues to late spring of the following year, a calendar should be devised that covers this period of time. Approximate beginning and completion dates can be noted on the calendar as well as special occasions such as holidays, vacations and birthdays. Since each LIFEPAC takes three to four weeks or 18 days to complete, it should take about 180 school days to finish a set of ten LIFEPACs. Starting at the beginning school date, mark off 18 school days on the calendar and that will become the targeted completion date for the first LIFEPAC. Continue marking the calendar until you have established dates for the remaining nine LIFEPACs making adjustments for previously noted holidays and vacations. If all five subjects are being used, the ten established target dates should be the same for the LIFEPACs in each subject.

TEACHING SUPPLEMENTS

The sample weekly lesson plan and student grading sheet forms are included in this section as teacher support materials and may be duplicated at the convenience of the teacher.

The student grading sheet is provided for those who desire to follow the suggested guidelines for assignment of letter grades as previously discussed. The student's self test scores should be posted as percentage grades. When the LIFEPAC is completed, the teacher should average the self test grades, multiply the average by .25, and post the points in the box marked self test points. The LIFEPAC percentage grade should be multiplied by .60 and posted. Next, the teacher should award and post points for written reports and oral work. A report may be any type of written work assigned to the student whether it is a LIFEPAC or additional learning activity. Oral work includes the student's ability to respond orally to questions which may or may not be related to LIFEPAC activities or any type of oral report assigned by the teacher. The points may then be totaled and a final grade entered along with the date that the LIFEPAC was completed.

The Student Record Book which was specifically designed for use with the Alpha Omega curriculum provides space to record weekly progress for one student over a nine-week period as well as a place to post self test and LIFEPAC scores. The Student Record Books are available through the current Alpha Omega catalog; however, unlike the enclosed forms these books are not for duplication and should be purchased in sets of four to cover a full academic year.

WEEKLY LESSON PLANNER

Week of:

Monday	Subject	Subject	Subject	Subject
Tuesday	Subject	Subject	Subject	Subject
Wednesday	Subject	Subject	Subject	Subject
Thursday	Subject	Subject	Subject	Subject
Friday	Subject	Subject	Subject	Subject

WEEKLY LESSON PLANNER

Week of:

	Subject	Subject	Subject	Subject
Monday				
Tuesday	Subject	Subject	Subject	Subject
Wednesday	Subject	Subject	Subject	Subject
Thursday	Subject	Subject	Subject	Subject
Friday	Subject	Subject	Subject	Subject

Student Name _____   Year _____

Bible

LP	Self Test Scores by Sections					Self Test Points	LIFEPAC Test	Oral Points	Report Points	Final Grade	Date
	1	2	3	4	5						
01											
02											
03											
04											
05											
06											
07											
08											
09											
10											

History & Geography

LP	Self Test Scores by Sections					Self Test Points	LIFEPAC Test	Oral Points	Report Points	Final Grade	Date
	1	2	3	4	5						
01											
02											
03											
04											
05											
06											
07											
08											
09											
10											

Language Arts

LP	Self Test Scores by Sections					Self Test Points	LIFEPAC Test	Oral Points	Report Points	Final Grade	Date
	1	2	3	4	5						
01											
02											
03											
04											
05											
06											
07											
08											
09											
10											

Student Name _____   Year _____

Math

LP	Self Test Scores by Sections 1	2	3	4	5	Self Test Points	LIFEPAC Test	Oral Points	Report Points	Final Grade	Date
01											
02											
03											
04											
05											
06											
07											
08											
09											
10											

Science

LP	Self Test Scores by Sections 1	2	3	4	5	Self Test Points	LIFEPAC Test	Oral Points	Report Points	Final Grade	Date
01											
02											
03											
04											
05											
06											
07											
08											
09											
10											

Spelling/Electives

LP	Self Test Scores by Sections 1	2	3	4	5	Self Test Points	LIFEPAC Test	Oral Points	Report Points	Final Grade	Date
01											
02											
03											
04											
05											
06											
07											
08											
09											
10											

Math Symbols and Signs

NUMBER SYMBOLS
Digits
1
2
3
4
5
6
7
8
9

NUMBER-OPERATION SYMBOLS

Symbol	Meaning	Example
+	addition	1 + 2 = 3
−	subtraction	3 − 2 = 1
× • ( )	multiplication	2 × 3 = 6 2 • 3 = 6 (2)(3) = 6
÷	division	6 ÷ 3 = 2

SET-OPERATIONS SYMBOLS

Symbol	Meaning	Example
∪	union	$A \cup B = M$
∩	intersection	$A \cap B = K$

PUNCTUATION SYMBOLS

Symbol	Meaning	Example
.	decimal point	π = 3.1416
,	comma	A = {3, 4, 5}
( )	parenthesis	2 + (3 + 1) = 6
[ ]	brackets	2 + [1 • (3 + 1)] − 7
{ }	braces	{1, 2} = {2, 1}

NUMBER-RELATION SYMBOLS

Symbol	Meaning	Example
=	is equal to	2 + 3 = 5
≠	is not equal to	8 + 1 ≠ 7
<	is less than	3 < 4
≮	is not less than	3 ≮ 2
>	is greater than	9 > 7
≯	is not greater than	7 ≯ 9
≤	is less than or equal to	4 ≤ 4
≰	is not less than or equal to	4 ≰ 3
≥	is greater than or equal to	6 ≥ 5
≱	is not greater than or equal to	5 ≱ 6

SET-RELATION SYMBOLS

Symbol	Meaning	Example
∈	is an element of	1 ∈ {1, 2}
∉	is not an element of	3 ∉ ∅
⊂	is a subset of	∅ ⊂ A
⊄	is not a subset of	{1, 2} ⊄ {2, 3}
↔	is equivalent to	{1, 2} ↔ {a, b}
↮	is not equivalent	A ↮ {3, 4}
=	is equal to	A = A
≠	is not equal to	{1, 2} ≠ ∅

INSTRUCTIONS FOR MATH

The LIFEPAC curriculum from grades two through twelve is structured so that the daily instructional material is written directly into the LIFEPACs. The student is encouraged to read and follow this instructional material in order to develop independent study habits. The teacher should introduce the LIFEPAC to the student, set a required completion schedule, complete teacher checks, be available for questions regarding both content and procedures, administer and grade tests, and develop additional learning activities as desired. Teachers working with several students may schedule their time so that students are assigned to a quiet work activity when it is necessary to spend instructional time with one particular student.

Math is a subject that requires skill mastery. But skill mastery needs to be applied toward active student involvement. Measurements require measuring cups, rulers, and empty containers. Boxes and other similar items help the study of solid shapes. Construction paper, beads, buttons, and beans are readily available and can be used for counting, base ten, fractions, sets, grouping, and sequencing. Students should be presented with problem situations and be given the opportunity to find their solutions.

Any workbook assignment that can be supported by a real world experience will enhance the student's ability for problem solving. There is an infinite challenge for the teacher to provide a meaningful environment for the study of math. It is a subject that requires constant assessment of student progress. Do not leave the study of math in the classroom.

This section of the Math Teacher's Guide includes the following teacher aids: Suggested and Required Material (supplies), Additional Learning Activities, Answer Keys, and Alternate LIFEPAC Tests.

The Teacher Notes section of the Teacher's Guide lists the required or suggested materials for the LIFEPACs and provides additional learning activities for the students. Additional learning activities provide opportunities for problem solving, encourage the student's interest in learning and may be used as a reward for good study habits.

MATH 1101

Unit 1: Sets, Structure, and Function

TEACHER NOTES

MATERIALS NEEDED FOR LIFEPAC	
Required	Suggested
(none)	• straightedges

ADDITIONAL LEARNING ACTIVITIES

Section 1: Sets

1. Discuss the use of Venn diagrams as pictorial representations of relationships involving sets. Illustrate with the following examples.

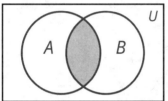 a. $A \cap B$ 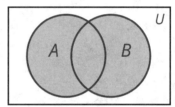 b. $A \cup B$

2. Divide the class into three groups. Each group writes a description of each of the following sets using set notation.

    a. The set *S* of states having a border on the Pacific Ocean.

    b. The set *C* of consonants in the word Mississippi.

    c. The set *F* of numbers between 3 and 21 that are divisible by 4.

    Each group exchanges its answers with the other groups and critiques one another's solutions.

Section 2: Structure

1. Write the following statements on the board and have the students respond with the correct property name. Many other possibilities exist; just change the numbers or variables.

$10 = 10$	reflexive
$5 + 7 = 7 + 5$	commutative—addition
$2(3 \cdot 9) = (2 \cdot 3)9$	associative—multiplication
$22 + 0 = 22$	identity—addition
If $u = v$ and $v = 6$, then $u = 6$.	transitive
$4(2 + 7) = 4 \cdot 2 + 4 \cdot 7$	distributive
$3 \cdot \frac{1}{3} = 1$	multiplicative inverse
If $d = e$, then $e = d$.	symmetric
$8 \cdot 9 = 9 \cdot 8$	commutative—multiplication
$6 \cdot 0 = 0$	zero—multiplication
$4 + (2 + 5) = (4 + 2) + 5$	associative—addition
$3 + (-3) = 0$	additive inverse
$5 \cdot 1 = 5$	identity—multiplication

2. Let groups of two to four students make up their own examples of each of the properties and quiz each other for the correct property name.

Section 3: Relations and Functions

1. Draw the graph for each of the following three functions on one pair of axes. Write each equation along its line.

$$y = x \qquad y = \tfrac{1}{2}x \qquad y = 2x$$

Indicate the symmetry in the differences among the three slopes. Point out the relative steepness of the line $y = 2x$ compared to the other equations.

2. Give the following equations and have the students indicate without drawing the graphs which is the steepest line.

$$y = \tfrac{1}{3}x \qquad y = 3x \qquad y = x$$

3. Have the students draw the graph for each of the following three functions on one pair of axes and write the equation for each one along its line.

$$y = x + 1 \qquad y = x + 4 \qquad y = x + 5$$

Have the students describe the relationship among the lines. Then have them write a formula for another line in the same direction.

Section 4: Algebraic Expressions

1. Explain scientific notation to your class as a useful method for writing very large and very small numbers. Illustrate with these examples:
   a. Convert 465,000 to scientific notation.
   b. Convert 0.000145 to scientific notation.

2. Demonstrate how to easily multiply and divide large numbers that end in zeros. To multiply these numbers, multiply all the numbers except the zeros; count the number of zeros and write them after the product. To divide these numbers, "cancel" as many zeros as possible and then divide. For example, to divide 6,000,000 by 2,000, "cancel" the three zeros at the end of each number and then divide 6,000 by 2. Illustrate with these examples:
   a. Multiply 48,000,000 by 3,000.
   b. Divide 58,000,000 by 2,000.

   To multiply decimals with zeros, multiply all the numbers except the zeros; count the number of zeros after the decimal point and write them before the product. To divide decimals with zeros, move the decimal point to the right the required number of places in the divisor and in the dividend to make the divisor a whole number; divide. Illustrate with these examples:
   a. Multiply 0.0000678 by 0.0015.
   b. Divide 0.00116 by 0.000029.

3. Have each student bring to class any recent news or magazine article in which some form of exponential notation is expressed. Have the student indicate whether he would use another technique for clarification or simplification rather than the exponential notation used in the article.

Additional Activities

The following activities may be reproduced as a student worksheet.

» FUNCTIONS

1. Draw a graph for each of these two functions on one pair of axes.

$f(x) = 2x + 1$ $f(x) = 2x + 3$

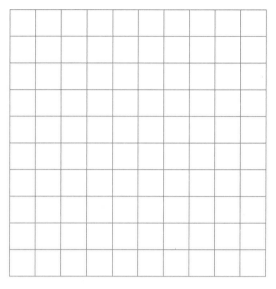

2. Write the equation for the line midway between the two lines.

3. Draw the graph for each of these two functions on one pair of axes.

$f(x) = x - 4$ $f(x) = 4 - x$

x	0	1	2	3	4	5
$f(x)$	-4	-3	___	___	___	1

What do you notice about these two lines?

_____

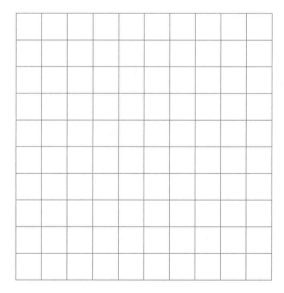

ADDITIONAL ACTIVITY, SOLUTION KEY

1. $f(x) = 2x + 1$

x	0	$-\frac{1}{2}$	-2
$f(x)$	1	0	-3

$f(x) = 2x + 3$

x	0	$-\frac{3}{2}$	2
$f(x)$	3	0	7

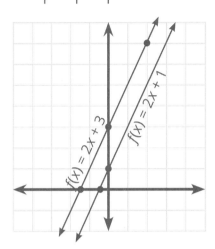

2. $f(x) = \frac{1}{2}(2x + 1 + 2x + 3) =$

$\frac{1}{2}(4x + 4) = 2x + 2$

$f(x) = 2x + 2$

3. $f(x) = x - 4$

x	0	1	2	3	4	5
$f(x)$	-4	-3	-2	-1	0	1

$f(x) = 2 - 4 = -2$
$f(x) = 3 - 4 = -1$
$f(x) = 4 - 4 = 0$

$f(x) = 4 - x$

x	0	1	2	3	4	5
$f(x)$	4	3	2	1	0	-1

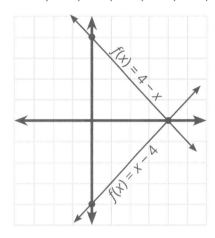

The two lines are perpendicular.

ANSWER KEY

SECTION 1

1.1	{3, 5, 7, 9, 11, 13}		**1.30**	{1}, {2}, {3}, {4}
1.2	{6, 4, 2, 0}		**1.31**	{1, 2}, {1, 3}, {1, 4}, {2, 3}, {2, 4}, {3, 4}
1.3	{1, 4, 9, 16, 25, 36, 49, 64}		**1.32**	{1, 2, 3}, {1, 2, 4}, {1, 3, 4}, {2, 3, 4}
1.4	answers will vary;		**1.33**	{1, 2, 3, 4}
	example: {Jones, Tate, Marsh}		**1.34**	16
1.5	{13, 26, 39}		**1.35**	32
1.6	$A = \{x \mid x$ is an even whole number between 0 and 13$\}$		**1.36**	2^n where n = number of elements in the set
1.7	$A = \{x \mid x$ is a perfect cube number between 0 and 100$\}$		**1.37**	{1, 2, 3, 4, 5, 6}
			1.38	{1, 2, 3, 4, 5}
1.8	$A = \{x \mid x$ is a letter in the word *algebra*$\}$		**1.39**	{1, 2, 3, 4, 5, 6}
1.9	$A = \{x \mid x$ is an even number between 0 and 8$\}$		**1.40**	{2, 4}
1.10	$A = \{x \mid x$ is a whole number less than 1$\}$		**1.41**	{1, 3, 5}
1.11	=		**1.42**	∅
1.12	≠		**1.43**	{1, 2, 3, 4, 5, 6}
1.13	≠; {0} has one element, { } has none		**1.44**	∅
1.14	=		**1.45**	{1, 2, 3, 4, 5}
1.15	≠		**1.46**	{1, 2, 3, 4, 5}
1.16	3		**1.47**	set of all whole numbers
1.17	1		**1.48**	set of all whole numbers
1.18	0		**1.49**	{1, 4, 9, 16, 25, 36, 49, 64, 81, 12, 14, 18}
1.19	answers will vary		**1.50**	{1, 4, 9, 16, 25, 36, 49, 64, 81}
1.20	11		**1.51**	{12, 14, 16, 18}
1.21	8		**1.52**	{16}
1.22	6		**1.53**	{all whole numbers}
1.23	⊂		**1.54**	{16}
1.24	⊂		**1.55**	{all whole numbers}
1.25	=		**1.56**	{1, 4, 9, 16, 25, 36, 49, 64, 81, 12, 14, 18}
1.26	{*a*}, {*b*}, {*c*}		**1.57**	c
1.27	{*a, b*}, {*a, c*}, {*b, c*}		**1.58**	e
1.28	{*a, b, c*}		**1.59**	d
1.29	8		**1.60**	a
			1.61	b

SELF TEST 1

1.01	true
1.02	true
1.03	$A = B$
1.04	{a}, {b}, {c}, {a, b}, {a, c}, {b, c}, {a, b, c}, Ø
1.05	$2^n = 2^6 = 64$
1.06	{$x : x$ is an integer and $0 < x \leq 10$} or {1, 2, 3, 4, 5, 6, 7, 8, 9, 10}
1.07	Ø
1.08	{1, 3, 5, 6, 7, 9}
1.09	{1, 5, 7, 9}
1.010	Ø

SECTION 2

2.1	d
2.2	a
2.3	k
2.4	l
2.5	g
2.6	h
2.7	e
2.8	b
2.9	f
2.10	i
2.11	j
2.12	c
2.13	associative—addition
2.14	associative—addition and identity—addition
2.15	associative—multiplication
2.16	commutative—addition and associative—addition
2.17	commutative—multiplication and associative—multiplication
2.18	associative—multiplication
2.19	commutative multiplication used twice
2.20	$800 + 24 = 824$
2.21	$240 + 24 = 264$
2.22	$9(30 + 3) = 270 + 27 = 297$
2.23	$13(10 + 2) = 130 + 26 = 156$
2.24	$17(10 - 1) = 170 - 17 = 153$
2.25	$22(20 + 3) = 440 + 66 = 506$
2.26	$2 + 3 \cdot 6 = 2 + 18 = 20$
2.27	$18 - 5 \cdot 3 = 18 - 15 = 3$
2.28	$4 \cdot 6 + 3 \cdot 8 = 24 + 24 = 48$
2.29	$6 \cdot 2 \div 6 + 1 = 12 \div 6 + 1 = 2 + 1 = 3$
2.30	$10 \div 5 + 6 \div 3 = 2 + 2 = 4$
2.31	$5(4 \cdot 3 + 3 \cdot 4) = 5(12 + 12) = 5(24) = 120$
2.32	$8 - 2 \cdot 2 = 8 - 4 = 4$
2.33	$(16 + 0) \cdot 0 = 16 \cdot 0 = 0$
2.34	$\frac{1}{2} \cdot 8 + \frac{1}{3} \cdot 12 \div 2 = 4 + \frac{4}{2} = 4 + 2 = 6$
2.35	$5(2 + 3) \div 25 + 8 \div 4 =$ $5(5) \div 25 + 2 = 1 + 2 = 3$
2.36	$3 + 4 \div 2 + 6(9 - 3) \div 12 + 1 =$ $3 + 2 + \frac{36}{12} + 1 =$ $3 + 2 + 3 + 1 =$ 9
2.37	$8 + [13 - (2 + 1)] =$ $8 + [10] =$ 18
2.38	$5(5 + 2) - 2(5 - 4) =$ $5(7) - 2(1) =$ $35 - 2 =$ 33

2.39 $4[(6-1)+3(5-2)] =$
$4[5+9] =$
$4 \cdot 14 =$
56

2.40 $2[3+5(1+2)] =$
$2[3+15] =$
$2[18] =$
36

SELF TEST 2

2.01 $10+4(3+2)+5+12 \div 6$
$= 10+20+5+2$
$= 37$

2.02 commutative—multiplication

2.03 commutative and associative for addition

2.04 symmetric

2.05 $3\{5+3[10+(4 \cdot 8)]\}$
$= 3\{5+3[42]\}$
$= 3\{5+126\}$
$= 3\{131\}$
$= 393$

2.06 $\{1\}, \{3\}, \{5\}, \{1, 3\}, \{1, 5\}, \{3, 5\}, \{1, 3, 5\}, \varnothing$

2.07 $2^n = 2^8 = 256$

2.08 $A \cup B = \{1, 2, 3, 4, 5, 6\}$

2.09 $A \cap C = A = \{1, 3, 5\}$

2.010 $\varnothing$

SECTION 3

3.1 neither: not a set of paired numbers
3.2 function
3.3 relation
3.4 function
3.5 function
3.6 function
3.7 {2}
3.8 {3, 4, 5, 6}
3.9 domain = range = {set of all real numbers}
3.10 domain = {all real numbers}
range = {$y : y \geq 0$}

3.11

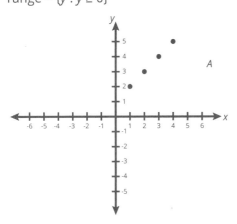

3.12

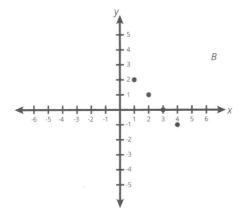

3.13

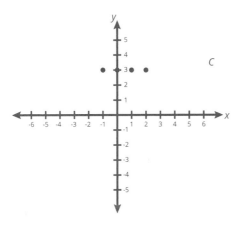

3.14

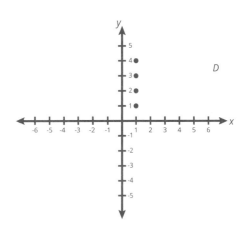

3.15

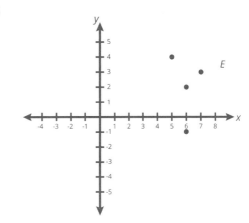

3.16 *D* and *E*, Problems 3.14 and 3.15 (vertical-line test)
3.17 Use *x* = 0, 2, 4.

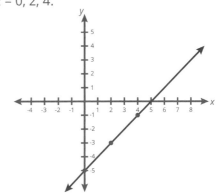

3.18 yes
3.19 yes
3.20 no
3.21 $f(x) = x^2 + 1$
$f(2) = 2^2 + 1 = 4 + 1 = 5$
3.22 $f(x) = x^2 + 1$
$f(6) = 6^2 + 1 = 36 + 1 = 37$
3.23 $f(x) = x^2 + 1$
$f(-1) = (-1)^2 + 1 = 1 + 1 = 2$

3.24 $f(x) = x^2 + 1$
$f(-6) = (-6)^2 + 1 = 36 + 1 = 37$

3.25 $f(x) = x^2 + 1$
$f(10) = 10^2 + 1 = 100 + 1 = 101$

3.26 $g(x) = 3x + 1$
$g(3) = 3 \cdot 3 + 1 = 9 + 1 = 10$

3.27 $g(x) = 3x + 1$
$g(-2) = 3(-2) + 1 = -6 + 1 = -5$

3.28 $g(x) = 3x + 1$
$g(0) = 3 \cdot 0 + 1 = 0 + 1 = 1$

3.29 $g(x) = 3x + 1$
$g(-14) = 3(-14) + 1 = -42 + 1 = -41$

3.30 $g(x) = 3x + 1$
$g(22) = 3(22) + 1 = 66 + 1 = 67$

3.31 $f(2) + g(3) = 5 + 10 = 15$

3.32 $f(5) = 5^2 + 1 = 26$
$g(1) = 3(1) + 1 = 4$
$f(5) - g(1) = 26 - 4 = 22$

3.33 $g(20) = 3(20) + 1 = 61$
$f(6) = 6^2 + 1 = 37$
$g(20) + f(6) = 61 + 37 = 98$

3.34 $f(3) = 3^2 + 1 = 10$
$g(-2) = 3(-2) + 1 = -5$
$[f(3) + g\{-2\}]^2 = [10 - 5]^2 = 25$

3.35 $f(-1) = (-1)^2 + 1 = 2$
$g(-3) = 3(-3) + 1 = -8$
$2 + 5(-8) = 2 - 40 = -38$

3.36 $f(2) = 2^2 + 1 = 5$
$g(10) = 3(10) + 1 = 31$
$[f(2) + g(10)] \div 12 = [5 + 31] \div 12 = 3$

3.37 $f(4) = 4^2 + 1 = 17$
$2f(4) = 2(17) = 34$

3.38 $g(5) = 3(5) + 1 = 16$
$3g(5) = 3(16) = 48$

3.39 $f(4) = 4^2 + 1 = 17$
$[f(4)]^2 = 17^2 = 289$

3.40 $g(1) = 3 \cdot 1 + 1 = 4$
$[g(1)]^3 = 4^3 = 64$

3.41 $f(1) = 1^2 + 1 = 2$
$g(4) = 3 \cdot 4 + 1 = 13$
$2f(1) + 3g(4) = 2(2) + 3(13) =$
$4 + 39 = 43$

3.42 $f(3) = 3^2 + 1 = 10$
$g(5) = 3 \cdot 5 + 1 = 16$
$[f(3)]^2 + g(5) = 10^2 + 16 = 116$

3.43 $f(2) = 2^2 + 1 = 5$
$g(1) = 3 \cdot 1 + 1 = 4$
$[f(2) - g(1)]^2 = (5 - 4)^2 = 1^2 = 1$

3.44 $[f(6)]^2 - [g(3)]^2 = 37^2 - 10^2 = 1{,}269$

3.45 $10f(101) - 10g(31)$
$10(101^2 + 1) - 10(31 \cdot 3 + 1)$
$10(10{,}202) - 10(94)$
$102{,}020 - 940$
$101{,}080$

3.46 $F(x) = 3x + 1$
$F(a) = 3 \cdot a + 1 = 3a + 1$

3.47 $F(x) = 3x + 1$
$F(a + 1) = 3(a + 1) + 1 =$
$3a + 3 + 1 = 3a + 4$

3.48 $F(x) = 3x + 1$
$F(a + h) = 3(a + h) + 1 =$
$3a + 3h + 1$

3.49 $F(x) = 3x + 1$
$F(a + h) = 3a + 3h + 1$
$F(a) = 3a + 1$
$F(a + h) - F(a) =$
$3a + 3h + 1 - (3a + 1) = 3h$

3.50 $\dfrac{F(a + h) - F(a)}{h} = \dfrac{3h}{h} = 3$

3.51 $f(x) = 3x + 1$
$f(2) = 3 \cdot 2 + 1 = 7$

3.52 $f^{-1}(x) = \dfrac{x - 1}{3}$
$f^{-1}(7) = \dfrac{7 - 1}{3} = 2$

3.53 $f(x) = 3x + 1$
$f(3) = 3 \cdot 3 + 1 = 10$

3.54 $f^{-1}(x) = \dfrac{x - 1}{3}$
$f^{-1}(10) = \dfrac{10 - 1}{3} = 3$

3.55 $f(0) = 3 \cdot 0 + 1 = 1$

3.56 $f^{-1}(1) = \dfrac{1 - 1}{3} = 0$

3.57 $(x, f(x)) = (2, 7)$

3.58 $(x, f^{-1}(x)) = (7, 2)$

3.59 $(x, f(x)) = (3, 10)$

3.60 $(x, f^{-1}(x)) = (10, 3)$

3.61 $(x, f(x)) = (0, 1)$

3.62 $(x, f^{-1}(x)) = (1, 0)$

3.63   yes

SELF TEST 3

3.01 $\{1, 2, 3, 4, 5, 6, 7, 8, 9, 10, 11\}$

3.02 finite

3.03 a. $B \cap C = \{3, 4, 5\}$
b. $B \cup C = \{1, 2, 3, 4, 5, 6, 7\}$

3.04 $\{A\}, \{B\}, \{C\}, \{D\}, \{A, B\}, \{A, C\},$
$\{A, D\}, \{B, C\}, \{B, D\}, \{C, D\},$
$\{A, B, C\}, \{A, B, D\}, \{A, C, D\},$
$\{B, C, D\}, \{A, B, C, D\}, \varnothing$

3.05 6

3.06 true

3.07 false

3.08 true

3.09 false

3.010 true

3.011 commutative—addition

3.012 distributive

3.013 associative—addition

3.014 additive—identity

3.015 Symmetric

3.016 $3 + 2 \cdot 8 \div 4$
$= 3 + 16 \div 4$
$= 3 + 4$
$= 7$

3.017 $[3(5 + 6) + 2] \div 7$
$= [3(11) + 2] \div 7$
$= [35] \div 7$
$= 5$

3.018 $F(x) = x^2 + 2$
$F(2) = 2^2 + 2 = 6$

3.019 $G(x) = 3x + 1$
$G(-1) = 3(-1) + 1 = -3 + 1 = -2$

3.020 $H(x) = x$
$H(5) = 5$

3.021 $F(1) + F(5) = 1^2 + 2 + 5^2 + 2 =$
$3 + 27 = 30$

3.022 $F(2) - F(8) + G(1)$
$2^2 + 2 - (8^2 + 2) + 3 \cdot 1 + 1$
$4 + 2 - 66 + 3 + 1$
-56

3.023 $F(a) + G(a) + H(a)$
$a^2 + 2 + 3 \cdot a + 1 + a$
$a^2 + 4a + 3$

3.024 domain $= \{1, 2, 3, 4, 5\}$

3.025 range $= \{2, 3, 7\}$

3.026 $P^{-1} = \{(2, 1), (2, 2), (3, 3), (3, 4), (7, 5)\}$

SECTION 4

4.1 6^3

4.2 7^4

4.3 x^2

4.4 $(3a)^3$

4.5 r^5

4.6 $(8y)^3$

4.7 $5^3 b^4$

4.8 $10^2 a^2 b$

4.9 $4^3 a^2 b^2$

4.10 $5^2 = 5 \cdot 5$

4.11 $(-2)^3 = (-2)(-2)(-2)$

4.12 $(ab)^4 = ab \cdot ab \cdot ab \cdot ab$

4.13 $10^4 = 10 \cdot 10 \cdot 10 \cdot 10$

4.14 $(-a)^3 = (-a)(-a)(-a)$

4.15 $(2c)^5 = (2c)(2c)(2c)(2c)(2c)$

4.16 $(3x)^2 = (3x)(3x)$

4.17 $(-3x)^4 = (-3x)(-3x)(-3x)(-3x)$

4.18 $8^3 = 8 \cdot 8 \cdot 8$

4.19 $2^0 = 1$

4.20 $6^{-1} = \dfrac{1}{6}$

4.21 $6^{-3} = \dfrac{1}{6^3} = \dfrac{1}{216}$

4.22 $(a + b)^0 = 1$

4.23 $3^1 = 3$

4.24 $8^{-1} = \dfrac{1}{8}$

4.25 $\dfrac{1}{10^0} = \dfrac{1}{1} = 1$

4.26 $(xy)^0 = 1$

4.27 $(5x)^0 = 1$

4.28 $2^{-2} = \dfrac{1}{2^2} = \dfrac{1}{4}$

4.29 $\dfrac{5^{-1}}{5^0} = \dfrac{\frac{1}{5}}{1} = \dfrac{1}{5}$

4.30 $(-7)^{-1} = \dfrac{1}{-7} = -\dfrac{1}{7}$

4.31 $\dfrac{1}{3^2} = 3^{-2}$

4.32 $\dfrac{1}{(xy)} = (xy)^{-1}$

4.33 $\dfrac{1}{a^4} = a^{-4}$

4.34 $\dfrac{1}{8^6} = 8^{-6}$

4.35 $\dfrac{5}{x^2} = 5x^{-2}$

4.36 $\dfrac{1}{16^2} = 16^{-2}$

4.37 $x^2 \cdot x^5 = x^{2+5} = x^7$

4.38 $r^2 \cdot r \cdot r^5 = r^{2+1+5} = r^8$

4.39 $\dfrac{x^{10}}{x^4} = x^{10-4} = x^6$

4.40 $\dfrac{(a + b)^9}{(a + b)^4} = (a + b)^{9-4} = (a + b)^5$

4.41 $\dfrac{10x^5}{2x^2} = 5x^{5-2} = 5x^3$

4.42 $\dfrac{3.6x^5}{1.2x^2} = 3x^{5-2} = 3x^3$

4.43 $y^7 \cdot y^9 = y^{7+9} = y^{16}$

4.44 $2x \cdot 3x^2 = 6x^3$

4.45 $\dfrac{a^5}{a} = a^{5-1} = a^4$

4.46 $\dfrac{(3x)^{12}}{(3x)^4} = (3x)^{12-4} = (3x)^8$

4.47 $\dfrac{15a^4}{3a^2} = 5a^{4-2} = 5a^2$

4.48 $\dfrac{0.105p^6}{0.5p^3} = 0.21p^{6-3} = 0.21p^3$

4.49 $p^3 \cdot p^2 \cdot p = p^{3+2+1} = p^6$

4.50 $5a^2 \cdot 6a^4 = 30a^{2+4} = 30a^6$

4.51 $\dfrac{b^7}{b^6} = b^{7-6} = b^1$ or b

4.52 $\dfrac{a^5}{a^3} = a^{5-3} = a^2$

4.53 $\dfrac{20b^2c^3}{4bc} = 5b^{2-1}\,c^{3-1} = 5bc^2$

4.54 $\dfrac{7.2q^4r^5}{0.6q^3r^3} = 12q^{4-3}r^{5-3} = 12qr^2$

4.55 $x^4 \cdot x^{-2} = x^{4-2} = x^2$

4.56 $p^8 \cdot p^{-3} \cdot p^2 = p^{8-3+2} = p^7$

4.57 $\dfrac{x^5}{x^{-3}} = x^{5-(-3)} = x^{5+3} = x^8$

4.58 $\dfrac{a^3b^2}{a^{-1}b^{-3}} = a^{3+1}b^{2+3} = a^4b^5$

4.59 $x^{-3}x^7 = x^{7-3} = x^4$

4.60 $y^{-9}y^{-8}y^{10} = y^{10-9-8} = y^{-7}$

4.61 $\dfrac{x^{-8}}{x^{-7}} = x^{-8+7} = x^{-1}$

4.62 $\dfrac{p^{-4}q^5r^6}{p^{-3}qr^{-2}} = p^{-4+3}q^{5-1}r^{6+2} = p^{-1}q^4r^8$

4.63 $x^{-8} \cdot x^{-2} = x^{-8-2} = x^{-10}$

4.64 $b^3 \cdot b^{-3} = b^{3-3} = b^0 = 1$

4.65 $\dfrac{x^{-8}}{x^5} = x^{-8-5} = x^{-13}$

4.66 $\dfrac{10}{10^{-2}} = 10^{1+2} = 10^3 = 1{,}000$

4.67 $(x^2)^4 = x^{2 \cdot 4} = x^8$

4.68 $(r^3)^{-2} = r^{-6}$

4.69 $(a^2b^2)^3 = a^6b^6$

4.70 6^{-9}

4.71 $x^4y^6z^8$

4.72 $2^3a^6 = 8a^6$

4.73 $(-5)^3x^{2 \cdot 3} = -125x^6$

4.74 x^{10}

4.75 8^{-9} $\quad s^{-9}$

4.76 $x^{12}y^6$ $\quad x^{12}y^8$

4.77 $\dfrac{1}{x^{-8}} = x^8$

4.78 $a^{-2}b^{-4}c^{-6}$

4.79 $3^4b^{12} = 81b^{12}$

4.80 $(-4)^2x^4 = 16x^4$

4.81 p^8

4.82 t^{-72}

4.83 $x^{12}y^6$

4.84 $\dfrac{1}{y^{-12}} = y^{12}$

4.85 $r^{-12}s^8t^4$

4.86 $4^3c^6 = 64c^6$

4.87 $3^2a^4b^2 = 9a^4b^2$

4.88 $5x + 3x = (5 + 3)x = 8x$

4.89 $8x^2 - 2x^2 = (8 - 2)x^2 = 6x^2$

4.90 $3a + 3a - 2a = (3 + 3 - 2)a = 4a$

4.91 $11x^2 - y$

4.92 $5x + 9y$

4.93 $3x$

4.94 $6b^3$

4.95 $8a$

4.96 $3x + y$

4.97 $9x + 3y$

4.98 $23a$

4.99 $2x$

4.100 $-2b$

4.101 $9x - 6y$

4.102 $7x + 3y$

4.103 $2x + 3y$

4.104 $6ab$

4.105 $7ab + 5$

4.106 $2x + y - 1$

4.107 $11xy$

4.108 $6x^2y - 4xy^2$

4.109 $14a - 13b$

4.110 $12abc$

4.111 $4p^2q^2$

4.112 $5(x - 2) + 6$
$= 5x - 10 + 6$
$= 5x - 4$

4.113 $7(x + 6) - 4$
$= 7x + 42 - 4$
$= 7x + 38$

4.114 $15(2 - x) + 17x$
$= 30 - 15x + 17x$
$= 30 + 2x$

4.115 $7(x + 2) + 3(x + 1)$
$= 7x + 14 + 3x + 3$
$= 10x + 17$

4.116 $8(x + 3) - 2x$
$= 8x + 24 - 2x$
$= 6x + 24$

4.117 $10(x - 5) + 20$
$= 10x - 50 + 20$
$= 10x - 30$

4.118 $13 - 3(5 - 2x)$
$= 13 - 15 + 6x$
$= 6x - 2$

4.119 $10(x + 4) + 15(x + 1)$
$= 10x + 40 + 15x + 15$
$= 25x + 55$

4.120 $13(x - 2) + 5(x + 1)$
$= 13x - 26 + 5x + 5$
$= 18x - 21$

4.121 $8(2x + 2) + 5(3x - 1)$
$= 16x + 16 + 15x - 5$
$= 31x + 11$

4.122 $7(9x - 3) - 4(2x - 1)$
$= 63x - 21 - 8x + 4$
$= 55x - 17$

4.123 $10(7 - 2x) + 4(3 - x)$
$= 70 - 20x + 12 - 4x$
$= 82 - 24x$

4.124 $2(x + 1) + 2(x + 2) + 3(x - 1)$
$= 2x + 2 + 2x + 4 + 3x - 3$
$= 7x + 3$

4.125 $3(1 - 2x) + 2(x - 1) - 3(x - 4)$
$= 3 - 6x + 2x - 2 - 3x + 12$
$= 13 - 7x$

4.126 $2(x^2 - 1) + 3(x^2 + 1)$
$= 2x^2 - 2 + 3x^2 + 3$
$= 5x^2 + 1$

4.127 $6(x - 3) - 4(x + 1)$
$= 6x - 18 - 4x - 4$
$= 2x - 22$

4.128 $4(5x - 6) - 4(2x + 1)$
$= 20x - 24 - 8x - 4$
$= 12x - 28$

4.129 $4(6 - 2x) - 3(3 - 4x)$
$= 24 - 8x - 9 + 12x$
$= 4x + 15$

4.130 $20(1 - 2x) + 4(7 - 2x)$
$= 20 - 40x + 28 - 8x$
$= 48 - 48x$

4.131 $7(x - 1) - 2(x + 1) + 3(x - 4)$
$= 7x - 7 - 2x - 2 + 3x - 12$
$= 8x - 21$

4.132 $5(a - b) + 6(a + b) - 7(a - 2b)$
$= 5a - 5b + 6a + 6b - 7a + 14b$
$= 4a + 15b$

4.133 $5(a^3 - 2) + 6(a^3 - 4)$
$= 5a^3 - 10 + 6a^3 - 24$
$= 11a^3 - 34$

SELF TEST 4

4.01 $A = \{-6, -5, -4, -3, -2, -1\}$

4.02 $A = \{x \mid x$ is a whole number multiple of 3 that is less than 27$\}$

4.03 $2^n = 2^5 = 32$

4.04 $A \cup B = \{a, e, i, o, u, l, g, b, r\}$

4.05 $A \cap B = \{a, e\}$

4.06 $B \cup C = \{a, l, g, e, b, r, m, t, h\}$

4.07 $B \cap C = \{a\}$

4.08 $A \cup C = \{a, e, i, o, u, m, t, h\}$

4.09 $A \cap C = \{a\}$

4.010 $A \cap B \cap C = \{a\}$

4.011 $7 \cdot 5 + 12 \div 4 = 35 + 3 = 38$

4.012 $8 + 3 \cdot 4 \div 6 = 8 + \frac{12}{6} = 8 + 2 = 10$

4.013 $F(x) = 2x^2 - 3$
$F(-2) = 2(-2)^2 - 3 = 2 \cdot 4 - 3 =$
$8 - 3 = 5$

4.014 $f(x) = 3x - 1$
$f(-2) = 3(-2) - 1 = -7$
$g(x) = -x + 6$
$g(5) = -5 + 6 = 1$
$f(-2) + g(5) = -7 + 1 = -6$

4.015 $\{-1, -8, 0, 6\}$

4.016 $\{7, 2, 0, 6\}$

4.017 $F(x) = x^2$
range of $F(x) \geq 0$

4.018 $h(p) = p^2 - 3p + q$
$h(x) = x^2 - 3x + q$

4.019 $3^4 = 3 \cdot 3 \cdot 3 \cdot 3 = 81$

4.020 $(2x^2) = 2 \cdot x \cdot x$

4.021 $(3a^2)^3 = 3^3 a^6 = 27a^6$

4.022 $(-2x^3)$
$-2(-2)^3 = -2(-8) = 16$

4.023 $6^0 + 6^1 + 6^2 = 1 + 6 + 36 = 43$

4.024   true

4.025   true

4.026   false

4.027   false

4.028   true

4.029   false

4.030   true

4.031   false

4.032   true

4.033   true

4.034   true

4.035   true

4.036   false

4.037   true; $\frac{1}{5^{-2}} = 5^2 = 25$

4.038   false

4.039 $\dfrac{32a^3b^2}{8ab^2} = 4a^2$

4.040 $48x^2(16x)^{-1} = \dfrac{48x^2}{16x} = 3x$

4.041 $x^5 \cdot x^{-5} \cdot x^2 = x^{0+2} = x^2$

4.042 $3(x + 2) - 4x$
$= 3x + 6 - 4x$
$= -x + 6$

4.043 $5(2x - 3) + 4(x + 1)$
$= 10x - 15 + 4x + 4$
$= 14x - 11$

4.044 $5(x + y) + 3(x - y)$
$= 5x + 5y + 3x - 3y$
$= 8x + 2y$

4.045 $3x^2 + 2x + 4 - x^2 + 5x$
$= 2x^2 + 7x + 4$

LIFEPAC TEST

1. $K \cup G = \{O, \square, \triangle, I, \varDiamond\}$
2. $K \cap H = \{\square\}$
3. $K \cap G \cap H = \{\ \} = \emptyset$
4. $\{\square\}, \{\boxtimes\}, \{\otimes\}, \{\square, \boxtimes\}, \{\square, \otimes\}, \{\boxtimes, \otimes\}, \{\square, \boxtimes, \otimes\}, \emptyset$
5. $2^n = 2^6 = 64$
6. 7
7. $12 + 8 \div 2 + 10 = 12 + 4 + 10 = 26$
8. $15 \div 3 + 10 \div 2 = 5 + 5 = 10$
9. associative—addition and commutative—addition
10. multiplicative inverse
11. multiplicative inverse, additive and multiplicative inverse, commutative (addition and multiplication), associative (addition and multiplication)
12. commutative—addition and multiplication
13. range = {1, 2, 3, 7}
14. domain = {5, 6, 7, 8, 9}
15. no: double-valued points, (1, 5) and (1, 8)
16. $f(x) = x^2 + 5x$
    $f(-2) = (-2)^2 + 5(-2) = 4 - 10 = -6$
17. $g(x) = 2x + 1$
    $g(3) = 2 \cdot 3 + 1 = 6 + 1 = 7$
18. $f(5) + g(6) = 5^2 + 5(5) + 2(6) + 1 = 50 + 13 = 63$
19. $g(3) - f(4) = 2(3) + 1 - (4^2 + 5 \cdot 4) = 7 - 36 = -29$
20. $g(a + h) - g(a)$
    $= 2(a + h) + 1 - (2a + 1)$
    $= 2a + 2h + 1 - 2a - 1$
    $= 2h$
21. a^3
22. $(3b)^4 = 81b^4$
23. $2a^2b^2$
24. $3 \cdot x \cdot x$
25. $3a \cdot 3a \cdot 3a$
26. $abc \cdot abc$
27. $10^2 \cdot 10^3 = 10^{2+3} = 10^5$
28. $x^3x^5 = x^{3+5} = x^8$
29. $a^2 \cdot a^{-3} \cdot a = a^{2-3+1} = a^0 = 1$
30. $\dfrac{18a^3b^2}{2ab} = 9a^2b$
31. $\dfrac{12ab^3c^2}{4a^{-2}bc^{-2}} = 3a^{1+2}b^{3-1}c^{2+2} = 3a^3b^2c^4$
32. 8
33. $3^{-2} = \dfrac{1}{3^2} = \dfrac{1}{9}$
34. $7^0 = 1$
35. $5h - 2h = (5 - 2)h = 3h$
36. $2a$
37. $7x^2 + 3x$
38. $5(x - 2) + 3x$
    $= 5x - 10 + 3x$
    $= 8x - 10$
39. $7 - 2(5 - 2x)$
    $= 7 - 10 + 4x$
    $= -3 + 4x$ or $4x - 3$
40. $3(x + 2) + 4(x - 5)$
    $= 3x + 6 + 4x - 20$
    $= 7x - 14$

ALTERNATE LIFEPAC TEST

1. {a, b, c, d, e, k, m, o}
2. { } or Ø
3. $A \cap B = \{a, e\}$
   $A \cap B \cup C = \{a, e, k, m, o\}$
4. {k}, {m}, {o}, {k, m},
   {k, o}, {m, o}, {k, m, o}, Ø
5. 8 elements are in $A \cup C$; therefore, the number of subsets is $2^8 = 256$.
6. 0
7. $16 + 12 \div 3 - 10 =$
   $16 + 4 - 10 =$
   10
8. $22 \div 11 + 9 \div 3 =$
   $2 + 3 =$
   5
9. associative—addition and commutative—addition
10. multiplicative inverse
11. multiplicative inverse and additive inverse
12. distributive
13. {-7, -1, 1, 2}
14. {-2, 3, 4, 6}
15. $F^{-1} = \{(2, 6), (1, 3), (-7, 4), (-1, -2)\}$
    yes
16. $F(-2) = (-2)^2 - 24$
    $= 4 - 24$
    $= -20$
17. $G(3) = 54 - 2(3)$
    $= 54 - 6$
    $= 48$
18. $F(5) = 5^2 - 24$
    $= 25 - 24$
    $= 1$
    $G(6) = 54 - 2(6)$
    $= 54 - 12$
    $= 42$
    $F(5) + G(6) = 1 + 42$
    $= 43$
19. $G(2) = 54 - 2(2)$
    $= 54 - 4$
    $= 50$
    $F(7) = 54 - 2(7)$
    $= 54 - 14$
    $= 40$
    $G(2) - F(7) = 50 - 40$
    $= 10$

20. $G(a + h) = 54 - 2(a + h)$
    $= 54 - 2a - 2h$
    $G(a) = 54 - 2(a)$
    $= 54 - 2a$
    $G(a + h) - G(a) = 54 - 2a - 2h - (54 - 2a)$
    $= 54 - 2a - 2h - 54 + 2a$
    $= -2h$
21. x^4
22. $2^3x^3 = 8x^3$
23. $15x^2y$
24. $5 \cdot x \cdot x \cdot x$
25. $2x \cdot 2x \cdot 2x$
26. $xyz \cdot xyz$ or $x \cdot x \cdot y \cdot y \cdot z \cdot z$
27. $5^2 \cdot 5^4 = 5^{2+4} = 5^6$
28. $a \cdot a^2 \cdot a^4 = a^{1+2+4} = a^7$
29. $x^3 \cdot x^{-3} \cdot x^2 = x^{3-3+2} = x^2$
30. $\dfrac{12x^2y^3}{4xy} = (12 \div 4)x^{2-1}y^{3-1} = 3xy^2$
31. $\dfrac{27a^3b^2c}{3a^{-2}bc^{-1}} = (27 \div 3)a^{3-(-2)} \cdot b^{2-1} \cdot c^{1-(-1)} = 9a^5bc^2$
32. $3^3 = 3 \cdot 3 \cdot 3 = 27$
33. $5^{-2} = \dfrac{1}{5^2} = \dfrac{1}{25}$
34. $6^0 = 1$
35. $3x$
36. $10y$
37. $2x^2 - 3x - x^2 - 5x =$
    $2x^2 - x^2 - 3x - 5x =$
    $x^2 - 8x$
38. $4(2x - 3) + 7x =$
    $8x - 12 + 7x =$
    $15x - 12$
39. $8 - 2(x + 6) + x =$
    $8 - 2x - 12 + x =$
    $-x - 4$
40. $7(x - 3) + 3(x + 2) =$
    $7x - 21 + 3x + 6 =$
    $10x - 15$

MATH 1101

ALTERNATE LIFEPAC TEST

NAME _____

DATE _____

SCORE _____

106

133

Complete these activities (each answer, 4 points).

Given A = {a, b, c, d, e}, B = {a, e, i, o, u}, C = {k, m, o}

1. $A \cup C$ _____

2. $A \cap C$ _____

3. $A \cap B \cup C$ _____

4. All subsets of C _____

5. Number of subsets of $A \cup C$ _____

6. Number of elements of $A \cap B \cap C$ _____

Evaluate each expression (each question, 3 points).

7. $16 + 12 \div 3 - 10$ _____

8. $22 \div 11 + 9 \div 3$ _____

Name the axiom(s) that justifies each of the following statements (each answer, 2 points).

9. $6 + (x - 3) = x + 3$ _____

10. $A \cdot \frac{1}{A} = 1$ _____

11. $6 \cdot \frac{1}{6} + 2 + (-1) = 2$ _____

12. $6x + 7x = 13x$ _____

Complete these activities (each answer, 3 points).

Given $F = \{(6, 2), (3, 1), (4, -7), (-2, -1)\}$

13. Write the range set of F. _____

14. Write the domain set of F. _____

15. Is F^{-1} a function? _____

Complete these activities (each answer, 4 points).

Given $F(x) = x^2 - 24$ and $G(x) = 54 - 2x$

16. $F(-2)$ _____

17. $G(3)$ _____

18. $F(5) + G(6)$ _____

19. $G(2) - F(7)$ _____

20. $G(a + h) - G(a)$ _____

Write each expression in exponential notation (each answer, 3 points).

21. $x \cdot x \cdot x \cdot x$ _____

22. $2x \cdot 2x \cdot 2x$ _____

23. $5 \cdot x \cdot y \cdot x \cdot 3$ _____

Write each expression without exponents (each answer, 3 points).

24. $5x^3$ _____

25. $(2x)^3$ _____

26. $(xyz)^2$ _____

Express in simplified exponential notation (each answer, 3 points).

27. $5^2 \cdot 5^4$ _____

28. $a \cdot a^2 \cdot a^4$ _____

29. $x^3 \cdot x^{-3} \cdot x^2$ _____

30. $\dfrac{12x^2y^3}{4xy}$ _____

31. $\dfrac{27a^3b^2c}{3a^{-2}bc^{-1}}$ _____

Evaluate each expression (each answer, 3 points).

32. 3^3 _____

33. 5^{-2} _____

34. 6^0 _____

Combine like terms (each answer, 4 points).

35. $6x - 3x$ _____

36. $5y + 7y - 2y$ _____

37. $2x^2 - 3x - x^2 - 5x$ _____

38. $4(2x - 3) + 7x$ _____

39. $8 - 2(x + 6) + x$ _____

40. $7(x - 3) + 3(x + 2)$ _____

MATH 1102

Unit 2: Numbers, Sentences, and Problems

TEACHER NOTES

MATERIALS NEEDED FOR LIFEPAC	
Required	Suggested
(none)	• straightedges

ADDITIONAL LEARNING ACTIVITIES

Section 1: Numbers

1. Discuss the difference between rational numbers and irrational numbers.

Section 2: Sentences

1. Discuss how inequalities involving absolute value can be used to describe certain neighborhoods of a real number c, e.g., $|x - 3| < 2$ is a way to write the open interval $-2 < (x - 3) < 2$ or $1 < x < 5$ or $(1, 5)$, which is a neighborhood of $c = 3$.

2. Show the class how not all inequalities involving absolute values describe neighborhoods, e.g., $|x - 3| > 2$ may be written $-2 > (x - 3)$ or $(x - 3) > 2$, or as $1 > x$ or $x < 5$, which does not describe a neighborhood of $c = 3$. The following figure illustrates the set of numbers x such that $1 > x$ or $x > 5$ is not an open interval that contains $c = 3$.

$$1 > x > 5$$

3. Divide students into four groups. Each group is to tell whether or not each of the following inequalities describes a neighborhood of $c = 4$. If not, the group is to explain why not. Each group takes turns giving its solution and the other groups critiquing their solution.

   a. $|x - 4| < 2$ b. $|x - 4| \leq \frac{1}{2}$

   c. $|x - 3| < 2$ d. $|x - 4| \geq 2$

Section 3: Applications

1. Demonstrate to the class the use of deductive reasoning with number tricks. For example, tell the class to "choose a number. Add five. Double the result. Subtract four. Divide by two. Subtract the number you started with. Your result is three."

   The number will always be three. Demonstrate this fact with several different numbers. Even though the result is always three, this fact does not prove that the trick will always work. We are reasoning inductively, and inductive reasoning cannot prove anything. For a proof we need to use the deductive method. Let's go through the trick again, but this time let's use a variable to represent the original number and use numerals for the other numbers.

   Proof

Choose a number.	n
Add five.	$n + 5$
Double the result.	$2n + 10$
Subtract four.	$2n + 6$
Divide by two.	$n + 3$
Subtract the number you started with.	$n - n + 3$
Your result is three.	3

2. Divide the class into four groups. Each group is to copy each of the following tricks, writing each step on a separate line. Each group tries each trick, with at least two different numbers. Then, they are to prove that the tricks work with the numbers they have chosen by using algebraic symbols. The groups then exchange solutions and proofs and critique each other.

   a. Choose a number. Double it. Add nine. Add your original number. Divide by three. Add four. Subtract your original number. Your result is seven.

   b. Choose a number. Triple it. Add the number one larger than your original number. Add eleven. Divide by four. Subtract three. The result is your original number.

Additional Activities

The following activities may be reproduced as student worksheets.

» NUMBERS

Complete these activities.

1.   Let *A*, *B*, and *C* be points on a line with coordinates -6, -2, and 3 respectively. Determine the possible coordinates of point *D* if $|AC| = |BD|$.

2.   *A*, *B*, and *C* are points on a line with coordinates *a*, *b*, and *c* respectively.

a. Prove that $AB + BC + CA = 0$.

b. Can $|AB| + |BC| + |CA| = 0$?

3.   Albrech Dürer, a sixteenth-century German painter, engraver, and designer, made a famous engraving entitled "Melancholy" that contains an interesting square of numbers. Two of the numbers in the square have been omitted for you to find.

16	3	2	13
5	10	11	8
9	6	__	12
4	15	14	__

a. When you assume that a rule exists for finding numbers, what kind of reasoning are you using?

_____

b. When you use the rule you think will work to tell what the missing numbers are, what kind of reasoning are you using?

_____

c. What are the missing numbers?

_____

» SENTENCES

Solve and graph each of the following equations or inequalities.

1. $|x| = 6$

2. $|x - 1| > 4$

3. $|\frac{1}{2}x - 1| \geq 4$

4. $|5 - 10x| \geq 25$

5. $|3x| = 9$

6. $4x + 1 > 17$

7. $\frac{x}{3} - 6 \leq 9$

8. $|P| \geq -1$

9. $|2 - 2x| < 8$

10. $|3(2x + 1)| = 12$

11. $10x + 8 > 18$

12. $3(P + 4) + 2(P - 6) \geq 4(2P - 1)$

13. $2y + 1 = 5y - 7$

14. $3(y - 8) + 5(y + 2) < 14y + 2(y + 6)$

ADDITIONAL ACTIVITIES, SOLUTION KEY

Numbers

1.

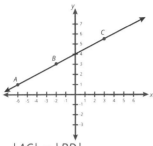

$$|AC| = |BD|$$
$$|-6 \cdot 3| = |-2 \cdot D|$$
$$|-18| = |-2D|$$
$$18 = 2D$$
$$2D = \pm 18$$
$$\tfrac{1}{2}(2D) = \tfrac{1}{2}(\pm 18)$$
$$D = \pm 9$$
$$D = 9 \ \text{ or } \ D = -9$$

2.
a. Draw a straight line and mark points *A*, *B*, and *C* with coordinates *a*, *b*, and *c* respectively at random intervals from point 0 (zero).

The distance *AB* equals the distance from 0 to *b* minus the difference from 0 to *a*, or *b* − *a*.

The distance *BC* equals the distance from 0 to *c* minus the distance from 0 to *b*, or *c* − *b*.

The distance *CA* equals the distance from 0 to *a* minus the distance from 0 to *c*, or *a* − *c*.

Add the measures.
$$(b - a) + (c - b) + (a - c) =$$
$$b - a + c - b + a - c = 0$$
$$\therefore AB + BC + CA = 0.$$

b. Assume that the distance from 0 to *A* on the line equals the distance from *A* to *B* equals the distance from *B* to *C*, or $0A = AB = BC$.

$\overline{AB}$ = the distance from 0 to *b* minus the distance from 0 to *a*, or *b* − *a*.

$\overline{BC}$ = the distance from 0 to *c* minus the distance from 0 to *b*, or *c* − *b*.

$\overline{CA}$ = the distance from 0 to *a* minus the distance from 0 to *c*, or *a* − *c*.

$$|b - a| + |c - b| + |a - c| =$$
$$b - a + c - b + a - c = 0$$
$\therefore |AB| + |BC| + |CA|$ can equal 0; the answer is yes.

3.
a. inductive reasoning
b. deductive reasoning
c. Each row across, down, and diagonally adds to 34. Therefore, the number in the third row is 34 − (9 + 6 + 12) = 34 − 27 = 7. The number in the fourth row is 34 − (4 + 15 + 14) = 34 − 33 = 1.

Sentences

1. $x = 6$ or $x = -6$

2.
$$|x - 1| > 4$$
$$x - 1 > 4$$
$$x - 1 + 1 > 4 + 1$$
$$x > 5$$
or
$$x - 1 < -4$$
$$x - 1 + 1 < -4 + 1$$
$$x < 3$$

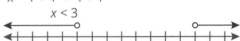

3.
$$\left|\tfrac{1}{2}x - 1\right| \geq 4$$
$$\tfrac{1}{2}x - 1 \geq 4$$
$$x - 2 \geq 8$$
$$x - 2 + 2 \geq 8 + 2$$
$$x \geq 10$$
or
$$\tfrac{1}{2}x - 1 \leq -4$$
$$x - 2 \leq -8$$
$$x - 2 + 2 \leq -8 + 2$$
$$x \leq -6$$

4.
$$|5 - 10x| \geq 25$$
$$5 - 10x \geq 25$$
$$5 - 5 - 10x \geq 25 - 5$$
$$-10x \geq 20$$
$$-\tfrac{1}{10}(-10x) \geq -\tfrac{1}{10}(20)$$
$$x \leq -2$$
or
$$5 - 10x \leq -25$$
$$5 - 5 - 10x \leq -25 - 5$$
$$-10x \leq -30$$
$$-\tfrac{1}{10}(-10x) \leq -\tfrac{1}{10}(-30)$$
$$x \geq 3$$

5.
$$|3x| = 9$$
$$3x = 9$$
$$\frac{1}{3} \cdot 3x = \frac{1}{3} \cdot 9$$
$$x = 3$$
or
$$3x = -9$$
$$\frac{1}{3}(3x) = \frac{1}{3}(-9)$$
$$x = -3$$

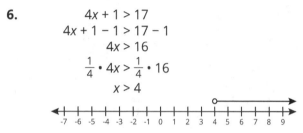

6.
$$4x + 1 > 17$$
$$4x + 1 - 1 > 17 - 1$$
$$4x > 16$$
$$\frac{1}{4} \cdot 4x > \frac{1}{4} \cdot 16$$
$$x > 4$$

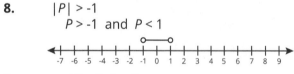

7.
$$\frac{x}{3} - 6 \leq 9$$
$$x - 18 \leq 27 \qquad \text{(multiply by 3)}$$
$$x - 18 + 18 \leq 27 + 18$$
$$x \leq 45$$

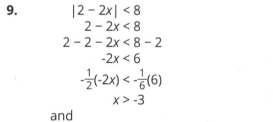

8.
$$|P| > -1$$
$$P > -1 \text{ and } P < 1$$

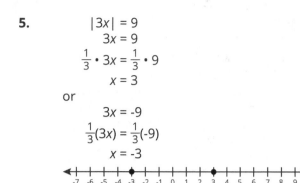

9.
$$|2 - 2x| < 8$$
$$2 - 2x < 8$$
$$2 - 2 - 2x < 8 - 2$$
$$-2x < 6$$
$$-\frac{1}{2}(-2x) < -\frac{1}{6}(6)$$
$$x > -3$$
and
$$2 - 2x > -8$$
$$2 - 2 - 2x > -8 - 2$$
$$-2x > -10$$
$$-\frac{1}{2}(-2x) > -\frac{1}{2}(-10)$$
$$x < 5$$

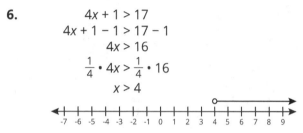

10.
$$|3(2x + 1)| = 12$$
$$3(2x + 1) = 12$$
$$6x + 3 = 12$$
$$6x + 3 - 3 = 12 - 3$$
$$6x = 9$$
$$\frac{1}{6} \cdot 6x = \frac{1}{6} \cdot 9$$
$$x = \frac{3}{2}$$

or
$$6x + 3 = -12$$
$$6x + 3 - 3 = -12 - 3$$
$$6x = -15$$
$$\frac{1}{6}(6x) = \frac{1}{6}(-15)$$
$$x = -\frac{5}{2}$$

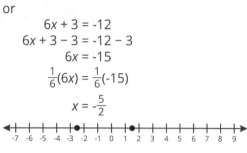

11.
$$10x + 8 > 18$$
$$10x + 8 - 8 > 18 - 8$$
$$10x > 10$$
$$\frac{1}{10} \cdot 10x > \frac{1}{10} \cdot 10$$
$$x > 1$$

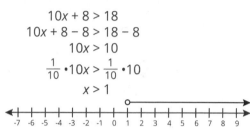

12.
$$3(P + 4) + 2(P - 6) \geq 4(2P - 1)$$
$$3P + 12 + 2P - 12 \geq 8P - 4$$
$$5P \geq 8P - 4$$
$$5P - 8P \geq 8P - 8P - 4$$
$$-3P \geq -4$$
$$-\frac{1}{3}(-3P) \geq -\frac{1}{3}(-4)$$
$$P \leq \frac{4}{3}$$

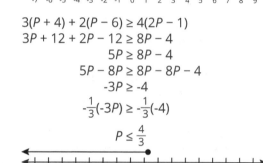

13.
$$2y + 1 = 5y - 7$$
$$2y + 1 - 1 = 5y - 7 - 1$$
$$2y = 5y - 8$$
$$2y - 5y = 5y - 5y - 8$$
$$-3y = -8$$
$$-\frac{1}{3}(-3y) = -\frac{1}{3}(-8)$$
$$y = \frac{8}{3}$$

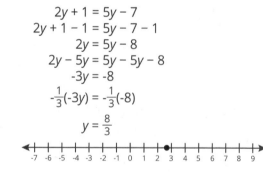

14.
$$3(y - 8) + 5(y + 2) \leq 14y + 2(y + 6)$$
$$3y - 24 + 5y + 10 \leq 14y + 2y + 12$$
$$8y - 14 \leq 16y + 12$$
$$8y - 14 + 14 \leq 16y + 12 + 14$$
$$8y \leq 16y + 26$$
$$8y - 16y \leq 16y - 16y + 26$$
$$-8y \leq 26$$
$$-\frac{1}{8}(-8y) \leq -\frac{1}{8}(26)$$
$$y \geq -\frac{13}{4}$$

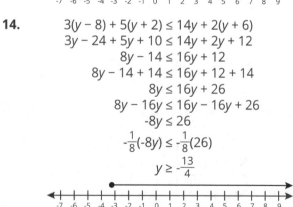

54

ANSWER KEY

SECTION 1

1.1 $|-3| = 3$

1.2 $|6| + |-4| = 6 + 4 = 10$

1.3 $|-7| + 3|4| = 7 + 12 = 19$

1.4 $|8 + 3| = |11| = 11$

1.5 $2|-1| = 2 \cdot 1 = 2$

1.6 $-|0| = -0 = 0$

1.7 $3|-4| = 3 \cdot 4 = 12$

1.8 $4|-2| - 3|-3| = 4 \cdot 2 - 3 \cdot 3 = 8 - 9 = -1$

1.9 $-|-8 - 2| = -|-10| = -(10) = -10$

1.10 $4 - |-4| = 4 - 4 = 0$

1.11 $|a| = 4, a = \pm 4, a = \{4, -4\}$

1.12 $|a + 1| = 4, a + 1 = \pm 4,$
$a = 3, a = -5, a = \{3, -5\}$

1.13 $|x - 1| = 3, x - 1 = \pm 3,$
$x = 4, x = -2, x = \{4, -2\}$

1.14 $|K| = -5$
impossible, $\emptyset$

1.15 $|x| = x$, zero or any positive number, $x \geq 0$

1.16 $|x| + |7| = 10$
$|x| + 7 = 10$
$|x| = 3$
$x = \pm 3, x = \{3, -3\}$

1.17 $|p| = \frac{2}{3}, p = \pm \frac{2}{3}, p = \left\{ \frac{2}{3}, -\frac{2}{3} \right\}$

1.18 $2|x| = 20, |x| = 10$
$x = \pm 10, x = \{10, -10\}$

1.19 $|R - 3| = 10$
$R - 3 = \pm 10$
$R - 3 = 10$ or $R - 3 = -10$
$R = 13 \qquad\quad R = -7$
$R = \{13, -7\}$

1.20 $|2x + 6| = 12$
$2x + 6 = \pm 12$
$2x + 6 = 12$ or $2x + 6 = -12$
$2x = 6 \qquad\qquad 2x = -18$
$x = 3 \qquad\qquad\quad x = -9$
$x = \{3, -9\}$

1.21 $6 < 8$

1.22 $\frac{1}{2} > \frac{1}{3}$

1.23 $|-a| = |a|$

1.24 $|x| + 1 > |x|$

1.25 $-|y| \leq |-y|$

1.26 $|-x| \geq 0$

1.27 $3 < 4 < 5$

1.28 $|-4| > -|-4|$

1.29 $|x| = 2$
$x = \pm 2$
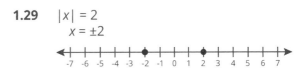

1.30 $|x + 1| = 2$
$x + 1 = \pm 2$
$x + 1 = 2$ or $x + 1 = -2$
$x = 1 \qquad\qquad x = -3$
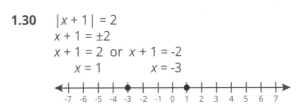

1.31 $|x - 1| = 3$
$x - 1 = \pm 3$
$x - 1 = 3$ or $x - 1 = -3$
$x = 4 \qquad\qquad x = -2$
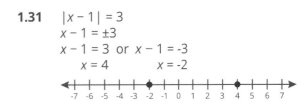

1.32 $|2x| = 6$
$2x = \pm 6$
$x = \pm 3$
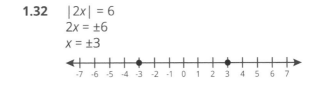

1.33 $|2x - 1| = 7$
$2x - 1 = \pm 7$
$2x - 1 = 7$ or $2x - 1 = -7$
$2x = 8 \qquad\qquad 2x = -6$
$x = 4 \qquad\qquad\quad x = -3$
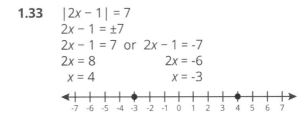

1.34 $|x| = 0$
$x = 0$
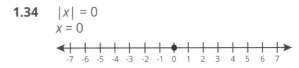

1.35 $|2 - x| = 4$
$2 - x = \pm 4$
$2 - x = 4$ or $2 - x = -4$
$-x = 2 \qquad\qquad -x = -6$
$x = -2 \qquad\qquad x = 6$
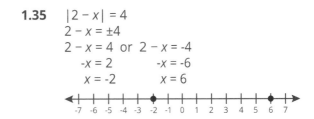

1.36	7
1.37	-3
1.38	3
1.39	-7
1.40	-7
1.41	6
1.42	2
1.43	-2
1.44	0
1.45	-5
1.46	-17
1.47	1
1.48	184
1.49	-15
1.50	24
1.51	-6.1
1.52	-30.6
1.53	-5.3
1.54	1.24
1.55	-5.94
1.56	12
1.57	80
1.58	-24
1.59	16
1.60	-150
1.61	-3
1.62	4
1.63	21
1.64	24
1.65	4

SELF TEST 1

1.01 $|-5| = 5$

1.02 $4|-2| - |-3| = 8 - 3 = 5$

1.03 $(-12)(-2) = 24$

1.04 $3(5 - 8) - 7 = 3(-3) - 7 = -9 - 7 = -16$

1.05 $10 \div (-2) + 6 = -5 + 6 = 1$

1.06 $15 - 12 - 8 + 4 - 6 + 1 = -6$

1.07 $8 - |-8| = 8 - 8 = 0$

1.08 $|x| = 5, x = \pm 5$

1.09 $|a| = -6;$
impossible

1.010 $|p + 2| = 10$
$p + 2 = \pm 10$
$p + 2 = 10$ or $p + 2 = -10$
$p = 8 \qquad p = -12$

1.011 $|3x - 4| = 6$
$3x - 4 = \pm 6$
$3x = 10$ or $3x = -2$
$x = \frac{10}{3} \qquad x = -\frac{2}{3}$

1.012 $2|x| = 3$
$|x| = \frac{3}{2}$
$x = \pm\frac{3}{2}$

1.013 $|x| = 6$
$x = \pm 6$

1.014 $|x - 1| = 5$
$x - 1 = \pm 5$
$x = 6$ or $x = -4$

1.015 $|2 - x| = 8$
$2 - x = \pm 8$
$-x = -10$ or $-x = 6$
$x = 10 \qquad x = -6$

1.016 true

1.017 false

1.018 false

1.019 true

1.020 true

SECTION 2

2.1
$$x + 2 = 10$$
$$x + 2 - 2 = 10 - 2$$
$$x + 0 = 8$$
$$x = 8$$

2.2
$$x + 8 = 6$$
$$x + 8 - 8 = 6 - 8$$
$$x + 0 = -2$$
$$x = -2$$

2.3
$$x - 5 = 10$$
$$x - 5 + 5 = 10 + 5$$
$$x + 0 = 15$$
$$x = 15$$

2.4
$$x - 8 = 2$$
$$x - 8 + 8 = 2 + 8$$
$$x + 0 = 10$$
$$x = 10$$

2.5
$$x + 6 = 6$$
$$x + 6 - 6 = 6 - 6$$
$$x + 0 = 0$$
$$x = 0$$

2.6
$$x + 6 - 5 = 8 - 2$$
$$x + 1 = 6$$
$$x + 1 - 1 = 6 - 1$$
$$x + 0 = 5$$
$$x = 5$$

2.7
$$3 + x + 1 = 2$$
$$x + 4 = 2$$
$$x + 4 - 4 = 2 - 4$$
$$x + 0 = -2$$
$$x = -2$$

2.8
$$3 - x = -4$$
$$3 - x + x = -4 + x$$
$$3 + 4 = -4 + 4 + x$$
$$7 = 0 + x$$
$$7 = x$$

2.9
$$7 - x = 7$$
$$7 - x + x = 7 + x$$
$$7 + 0 = 7 + x$$
$$x + 7 = 7$$
$$x + 7 - 7 = 7 - 7$$
$$x + 0 = 0$$
$$x = 0$$

2.10
$$7 + x + 2 = 9 + 3$$
$$x + 9 = 12$$
$$x + 9 - 9 = 12 - 9$$
$$x + 0 = 3$$
$$x = 3$$

2.11
$$x + 5 = 2x$$
$$2x = x + 5$$
$$2x - x = x - x + 5$$
$$x = 0 + 5$$
$$x = 5$$

2.12
$$3x = 2x + 7$$
$$3x - 2x = 2x - 2x + 7$$
$$x = 0 + 7$$
$$x = 7$$

2.13
$$5x = 7.3 + 4x$$
$$5x - 4x = 7.3 + 4x - 4x$$
$$x = 7.3$$

2.14
$$3x + 1 = 2x + 12$$
$$3x - 2x + 1 - 1 = 2x - 2x + 12 - 1$$
$$x + 0 = 0 + 11$$
$$x = 11$$

2.15
$$9x - 3.2 = 6.8 + 8x$$
$$9x - 8x = 6.8 + 3.2$$
$$x = 10$$

2.16
$$4 + 12x = 11x + 10$$
$$12x - 11x = 10 - 4$$
$$x = 6$$

2.17
$$8 + x = 13 + 2x$$
$$8 - 13 = 2x - x$$
$$-5 = x$$

2.18
$$3x + 1 + 5x = 7 + 15 + 7x$$
$$3x + 5x - 7x = 7 + 15 - 1$$
$$x = 21$$

2.19
$$4 - 7x + 10 = 15 - 6x - 8$$
$$14 - 7x = 7 - 6x$$
$$14 - 7 = 7x - 6x$$
$$7 = x$$

2.20
$$5 - 8.5x = 6.7 - 7.5x$$
$$5 - 6.7 = 8.5x - 7.5x$$
$$-1.7 = x$$

2.21
$$3x = 12$$
$$\frac{1}{3} \cdot 3x = \frac{1}{3} \cdot 12$$
$$x = 4$$

2.22
$$5x = 25$$
$$\frac{1}{5} \cdot 5x = \frac{1}{5} \cdot 25$$
$$x = 5$$

2.23
$$7x = 84$$
$$\frac{1}{7} \cdot 7x = \frac{1}{7} \cdot 84$$
$$x = 12$$

2.24
$$3.2x = 64$$
$$\frac{1}{3.2} \cdot 3.2x = \frac{1}{3.2} \cdot 64$$
$$x = 20$$

2.25
$$5.1x = 1.02$$
$$\frac{1}{5.1} \cdot 5.1x = \frac{1}{5.1} \cdot 1.02$$
$$x = 0.2$$

2.26
$$18x = 60$$
$$\frac{1}{18} \cdot 18x = \frac{1}{18} \cdot 60$$
$$x = \frac{60}{18} = \frac{10}{3} \text{ or } 3\frac{1}{3}$$

2.27 $\frac{x}{6} = 3$

$6 \cdot \frac{x}{6} = 6 \cdot 3$

$x = 18$

2.28 $\frac{x}{9} = 1$

$9 \cdot \frac{x}{9} = 9 \cdot 1$

$x = 9$

2.29 $\frac{x}{10} = 4$

$10 \cdot \frac{x}{10} = 10 \cdot 4$

$x = 40$

2.30 $\frac{x}{1.2} = 15$

$1.2 \cdot \frac{x}{1.2} = 1.2 \cdot 15$

$x = 18$

2.31 $\frac{x}{8} = 0.42$

$8 \cdot \frac{x}{8} = 8 \cdot 0.42$

$x = 3.36$

2.32 $\frac{3x}{2} = 5$

$\frac{2}{3} \cdot \frac{3x}{2} = \frac{2}{3} \cdot 5$

$x = \frac{10}{3}$ or $3\frac{1}{3}$

2.33 $\frac{8x}{7} = 8$

$\frac{7}{8} \cdot \frac{8x}{7} = \frac{7}{8} \cdot 8$

$x = 7$

2.34 $\frac{4x}{3} = 8$

$\frac{3}{4} \cdot \frac{4x}{3} = \frac{3}{4} \cdot 8$

$x = 6$

2.35 $\frac{5x}{7} = 22$

$\frac{7}{5} \cdot \frac{5x}{7} = \frac{7}{5} \cdot 22$

$x = \frac{154}{5}$ or $30\frac{4}{5}$

2.36 $5x + 2 = 12$

$5x = 10$

$x = 2$

2.37 $6x - 8 = 16$

$6x = 24$

$x = 4$

2.38 $12x + 1 = 25$

$12x = 24$

$x = 2$

2.39 $2x - 20 = 32$

$2x = 52$

$x = 26$

2.40 $20 - 3x = 8$

$-3x = -12$

$x = 4$

2.41 $-13 - 3x = -10$

$-3x = 3$

$x = -1$

2.42 $\frac{x}{6} + 2 = 8$

$\frac{x}{6} = 6$

$x = 36$

2.43 $\frac{x}{3} - 4 = 10$

$\frac{x}{3} = 14$

$x = 42$

2.44 $\frac{x}{6} + 7 = 20$

$\frac{x}{6} = 13$

$x = 78$

2.45 $\frac{x}{9} + 8 = 8$

$\frac{x}{9} = 0$

$x = 0$

2.46 $\frac{x}{6} + 4 = 20$

$\frac{x}{6} = 16$

$x = 96$

2.47 $\frac{2x}{5} + 1 = 7$

$\frac{2x}{5} = 6$

$2x = 30$

$x = 15$

2.48 $\frac{3x}{7} - 2 = 15$

$\frac{3x}{7} = 17$

$3x = 119$

$x = \frac{119}{3}$ or $39\frac{2}{3}$

2.49 $\frac{5x}{8} + 10 = 2$

$\frac{5x}{8} = -8$

$5x = -64$

$x = -\frac{64}{5}$ or $-12\frac{4}{5}$

2.50 $\frac{7x}{15} - 1 = 22$

$\frac{7x}{15} = 23$

$7x = 345$

$x = \frac{345}{7}$ or $49\frac{2}{7}$

2.51 $3(x + 2) = 6$
$3x + 6 = 6$
$3x = 0$
$x = 0$

2.52 $5(x - 4) = 12$
$5x - 20 = 12$
$5x = 32$
$x = \frac{32}{5}$ or $6\frac{2}{5}$

2.53 $7(2x + 6) = 1$
$14x + 42 = 1$
$14x = -41$
$x = -\frac{41}{14}$ or $-2\frac{13}{14}$

2.54 $4(3 - 2x) = 15$
$12 - 8x = 15$
$-8x = 3$
$x = -\frac{3}{8}$

2.55 $8(1 - 5x) = 13$
$8 - 40x = 13$
$-40x = 5$
$x = -\frac{5}{40} = -\frac{1}{8}$

2.56 $6(x - 1) = 4(x - 2)$
$6x - 6 = 4x - 8$
$6x - 4x = -8 + 6$
$2x = -2$
$x = -1$

2.57 $9(x - 6) = 8(x + 6)$
$9x - 54 = 8x + 48$
$9x - 8x = 48 + 54$
$x = 102$

2.58 $15(2 - x) = 13(3 - x)$
$30 - 15x = 39 - 13x$
$-15x + 13x = 39 - 30$
$-2x = 9$
$x = -\frac{9}{2}$ or $-4\frac{1}{2}$

2.59 $12(x - 6) = 2(x - 9)$
$12x - 72 = 2x - 18$
$12x - 2x = 72 - 18$
$10x = 54$
$x = \frac{54}{10} = \frac{27}{5}$ or $5\frac{2}{5}$

2.60 $4(7 - 3x) = 7(4 - 2x)$
$28 - 12x = 28 - 14x$
$14x - 12x = 28 - 28$
$2x = 0$
$x = 0$

2.61 $7(x - 2) + 3(x + 2) = 5(x - 6)$
$7x - 14 + 3x + 6 = 5x - 30$
$10x - 8 = 5x - 30$
$5x = -22$
$x = -\frac{22}{5}$ or $-4\frac{2}{5}$

2.62 $4(2x - 3) + 8(x - 4) = 2(2x + 6)$
$8x - 12 + 8x - 32 = 4x + 12$
$16x - 44 = 4x + 12$
$12x = 56$
$x = \frac{56}{12} = \frac{14}{3}$ or $4\frac{2}{3}$

2.63 $4(7x - 1) = 3(2x + 1) - 4(x + 6)$
$28x - 4 = 6x + 3 - 4x - 24$
$28x - 4 = 2x - 21$
$26x = -17$
$x = -\frac{17}{26}$

2.64 $12(2x - 8) = 4(5 - 2x) + 3(7 - 3x)$
$24x - 96 = 20 - 8x + 21 - 9x$
$24x - 96 = 41 - 17x$
$41x = 137$
$x = \frac{137}{41}$ or $3\frac{14}{41}$

2.65 $3(x - 2) + 4(2x - 6) = 6(x - 4) + 8(2x + 1)$
$3x - 6 + 8x - 24 = 6x - 24 + 16x + 8$
$11x - 30 = 22x - 16$
$-11x = 14$
$x = -\frac{14}{11}$ or $-1\frac{3}{11}$

2.66 $a + b + c = 3 + 4 + 5 = 12$
2.67 $a - b - c = 3 - 4 - 5 = -6$
2.68 $\frac{a + b}{c} = \frac{3 + 4}{5} = \frac{7}{5}$ or $1\frac{2}{5}$
2.69 $a^2 + b^2 = 3^2 + 4^2 = 9 + 16 = 25$
2.70 $c^2 - b^2 = 5^2 - 4^2 = 25 - 16 = 9$
2.71 $D + E + F = 5 + 10 + 4 = 19$
2.72 $D - E - F = 5 - 10 - 4 = -9$
2.73 $2D - 3E + 4F = 10 - 30 + 16 = -4$
2.74 $D^2 - E^2 + F^2 = 25 - 100 + 16 = -59$
2.75 $D \cdot \frac{E}{F} = 5 \cdot \frac{10}{4} = \frac{50}{4} = \frac{25}{2}$ or $12\frac{1}{2}$
2.76 $A = LW, LW = A, \frac{LW}{W} = \frac{A}{W}, L = \frac{A}{W}$
2.77 $A = LW, LW = A, \frac{LW}{L} = \frac{A}{L}, W = \frac{A}{L}$
2.78 $3r + 2s = P$
$2s = P - 3r$
$s = \frac{P - 3r}{2}$

2.79 $A = 1 + prt$
$prt + 1 = A$
$prt = A - 1$
$\frac{ptr}{pt} = \frac{A - 1}{pt}$
$r = \frac{A - 1}{pt}$

2.80
$$C = \frac{5(F - 32)}{9}$$
$$\frac{5(F - 32)}{9} = C$$
$$5(F - 32) = 9C$$
$$5F - 160 = 9C$$
$$5F = 9C + 160$$
$$F = \frac{9}{5}C + 32$$

2.81
$R = 3(p + s) - 4(p - s)$
$R = 3p + 3s - 4p + 4s$
$R = 7s - p$
$p = 7s - R$

2.82
$$A = \frac{h}{2}(a + b)$$
$$2A = h(a + b)$$
$$h(a + b) = 2A$$
$$h = \frac{2A}{a + b}$$

2.83
$$C = 2\pi r$$
$$2\pi r = C$$
$$r = \frac{C}{2\pi}$$

2.84
$$P = 2l + 2w$$
$$2l + 2w = P$$
$$2l = P - 2w$$
$$l = \frac{P - 2w}{2}$$

2.85
$K^2 (m - p) = 2K^2 p$
$K^2 m - K^2 p = 2K^2 p$
$K^2 m = 3K^2 p$
$3K^2 p = K^2 m$
$$p = \frac{K^2 m}{3K^2} = \frac{m}{3}$$

2.86
$2x < 8$
$\frac{1}{2} \cdot 2x < \frac{1}{2} \cdot 8$
$x < 4$

2.87
$2x + 1 < 9$
$2x < 8$
$x < 4$

2.88
$7x - 2 < 10$
$7x < 12$
$x < \frac{12}{7}$

2.89
$8x - 1 < 15$
$8x < 16$
$x < 2$

2.90
$3y + 5 < 10$
$3y < 5$
$y < \frac{5}{3}$

2.91
$2P - 3 > P + 6$
$2P - P > 6 + 3$
$P > 9$

2.92
$8P + 2 > 3P - 15$
$8P - 3P > -15 - 2$
$5P > -17$
$P > -\frac{17}{5}$

2.93
$2(P + 1) > 7 + P$
$2P + 2 > 7 + P$
$2P - P > 7 - 2$
$P > 5$

2.94
$6(2P - 1) > 5P + 2$
$12P - 6 > 5P + 2$
$12P - 5P > 6 + 2$
$7P > 8$
$P > \frac{8}{7}$

2.95
$2(P + 1) + 3(P + 2) > 2$
$2P + 2 + 3P + 6 > 2$
$5P + 8 > 2$
$5P > -6$
$P > -\frac{6}{5}$

2.96
$3y + 2 \geq 5y + 8$
$3y - 5y \geq 8 - 2$
$-2y \geq 6$
$y \leq -3$

2.97
$7y - 3 \leq 10y + 9$
$-3y \leq 12$
$y \geq -4$

2.98
$12z - 3 \geq 2z - 15$
$12z - 2z \geq -15 + 3$
$10z \geq -12$
$z \geq -\frac{6}{5}$

2.99
$-7z - 7 \leq -5z + 5$
$-7z + 5z \leq 5 + 7$
$-2z \leq 12$
$z \geq -6$

2.100
$2(z + 1) - 4(z - 4) \leq 2(z + 5)$
$2z + 2 - 4z + 16 \leq 2z + 10$
$-2z + 18 \leq 2z + 10$
$-4z \leq -8$
$z \geq 2$

2.101
$2x < 6$
$x < 3$

2.102
$3x > -3$
$x > -1$

2.103 $2x - 1 \leq x + 5$
$2x - x \leq 5 + 1$
$x \leq 6$

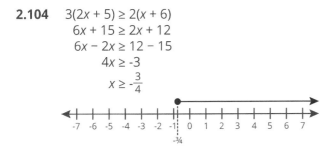

2.104 $3(2x + 5) \geq 2(x + 6)$
$6x + 15 \geq 2x + 12$
$6x - 2x \geq 12 - 15$
$4x \geq -3$
$x \geq -\frac{3}{4}$

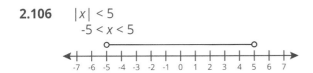

2.105 $2(x + 1) - 3(x + 5) \geq 0$
$2x + 2 - 3x - 15 \geq 0$
$-x - 13 \geq 0$
$-x \geq 13$
$x \leq -13$

2.106 $|x| < 5$
$-5 < x < 5$

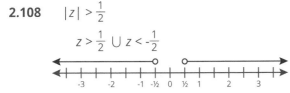

2.107 $|x| < 4$
$-4 < x < 4$

2.108 $|z| > \frac{1}{2}$
$z > \frac{1}{2} \cup z < -\frac{1}{2}$

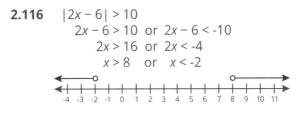

2.109 $|z| \leq 6$
$-6 \leq z \leq 6$

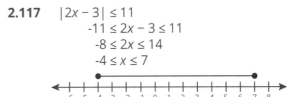

2.110 $|P| > 3$
$P > 3 \cup P < -3$

2.111 $|x + 1| \leq 4$
$-4 \leq x + 1 \leq 4$
$-5 \leq x \leq 3$

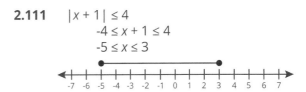

2.112 $|x - 1| \leq 4$
$-4 \leq x - 1 \leq 4$
$-3 \leq x \leq 5$

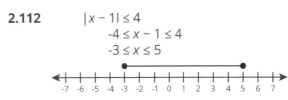

2.113 $|y - 2| > 6$
$y - 2 > 6$ or $y - 2 < -6$
$y > 8$ or $y < -4$

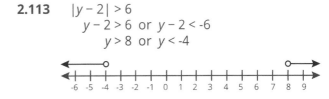

2.114 $|y + 2| > 6$
$y + 2 > 6$ or $y + 2 < -6$
$y > 4$ or $y < -8$

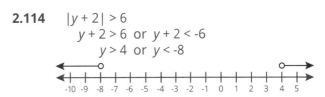

2.115 $|3x + 5| \leq 12$
$-12 \leq 3x + 5 \leq 12$
$-17 \leq 3x \leq 7$
$-\frac{17}{3} \leq x \leq \frac{7}{3}$

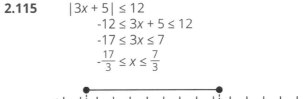

2.116 $|2x - 6| > 10$
$2x - 6 > 10$ or $2x - 6 < -10$
$2x > 16$ or $2x < -4$
$x > 8$ or $x < -2$

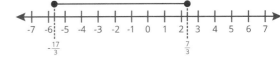

2.117 $|2x - 3| \leq 11$
$-11 \leq 2x - 3 \leq 11$
$-8 \leq 2x \leq 14$
$-4 \leq x \leq 7$

2.118 $|1 - 4x| > 7$
   $1 - 4x > 7$ or $1 - 4x < -7$
   $-4x > 6$ or $-4x < -8$
   $x < -\frac{3}{2}$ or $x > 2$

2.119 $|2(x - 3)| < 1$
   $-1 < 2x - 6 < 1$
   $5 < 2x < 7$
   $\frac{5}{2} < x < \frac{7}{2}$

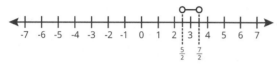

2.120 $|5x - 1| < 1$
   $-1 < 5x - 1 < 1$
   $0 < 5x < 2$
   $0 < x < \frac{2}{5}$

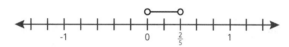

SELF TEST 2

2.01 $|-6| + 2|-4| - 3|6|$
   $= 6 + 8 - 18$
   $= 14 - 18$
   $= -4$

2.02 $5 - |-6|$
   $= 5 - 6$
   $= -1$

2.03 $16 - 4 + 2|-4| - 3$
   $= 12 + 8 - 3$
   $= 17$

2.04 $15 \div (-3) + 5|-2| \div (-5)$
   $= -5 + 10 \div (-5)$
   $= -5 - 2$
   $= -7$

2.05 $-8 + 2 \div (-2) + |-3|$
   $= -8 - 1 + 3$
   $= -6$

2.06 $a + b + c = 4 + (-2) + 8$
   $= 4 - 2 + 8 = 10$

2.07 $a - b - c = 4 - (-2) - 8$
   $= 4 + 2 - 8 = -2$

2.08 $ab - bc = 4(-2) - (-2)(8)$
   $= -8 + 16 = 8$

2.09 $3abc = 3(4)(-2)(8)$
   $= (12)(-16) = -192$

2.010 $2ab - 2bc + 2ac = 2(4)(-2) - 2(-2)(8) + 2(4)(8)$
   $= -16 + 32 + 64 = 16 + 64 = 80$

2.011 $3x - 2 = 13$
   $3x = 15$
   $x = 5$

2.012 $3(2x - 4) = 4(x + 1)$
   $6x - 12 = 4x + 4$
   $6x - 4x = 4 + 12$
   $2x = 16$
   $x = 8$

2.013 $|x| = 10$
   $x = \pm 10$

2.014 $|3 - x| = 8$
   $3 - x = \pm 8$
   $3 - x = 8$ or $3 - x = -8$
   $-x = 5$ $-x = -11$
   $x = -5$ $x = 11$

2.015 $|x| = -15$
   impossible

2.016 $3x < 18$
   $\frac{1}{3} \cdot 3x < \frac{1}{3} \cdot 18$
   $x < 6$

2.017　　$6(x + 1) > 2x - 1$
　　　　　$6x + 6 > 2x - 1$
　　　　　$6x - 2x > -1 - 6$
　　　　　　$4x > -7$
　　　　　　　$x > -\frac{7}{4}$

2.018　　$\frac{x}{5} - 3 < 5$
　　　　　　　$\frac{x}{5} < 8$
　　　　　$5 \cdot \frac{x}{5} < 8 \cdot 5$
　　　　　　　$x < 40$

2.019　　$|x| < 5$
　　　　　$-5 < x < 5$

2.020　　$|P| > 3$
　　　　　$P > 3$ or $P < -3$

2.021　　$|y - 2| < 10$
　　　　　$-10 < y - 2 < 10$
　　　　　　$-8 < y < 12$

2.022　　$|2x - 2| < 8$
　　　　　$-8 < 2x - 2 < 8$
　　　　　$-6 < 2x < 10$
　　　　　$-3 < x < 5$

2.023　　$|x| > 5$
　　　　　　$x > 5$ or $x < -5$

2.024　$2(x + 1) < 3x - 2$
　　　　$2x + 2 < 3x - 2$
　　　　$2x - 3x < -2 - 2$
　　　　　$-x < -4$
　　　　　　$x > 4$

2.025　$3(x - 2) = 5(x + 1)$
　　　　$3x - 6 = 5x + 5$
　　　　$3x - 5x = 5 + 6$
　　　　　$-2x = 11$
　　　　　　$x = -\frac{11}{2}$

SECTION 3

3.1　　　Let x = small number
　　　　$10x$ = large number
　　　$10x - x = 81$
　　　　　$9x = 81$
　　　　　　$x = 9$
　　　　$10x = 90$
　　　　　{9, 90}

3.2　　　Let x = small number
　　　$3 + 2x$ = large number
　　　$x + (3 + 2x) = 27$
　　　　$3x + 3 = 27$
　　　　　$3x = 24$
　　　　　　$x = 8$
　　　$3 + 2x = 19$
　　　　　{8, 19}

3.3　　　Let x = small number
　　　$x + 1$ = large number
　　　$x + (x + 1) = 37$
　　　　$2x + 1 = 37$
　　　　　$2x = 36$
　　　　　　$x = 18$
　　　　$x + 1 = 19$
　　　　　{18, 19}

3.4　　　Let x = small number
　　　$x + 2$ = large number
　　　$x + (x + 2) = 92$
　　　　$2x + 2 = 92$
　　　　　$2x = 90$
　　　　　　$x = 45$
　　　　$x + 2 = 47$
　　　　　{45, 47}

3.5　　　Let x = small number
　　　$x + 1$ = second number
　　　$x + 2$ = large number
　　$x + (x + 1) + (x + 2) = 117$
　　　　　$3x + 3 = 117$
　　　　　　$3x = 114$
　　　　　　　$x = 38$
　　　　　$x + 1 = 39$
　　　　　$x + 2 = 40$
　　　　　　{38, 39, 40}

3.6　　　Let x = small number
　　　$x + 1$ = second number
　　　$x + 2$ = large number
　　$x + (x + 1) + (x + 2) = 21 + x$
　　　　　$3x + 3 = 21 + x$
　　　　　　$2x = 18$
　　　　　　　$x = 9$
　　　　　$x + 1 = 10$
　　　　　$x + 2 = 11$
　　　　　　{9, 10, 11}

3.7   Let x = small number
$3x - 800$ = large number
$x + (3x - 800) = 1{,}200$
$4x - 800 = 1{,}200$
$4x = 2{,}000$
$x = 500$
$3x - 800 = 3(500) - 800 = 700$
{500, 700}

3.8   Let x = width of rectangle
$3x$ = length of rectangle
$2x + 2(3x) = 22$
$2x + 6x = 22$
$8x = 22$
$x = \frac{22}{8} = \frac{11}{4} = 2\frac{3}{4}$
$3x = \frac{33}{4} = 8\frac{1}{4}$
{width = $2\frac{3}{4}$, length = $8\frac{1}{4}$}

3.9   Let x = small angle
$x + 4$ = large angle
$x + (x + 4) = 90°$
$2x + 4 = 90°$
$2x = 86°$
$x = 43°$
$x + 4 = 47°$
{43°, 47°}

3.10   Let x = small angle
$5x$ = large angle
$x + 5x = 180°$
$6x = 180°$
$x = 30°$
$5x = 150°$
{30°, 150°}

3.11   Let x = length of equal sides
$x - 4$ = base side
$x + x + x - 4 = 32$
$3x - 4 = 32$
$3x = 36$
$x = 12$
$x - 4 = 8$
{12, 12, 8}

3.12   Let x = Henry's age
$2x$ = Frank's age
$x + 2x = 45$
$3x = 45$
$x = 15$
$2x = 30$
{Henry: 15 yrs. old; Frank: 30 yrs. old}

3.13   Let x = son's age 2 years ago
$4x$ = man's age 2 years ago

	2 years ago	now	in 3 years
son	x	$x + 2$	$x + 5$
man	$4x$	$4x + 2$	$4x + 5$

$4x + 5 = 3(x + 5)$
$4x + 5 = 3x + 15$
$x = 10$
$x + 2 = 12$
$4x + 2 = 42$
{son: 12 yrs. old; father: 42 yrs. old}

3.14   Let x = James's age
$x + 10$ = Joe's age
$x + 8$ = James's age in 8 years
$x + 18$ = Joe's age in 8 years
$2(x + 18) = 3(x + 8)$
$2x + 36 = 3x + 24$
$12 = x$
$x + 10 = 22$
{James: 12 yrs. old; Joe: 22 yrs. old}

3.15   Let x = number of dimes
$x + 2$ = number of nickels
$10x + 5(x + 2) = 115$
$10x + 5x + 10 = 115$
$15x = 105$
$x = 7$
$x + 2 = 9$
{7 dimes, 9 nickels}

3.16   Let x = number of quarters
$10 + x$ = number of dimes
$25x + 10(10 + x) = 345$
$25x + 100 + 10x = 345$
$35x + 100 = 345$
$35x = 245$
$x = 7$
$10 + x = 17$
{7 quarters, 17 dimes}

3.17   Let x = number of dimes
$2 + x$ = number of nickels
$3 + 2 + x$ = number of quarters
$10x + 5(2 + x) + 25(5 + x) = 335$
$10x + 10 + 5x + 125 + 25x = 335$
$40x + 135 = 335$
$40x = 200$
$x = 5$
$2 + x = 7$
$5 + x = 10$
{5 dimes, 7 nickels, 10 quarters}

3.18   Let x = small number
$x + 5$ = large number
$x + (x + 5) = 3x - 3$
$x + x + 5 = 3x - 3$
$2x + 5 = 3x - 3$
$-x = -8$
$x = 8$
$x + 5 = 13$
{8, 13}

3.19   Let x = number of children
$30 - x$ = number of adults
$50(30 - x) + 25(x) = 1,225$
$1,500 - 50x + 25x = 1,225$
$1,500 - 25x = 1,225$
$-25x = -275$
$x = 11$
$30 - x = 19$
{11 children, 19 adults}

3.20   Let x = speed of slower car
$x + 10$ = speed of faster car
$r \cdot t = d, t = 3$
$3x + 3(x + 10) = 240$
$3x + 3x + 30 = 240$
$6x + 30 = 240$
$6x = 210$
$x = 35$
$x + 10 = 45$
{35 mph, 45 mph}

3.21   Let t = flying time
$d = r \cdot t$
$280t + 320t = 1,000$
$600t = 1,000$
$t = \frac{1,000}{600} = \frac{5}{3}$ hours
$\frac{5}{3} = 1\frac{2}{3}$ = 1 hr. 40 min.
10:00 + 1:40 = 11:40 A.M.
{11:40 A.M.}

3.22   Let r = rate of car
$d = r \cdot t$
$8(1\frac{1}{4}) = \frac{1}{4}(r)$
$8 \cdot \frac{5}{4} = \frac{r}{4}$
$r = 40$ mph
{40 mph}

3.23   Let t = time of Express
$t + 1\frac{1}{2}$ = time of Local
$35(t + 1\frac{1}{2}) = 56 \cdot t$
$35t + \frac{105}{2} = 56t$

$\frac{105}{2} = 21t$
$t = \frac{105}{42} = 2\frac{1}{2}$ hours
{$2\frac{1}{2}$ hours}

3.24   Let t = hours Ben travels
$8t + 20t = 180$
$28t = 180$
$t = \frac{180}{28} = 6\frac{3}{7}$ hours
t = 6 hours, 26 minutes
{6 hours, 26 minutes}

3.25   Let r = Charles's rate
$d = rt$
$2r = 9(4 + 2)$
$2r = 54$
$r = 27$ mph
{27 mph}

3.26   Let t = time of second train
$50(t + \frac{1}{2}) = 55t$
$50t + 25 = 55t$
$25 = 5t$
t = 5 hours
{5 hours}

3.27   Let x = yards handicap
rate of Jack = $\frac{440}{88}$ = 5 yds./sec.
Jack must run shorter portion in 55 sec. or a total distance of 55 $\cdot$ 5 = 275 yds.
$x + 275 = 440$
$x = 165$ yards
{165 yards}

3.28   Let r = rate of plane
w = rate of wind
$3(r + w) = 1,890$
$3r + 3w = 1,890$
$3r = 1,890 - 3w$
$r = 630 - w$
$3\frac{3}{8}(r - w) = 1,890$
$3\frac{3}{8}(630 - w - w) = 1,890$
$\frac{27}{8}(630 - 2w) = 1,890$
$630 - 2w = 560$
$-2w = -70$
$w = 35$
$r = 630 - 35 = 55$
{wind speed: 35 mph;
air speed: 595 mph}

3.29   Let r = rate of plane
w = rate of wind
$(r - w)\frac{1}{2} = 125$
$r - w = 250$
$r = 250 + w$
$\frac{25}{60}(r + w) = 125$
$\frac{25}{60}(250 + w + w) = 125$
$250 + 2w = 300$
$2w = 50$
$w = 25$
$r = 250 + 25 = 275$
{wind speed: 25 mph;
air speed: 275 mph}

3.30   Let r = rate of current
$5r$ = rate of boat
$t = \frac{d}{r}$
$\frac{12}{5r - r} + \frac{12}{5r + r} = 2\frac{1}{2}$
$\frac{12}{4r} + \frac{12}{6r} = \frac{5}{2}$
$\frac{3}{r} + \frac{2}{r} = \frac{5}{2}$ (multiply by the L.C.D., 2r)
$6 + 4 = 5r$
$10 = 5r$
$r = 2$
{2 mph}

3.31   Let r = speed of aircraft
w = speed of wind
$d = r \cdot t$
$(r + w) \cdot 1\frac{1}{2} = 630$
$(r + w) \cdot \frac{3}{2} = 630$
$3r + 3w = 1{,}260$
$3r = 1{,}260 - 3w$
$r = 420 - w$
$(r - w) \cdot 1\frac{3}{4} = 630$
$(420 - w - w) \cdot \frac{7}{4} = 630$
$(420 - 2w) \cdot 7 = 2{,}520$
$2{,}940 - 14w = 2{,}520$
$-14w = -420$
$w = 30$
$r = 420 - 30 = 390$
{wind speed: 30 mph;
air speed: 390 mph}

3.32   Let x = number of coins Ted has
$2x + 8$ = number of coins Mac has
$(2x + 8) + x = 74$
$3x + 8 = 74$
$3x = 66$
$x = 22$
$2x + 8 = 2(22) + 8 = 52$
{Ted: 22; Mac: 52}

3.33   Let w = width of rectangle
$3w$ = length of rectangle
$w + 1$ = width of new rectangle
$3w + 2$ = length of new rectangle
$2(3w + 2) + 2(w + 1) = 62$
$6w + 4 + 2w + 2 = 62$
$8w + 6 = 62$
$8w = 56$
$w = 7$
$3w = 21$
{width: 7 in.; length: 21 in.}

3.34   Let w = width
$l = 3w - 2$ = length
$2(3w - 2) + 2w = 28$
$6w - 4 + 2w = 28$
$8w = 32$
$w = 4$
$3w - 2 = 10$
{width: 4 in; length: 10 in.}

3.35   Let x = number of years ago
$12 - x$ = Ann's age x years ago
$36 - x$ = mother's age x years ago
$36 - x = 4(12 - x)$
$36 - x = 48 - 4x$
$3x = 12$
$x = 4$
{4 years ago}

3.36   Let x = number of books five years ago
$3x + 10$ = number of books now
$3x + 10 = 1{,}510$
$3x = 1{,}500$
$x = 500$
{500 books}

3.37   Let x = the number
$x + 1$ = successor
$(x + 1) + 2x = 61$
$3x + 1 = 61$
$3x = 60$
$x = 20$
{20}

3.38   Let x = pounds of cashew nuts
$75x$ = worth of cashew nuts
$10(150)$ = worth of pecans
$75x + 10(150) = (x + 10)(100)$
$75x + 1{,}500 = 100x + 1{,}000$
$500 = 25x$
$20 = x$
{20 lbs.}

3.39   Let x = gallons of maple syrup
$50 - x$ = gallons of corn syrup
$600x$ = worth of maple syrup
$80(50 - x)$ = worth of corn syrup
$600x + 80(50 - x) = 50(236)$
$600x + 4,000 - 80x = 11,800$
$520x = 7,800$
$x = 15$
$50 - x = 35$
{maple syrup: 15 gal.;
corn syrup: 35 gal.}

3.40   Let d = number of dimes
$2d$ = number of nickels
$2d + 5$ = number of half-dollars
$10d + 5(2d) + 50(2d + 5) = 610$
$10d + 10d + 100d + 250 = 610$
$120d = 360$
$d = 3$
$2d = 6$
$2d + 5 = 11$
{3 dimes, 6 nickels, 11 half-dollars}

3.41   Let x = number of nickels
$21 - x$ = number of dimes
$5x + 10(21 - x) = 165$
$5x + 210 - 10x = 165$
$-5x = -45$
$x = 9$
$21 - x = 12$
{9 nickels, 12 dimes}

3.42   Let x = number of two-cent stamps
$36 - x$ = number of three-cent stamps
$2x + 3(36 - x) = 100$
$2x + 108 - 3x = 100$
$-x = -8$
$x = 8$
$36 - x = 28$
{2¢ stamps: 8; 3¢ stamps: 28}

3.43   Let x = number of trips of large truck
$x + 18$ = number of trips of small truck
$5x$ = tons capacity of large truck
$3(x + 18)$ = tons capacity of small truck
$3(x + 18) - 5x = 12$
$3x + 54 - 5x = 12$
$-2x = -42$
$x = 21$
$x + 18 = 39$
{small truck: 39; large truck: 21}

3.44   Let x = number of trips of small truck
$x + 3$ = number of trips of large truck
$4(x + 3) - 3(x) = 20$
$4x + 12 - 3x = 20$
$x = 8$
$x + 3 = 11$
{small truck: 3; large truck: 11}

3.45   Let x = number of years
$11 + x$ = age of A in x years
$68 + x$ = age of B in x years
$68 + x = 4(11 + x)$
$68 + x = 44 + 4x$
$24 = 3x$
$8 = x$
{8 years}

3.46   Let x = years under 60
$x + 14$ = years over 40
$60 - x = 40 + x + 14$
$20 = 2x + 14$
$6 = 2x$
$3 = x$
$60 - 3 = 57$ is aunt's age
$40 + 3 = 43$ is Mrs. West's age
{aunt: 57 yrs. old;
Mrs. West: 43 yrs. old}

3.47   Let x = width of rectangle
$x + 16$ = length of rectangle
$2(x + 16) + 2x = 256$
$2x + 32 + 2x = 256$
$4x = 224$
$x = 56$
$x + 16 = 72$
{width: 56 in.; length: 72 in.}

3.48   Let x = smaller number
$2x + 11$ = larger number
$x + (2x + 11) = 2(2x + 11 - x)$
$x + 2x + 11 = 4x + 22 - 2x$
$3x + 11 = 2x + 22$
$x = 11$
$2x + 11 = 33$
{11, 33}

3.49   Let q = number of quarters
$q + 2$ = number of nickels
$25q + 5(q + 2) = 100$
$25q + 5q + 10 = 100$
$30q = 90$
$q = 3$
$q + 2 = 5$
{3 quarters, 5 nickels}

3.50   Let x = number of $10 checks
$22 - x$ = number of $20 checks
$10x + 20(22 - x) = 300$
$10x + 440 - 20x = 300$
$-10x = -140$
$x = 14$
$22 - x = 8$
{$10 checks: 14;
$20 checks: 8}

3.51   Let x = the angle
$90 - x$ = the complement
$x = \frac{1}{2}(90 - x) - 18$
$2x = (90 - x) - 36$
$2x = 54 - x$
$3x = 54$
$x = 18°$
{18°}

SELF TEST 3

3.01 $|{-10}| - |{-8}| = 10 - 8 = 2$
3.02 $15 + |{-3}| - 4 = 15 + 3 - 4 = 14$
3.03 $10 + 8 \div 4 - 12 = 10 + 2 - 12 = 0$
3.04 $2P - 3R + T$
$= 2(10) - 3(-4) + 5$
$= 20 + 12 + 5$
$= 32 + 5$
$= 37$
3.05 $PRT = 10(-4)(5) = -200$
3.06 $P^2 - R^2 = 10^2 - (-4)^2 = 100 - 16 = 84$
3.07 $5x - 1 = 24$
$5x = 25$
$x = 5$
3.08 $6x + 2 = 2x - 18$
$4x = -20$
$x = -5$
3.09 $5(x - 6) = 2(x - 1)$
$5x - 30 = 2x - 2$
$3x = 28$
$x = \frac{28}{3}$ or $9\frac{1}{3}$
3.010 $|x| = 11$
$x = \pm 11$
3.011 $|x + 2| = 10$
$x + 2 = \pm 10$
$x + 2 = 10$ or $x + 2 = -10$
$x = 8$ or $x = -12$
{8, -12}
3.012 $|3x - 4| = 15$
$3x - 4 = \pm 15$
$3x - 4 = 15$ or $3x - 4 = -15$
$3x = 19$ or $3x = -11$
$x = \frac{19}{3}$ or $x = -\frac{11}{3}$
$\{\frac{19}{3}, -\frac{11}{3}\}$
3.013 $|x| < 6$
$-6 < x < 6$
3.014 $|x - 1| > 4$
$x - 1 > 4$ or $x - 1 < -4$
$x > 5$ or $x < -3$
3.015 $|2x + 6| < 16$
$-16 < 2x + 6 < 16$
$-22 < 2x < 10$
$-11 < x < 5$
3.016 $|x| > 2$
$-2 > x > 2$

3.017 $5x + 1 \leq 11$
$5x \leq 10$
$x \leq 2$

3.018   Let x = smaller number
$x + 5$ = larger number
$(x + 5) + x = 3x - 3$
$2x + 5 = 3x - 3$
$8 = x$
$x + 5 = 13$
{8, 13}

3.019   Let x = one number
$3x - 2$ = other number
$3x - 2 = 2x - 6$
$x = -4$
$3x - 2 = -14$
{-4, -14}

3.020   Let x = first number
$x + 2$ = second number
$x + 4$ = third number
$x = (x + 2) + (x + 4)$
$x = 2x + 6$
$-x = 6$
$x = -6$
$x + 2 = -4$
$x + 4 = -2$
{-6, -4, -2}

3.021   Let x = son's age
$x + 20$ = Dad's age
$x + x + 20 = 40$
$2x = 20$
$x = 10$
$x + 20 = 30$
{son: 10 yrs. old; Dad: 30 yrs. old}

3.022   Let x = Jill's age now
$50 - x$ = Dad's age now
$50 - x + 5 = 3(x + 5)$
$55 - x = 3x + 15$
$40 = 4x$
$10 = x$
$50 - x = 40$
{Jill: 10 yrs. old; Dad: 40 yrs. old}

3.023   Let w = width
$2w + 2$ = length
$2(2w + 2) + 2w = 76$
$4w + 4 + 2w = 76$
$6w + 4 = 76$
$6w = 72$
$w = 12$
$2w + 2 = 26$
{width: 12; length: 26}

3.024   Let x = number of half-dollars, quarters, and dimes each
$50x + 25x + 10x = 1,500$
$85x = 1,500$
$x = 17.65$
Answer is no.

3.025   Let t = time going
$12 - t$ = time returning
$d = rt$
$20t = 30(12 - t)$
$20t = 360 - 30t$
$50t = 360$
$t = \dfrac{360}{50} = 7\frac{1}{5}$ or 7.2 hrs.
$= 7$ hrs., 12 min.

$12 - t = 4\frac{4}{5}$ or 4.8 hrs.
$= 4$ hrs., 48 min.
{out: 7.2 hrs.; back: 4.8 hrs.}

LIFEPAC TEST

1. $5 - 3(-2) + |-3| = 5 + 6 + 3 = 14$
2. $7(-4) - |-6| + |4| = -28 - 6 + 4 = -30$
3. $15 \div 3 \cdot (-2) + |-10| = 5(-2) + 10 = 0$
4. $A^2 - B^2 = 4^2 - 5^2 = 16 - 25 = -9$
5. $2A - 3B = 2(7) - 3(-2) = 14 + 6 = 20$
6. $x^2 - 7x + 10 = (-3)^2 - 7(-3) + 10 = 9 + 21 + 10$
    $= 40$

7. $3x + 1 = 10$
    $3x = 9$
    $x = 3$

8. $7x - 4 = 5x + 15$
    $2x = 19$
    $x = \frac{19}{2}$ or $9\frac{1}{2}$

9. $7(x - 2) = 3(x + 4)$
    $7x - 14 = 3x + 12$
    $4x = 26$
    $x = \frac{26}{4} = \frac{13}{2}$ or $6\frac{1}{2}$

10. $2x + 1 < 5$
    $2x < 4$
    $x < 2$

11. $3x + 5 < 6x - 1$
    $3x - 6x < -5 - 1$
    $-3x < -6$
    $x > 2$

12. $|2x + 1| = 10$
    $2x + 1 = \pm 10$
    $2x + 1 = 10$ or $2x + 1 = -10$
    $2x = 9$ or $2x = -11$
    $x = \frac{9}{2}$ $\qquad$ $x = -\frac{11}{2}$
    $\{\frac{9}{2}, -\frac{11}{2}\}$

13. $|x| > 5$
    $x > 5$ or $x < -5$

14. $|x| < 12$
    $-12 < x < 12$

15. $|4x - 8| < 12$
    $-12 < 4x - 8 < 12$
    $-4 < 4x < 20$
    $-1 < x < 5$

16. $|x| > 5$
    $-5 > x > 5$

17. $4x - 2 < 10$
    $4x < 12$
    $x < 3$

18. Let t = flying time
    $d = rt$
    $560t + 500t = 2,000$
    $1,060t = 2,000$
    $t = \frac{2,000}{1,060}$
    $t = 1\frac{47}{53}$ hr.
    $= 1$ hr., 53 min.
    Added to 12 noon = 1:53 P.M.
    $\{1:53$ P.M.$\}$

19. Let N = number of nickels
    $3N$ = number of dimes
    $2N$ = number of quarters
    $5N + 10(3N) + 25(2N) = 340$
    $5N + 30N + 50N = 340$
    $85N = 340$
    $N = 4$
    $3N = 12$
    $2N = 8$
    $\{4$ nickels, 12 dimes, 8 quarters$\}$

20. Let x = number of children
    $30 - x$ = number of adults
    $50(30 - x) + 25x = 1,225$
    $1500 - 50x + 25x = 1,225$
    $-25x = -275$
    $x = 11$
    $30 - x = 19$
    $\{11$ children, 19 adults$\}$

ALTERNATE LIFEPAC TEST

1. $7 - 4(-3) + |-5| = 7 + 12 + 5 = 24$
2. $8(-5) - |-4| + |3| = -40 - 4 + 3 = -41$
3. $18 \div (-3)(-6) - |-4| = -6(-6) - 4 = 36 - 4 = 32$
4. $x^2 - y^2 = 9^2 - (-2)^2 = 81 - 4 = 77$
5. $7x - 2y = 7 \cdot 3 - 2(-4) = 21 + 8 = 29$
6. $a^2 - 7a + 2 = (-2)^2 - 7(-2) + 2 = 4 + 14 + 2 = 20$
7.
$$5x - 6 = 20$$
$$5x - 6 + 6 = 20 + 6$$
$$5x = 26$$
$$\tfrac{1}{5} \cdot 5x = \tfrac{1}{5} \cdot 26$$
$$x = \tfrac{26}{5}$$

8.
$$7x - 8 = 2x + 5$$
$$7x - 2x - 8 = 2x - 2x + 5$$
$$5x - 8 = 5$$
$$5x - 8 + 8 = 5 + 8$$
$$5x = 13$$
$$\tfrac{1}{5} \cdot 5x = \tfrac{1}{5} \cdot 13$$
$$x = \tfrac{13}{5}$$

9.
$$5(x + 1) = 3(x - 4)$$
$$5x + 5 = 3x - 12$$
$$5x - 3x + 5 = 3x - 3x - 12$$
$$2x + 5 = -12$$
$$2x + 5 - 5 = -12 - 5$$
$$2x = -17$$
$$\tfrac{1}{2}(2x) = \tfrac{1}{2}(-17)$$
$$x = -\tfrac{17}{12}$$

10.
$$7x - 1 < 13$$
$$7x - 1 + 1 < 13 + 1$$
$$7x < 14$$
$$\tfrac{1}{7} \cdot 7x < \tfrac{1}{7} \cdot 14$$
$$x < 2$$

11.
$$4x + 5 > 3x - 2$$
$$4x + 5 - 5 > 3x - 2 - 5$$
$$4x > 3x - 7$$
$$4x - 3x > 3x - 3x - 7$$
$$x > -7$$

12.
$$|3x - 1| = 10$$
$$3x - 1 = 10$$
$$3x - 1 + 1 = 10 + 1$$
$$3x = 11$$
$$\tfrac{1}{3} \cdot 3x = \tfrac{1}{3} \cdot 11$$
$$x = \tfrac{11}{3}$$
or
$$3x - 1 = -10$$
$$3x - 1 + 1 = -10 + 1$$
$$3x = -9$$
$$\tfrac{1}{3}(3x) = \tfrac{1}{3}(-9)$$
$$x = -3$$
$$\therefore x = \tfrac{11}{3} \text{ or } -3$$

13. $x > 3$ or $x < -3$
14. $x < 5$ and $x > -5$
$$-5 < x < 5$$
15.
$$|2x - 4| < 10$$
$$2x - 4 < 10$$
$$2x - 4 + 4 < 10 + 4$$
$$2x < 14$$
$$\tfrac{1}{2} \cdot 2x < \tfrac{1}{2} \cdot 14$$
$$x < 7$$
and
$$2x - 4 > -10$$
$$2x - 4 + 4 > -10 + 4$$
$$2x > -6$$
$$\tfrac{1}{2}(2x) > \tfrac{1}{2}(-6)$$
$$x > -3$$
$$-3 < x < 7$$

16. $x < 3$ and $x > -3$
$$-3 < x < 3$$

17.
$$5x - 7 < 23$$
$$5x - 7 + 7 < 23 + 7$$
$$5x < 30$$
$$\tfrac{1}{5} \cdot 5x < \tfrac{1}{5} \cdot 30$$
$$x < 6$$

18. $500t + 350t = 2,000$

$850t = 2,000$

$\frac{1}{850} \cdot 850t = \frac{1}{850} \cdot 2,000$

$t = \frac{2,000}{850} = 2.35$ hrs.

or 2 hrs., 21 min.

time = 4:00 P.M. + 2 hrs., 21 min.

= 6:21 P.M.

{6:21 P.M.}

19.   Joe = 18 yrs. old now

Bill = 3 • 18 = 54 yrs. old now

Let x = number of years

$54 + x = 2(18 + x)$

$54 + x = 36 + 2x$

$54 + x - x = 36 + 2x - x$

$54 = 36 + x$

$54 - 36 = 36 - 36 + x$

$18 = x$

In 18 years Bill will be twice as old as Joe.

20.   Let x = number of dimes

$x + 4$ = number of quarters

$3x + 5$ = number of nickels

$5(3x + 5) + 10x + 25(x + 4) = 425$

$15x + 25 + 10x + 25x + 100 = 425$

$50x + 125 = 425$

$50x + 125 - 125 = 425 - 125$

$50x = 300$

$\frac{1}{50} \cdot 50x =$

$\frac{1}{50} \cdot 300$

$x = 6$

$x + 4 =$

$6 + 4 = 10$

$3x + 5 =$

$3 \cdot 6 + 5 =$

$18 + 5 = 23$

{6 dimes, 10 quarters, 23 nickels}

MATH 1102
ALTERNATE LIFEPAC TEST

NAME _____

DATE _____

SCORE _____

$\dfrac{73}{91}$

Evaluate each of the following expressions (each answer, 3 points).

1. $7 - 4(-3) + |-5|$

2. $8(-5) - |-4| + |3|$

3. $18 \div (-3)(-6) - |-4|$

4. $x^2 - y^2$ for $x = 9$ and $y = -2$

5. $7x - 2y$ for $x = 3$ and $y = -4$

6. $a^2 - 7a + 2$ for $a = -2$

Solve each of the following sentences (each answer, 5 points).

7. $5x - 6 = 20$

8. $7x - 8 = 2x + 5$

9. $5(x + 1) = 3(x - 4)$

10. $7x - 1 < 13$

11. $4x + 5 > 3x - 2$

12. $|3x - 1| = 10$

13. $|x| > 3$

14. $|x| < 5$

15. $|2x - 4| < 10$

Graph each of the following sentences (each answer, 5 points).

16. $|x| < 3$

17. $5x - 7 < 23$

Solve the following problems (each answer, 4 points for set-up, 2 points for solution).

18. Two planes leave an airport at 4:00 P.M. If the northbound plane flies at 500 mph and the southbound plane flies at 350 mph, at what time will the planes be 2,000 miles apart?

19. Bill is three times as old as Joe. In how many years will Bill be twice as old as Joe if Joe is 18 years old now?

20. Dan has $4.25 in quarters, dimes, and nickels. If he has four more quarters than dimes and the number of nickels is five more than three times the number of dimes, how many coins of each kind does Dan have?

MATH 1103

Unit 3: Linear Equations and Inequalities

TEACHER NOTES

MATERIALS NEEDED FOR LIFEPAC	
Required	Suggested
(none)	• straightedges • graph paper

ADDITIONAL LEARNING ACTIVITIES

Section 1: Lines

1. Discuss the distance formula between two points whose coordinates are known.

   $$d = (x_1 - x_2)^2 + (y_1 - y_2)^2$$

   Demonstrate with the following diagram how this formula is a special case of the Pythagorean Theorem.

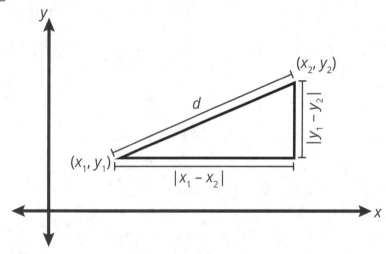

2. Divide the class into four groups—*A*, *B*, *C*, and *D*. Group *A* is to decide if the points (11, 1), (6, 6), and (2, 2) are vertices of a right triangle. Group *B* is to decide the same as Group *A*, but with points (10, -4), (3, 5), and (0, 0). Group *C* has points (9, 6), (-1, 2), and (1, -3) with which to decide. Group *D* has points (-5, -8), (1, 6), and (5, -4) with which to decide. Groups present their findings to each other and critique their solutions.

Section 2: Systems of Equations

1. Discuss how to determine if nonvertical lines are parallel by determining whether they have the same slope and different *y*-intercepts.

2. Discuss how to determine if two nonvertical lines are perpendicular by examining their equations in slope-intercept form. If the slope of one of the lines is the negative reciprocal of the slope of the other line, the lines are perpendicular.

3. Divide the class into four groups. Assign one of the following systems to each group. Have each group tell whether each pair of lines is parallel, perpendicular, or neither without graphing. Answers are given for the teacher's information.

   a. $2x - 5y = -3$
      $2x + 5y = 4$
      (perpendicular; slopes are $\frac{2}{5}$ and $-\frac{2}{5}$ respectively)

   b. $x + 2y = 5$
      $2x + 4y = 8$
      (parallel; slopes are both $-\frac{1}{2}$ and y-intercepts are different)

   c. $y = 4x - 5$
      $4y = 8 + 16x$
      (parallel; slopes are both 4, and y-intercepts are different)

   d. $y = -x + 7$
      $y = x + 3$
      (neither)

Section 3: Inequalities

1. Have the class solve each of the following inequalities for y and, without plotting any points, tell whether the graph of each inequality is shaded above the line or below the line. Answers are given for the teacher's information.

   a. $x > 3$ (above)

   b. $y \leq x + 2$ (below)

   c. $y < 2x$ (below)

   d. $x + 2 \geq y$ ($y \leq x + 2$; below)

   e. $2x + y > 5$ ($y > -2x + 5$; above)

   f. $3x - y < 6$ ($y > 3x - 6$; above)

   g. $x \leq 8$ (below or left)

   h. $3x + 2y > -7$ ($y > -\frac{3}{2}x - \frac{7}{2}$; above)

   i. $4x < y - 2$ ($y > 4x + 2$; above)

   j. $4x - y \geq 4$ ($y \leq 4x - 4$; below)

Additional Activity

The following may be reproduced as a student worksheet.

» EQUATIONS

Write the equation for each of the following lines.

1. The line that passes through (-3, -5) and is perpendicular to $5x - 2y = 4$.

    _____

2. The line that passes through (0, 3) and is perpendicular to $2x - y = 7$.

    _____

3. The line that passes through (-1, 3) and is perpendicular to the line containing (3, -5) and (-2, 7).

    _____

4. The line with y-intercept of 4 and is parallel to $2x + 3y = 8$.

    _____

5. The line with y-intercept of 3 and is parallel to $x - 5y = 10$.

    _____

6. The line that passes halfway between and is parallel to both $x + y = 2$ and $x + y = 8$.

    _____

7. The line with $m = \frac{1}{2}$ and $b = 6$.

    _____

8. The line with $m = \frac{2}{3}$ and $b = 5$.

    _____

9. The line with $m = -3$ and intersects $2x + 3y = 9$ at $x = 3$.

    _____

10. The line with y-intercept of -2 and intersects $4x + 2y = 15$ at $x = 3$.

    _____

ADDITIONAL ACTIVITIES, SOLUTION KEY

1. Find the slope of the given line; since the lines are perpendicular, the negative reciprocal of this slope equals the slope of the other line.

$$5x - 2y = 4$$
$$5x - 5x - 2y = 4 - 5x$$
$$-2y = -5x + 4$$
$$-\frac{1}{2}(-2y) = -\frac{1}{2}(-5x + 4)$$
$$y = \frac{5}{2}x - 2$$
$$m = \frac{5}{2}$$

m of other line is therefore $-\frac{2}{5}$.

$$y - y_1 = m(x - x_1)$$
$$y - (-5) = -\frac{2}{5}[x - (-3)]$$
$$y + 5 = -\frac{2}{5}(x + 3)$$
$$5y + 25 = -2(x + 3) \quad \text{(multiply by 5)}$$
$$5y + 25 = -2x - 6$$
$$5y + 25 + 2x = -2x + 2x - 6$$
$$2x + 5y + 25 = -6$$
$$2x + 5y + 25 - 25 = -6 - 25$$
$$2x + 5y = -31$$

2. Find the slope of the given line; since the lines are perpendicular, the negative reciprocal of this slope equals the slope of the other line.

$$2x - y = 7$$
$$2x - 2x - y = 7 - 2x$$
$$-y = -2x + 7$$
$$y = 2x - 7 \quad \text{(multiply by -1)}$$
$$m = 2$$

m of other line is therefore $-\frac{1}{2}$.

$$y - y_1 = m(x - x_1)$$
$$y - 3 = -\frac{1}{2}(x - 0)$$
$$y - 3 = -\frac{1}{2}x$$
$$2y - 6 = -x \quad \text{(multiply by 2)}$$
$$2y - 6 + x = -x + x$$
$$x + 2y - 6 = 0$$
$$x + 2y - 6 + 6 = 0 + 6$$
$$x + 2y = 6$$

3. Find the slope of the line containing (3, -5) and (-2, 7); since the lines are perpendicular, the negative reciprocal of this slope equals the slope of the other line.

$$m = \frac{\Delta y}{\Delta x} = \frac{7 - (-5)}{-2 - 3} = -\frac{12}{5}$$

m of other line is therefore $\frac{5}{12}$.

$$y - y_1 = m(x - x_1)$$
$$y - 3 = \frac{5}{12}[x - (-1)]$$
$$y - 3 = \frac{5}{12}(x + 1)$$
$$12y - 36 = 5(x + 1) \quad \text{(multiply by 12)}$$
$$12y - 36 = 5x + 5$$
$$12y - 36 - 5x = 5x - 5x + 5$$
$$-5x + 12y - 36 = 5$$
$$-5x + 12y - 36 + 36 = 5 + 36$$
$$-5x + 12y = 41$$
$$5x - 12y = -41 \quad \text{(multiply by -1)}$$

4. Find the slope of the given line; since the lines are parallel, the slopes are equal.

$$2x + 3y = 8$$
$$2x - 2x + 3y = 8 - 2x$$
$$3y = -2x + 8$$
$$\frac{1}{3}(3y) = \frac{1}{3}(-2x + 8)$$
$$y = -\frac{2}{3}x + \frac{8}{3}$$
$$m = -\frac{2}{3}$$

Use this slope and point (0, 4) to find the equation of the line.

$$y - y_1 = m(x - x_1)$$
$$y - 4 = -\frac{2}{3}(x - 0)$$
$$y - 4 = -\frac{2}{3}x$$
$$3y - 12 = -2x \quad \text{(multiply by 3)}$$
$$3y - 12 + 2x = -2x + 2x$$
$$2x + 3y - 12 = 0$$
$$2x + 3y - 12 + 12 = 0 + 12$$
$$2x + 3y = 12$$

5. Find the slope of the given line; since the lines are parallel, the slopes are equal.

$$x - 5y = 10$$
$$x - x - 5y = 10 - x$$
$$-5y = -x + 10$$
$$-\frac{1}{5}(-5y) = -\frac{1}{5}(-x + 10)$$
$$y = \frac{1}{5}x - 2$$
$$m = \frac{1}{5}$$

Use this slope and point (0, 3) to find the equation of the line.

$$y - y_1 = m(x - x_1)$$
$$y - 3 = \frac{1}{5}(x - 0)$$
$$y - 3 = \frac{1}{5}x$$
$$5y - 15 = x \quad \text{(multiply by 5)}$$
$$5y - 15 - x = x - x$$
$$-x + 5y - 15 = 0$$
$$-x + 5y - 15 + 15 = 0 + 15$$
$$-x + 5y = 15$$
$$x - 5y = -15 \quad \text{(multiply by -1)}$$

6. Add the equations together and multiply by $\frac{1}{2}$ to find the equation of the other line.

$$\begin{array}{rcl} x + y &=& 2 \\ \underline{x + y} &=& \underline{8} \\ 2x + 2y &=& 10 \end{array}$$

$$\frac{1}{2}(2x + 2y = 10)$$

$$x + y = 5$$

7.
$$y = mx + b$$
$$y = \frac{1}{2}x + 6$$
$$2y = x + 12 \quad \text{(multiply by 2)}$$
$$2y - x = x - x + 12$$
$$-x + 2y = 12$$
$$x - 2y = -12 \quad \text{(multiply by -1)}$$

8.
$$y = mx + b$$
$$y = \frac{2}{3}x + 5$$
$$3y = 2x + 15 \quad \text{(multiply by 3)}$$
$$3y - 2x = 2x - 2x + 15$$
$$-2x + 3y = 15$$
$$2x - 3y = -15 \quad \text{(multiply by -1)}$$

9. When $x = 3$:
$$2x + 3y = 9$$
$$2 \cdot 3 + 3y = 9$$
$$6 + 3y = 9$$
$$6 - 6 + 3y = 9 - 6$$
$$3y = 3$$
$$\frac{1}{3} \cdot 3y = \frac{1}{3} \cdot 3$$
$$y = 1$$

The point of intersection is (3, 1). Use the given slope and this point to find the equation of the other line.

$$y - y_1 = m(x - x_1)$$
$$y - 1 = -3(x - 3)$$
$$y - 1 = -3x + 9$$
$$y - 1 + 3x = -3x + 3x + 9$$
$$3x + y - 1 = 9$$
$$3x + y - 1 + 1 = 9 + 1$$
$$3x + y = 10$$

10. When $x = 3$:
$$4x + 2y = 15$$
$$4 \cdot 3 + 2y = 15$$
$$12 + 2y = 15$$
$$12 - 12 + 2y = 15 - 12$$
$$2y = 3$$
$$\frac{1}{2} \cdot 2y = \frac{1}{2} \cdot 3$$
$$y = \frac{3}{2}$$

The point of intersection is $(3, \frac{3}{2})$. Use this point and the given y-intercept (0, -2) to find the slope and then the equation of the line.

$$m = \frac{\Delta y}{\Delta x} = \frac{-2 - \frac{3}{2}}{0 - 3} = \frac{-\frac{7}{2}}{-3} = \frac{7}{6}$$

$$y - y_1 = m(x - x_1)$$
$$y - (-2) = \frac{7}{6}(x - 0)$$
$$y + 2 = \frac{7}{6}x$$
$$6y + 12 = 7x$$
$$6y + 12 - 7x = 7x - 7x$$
$$-7x + 6y + 12 = 0$$
$$-7x + 6y + 12 - 12 = 0 - 12$$
$$-7x + 6y = -12$$
$$7x - 6y = 12 \quad \text{(multiply by -1)}$$

ANSWER KEY

SECTION 1

1.1 a. $y = 2x - 3$
$\quad= 2(1) - 3$
$\quad= -1$
b. $y = 2x - 3$
$\quad= 2(2) - 3$
$\quad= 4 - 3$
$\quad= 1$
c. $y = 2x - 3$
$\quad= 2(3) - 3$
$\quad= 6 - 3$
$\quad= 3$

1.2 a. $y = 3x + 1$
$\quad= 3(-1) + 1$
$\quad= -3 + 1$
$\quad= -2$
b. $y = 3x + 1$
$\quad= 3(-2) + 1$
$\quad= -6 + 1$
$\quad= -5$
c. $y = 3x + 1$
$\quad= 3(0) + 1$
$\quad= 0 + 1$
$\quad= 1$

1.3 a. $y = 5x - 5$
$\quad= 5(0) - 5$
$\quad= 0 - 5$
$\quad= -5$
b. $y = 5x - 5$
$\quad= 5(1) - 5$
$\quad= 5 - 5$
$\quad= 0$
c. $y = 5x - 5$
$\quad= 5(2) - 5$
$\quad= 10 - 5$
$\quad= 5$

1.4 a. $y = -2x + 1$
$\quad= -2(1) + 1$
$\quad= -2 + 1$
$\quad= -1$
b. $y = -2x + 1$
$\quad= -2(5) + 1$
$\quad= -10 + 1$
$\quad= -9$
c. $y = -2x + 1$
$\quad= -2(-5) + 1$
$\quad= 10 + 1$
$\quad= 11$

1.5 a. $y = 7 - 2x$
$\quad= 7 - 2(3)$
$\quad= 7 - 6$
$\quad= 1$
b. $y = 7 - 2x$
$\quad= 7 - 2(4)$
$\quad= 7 - 8$
$\quad= -1$
c. $y = 7 - 2x$
$\quad= 7 - 2(-2)$
$\quad= 7 + 4$
$\quad= 11$

1.6 $2 \neq 2 - 4$
$2 \neq -2$

1.7 $3 \neq 5 - 2(0)$
$3 \neq 5$

1.8 $2 \neq \dfrac{0}{5} + 1$
$2 \neq 1$

1.9 $2 \neq \dfrac{2(1) + 1}{3}$
$2 \neq 1$

1.10 $-1 \neq 3 - (-1)$
$-1 \neq 4$

1.11 through 1.20 Examples:
1.11 (1,4), (2, 3), (3, 2)
1.12 (1, 1), (2, 7), (3, 13)
1.13 (1, 0), (2, 2), (3, 4)
1.14 (1, 5), (2, 5), (3, 5)
1.15 $(1, \frac{1}{2}), (2, \frac{3}{2}), (3, \frac{5}{2})$
1.16 $(1, 2), (2, \frac{5}{2}), (3, 3)$
1.17 (-2, 1), (-2, 2), (-2, 3)
1.18 (1, 0), (2, 1), (3, 2)
1.19 $(1, \frac{2}{5}), (2, 0), (3, -\frac{2}{5})$
1.20 $(1, \frac{1}{5}), (2, \frac{3}{5}), (3, 1)$
1.21 $x^2 + y = 4; \frac{x}{2} - y^3 = 1$
1.22 $x^2 + y^2 = 5; y = x^2 + 3$
1.23 through 1.30 Examples:
1.23 (1, 5), (3, 3), (5, 1)
1.24 (5, 0), (8, 3), (10, 5)
1.25 (1, 5), (2, 3), (3, 1)
1.26 (2, -1), (-4, 2), (6, -3)
1.27 (0, 2), (1, 1), (2, 0)

1.28   (2, 0), (4, 3), (0, -3)

1.29   (3, 0), (1, $\frac{4}{3}$), (0, 2)

1.30   (-1, 0), (1, $\frac{6}{5}$), (0, $\frac{3}{5}$)

1.31

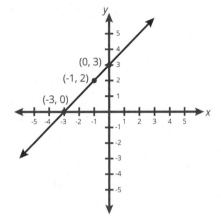

1.32

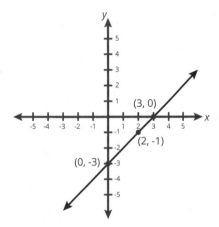

1.33

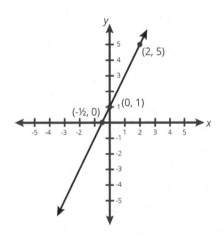

1.34

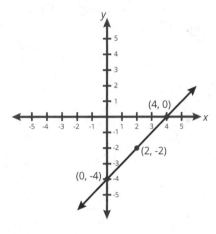

1.35

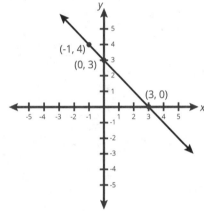

1.36

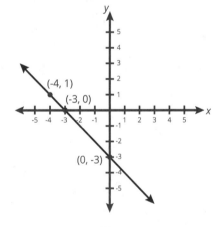

1.37

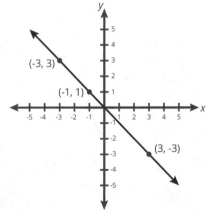

1.38

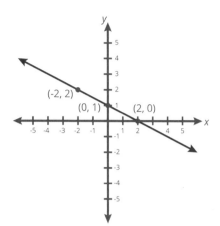

1.42

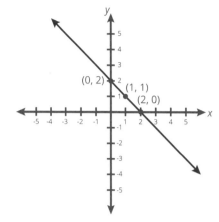

1.39

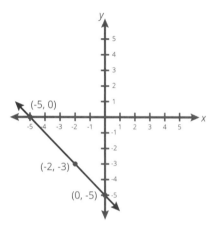

1.43

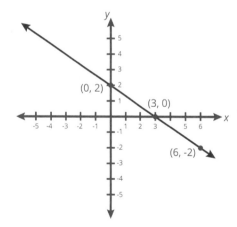

1.40

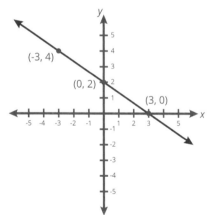

1.44

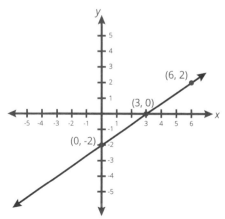

1.41

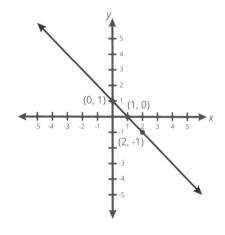

1.45

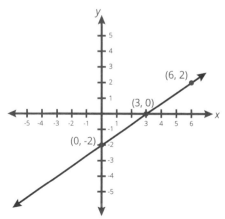

1.46

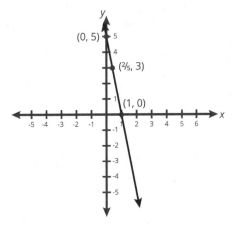

1.47

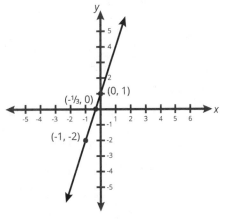

1.48

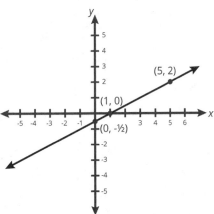

1.49

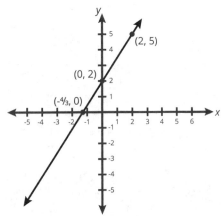

1.50

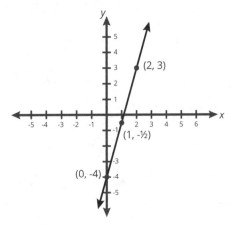

1.51 The lines are parallel by equal slopes.

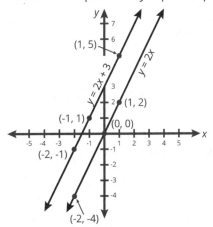

1.52 The lines are parallel by equal slopes.

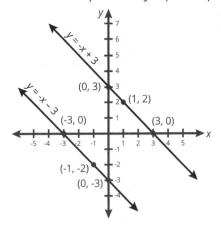

1.53 They are ⊥ and can be checked by the Pythagorean Theorem or negative reciprocal slopes.

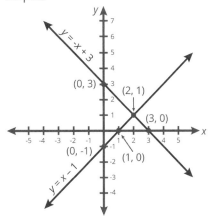

1.54 $m = \frac{\Delta y}{\Delta x} = \frac{-2-2}{-2-2} = \frac{-4}{-4} = 1$

1.55 $m = \frac{\Delta y}{\Delta x} = \frac{-2-2}{-1-1} = \frac{-4}{-2} = 2$

1.56 $m = \frac{\Delta y}{\Delta x} = \frac{-1-1}{-2-2} = \frac{-2}{-4} = \frac{1}{2}$

1.57 $m = \frac{\Delta y}{\Delta x} = \frac{-2-2}{2-(-2)} = \frac{-4}{4} = -1$

1.58 $m = \frac{\Delta y}{\Delta x} = \frac{2-0}{-2-4} = \frac{2}{-6} = -\frac{1}{3}$

1.59 $m = \frac{\Delta y}{\Delta x} = \frac{-4-4}{1-(-1)} = \frac{-8}{2} = -4$

1.60 Choose another point such as (1, 1).
$m = \frac{\Delta y}{\Delta x} = \frac{1-1}{1-0} = \frac{0}{1} = 0$

1.61 $m = \frac{\Delta y}{\Delta x} = \frac{-3-(-1)}{0-4} = \frac{-2}{-4} = \frac{1}{2}$

1.62 $m = \frac{\Delta y}{\Delta x} = \frac{-3-(-1)}{3-(-4)} = -\frac{2}{7}$

1.63 Choose another point (2, 1).
$m = \frac{\Delta y}{\Delta x} = \frac{1-0}{2-2} = \frac{1}{0}$ = undefined; no slope

1.64 $m = \frac{\Delta y}{\Delta x} = \frac{3-0}{0-4} = -\frac{3}{4}$

1.65 $m = \frac{\Delta y}{\Delta x} = \frac{0-(-4)}{3-0} = \frac{4}{3}$

1.66 $m = \frac{3-2}{7-6} = 1$

1.67 $m = \frac{7-3}{5-0} = \frac{4}{5}$

1.68 $m = \frac{7-3}{4-1} = \frac{4}{3}$

1.69 $m = \frac{4-1}{5-1} = \frac{3}{4}$

1.70 $m = \frac{3-0}{2-0} = \frac{3}{2}$

1.71 $m = \frac{5-0}{7-0} = \frac{5}{7}$

1.72 $m = \frac{6-5}{1+1} = \frac{1}{2}$

1.73 $m = \frac{6-6}{4+2} = 0$

1.74 $m = \frac{3+3}{2+2} = \frac{3}{2}$

1.75 $m = \frac{-2+1}{7-6} = -1$

1.76 $m = \frac{-6-4}{-5+3} = \frac{-10}{-2} = 5$

1.77 $m = \frac{7-3}{5-5} = \frac{4}{0}$ = no slope

1.78 $\frac{y-3}{2-1} = 2$, $y - 3 = 2$, $y = 5$

1.79 $\frac{y-2}{2-1} = -1$, $y - 2 = -1$, $y = 1$

1.80 $\frac{7-y}{5-3} = \frac{1}{2}$, $14 - 2y = 2$, $-2y = -12$, $y = 6$

1.81 $\frac{y-5}{3-2} = 1$, $y - 5 = 1$, $y = 6$

1.82 $\frac{y-5}{4-3} = -2$, $y - 5 = -2$, $y = 3$

1.83 $\frac{7-9}{3-x} = \frac{2}{3}$, $3(-2) = 2(3 - x)$, $-6 = 6 - 2x$, $-12 = -2x$, $x = 6$

For Problems 1.84 through 1.93, compute each slope and use the definitions of slope, zero slope, and no slope:

$m \neq 0$ for neither horizontal nor vertical line,

$m = 0$ for horizontal line,

$m = \frac{x}{0}$ for vertical line.

1.84 $m = 3$; neither

1.85 $m = \frac{-12}{-4}$; neither

1.86 $m = \frac{0}{2}$; horizontal

1.87 $m = \frac{0}{1}$; horizontal

1.88 $m = \frac{0}{-1}$; horizontal

1.89 $m = -3$; neither

1.90 $m = \frac{-7}{0}$; vertical

1.91 $m = \frac{-4}{-10}$; neither

1.92 $m = \frac{0}{-1}$; horizontal

1.93 $m = \frac{0}{-7}$; horizontal

For Problems 1.94 through 1.97, check three slopes.

1.94 (1, 1) and (2, 2) $m = 1$
(2, 2) and (3, 3) $m = 1$
(1, 1) and (3, 3) $m = 1$
yes: collinear.

1.95   (-2, 1) and (0, 3) $m = \frac{2}{2} = 1$

(-2, 1) and (2, 5) $m = \frac{4}{4} = 1$

(0, 3) and (2, 5) $m = \frac{2}{2} = 1$
yes: collinear.

1.96   (1, 3) and (3, 5) $m = 1$

(1, 3) and (4, 7) $m = \frac{4}{3}$

(3, 5) and (4, 7) $m = 2$
no: not collinear.

1.97   (6, -2) and (3, 1) $m = \frac{3}{-3} = -1$

(6, -2) and (0, 4) $m = \frac{6}{-6} = -1$

(3, 1) and (0, 4) $m = \frac{3}{-3} = -1$
yes: collinear.

1.98 $m = 1$, (0, 0)
$y - 0 = 1(x - 0)$
$y = x$

1.99 $m = 2$, (0, 0)
$y - 0 = 2(x - 0)$
$y = 2x$

1.100 $m = \frac{1}{2}$, (0, 0)
$y - 0 = \frac{1}{2}(x - 0)$
$y = \frac{x}{2}$

1.101 $m = -1$, (0, 0)
$y - 0 = -1(x - 0)$
$y = -x$

1.102 $m = -\frac{1}{3}$, (4, 0)

$y - 0 = -\frac{1}{3}(x - 4)$

$y = -\frac{x}{3} + \frac{4}{3}$

1.103 $m = -4$, (0, 0)
$y - 0 = -4(x - 0)$
$y = -4x$

1.104 $m = 0$, (0, 1)
$y - 1 = 0(x - 0)$
$y - 1 = 0$
$y = 1$

1.105 $m = \frac{1}{2}$, (0, -3)

$y + 3 = \frac{1}{2}(x - 0)$

$y + 3 = \frac{x}{2}$

$y = \frac{x}{2} - 3$

1.106 $m = -\frac{2}{7}$, (-4, -1)

$y + 1 = -\frac{2}{7}(x + 4)$

$y + 1 = -\frac{2x}{7} - \frac{8}{7}$

$y = -\frac{2x}{7} - \frac{15}{7}$

1.107 no slope, (2, 0)
vertical line
$x = 2$

1.108 $m = -\frac{3}{4}$, (0, 3)

$y - 3 = \frac{-3}{4}(x - 0)$

$y - 3 = \frac{-3x}{4}$

$y = \frac{-3x}{4} + 3$

1.109 $m = \frac{4}{3}$, (3, 0)

$y - 0 = \frac{4}{3}(x - 3)$

$y = \frac{4x}{3} - 4$

1.110 $y - 0 = 2(x - 0)$
$y = 2x$

1.111 $y - 3 = 2(x - 1)$
$y - 3 = 2x - 2$
$y = 2x + 1$

1.112 $y - 3 = 3(x - 1)$
$y - 3 = 3x - 3$
$y = 3x$

1.113 $y - 5 = -1(x + 1)$
$y - 5 = -x - 1$
$y = -x + 4$

1.114 $y - 0 = -2(x + 1)$
$y = -2x - 2$

1.115 $y - 5 = -3(x - 5)$
$y - 5 = -3x + 15$
$y = -3x + 20$

1.116 $y - 3 = \frac{1}{3}(x - 0)$

$y - 3 = \frac{x}{3}$

$y = \frac{x}{3} + 3$

1.117 $y - 8 = -\frac{2}{3}(x + 6)$

$y - 8 = -\frac{2x}{3} - 4$

$y = -\frac{2x}{3} + 4$

1.118 $y + 5 = \frac{2}{5}(x - 5)$

$y + 5 = \frac{2x}{5} - 2$

$y = \frac{2x}{5} - 7$

1.119 $y - 1 = 0(x - 2)$
$y - 1 = 0$
$y = 1$

1.120 $y + 1 = -\frac{5}{8}(x + 5)$

$y + 1 = -\frac{5x}{8} - \frac{25}{8}$

$y = -\frac{5x}{8} - \frac{33}{8}$

1.121 $y - 1 = 10(x - 7)$
$y - 1 = 10x - 70$
$y = 10x - 69$

1.122 vertical line through (6, 6)
$x = 6$

1.123 $y - 1 = 6(x + 6)$
$y - 1 = 6x + 36$
$y = 6x + 37$

1.124 $y - 11 = -9(x - 10)$
$y - 11 = -9x + 90$
$y = -9x + 101$

1.125 $m = \frac{4 - 1}{5 - 6} = \frac{3}{-1} = -3$
$y - 1 = -3(x - 6)$
$y - 1 = -3x + 18$
$y = -3x + 19$

1.126 $m = \frac{4 - 2}{5 - 7} = -1$
$y - 2 = -1(x - 7)$
$y - 2 = -x + 7$
$y = -x + 9$

1.127 $m = \frac{9 - 1}{7 - 8} = -8$
$y - 1 = -8(x - 8)$
$y - 1 = -8x + 64$
$y = -8x + 65$

1.128 $m = 1$
$y - 2 = 1(x - 2)$
$y - 2 = x - 2$
$y = x$

1.129 $m = \frac{4}{5 + 1} = \frac{2}{3}$

$y - 0 = \frac{2}{3}(x + 1)$

$y = \frac{2}{3}x + \frac{2}{3}$

1.130 $m = \frac{-1}{6}$

$y - 0 = -\frac{1}{6}(x - 0)$

$y = -\frac{x}{6}$

1.131 $m = \frac{-4}{-5} = \frac{4}{5}$

$y - 2 = \frac{4}{5}(x - 10)$

$y - 2 = \frac{4x}{5} - 8$

$y = \frac{4x}{5} - 6$

1.132 $m = \frac{3}{-1} = -3$
$y - 2 = -3(x - 6)$
$y - 2 = -3x + 18$
$y = -3x + 20$

1.133 $m = \frac{4}{-4} = -1$
$y - 3 = -1(x - 7)$
$y - 3 = -x + 7$
$y = -x + 10$

1.134 $m = \frac{2}{0} =$ no slope
$x = 5$

1.135 $m = \frac{-2}{-3} = \frac{2}{3}$

$y + 3 = \frac{2}{3}(x + 1)$

$y + 3 = \frac{2}{3}x + \frac{2}{3}$

$y = \frac{2}{3}x - \frac{7}{3}$

1.136 $m = \frac{4}{4} = 1$
$y + 5 = 1(x - 1)$
$y + 5 = x - 1$
$y = x - 6$

1.137 $m = \frac{1}{2}$

$y - 2 = \frac{1}{2}(x - 7)$

$y - 2 = \frac{x}{2} - \frac{7}{2}$

$y = \frac{x}{2} - \frac{3}{2}$

1.138 $m = \frac{32}{112} = \frac{2}{7}$

$y - 0 = \frac{2}{7}(x - 100)$

$y = \frac{2x}{7} - \frac{200}{7}$

1.139 $m = \frac{6}{-3} = -2$
$y - 2 = -2(x - 7)$
$y - 2 = -2x + 14$
$y = -2x + 16$

1.140 a. $-x + 6$
b. -1
c. 6

1.141 a. $x - 7$
b. 1
c. -7

1.142 a. -x − 7
      b. -1
      c. -7

1.143 a. -2x + 4
      b. -2
      c. 4

1.144 a. $\frac{-x}{2} + \frac{3}{2}$
      b. $\frac{-1}{2}$
      c. $\frac{3}{2}$

1.145 a. 2x − 6
      b. 2
      c. -6

1.146 a. $\frac{x}{3} - \frac{1}{3}$
      b. $\frac{1}{3}$
      c. $\frac{-1}{3}$

1.147 a. $\frac{-2x}{3} + 2$
      b. $-\frac{2}{3}$
      c. 2

1.148 a. $\frac{7x}{4} - 2$
      b. $\frac{7}{4}$
      c. -2

1.149 a. $\frac{-5x}{3} - \frac{2}{3}$
      b. $\frac{-5}{3}$
      c. $-\frac{2}{3}$

1.150 a. $\frac{9x}{8} - \frac{1}{8}$
      b. $\frac{9}{8}$
      c. $\frac{-1}{8}$

1.151 a. $2x + \frac{2}{3}$
      b. 2
      c. $\frac{2}{3}$

1.152 $b = 1$

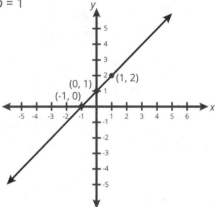

1.153 $b = 2$

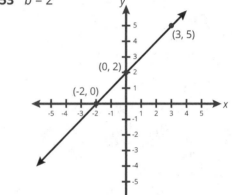

1.154 $b = 1$

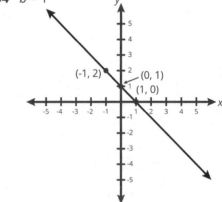

1.155 $b = -1$

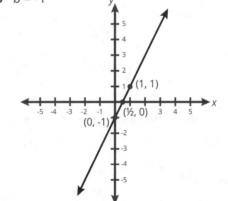

1.156 *b* = 4

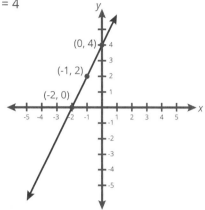

1.157 *b* = -4

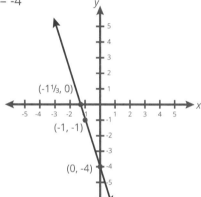

1.158 *b* = 1

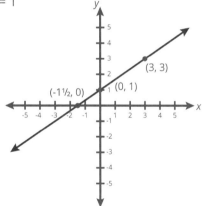

1.159 *b* = -2

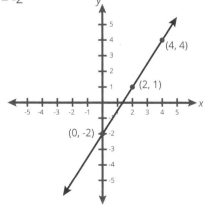

1.160 *b* = 1

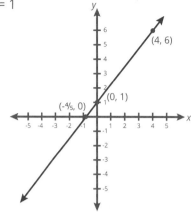

1.161 *b* = 1

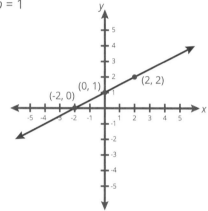

1.162 *b* = 2

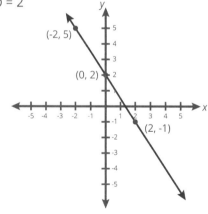

1.163 *b* = -3

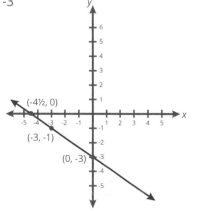

1.164 (1.140)

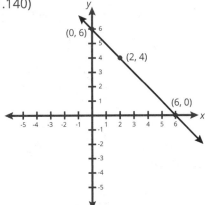

1.168 (1.144)

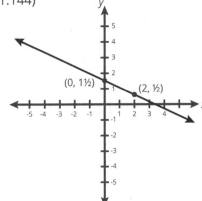

1.165 (1.141)

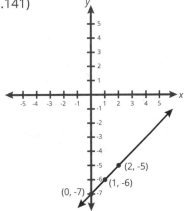

1.169 (1.145)

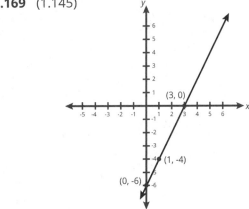

1.166 (1.142)

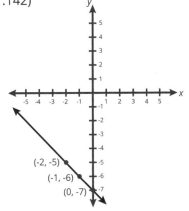

1.170 (1.146)

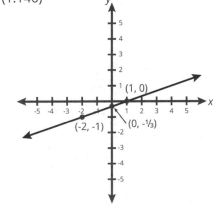

1.167 (1.143)

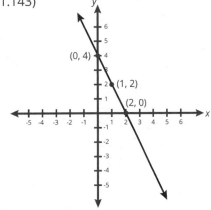

1.171 (1.147)

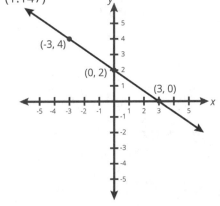

1.172 (1.148)

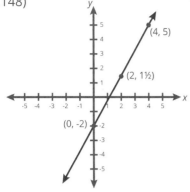

1.173 (1.149)

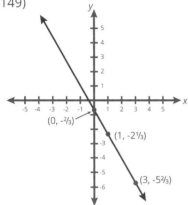

1.174 (1.150)

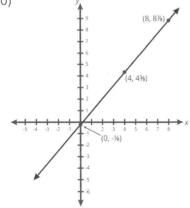

1.175 (1.151)

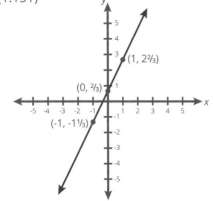

1.176 a. $m = \frac{-A}{B} = \frac{-2}{3}$

b. $b = \frac{C}{B} = \frac{6}{3} = 2$

1.177 a. $m = \frac{-A}{B} = \frac{-5}{6}$

b. $b = \frac{C}{B} = \frac{24}{6} = 4$

1.178 a. $m = \frac{-A}{B} = \frac{-7}{-8} = \frac{7}{8}$

b. $b = \frac{C}{B} = \frac{16}{-8} = -2$

1.179 a. $m = \frac{-A}{B} = \frac{-5}{-3} = \frac{5}{3}$

b. $b = \frac{C}{B} = \frac{-12}{-3} = 4$

1.180 a. $m = \frac{-A}{B} = \frac{-10}{9}$

b. $b = \frac{C}{B} = \frac{45}{9} = 5$

1.181 $6x + 5y = 15$

a. $m = \frac{-A}{B} = \frac{-6}{5}$

b. $b = \frac{C}{B} = \frac{15}{5} = 3$

1.182 a. $m = \frac{-A}{B} = \frac{-20}{-22} = \frac{10}{11}$

b. $b = \frac{C}{B} = \frac{88}{-22} = -4$

1.183 a. $m = \frac{-A}{B} = \frac{-17}{-12} = \frac{17}{12}$

b. $b = \frac{C}{B} = \frac{-36}{-12} = 3$

1.184 a. $m = \frac{-A}{B} = \frac{-1.5}{-2.5} = \frac{3}{5}$

b. $b = \frac{C}{B} = \frac{100}{-2.5} = -40$

1.185 $3x - 2y = -15$

a. $m = \frac{-A}{B} = \frac{-3}{-2} = \frac{3}{2}$

b. $b = \frac{C}{B} = \frac{-15}{-2} = \frac{15}{2}$

1.186 $7x - 3y = 17$

a. $m = \frac{-A}{B} = \frac{-7}{-3} = \frac{7}{3}$

b. $b = \frac{C}{B} = \frac{17}{-3}$

1.187 a. $m = \frac{-A}{B} = \frac{-5}{4}$

b. $b = \frac{C}{B} = \frac{14}{4} = \frac{7}{2}$

1.188 a. $m = \frac{-A}{B} = \frac{-1.6}{4.8} = \frac{-1}{3}$

b. $b = \frac{C}{B} = \frac{72}{4.8} = 15$

1.189 a. $m = \frac{-A}{B} = \frac{-0.05}{-0.03} = \frac{5}{3}$

b. $b = \frac{C}{B} = \frac{9}{-0.03} = -300$

1.190 a. $m = \frac{-A}{B} = \frac{-3}{-2}$

b. $b = \frac{C}{B} = \frac{0}{2} = 0$

1.191 $m = \frac{3}{-1} = -3$

$y - 1 = 3(x - 6)$
$y - 1 = -3x + 18$
$3x + y = 19$

1.192 $m = \frac{-5}{-3} = \frac{5}{3}$

$y + 3 = \frac{5}{3}(x - 7)$

$3y + 9 = 5x - 35$
$-5x + 3y = -35 - 9$
$5x - 3y = 44$

1.193 $m = \frac{-7}{7} = -1$

$y + 1 = -1(x + 2)$
$y + 1 = -x - 2$
$x + y = -3$

1.194 $m = \frac{5}{9}$

$y - 0 = \frac{5}{9}(x + 8)$

$9y = 5x + 40$
$5x - 9y = -40$

1.195 (1.191)

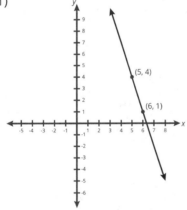

1.196 (1.192)

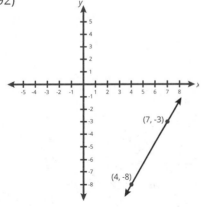

1.197 (1.193)

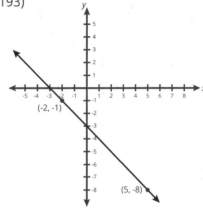

1.198 (1.194)

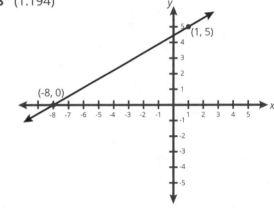

1.199 $m = -1$, $(0, 0)$
$y - 0 = -1(x - 0)$
$y = -x$ or $x + y = 0$

1.200 $m = 1$, $(5, 2)$
$y - 2 = 1(x - 5)$
$y - 2 = x - 5$
$y = x - 3$ or $x - y = 3$

1.201 $m = -2$, $(0, 2)$
$y - 2 = -2(x - 0)$
$y - 2 = -2x$
$2x + y = 2$

1.202 $m = 1$; select any point between the two given lines, such as $(0, 0)$.
$y - 0 = 1(x - 0)$
$y = x$
Other examples are $y = x + 1$ and $y = x - 1$.

1.203 Line 1: (0, 4) and (3, 7)

$m = \frac{3}{3} = 1$

$y - 4 = 1(x - 0)$
$y - 4 = x$
$y = x + 4$ or $x - y = -4$

Line 2: (3, 7) and (8, 2)

$m = \frac{-5}{5} = -1$

$y - 7 = -1(x - 3)$
$y - 7 = -x + 3$
$y = -x + 10$ or $x + y = 10$

Line 3: (0, 4) and (8, 2)

$m = \frac{-2}{8} = -\frac{1}{4}$

$y - 4 = -\frac{1}{4}(x - 0)$

$y - 4 = -\frac{x}{4}$

$4y - 16 = -x$
$x + 4y = 16$

1.204 Freezing temperature of water: $(C, F) = (0, 32)$
Boiling temperature of water: $(C, F) = (100, 212)$

$m = \frac{212 - 32}{100 - 0} = \frac{180}{100} = \frac{9}{5}$

$F - 32 = \frac{9}{5}(C - 0)$

$F - 32 = \frac{9}{5}C$

$F = \frac{9}{5}C + 32$

1.205 Counterclockwise:

Side 1: (0, 0) to (4, 0), $m = 0$
Side 2: (4, 0) to (6, 2), $m = \frac{2}{2} = 1$
Side 3: (6, 2) to (2, 2), $m = 0$
Side 4: (2, 2) to (0, 0), $m = 1$
Side 1 is parallel to side 3.
Side 2 is parallel to side 4.

If opposite sides of a quadrilateral are parallel, the quadrilateral is a parallelogram.

1.206 Counterclockwise:

Side 1: (0, 0) to (a, b), $m = \frac{b}{a}$

Side 2: (a, b) to $(a + c, b + d)$, $m = \frac{d}{c}$

Side 3: $(a + c, b + d)$ to (c, d), $m = \frac{-b}{-a} = \frac{b}{a}$

Side 4: (c, d) to (0, 0), $m = \frac{d}{c}$

Opposite sides are parallel; $\therefore$ the quadrilateral is a parallelogram.

1.207 $A_1 x + B_1 y = C_1$, $m_1 = \frac{-A_1}{B_1}$

$A_2 x + B_2 y = C_2$, $m_2 = \frac{-A_2}{B_2}$

If $m_1 = m_2$, Then $\frac{-A_1}{B_1} = \frac{-A_2}{B_2}$

or $-A_1 B_2 = -A_2 B_1$

or $A_1 B_2 = A_2 B_1$

SELF TEST 1

1.01 a. $y = 2(0) - 3$
            $y = 0 - 3$
            $y = -3$
     b. $y = 2(-3) - 3$
            $y = -6 - 3$
            $y = -9$
     c. $y = 2(3) - 3$
            $y = 6 - 3$
            $y = 3$

1.02 a. $1 + y = 7$
              $y = 6$
     b. $x + 3 = 7$
              $x = 4$
     c. $-10 + y = 7$
              $y = 17$

1.03 a. $2(0) - 3y = 6$
              $-3y = 6$
               $y = -2$
     b. $2x - 3(0) = 6$
              $2x = 6$
               $x = 3$
     c. $2x - 3(6) = 6$
          $2x - 18 = 6$
             $2x = 24$
              $x = 12$

1.04

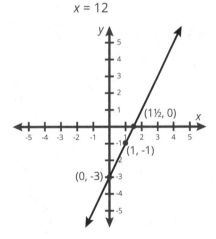

1.05

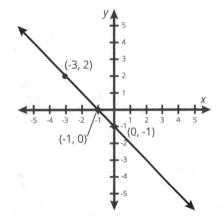

1.06

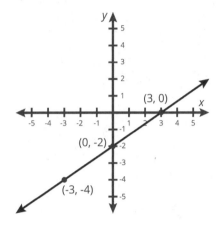

1.07 (1, 3), (-1, -3),
      $m = \frac{-6}{-2} = 3$

1.08 (-5, 2), (3, 1),
      $m = \frac{-1}{8}$

1.09 (0, 3), horizontal line, $m = 0$

1.010 $m = \frac{8 - 7}{-4 - 2} = \frac{1}{-6} = -\frac{1}{6}$

1.011 $y = mx + b$, $m = \frac{2}{3}$

1.012 $y = mx + b$, $m = -\frac{1}{2}$

1.013 $m = \frac{-A}{B}$, $m = \frac{-5}{-3} = \frac{5}{3}$

1.014 $x + 0y = 6$, $m = \frac{-A}{B} = \frac{-1}{0}$; no slope

1.015 $0x + y = -3$, $m = \frac{-A}{B} = \frac{0}{1} = 0$

1.016 $m = \frac{-5}{3}$, (5, 3)

        $y - 3 = \frac{-5}{3}(x - 5)$
       $3y - 9 = -5x + 25$
       $5x + 3y = 34$

1.017 $y = mx + b$
       $y = 3x - 2$

1.018 $y + 3 = -\frac{1}{2}(x + 2)$
      $2y + 6 = -x - 2$
      $x + 2y = -8$

1.019 $m = 1$
      $y - 0 = 1(x - 1)$
        $y = x - 1$

1.020 $m = 2$, (3, 0)
      $y - 0 = 2(x - 3)$
        $y = 2x - 6$

1.021 $m = 1, (0, -1)$
$y + 1 = 1(x - 0)$
$y + 1 = x$
$y = x - 1$

1.022 $m = -\frac{3}{2}, (-2, 0)$

$y - 0 = -\frac{3}{2}(x + 2)$

$y = -\frac{3x}{2} - 3$

1.023 $m = -\frac{1}{3}, (3, 0)$

$y - 0 = -\frac{1}{3}(x - 3)$

$y = -\frac{x}{3} + 1$
$3y = -x + 3$
$x + 3y = 3$

1.024 a. $y = -x + 6$
b. $m = -1$
c. $b = 6$

1.025 a. $y = x - 2$
b. $m = 1$
c. $b = -2$

1.026 a. $y = -\frac{2}{5}x + \frac{8}{5}$

b. $m = -\frac{2}{5}$

c. $b = \frac{8}{5}$

1.027 Counterclockwise:

Side 1: (1, 2) to (6, 6), $m = \frac{4}{5}$

Side 2: (6, 6) to (6, 8), vertical line

Side 3: (6, 8) to (1, 4), $m = \frac{4}{5}$

Side 4: (1, 4) to (1, 2), vertical line

Opposite sides are parallel; ∴ the quadrilateral is a parallelogram.

SECTION 2

2.1 Line 1: (0, 4), (4, 0)
Line 2: (0, 0), (4, 4)
Intersect at (2, 2).

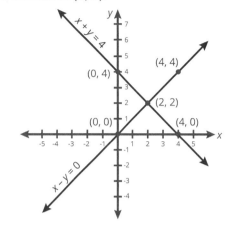

2.2 Line 1: (0, -5), (5, 0)
Line 2: (0, 1), (1, -1)
Intersect at (2, -3).

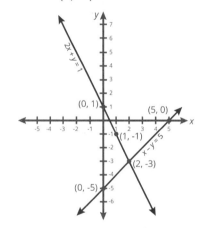

2.3 Line 1: (0, 5), (5, 0)
Line 2: (0, 7), (7, 0)
Lines are parallel.

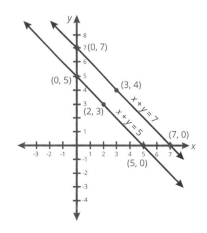

2.4   Line 1: (0, 3), (4, -3)
Line 2: (0, -2), (3, 1)
Intersect at (2, 0).

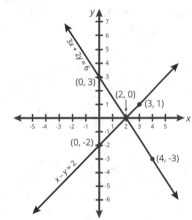

2.5   Line 1: (0, 1), (1, -3)
Line 2: (-3, 3), (0, 6)
Intersect at (-1, 5).

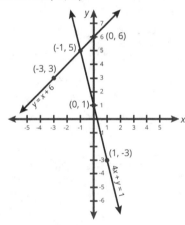

2.6   Line 1: (0, 1), (4, 5)
Line 2: (-5, 0), (0, -5)
Intersect at (-3, -2).

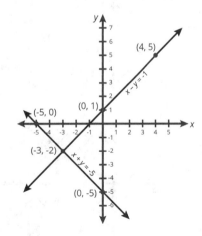

2.7   Line 1: (1, -5), (3, -1)
Line 2: same as Line 1
Lines are coincident; all points on line are solutions.

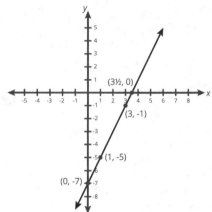

2.8
$$x + y = 5$$
$$\underline{2x + y = 7}$$
$$-x = -2$$
$$x = 2$$
$$2 + y = 5$$
$$y = 3$$

2.9
$$x - y = 4$$
$$\underline{x + y = 8}$$
$$2x = 12$$
$$x = 6$$
$$6 + y = 8$$
$$y = 2$$

2.10
$$2x + y = 6$$
$$\underline{3x - y = 4}$$
$$5x = 10$$
$$x = 2$$
$$2(2) + y = 6$$
$$y = 2$$

2.11
$$x + y = 7$$
$$\underline{2x - y = 2}$$
$$3x = 9$$
$$x = 3$$
$$3 + y = 7$$
$$y = 4$$

2.12
$$2x + y = -2$$
$$\underline{x + y = 5}$$
$$x = -7$$
$$-7 + y = 5$$
$$y = 12$$

2.13
$$3x + 2y = 1$$
$$\underline{2x + 2y = 3}$$
$$x = -2$$
$$3(-2) + 2y = 1$$
$$2y = 7$$
$$y = \frac{7}{2}$$

2.14
$$3x - 4y = 7$$
$$\underline{3x + 2y = -5}$$
$$-6y = 12$$
$$y = -2$$
$$3x + 2(-2) = -5$$
$$3x = -1$$
$$x = -\frac{1}{3}$$

2.15
$$5x + y = 6$$
$$\underline{5x + 3y = -4}$$
$$-2y = 10$$
$$y = -5$$
$$5x - 5 = 6$$
$$5x = 11$$
$$x = \frac{11}{5}$$

2.16
$$3x - 4y = 6$$
$$\underline{5x - 4y = 10}$$
$$-2x = -4$$
$$x = 2$$
$$3(2) - 4y = 6$$
$$-4y = 0$$
$$y = 0$$

2.17
$$x + y = K$$
$$\underline{x - y = K}$$
$$2x = 2K$$
$$x = K$$
$$K + y = K$$
$$y = 0$$

2.18
$$2x + y = 3l$$
$$\underline{x + y = 6l}$$
$$x = -3l$$
$$-3l + y = 6l$$
$$y = 9l$$

2.19
$$2x - y = 2s$$
$$\underline{2x - 2y = 4s}$$
$$y = -2s$$
$$2x + 2s = 2s$$
$$2x = 0$$
$$x = 0$$

2.20
$$3x + y = 7$$
$$\underline{3x + y = 8}$$
$$0x + 0y = -1$$
parallel lines; no solution

2.21
$$2x + y = 3 \longrightarrow 4x + 2y = 6$$
$$\underline{x - 2y = -1} \longrightarrow \underline{x - 2y = -1}$$
$$5x = 5$$
$$x = 1$$
$$2(1) + y = 3$$
$$2 + y = 3$$
$$y = 1$$

2.22
$$x - 2y = 3 \longrightarrow 5x - 10y = 15$$
$$\underline{5x + 3y = 2} \longrightarrow \underline{5x + 3y = 2}$$
$$-13y = 13$$
$$y = -1$$
$$x - 2(-1) = 3$$
$$x + 2 = 3$$
$$x = 1$$

2.23
$$a - b = 0 \longrightarrow 5a - 5b = 0$$
$$\underline{6a + 5b = -22} \longrightarrow \underline{6a + 5b = -22}$$
$$11a = -22$$
$$a = -2$$
$$-2 - b = 0$$
$$-b = 2$$
$$b = -2$$

2.24
$$3x + 5y = 78 \longrightarrow 3x + 5y = 78$$
$$\underline{2x - y = 0} \longrightarrow \underline{10x - 5y = 0}$$
$$13x = 78$$
$$x = 6$$
$$2(6) - y = 0$$
$$12 - y = 0$$
$$y = 12$$

2.25
$$a + 5b = -2 \longrightarrow 2a + 10b = -4$$
$$\underline{2a + b = 5} \longrightarrow \underline{2a + b = 5}$$
$$9b = -9$$
$$b = -1$$
$$2a - 1 = 5$$
$$2a = 6$$
$$a = 3$$

2.26
$$2x + y = 1 \longrightarrow 6x + 3y = 3$$
$$\underline{9x + 3y = -3} \longrightarrow \underline{9x + 3y = -3}$$
$$-3x = 6$$
$$x = -2$$
$$2(-2) + y = 1$$
$$-4 + y = 1$$
$$y = 5$$

2.27
$$5x + 2y = 6 \longrightarrow 5x + 2y = 6$$
$$\underline{3x + y = 4} \longrightarrow \underline{6x + 2y = 8}$$
$$-x = -2$$
$$x = 2$$
$$3(2) + y = 4$$
$$6 + y = 4$$
$$y = -2$$

2.28 $3x + y = 4 \longrightarrow 6x + 2y = 8$

$\underline{x - 2y = 3} \longrightarrow \underline{x - 2y = 3}$

$7x = 11$

$x = \frac{11}{7}$

$\frac{11}{7} - 2y = 3$

$-2y = 3 - \frac{11}{7}$

$2y = -\frac{10}{7}$

$y = \frac{5}{7}$

2.29 $2x + 3y = 6 \longrightarrow 4x + 6y = 12$

$\underline{5x + 2y = 4} \longrightarrow \underline{15x + 6y = 12}$

$-11x = 0$

$x = 0$

$2(0) + 3y = 6$

$0 + 3y = 6$

$y = 2$

2.30 $7x - 3y = 4 \longrightarrow 28x - 12y = 16$

$\underline{2x - 4y = 1} \longrightarrow \underline{6x - 12y = 3}$

$22x = 13$

$x = \frac{13}{22}$

$2\left(\frac{13}{22}\right) - 4y = 1$

$4y = \frac{13}{11} - 1$

$4y = \frac{2}{11}$

$y = \frac{1}{22}$

2.31 $x + y = k \longrightarrow 3x + 3y = 3k$

$\underline{2x + 3y = k + 1} \longrightarrow \underline{2x + 3y = k + 1}$

$x = 2k - 1$

$2k - 1 + y = k$

$y = -k + 1$

$y = 1 - k$

2.32 $3x + 2y = A \longrightarrow 3x + 2y = A$

$\underline{5x + y = B} \longrightarrow \underline{10x + 2y = 2B}$

$-7x = A - 2B$

$x = \frac{2B - A}{7}$

$5\left(\frac{2B - A}{7}\right) + y = B$

$y = B - \left(\frac{10B - 5A}{7}\right)$

$y = \frac{7B - 10B + 5A}{7}$

$= \frac{5A - 3B}{7}$

2.33 $ax + by = k_1 \longrightarrow a^2x + aby = ak_1$

$\underline{bx - ay = k_2} \longrightarrow \underline{b^2x - aby = bk_2}$

$a^2x + b^2x = ak_1 + bk_2$

$(a^2 + b^2)x = ak_1 + bk_2$

$x = \frac{ak_1 + bk_2}{a^2 + b^2}$

$a\left(\frac{ak_1 + bk_2}{a^2 + b^2}\right) + by = k_1$

$by = k_1 - a\left(\frac{ak_1 + bk_2}{a^2 + b^2}\right)$

$by = k_1 + \left(\frac{-a^2k_1 - abk_2}{a^2 + b^2}\right)$

$by = \frac{(a^2 + b^2)k_1}{a^2 + b^2} + \left(\frac{-a^2k_1 - abk_2}{a^2 + b^2}\right)$

$by = \frac{(a^2 + b^2)k_1 - a^2k_1 - abk_2}{a^2 + b^2}$

$by = \frac{a^2k_1 + b^2k_1 - a^2k_1 - abk_2}{a^2 + b^2}$

$by = \frac{b^2k_1 - abk_2}{a^2 + b^2}$

$y = \frac{b^2k_1 - abk_2}{b(a^2 + b^2)} = \frac{bk_1 - ak_2}{a^2 + b^2}$

2.34 $ax + by = c \longrightarrow aex + bey = ce$

$\underline{dx + ey = f} \longrightarrow \underline{dbx + bey = bf}$

$aex - dbx = ce - bf$

$(ae - db)x = ce - bf$

$x = \frac{ce - bf}{ae - bd}$

$adx + bdy = cd$

$\underline{adx + aey = af}$

$bdy - aey = cd - af$

$(bd - ae)y = cd - af$

$y = \frac{cd - af}{bd - ae}$

$\text{or } y = \frac{af - cd}{ae - bd}$

2.35 $2x + y = 7$

$y = x + 1$

$2x + (x + 1) = 7$

$3x + 1 = 7$

$3x = 6$

$x = 2$

$y = 2 + 1 = 3$

2.36 $3x - y = 2$

$y = x - 1$

$3x - (x - 1) = 2$

$3x - x + 1 = 2$

$2x = 1$

$x = \frac{1}{2}$

$y = \frac{1}{2} - 1 = -\frac{1}{2}$

2.37 $5x - 6y = 0$

$y = x$

$5x - 6x = 0$

$-x = 0$

$x = 0$

$y = 0$

2.38
$$x - y = 6$$
$$x = y + 2$$
$$y + 2 - y = 6$$
$$0y = 4$$
no solution

2.39
$$10x - 10y = 1$$
$$x = y - 3$$
$$10(y - 3) - 10y = 1$$
$$10y - 30 - 10y = 1$$
$$0y = 31$$
no solution

2.40
$$5x - 2y = 6$$
$$x = 5 - y$$
$$5(5 - y) - 2y = 6$$
$$25 - 5y - 2y = 6$$
$$-7y = -19$$
$$y = \frac{19}{7}$$
$$x = 5 - \frac{19}{7} = \frac{16}{7}$$

2.41
$$x + y = 6; y = 6 - x$$
$$2x + y = 4$$
$$2x + 6 - x = 4$$
$$x = -2$$
$$y = 6 - (-2)$$
$$y = 8$$

2.42
$$y = 5x - 6$$
$$2x - 3(5x - 6) = 4$$
$$2x - 15x + 18 = 4$$
$$-13x = -14$$
$$x = \frac{14}{13}$$
$$y = 5\left(\frac{14}{13}\right) - 6$$
$$y = \frac{70 - 78}{13}$$
$$y = \frac{-8}{13}$$

2.43
$$7x - 2 = 2y; y = \frac{7x - 2}{2}$$
$$3x = 2y - 1$$
$$3x = 2\left(\frac{7x - 2}{2}\right) - 1$$
$$3x = 7x - 2 - 1$$
$$-4x = -3$$
$$x = \frac{3}{4}$$
$$y = \frac{7\left(\frac{3}{4}\right) - 2}{2} = \frac{21 - 8}{8}$$
$$y = \frac{13}{8}$$

2.44
$$8x = 2y + 5$$
$$3x = y + 7; y = 3x - 7$$
$$8x = 2(3x - 7) + 5$$
$$8x = 6x - 14 + 5$$
$$2x = -9$$
$$x = -\frac{9}{2}$$
$$y = 3\left(-\frac{9}{2}\right) - 7$$
$$y = -\frac{27}{2} - 7$$
$$y = -\frac{41}{2}$$

2.45
$$8y - 1 = x$$
$$3x = 2y$$
$$3(8y - 1) = 2y$$
$$24y - 3 = 2y$$
$$22y = 3$$
$$y = \frac{3}{22}$$
$$x = 8\left(\frac{3}{22}\right) - 1$$
$$x = \frac{24}{22} - \frac{22}{22}$$
$$x = \frac{1}{11}$$

2.46
$$7 + 2y = 8x; x = \frac{7 + 2y}{8}$$
$$3x - 2y = 0$$
$$3\left(\frac{7 + 2y}{8}\right) - 2y = 0$$
$$3(7 + 2y) - 16y = 0$$
$$21 + 6y - 16y = 0$$
$$-10y = -21$$
$$y = \frac{21}{10}$$
$$x = \frac{7 + 2\left(\frac{21}{10}\right)}{8}$$
$$x = \frac{7 + \frac{21}{5}}{8} = \frac{56}{40} = \frac{7}{5}$$

2.47
$$x = 3y + 2$$
$$x = y - 4$$
$$3y + 2 = y - 4$$
$$2y = -6$$
$$y = -3$$
$$x = -3 - 4 = -7$$

2.48
$$y = 7x - 1$$
$$y = 5 - 2x$$
$$7x - 1 = 5 - 2x$$
$$9x = 6$$
$$x = \frac{2}{3}$$
$$y = 7\left(\frac{2}{3}\right) - 1$$
$$y = \frac{11}{3}$$

2.49

$2x = y - 1$
$y = 2x - 1$
$2x = (2x - 2) - 1$
$0x = -2$
no solution

2.50

$x = y + b$
$y = x + a$
$y = y + b + a$
$0y = a + b$
no solution

2.51

$2x - y = c; y = 2x - c$
$x + 2y = d$
$x + 2(2x - c) = d$
$x + 4x - 2c = d$
$5x = d + 2c$
$x = \frac{d + 2c}{5}$
$y = 2\left(\frac{2c + d}{5}\right) - c$
$y = \frac{2d - c}{5}$

2.52

$bx - ay = 2; x = \frac{ay + 2}{b}$
$ax + by = 3$
$a\left(\frac{ay + 2}{b}\right) + by = 3$
$a^2y + 2a + b^2y = 3b$
$(a^2 + b^2)y = 3b - 2a$
$y = \frac{3b - 2a}{a^2 + b^2}$
$x = \frac{a\left(\frac{3b - 2a}{a^2 + b^2}\right) + 2}{b}$
$x = \frac{3ab - 2a^2 + 2a^2 + 2b^2}{b(a^2 + b^2)}$
$x = \frac{3a + 2b}{a^2 + b^2}$

2.53

$x + y = ab; y = ab - x$
$bx - y = a$
$bx - (ab - x) = a$
$bx - ab + x = a$
$(b + 1)x = a + ab$
$x = \frac{a(1 + b)}{b + 1} = a$
$y = ab - a$

2.54

$cx - b = ay; x = \frac{ay + b}{c}$
$ax - c = by$
$a\left(\frac{ay + b}{c}\right) - c = by$
$a^2y + ab - c^2 = bcy$
$a^2y - bcy = c^2 - ab$
$(a^2 - bc)y = c^2 - ab$
$y = \frac{c^2 - ab}{a^2 - bc}$
$x = \frac{a\left(\frac{c^2 - ab}{a^2 - bc}\right) + b}{c}$
$x = \frac{ac^2 - a^2b + a^2b - b^2c}{c(a^2 - bc)}$
$x = \frac{ac^2 - b^2c}{c(a^2 - bc)} = \frac{c(ac - b^2)}{c(a^2 - bc)}$
$x = \frac{ac - b^2}{a^2 - bc}$

2.55

$x = 2y$
$x + y = 36$
$2y + y = 36$
$3y = 36$
$y = 12$
$x = 2(12) = 24$
24 and 12 are the numbers.

2.56

$x + y = 62$
$\underline{x - y = 16}$
$2x = 78$
$x = 39$
$39 + y = 62$
$y = 62 - 39$
$y = 23$
39 and 23 are the numbers.

2.57

$x = y + 3$
$x + y = 41$
$y + 3 + y = 41$
$2y = 38$
$y = 19$
$x = 19 + 3 = 22$
22 and 19 are the numbers.

2.58

$x = y - 8$
$x + y = 90$
$y - 8 + y = 90$
$2y = 98$
$y = 49$
$x = 49 - 8 = 41$
41° and 49° are the angles.

2.59

$$x = y + 5 \longrightarrow x = y + 5$$
$$2(x + 10) - (y + 10) = 35 \longrightarrow 2x - y = 25$$
$$2(y + 5) - y = 25$$
$$2y + 10 - y = 25$$
$$y = 15$$
$$x = 15 + 5$$
$$= 20$$

John is 20 yrs. old and Mary is 15 yrs. old.

2.60   Let r = speed of plane
w = speed of wind
Use $d = rt$.

$$3(r + w) = 1{,}890 \longrightarrow r + w = 630$$
$$3\tfrac{3}{8}(r - w) = 1{,}890 \longrightarrow \underline{r - w = 560}$$
$$2r = 1{,}190$$
$$r = 595 \text{ mph}$$
$$w = 630 - 595$$
$$= 35 \text{ mph}$$

wind speed = 35 mph
air speed = 595 mph

2.61   Let x = cost of jacket
y = cost of slacks
$$x + y = 63$$
$$x = 33 + y$$
$$33 + y + y = 63$$
$$2y = 30$$
$$y = 15$$
$$x = 33 + 15 = 48$$
jacket cost $48, slacks cost $15

2.62   Let x = amount invested at 4%
y = amount invested at 3%
Use $i = prt$.
$$0.04x + 0.03y = 194 \longrightarrow 4x + 3y = 19{,}400$$
$$\underline{x + y = 5{,}200} \longrightarrow \underline{3x + 3y = 15{,}600}$$
$$x = 3{,}800$$
$$y = 5{,}200 - 3{,}800 = 1{,}400$$
Mr. Rose invested $3,800 at 4%
and $1,400 at 3%.

2.63   Let x = larger number
y = smaller number
$$x - (2y) = 1 \longrightarrow x = 2y + 1$$
$$\underline{3y - x = 6}$$
$$3y - (2y + 1) = 6$$
$$y = 7$$
$$x = 2(7) + 1 = 15$$
15 and 7 are the numbers.

2.64   Let x = number of dimes
y = number of quarters
$$x + y = 60 \longrightarrow 10x + 10y = 600$$
$$\underline{0.10x + 0.25y = 12.30} \longrightarrow \underline{10x + 25y = 1{,}230}$$
$$-15y = -630$$
$$y = 42$$
$$x = 60 - 42 = 18$$
18 dimes, 42 quarters

2.65   Let u = units' digit
t = tens' digit
$$t + u = 14$$
$$\underline{t - u = 2}$$
$$2t = 16$$
$$t = 8$$
$$u = 6$$
86 = the number

2.66   Let u = units' digit
t = tens' digit
$10t + u$ = the number
$10u + t$ = the number reversed
$$t + u = 5 \longrightarrow t + u = 5$$
$$(10u + t) - 3t = 2 \longrightarrow -2t + 10u = 2$$
$$2t + 2u = 10$$
$$\underline{-2t + 10u = 2}$$
$$12u = 12$$
$$u = 1$$
$$t = 4$$
41 is the number.

2.67   Let x = the number of 13¢ stamps
y = the number of 18¢ stamps
$$x + y = 42 \longrightarrow 13x + 13y = 546$$
$$\underline{0.13x + 0.18y = 6.66} \longrightarrow \underline{13x + 18y = 666}$$
$$-5y = -120$$
$$y = 24$$
$$x = 18$$
eighteen 13¢ stamps,
twenty-four 18¢ stamps

SELF TEST 2

2.01 Line 1: (0, -3), (2, 1)
Line 2: (0, 6), (4, 2)
Intersect at (3, 3).

2.02 Line 1: (5, 0), (3, 1)
Line 2: (0, 0), (-2, 1)
Lines are parallel.

2.03 Line 1: (-2, -1), (0, -3)
Line 2: (0, -1), (2, 1)
Intersect at (-1, -2).

2.04
$$x + y = 6$$
$$\underline{x - y = 8}$$
$$2x = 14$$
$$x = 7$$
$$y = -1$$

2.05
$$2x + y = 8$$
$$\underline{x + y = 4}$$
$$x = 4$$
$$y = 0$$

2.06
$$3x + 2y = 5$$
$$\underline{5x + 2y = 7}$$
$$-2x = -2$$
$$x = 1$$
$$3(1) + 2y = 5$$
$$2y = 2$$
$$y = 1$$

2.07
$$2x - 6y = 5 \longrightarrow 2x - 6y = 5$$
$$\underline{x + y = 2} \longrightarrow \underline{2x + 2y = 4}$$
$$-8y = 1$$
$$y = -\tfrac{1}{8}$$
$$x - \tfrac{1}{8} = 2$$
$$x = \tfrac{17}{8}$$

2.08
$$3x + 2y = 6 \longrightarrow 3x + 2y = 6$$
$$\underline{4x + y = 1} \longrightarrow \underline{8x + 2y = 2}$$
$$-5x = 4$$
$$x = -\tfrac{4}{5}$$
$$y = 1 - 4(-\tfrac{4}{5})$$
$$y = 1 + \tfrac{16}{5}$$
$$y = \tfrac{21}{5}$$

2.09
$$6x - 2y = 5 \longrightarrow 6x - 2y = 5$$
$$\underline{3x - y = 10} \longrightarrow \underline{6x - 2y = 20}$$
$$0x + 0y = 25$$
lines are parallel; no solution

2.010
$$m = \frac{3 - 1}{-2 - 3} = \frac{2}{-5}$$
$$y - 1 = -\tfrac{2}{5}(x - 3)$$
$$5y - 5 = -2x + 6$$
$$2x + 5y = 11$$

2.011
$$m = \frac{7 - 7}{0 - 4} = 0$$
$$y - 7 = 0(x - 4)$$
$$y - 7 = 0$$
$$y = 7$$

2.012 $y = mx + b$
$y = 2x - 4$

2.013 $y = mx + b$
$$y = -1x + \tfrac{1}{2}$$
$$y = -x + \tfrac{1}{2}$$

2.014 $m = \dfrac{5 - 3}{2 - 2} = \dfrac{2}{0} = $ no slope
$x = 2$, vertical line

2.015
$$y - 1 = \tfrac{2}{3}(x - 1)$$
$$3y - 3 = 2x - 2$$
$$2x - 3y = -1$$

2.016
$$m = -\tfrac{2}{3}$$
$$y + 4 = -\tfrac{2}{3}(x - 1)$$
$$3y + 12 = -2x + 2$$
$$2x + 3y = -10$$

2.017 $m = \dfrac{-A}{B} = \dfrac{-3}{-2} = \dfrac{3}{2}$

2.018 $m = \dfrac{-A}{B} = \dfrac{-2}{0} = $ no slope

2.019 $2x + 3y = 1$
$$m = \frac{-A}{B} = \frac{-2}{3}$$

2.020 $m = \dfrac{-A}{B} = \dfrac{-0}{1} = 0$

2.021 $m = \dfrac{-5 - 1}{-4 - 2} = \dfrac{-6}{-6} = 1$

2.022 $m = \dfrac{-3 - 0}{-2 - 0} = \dfrac{3}{2}$

2.023 (2, 1), (3, 3); $m = \dfrac{2}{1} = 2$
(2, 1), (4, 5); $m = \dfrac{4}{2} = 2$
(3, 3), (4, 5); $m = \dfrac{2}{1} = 2$
Yes, the points are collinear.

2.024 Line 1: $m = \frac{2}{3}$

Line 2: $m = -\frac{2}{3}$

The lines are not parallel, therefore, they are intersecting.

2.025 The lines must have equal slopes.

Line 1: $m = -\frac{3}{1} = -3$

Line 2: $m = \frac{-b}{-1} = b$

$b = -3$

2.026 The lines must have equal slopes.

Line 1: $m = -\frac{5}{2}$

Line 2: $m = \frac{-3}{-a} = \frac{3}{a}$

$\frac{3}{a} = -\frac{5}{2}$

$-5a = 6$

$a = -\frac{6}{5}$

2.027 $\quad y = mx + b$

$y = -\frac{3}{4}x - 2$

$4y = -3x - 8$

$3x + 4y = -8$

2.028 $\quad 3x + 2y = 7$

$2y = -3x + 7$

$y = -\frac{3}{2}x + \frac{7}{2}$

2.029 $\quad x + y = -1$

$x = 2y - 5$

$2y - 5 + y = -1$

$3y = 4$

$y = \frac{4}{3}$

$x + \frac{4}{3} = -1$

$x = -1 - \frac{4}{3} = -\frac{7}{3}$

2.030 Let x = dimes

y = quarters

$x + y = 22 \longrightarrow 10x + 10y = 220$

$\underline{10x + 25y = 340} \longrightarrow \underline{10x + 25y = 340}$

$-15y = -120$

$y = 8$

$x = 14$

8 quarters, 14 dimes

SECTION 3

3.1

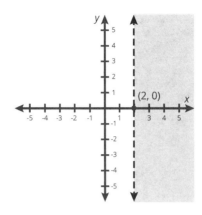

3.2

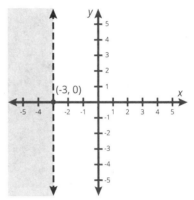

3.3

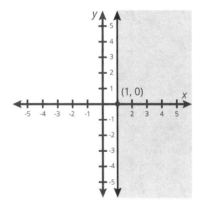

3.4

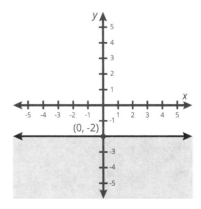

3.5

3.6

3.7

3.8

3.9

3.10

3.11

3.12

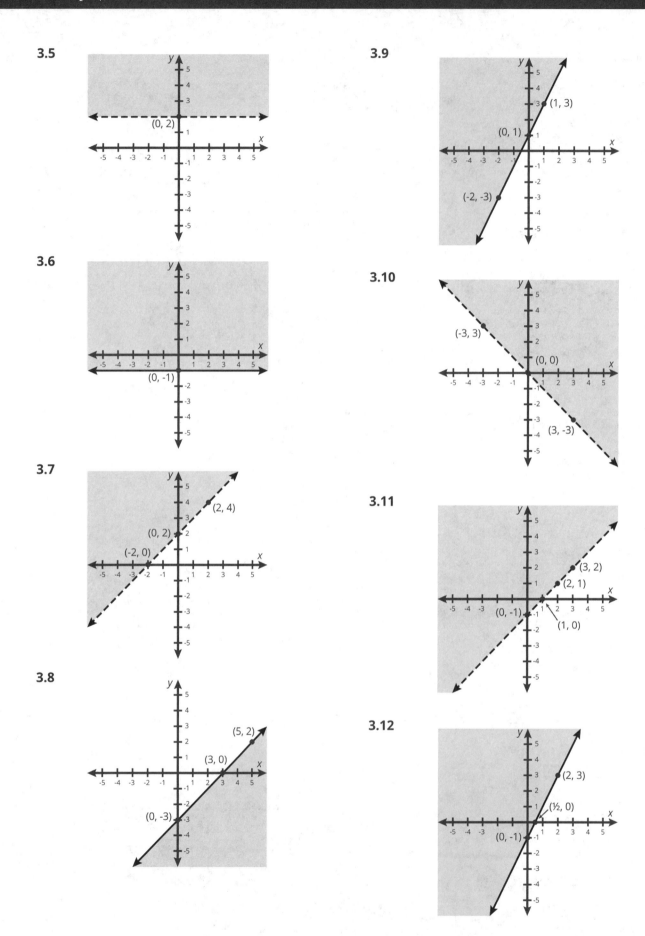

3.13

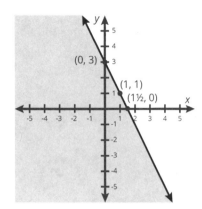

3.14

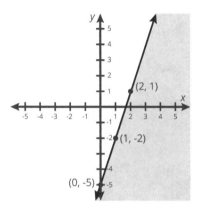

3.15

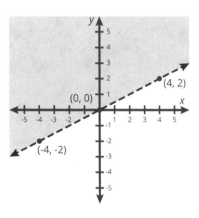

3.16

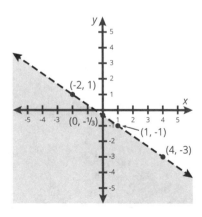

3.17

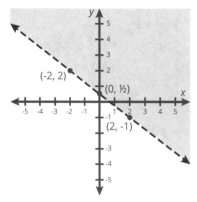

3.18

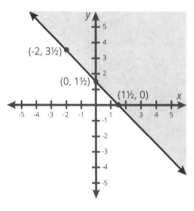

3.19

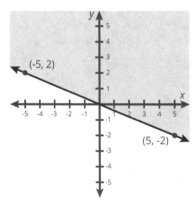

3.20

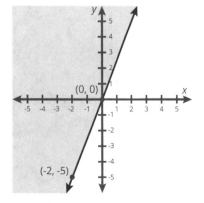

3.21

3.22

3.23

3.24

3.25

3.26

3.27

3.28

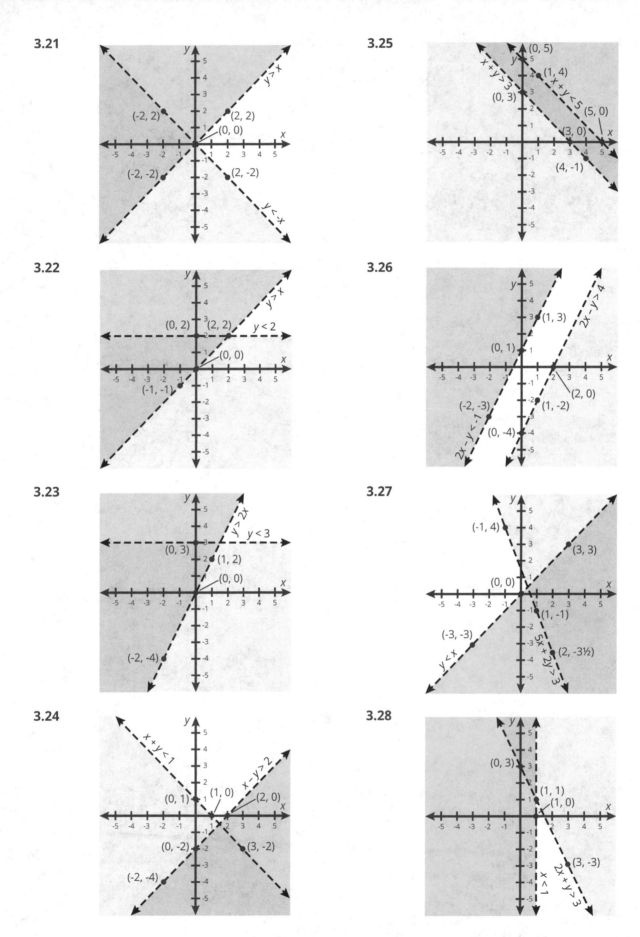

3.29

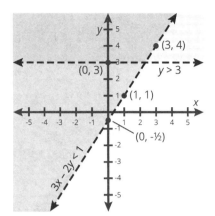

3.30

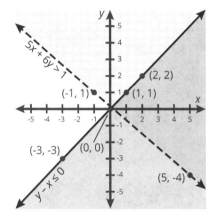

SELF TEST 3

3.01

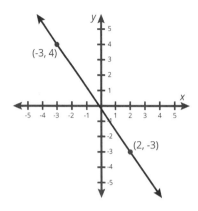

3.02

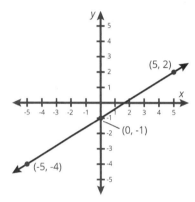

3.03

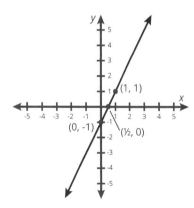

3.04

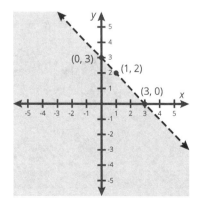

3.05

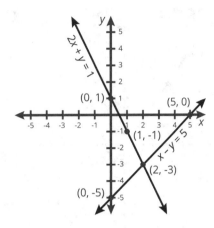

3.06

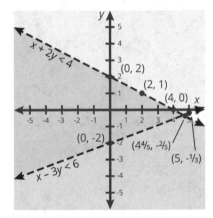

3.07 $m = \frac{3-6}{5-3} = \frac{-3}{2}$

3.08 $m = \frac{-6-4}{-5+2} = \frac{-10}{-3} = \frac{10}{3}$

3.09 $m = -2$

3.010 $y = mx + b$

$y = -\frac{3}{8}$

3.011 $m = \frac{-A}{B} = -\frac{9}{5}$

3.012 $-3x + 4y + 6 = 0$

$m = \frac{-A}{B} = \frac{3}{4}$

3.013 $m = \frac{-2-0}{0-(-4)} = \frac{-2}{4} = -\frac{1}{2}$

3.014 $m = \frac{3+1}{0+3} = \frac{4}{3}$

3.015 $m = \frac{3}{2}$

$y - 1 = \frac{3}{2}(x - 1)$

$2y - 2 = 3x - 3$

$3x - 2y = 1$

3.016 $m = \frac{-6-5}{-2+3} = \frac{-11}{1} = -11$

$y - 5 = -11(x + 3)$

$y - 5 = -11x - 33$

$11x + y = -28$

3.017 $y - 7 = 2(x - 1)$

$y - 7 = 2x - 2$

$2x - y = -5$

3.018 $y + 4 = -\frac{3}{8}(x - 5)$

$8y + 32 = -3x + 15$

$3x + 8y = -17$

3.019 $y = mx + b$

$y = -1x + \frac{1}{2}$

$2y = -2x + 1$

$2x + 2y = 1$

3.020 $y = mx + b$

$y = -\frac{3}{2}x + 6$

$2y = -3x + 12$

$3x + 2y = 12$

3.021 $m = \frac{1}{3}$

$y - 3 = \frac{1}{3}(x + 1)$

$3y - 9 = x + 1$

$x - 3y = -10$

3.022 $m = 0$

$y - 5 = 0(x - 1)$

$y - 5 = 0$

$y = 5$

3.023 (0, -3) and (3, 0)

$m = 1$

$y - 0 = 1(x - 3)$

$y = x - 3$

$x - y = 3$

3.024 (-3, 0) and (2, -2)

$m = \frac{-2}{5}$

$y - 0 = -\frac{2}{5}(x + 3)$

$5y = -2x - 6$

$2x + 5y = -6$

3.025 $3x - 2y = 6$

$-2y = 6 - 3x$

$y = \frac{3x - 6}{2}$

$y = \frac{3}{2}x - 3$

3.026 $\frac{x}{2} - 3y + 6 = 0$

$-3y = -\frac{x}{2} - 6$

$y = \frac{x}{6} + 2$

3.027 $x - y < 3$
              $-y < 3 - x$
              $y > x - 3$

3.028 $2x + 5y + 1 > 0$
              $5y > -2x - 1$
              $y > -\frac{2}{5}x - \frac{1}{5}$

3.029 $x + y = 6$
              $\underline{2x - y = 3}$
              $3x = 9$
              $x = 3$
              $3 + y = 6$
              $y = 3$
                  $(3, 3)$

3.030 $2x + y = 7$
              $\underline{5x + y = 9}$
              $-3x = -2$
              $x = \frac{2}{3}$
              $y = 7 - 2(\frac{2}{3})$
              $y = 7 - \frac{4}{3}$
              $y = \frac{17}{3}$
                  $(\frac{2}{3}, \frac{17}{3})$

3.031 $5x + 2y = 5$ $\longrightarrow$ $5x + 2y = 5$
              $\underline{3x - y = 14}$ $\longrightarrow$ $\underline{6x - 2y = 28}$
                                         $11x = 33$
                                         $x = 3$
                                         $3(3) - y = 14$
                                         $9 - y = 14$
                                         $-y = 5$
                                         $y = -5$
                                             $(3, -5)$

3.032 $x + 2y = 5$ $\longrightarrow$ $3x + 6y = 15$
              $\underline{3x + 5y = 14}$ $\longrightarrow$ $\underline{3x + 5y = 14}$
                                         $y = 1$
                                   $x + 2(1) = 5$
                                         $x = 3$
                                             $(3, 1)$

3.033 $7x + 2y = 4$
              $y = x + 1$
              $7x + 2(x + 1) = 4$
              $9x + 2 = 4$
              $9x = 2$
              $x = \frac{2}{9}$
              $y = \frac{2}{9} + 1$
              $y = \frac{11}{9}$
                  $(\frac{2}{9}, \frac{11}{9})$

3.034 $5x + 10y = 18$
              $x = y - 6$
              $5(y - 6) + 10y = 18$
              $5y - 30 + 10y = 18$
              $15y = 48$
              $y = \frac{16}{5}$
              $x = \frac{16}{5} - 6$
              $x = -\frac{14}{5}$
                  $(-\frac{14}{5}, \frac{16}{5})$

3.035 $x + y = 23$
              $\underline{x = 5 + 2y}$
              $5 + 2y + y = 23$
              $3y = 18$
              $y = 6$
              $x = 5 + 12 = 17$
                  17 and 6 are the numbers.

3.036 $x + y = 180$
              $\underline{x = 30 + 2y}$
              $30 + 2y + y = 180$
              $3y = 150$
              $y = 50$
              $x = 180 - 50 = 130$
                  130° and 50° are the angles.

LIFEPAC TEST

1.

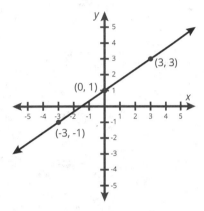

2.

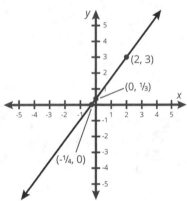

3.

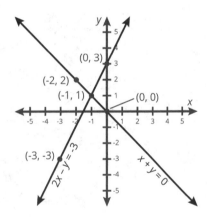

4.

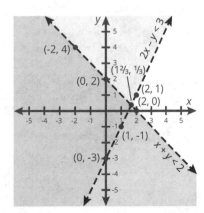

5. $m = \frac{5-8}{-2-3} = \frac{-3}{-5} = \frac{3}{5}$

6. $m = \frac{-A}{B} = \frac{-7}{-2} = \frac{7}{2}$

7. $y = mx + b$

$m = \frac{3}{7}$

8. $(-1, -1), (2, 1)$

$m = \frac{1+1}{2+1} = \frac{2}{3}$

9. $m = \frac{3-5}{-2-1} = \frac{-2}{-3} = \frac{2}{3}$

$y - 5 = \frac{2}{3}(x - 1)$

$3y - 15 = 2x - 2$

$2x - 3y = -13$

10. $m = \frac{1}{2}$

$y - 4 = \frac{1}{2}(x + 2)$

$2y - 8 = x + 2$

$x - 2y = -10$

11. $y = mx + b$

$y = \frac{1}{2}x + 3$

$2y = x + 6$

$x - 2y = -6$

12. $(2, 1), (-1, -3)$

$m = \frac{-3-1}{-1-2} = \frac{-4}{-3} = \frac{4}{3}$

$y - 1 = \frac{4}{3}(x - 2)$

$3y - 3 = 4x - 8$

$4x - 3y = 5$

13. $3x - 4y = -2$

$-4y = -3x - 2$

$y = \frac{3}{4}x + \frac{1}{2}$

14. $10x + 3y \geq 1$

$3y \geq -10x + 1$

$y \geq -\frac{10}{3}x + \frac{1}{3}$

15.
$$\begin{array}{ll} 3x + 2y = 4 & \longrightarrow \quad 3x + 2y = 4 \\ 2x - y = 5 & \longrightarrow \quad 4x - 2y = 10 \end{array}$$

$7x = 14$

$x = 2$

$2(2) - y = 5$

$4 - y = 5$

$-y = 1$

$y = -1$

$(2, -1)$

112

16.
$$8x + 13y = 2$$
$$y = x - 2$$
$$8x + 13(x - 2) = 2$$
$$21x - 26 = 2$$
$$21x = 28$$
$$x = \frac{4}{3}$$
$$y = \frac{4}{3} - 2 = -\frac{2}{3}$$
$$\left(\frac{4}{3}, -\frac{2}{3}\right)$$

17.
$$px + qy = r$$
$$\underline{2px - qy = 2r}$$
$$3px = 3r$$
$$x = \frac{r}{p}$$
$$y = \frac{r - px}{q}$$
$$y = \frac{r - p\left(\frac{r}{p}\right)}{q} = \frac{r - r}{q} = 0$$
$$\left(\frac{r}{p}, 0\right)$$

18. a. $m = \frac{-A}{B}$

$m = \frac{-p}{-q} = \frac{p}{q}$

b. $px - qy = r + 1$
$$-qy = -px + r + 1$$
$$y = \frac{p}{q}x - \frac{(r + 1)}{q}$$
$$b = -\frac{r + 1}{q}$$

19.
$$x + y = 39$$
$$x = 2y - 3$$
$$2y - 3 + y = 39$$
$$3y = 42$$
$$y = 14$$
$$x = 28 - 3 = 25$$
25 and 14 are the numbers.

20. Let l = length
w = width
$$2l + 2w = 28 \longrightarrow l + w = 14$$
$$w = 2 + \frac{l}{2} \longrightarrow l + (2 + \frac{l}{2}) = 14$$
$$2l + 4 + l = 28$$
$$3l = 24$$
$$l = 8$$
$$w = 2 + \frac{8}{2} = 6$$
length = 8
width = 6

ALTERNATE LIFEPAC TEST

1. $y = 2x - 6$
For $x = 0$: $y = 2 \cdot 0 - 6 = -6$
Solution: $(0, -6)$

For $y = 0$: $0 = 2x - 6$
$0 + 6 = 2x - 6 + 6$
$6 = 2x$
$\frac{1}{2} \cdot 6 = \frac{1}{2} \cdot 2x$
$3 = x$
Solution: $(3, 0)$

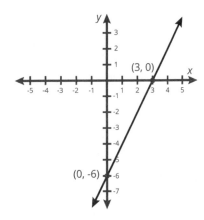

2. $2x + 3y = 4$
For $x = 0$: $2 \cdot 0 + 3y = 4$
$3y = 4$
$\frac{1}{3} \cdot 3y = \frac{1}{3} \cdot 4$
$y = \frac{4}{3}$

Solution: $(0, \frac{4}{3})$

For $y = 0$: $2x + 3 \cdot 0 = 4$
$2x = 4$
$\frac{1}{2} \cdot 2x = \frac{1}{2} \cdot 4$
$x = 2$
Solution: $(2, 0)$

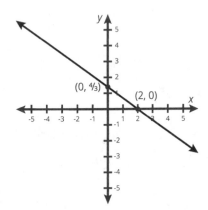

3. $3x + y = 1$
For $x = 0$: $3 \cdot 0 + y = 1$
$y = 1$
Solution: $(0, 1)$

For $y = 0$: $3x + 0 = 1$
$3x = 1$
$\frac{1}{3} \cdot 3x = \frac{1}{3} \cdot 1$
$x = \frac{1}{3}$

Solution: $(\frac{1}{3}, 0)$

$y + 2 = 0$
$y + 2 - 2 = 0 - 2$
$y = -2$

The common solution is $(1, -2)$.

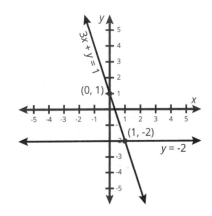

4. $x - y \geq -3$
For $x = 0$: $0 - y \geq -3$
                                   $y \leq 3$ (multiply by -1)
Solution: $(0, 3)$
For $y = 0$: $x - 0 \geq -3$
                                $x \geq -3$
Solution: $(-3, 0)$
$3x + 2y \geq 0$
For $x = 0$: $3 \cdot 0 + 2y \geq 0$
                             $2y \geq 0$
                             $\frac{1}{2} \cdot 2y \geq \frac{1}{2} \cdot 0$
                             $y \geq 0$
Solution: $(0, 0)$
For $x = 2$: $3 \cdot 2 + 2y \geq 0$
                             $6 + 2y \geq 0$
                             $6 - 6 + 2y \geq 0 - 6$
                             $2y \geq -6$
                             $\frac{1}{2}(2y) \geq \frac{1}{2}(-6)$
                             $y \geq -3$
Solution: $(2, -3)$
The common solution is $(-\frac{6}{5}, \frac{9}{5})$.

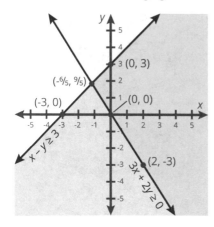

5. $m = \frac{\Delta y}{\Delta x} = \frac{1 - 3}{5 - (-2)} = -\frac{2}{7}$

6.   Write the equation in slope-intercept form.
$y = 6 - 2x$
$y = 2x + 6$
$m = -2$

7.   Write the equation in slope-intercept form.
$5x + 6y = 1$
$5x - 5x + 6y = 1 - 5x$
$6y = 1 - 5x$
$\frac{1}{6}(6y) = \frac{1}{6}(1 - 5x)$
$y = \frac{1 - 5x}{6}$
$y = \frac{1}{6} - \frac{5}{6}x$
$y = -\frac{5}{6}x + \frac{1}{6}$
$m = -\frac{5}{6}$

8. $m = \frac{\Delta y}{\Delta x} = \frac{1 - 2}{3 - (-3)} = \frac{-3}{6} = -\frac{1}{2}$

9. $m = \frac{\Delta y}{\Delta x} = \frac{-2 - 6}{-1 - 2} = \frac{-8}{-3} = \frac{8}{3}$
$y - y_1 = m(x - x_1)$
$y - 6 = \frac{8}{3}(x - 2)$
$3y - 18 = 8(x - 2)$ (multiply by 3)
$3y - 18 = 8x - 16$
$3y - 18 - 8x = 8x - 8x - 16$
$-8x + 3y - 18 + 18 = -16 + 18$
$-8x + 3y = 2$
$8x - 3y = -2$ (multiply by -1)

10. $y = mx + b$
$y = -\frac{2}{3}x + 4$
$3y = -2x + 12$ (multiply by 3)
$3y + 2x = -2x + 2x + 12$
$2x + 3y = 12$

11.   Find the slope of the given line.
$2x + 5y = 1$
$2x - 2x + 5y = 1 - 2x$
$5y = 1 - 2x$
$\frac{1}{5} \cdot 5y = \frac{1}{5}(-2x + 1)$
$y = -\frac{2}{5}x + \frac{1}{5}$
$m = -\frac{2}{5}$
Use this slope and the given point to find the equation of the line.
$y - y_1 = m(x - x_1)$
$y - 5 = -\frac{2}{5}(x - 1)$
$5y - 25 = -2(x - 1)$ (multiply by 5)
$5y - 25 = -2x + 2$
$5y - 25 + 2x = -2x + 2x + 2$
$2x + 5y - 25 = 2$
$2x + 5y - 25 + 25 = 2 + 25$
$2x + 5y = 27$

12. $m = \frac{\Delta y}{\Delta x} = \frac{-3 - 2}{1 - (-1)} = -\frac{5}{2}$
$y - y_1 = m(x - x_1)$
$y - 2 = -\frac{5}{2}[x - (-1)]$
$y - 2 = -\frac{5}{2}(x + 1)$
$2y - 4 = -5(x + 1)$ (multiply by 2)
$2y - 4 = -5x - 5$
$2y - 4 + 5x = -5x + 5x - 5$
$5x + 2y - 4 = -5$
$5x + 2y - 4 + 4 = -5 + 4$
$5x + 2y = -1$

13.
$$7x + 4y - 1 = 0$$
$$7x - 7x + 4y - 1 = 0 - 7x$$
$$4y - 1 = -7x$$
$$4y - 1 + 1 = -7x + 1$$
$$4y = -7x + 1$$
$$\tfrac{1}{4}(4y) = \tfrac{1}{4}(-7x + 1)$$
$$y = \frac{-7x + 1}{4} \text{ or } -\tfrac{7}{4}x + \tfrac{1}{4}$$

14.
$$6x - 2y + 3 \leq 0$$
$$6x - 6x - 2y + 3 \leq 0 - 6x$$
$$-2y + 3 \leq -6x$$
$$-2y + 3 - 3 \leq -6x - 3$$
$$-2y \leq -6x - 3$$
$$-\tfrac{1}{2}(-2y) \leq -\tfrac{1}{2}(-6x - 3)$$
$$y \geq \frac{6x + 3}{2} \text{ or } 3x + \tfrac{3}{2}$$

15.
$$6x - 5y = 19 \longrightarrow 12x - 10y = 38 \text{ (mult. × 2)}$$
$$\underline{5x + 2y = -15} \longrightarrow \underline{25x + 10y = -75} \text{ (mult. × 5)}$$
$$37x \quad\quad = -37$$
$$\tfrac{1}{37}(37x) = \tfrac{1}{37}(-37)$$
$$x = -1$$

Find y.
$$6(-1) - 5y = 19$$
$$-6 - 5y = 19$$
$$-6 + 6 - 5y = 19 + 6$$
$$-5y = 25$$
$$-\tfrac{1}{5}(-5y) = -\tfrac{1}{5}(25)$$
$$y = -5$$
The solution is (-1, -5).

16.
$$9x + 3y = -3$$
$$y = 1 - 2x$$
Substitute the quantity (1 – 2x) in place of y in the first equation.
$$9x + 3(1 - 2x) = -3$$
$$9x + 3 - 6x = -3$$
$$3x + 3 - 3 = -3 - 3$$
$$3x = -6$$
$$\tfrac{1}{3}(3x) = \tfrac{1}{3}(-6)$$
$$x = -2$$
Find y.
$$y = 1 - 2(-2) = 1 + 4 = 5$$
The solution is (-2, 5).

17.
$$ax + 2by = c \longrightarrow ax + 2by = c$$
$$\underline{2ax - by = c} \longrightarrow \underline{4ax - 2by = 2c} \text{ (mult. × 2)}$$
$$5ax \quad\quad = 3c$$
$$\tfrac{1}{5a} \cdot 5ax = \tfrac{1}{5a} \cdot 3c$$
$$x = \frac{3c}{5a}$$
Find y.
$$a\left(\frac{3c}{5a}\right) + 2by = c$$
$$\frac{3c}{5} + 2by = c$$
$$3c + 10by = 5c \quad\quad\quad \text{(multiply by 5)}$$
$$3c - 3c + 10by = 5c - 3c$$
$$10by = 2c$$
$$\tfrac{1}{10b} \cdot 10by = \tfrac{1}{10b} \cdot 2c$$
$$y = \frac{2c}{10b} = \frac{c}{5b}$$
The solution is $\left(\frac{3c}{5a}, \frac{c}{5b}\right)$.

18.   a.   Write the equation in slope-intercept form.
$$Ax + By + C = 0$$
$$Ax + By + C - C = 0 - C$$
$$Ax + By = -C$$
$$Ax - Ax + Bx = -Ax - C$$
$$By = -Ax - C$$
$$y = \frac{-Ax - C}{B}$$
$$y = -\frac{Ax}{B} - \frac{C}{B}$$
$$m = -\frac{A}{B}$$

b. $b = -\frac{C}{B}$

19.
Let x = one angle
y = other angle
$$x + y = 180$$
$$x = 2y - 6$$
Substitute the quantity (2y – 6) in place of x in the first equation.
$$(2y - 6) + y = 180$$
$$3y - 6 = 180$$
$$3y - 6 + 6 = 180 + 6$$
$$3y = 186$$
$$\tfrac{1}{3} \cdot 3y = \tfrac{1}{3} \cdot 186$$
$$y = 62°$$
Find x.
$$x = 2 \cdot 62 - 6 = 124 - 6 = 118°$$
The angles measure 118° and 62°.

20.   Let x = speed of plane
           y = speed of wind

$5(x - y) = 2,700 \longrightarrow 5x - 5y = 2,700$
$x - y = 540$
(multiply by $\frac{1}{5}$)

$4\frac{1}{2}(x + y) = 2,700 \longrightarrow \frac{9}{2}x + \frac{9}{2}y = 2,700$
$x + y = 600$
(multiply by $\frac{2}{9}$)

$$\begin{array}{r} x - y = 540 \\ x + y = 600 \\ \hline 2x = 1,140 \end{array}$$

$\frac{1}{2} \cdot 2x = \frac{1}{2} \cdot 1,140$

$x = 570$ mph

Find y.

$x + y = 600$
$570 + y = 600$
$570 - 570 + y = 600 - 570$
$y = 30$ mph

           Plane: 570 mph
           Wind: 30 mph

MATH 1103
ALTERNATE LIFEPAC TEST

NAME _____

DATE _____

SCORE _____

Construct the following graphs (each graph, 3 points).

1. $y = 2x - 6$

2. $2x + 3y = 4$

Find each solution by graphing (each answer, 3 points).

3. $3x + y = 1$ and $y + 2 = 0$

4. $x - y \geq -3$ and $3x + 2y \geq 0$

Find the slope of the given line (each answer, 3 points).

5.   The line including (-2, 3) and (5, 1)

   $m =$ _____

6. $y = 6 - 2x$

   $m =$ _____

7. $5x + 6y = 1$

   $m =$ _____

8. $m =$ _____

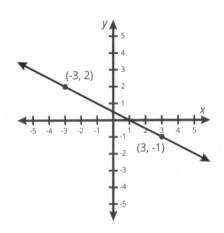

Write the equation of the line with the given information. Leave answers in standard form (each answer, 4 points).

9. The line including (2, 6) and (-1, -2) _____

10. The line with $m = -\frac{2}{3}$ and $b = 4$ _____

11. The line through (1, 5) and parallel to $2x + 5y = 1$ _____

12.

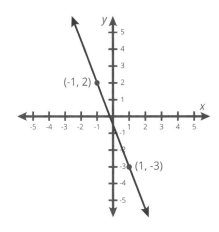

_____

Solve as indicated. Circle your answer (each answer, 3 points).

13. $7x + 4y - 1 = 0$, for y.

14. $6x - 2y + 3 \leq 0$, for y.

Find the common solution. Circle your answer (each answer, 3 points).

15. $6x - 5y = 19$
    $5x + 2y = -15$

16. $9x + 3y = -3$
    $y = 1 - 2x$

17. $ax + 2by = c$
    $2ax - by = c$

Complete this item (each answer, 3 points).

18. Find the slope and *y*-intercept of $Ax + By + C = 0$.

a. *m* = _____   b. *b* = _____

Solve, using a two-order system. Circle your answer (each answer, 5 points).

19. One of two supplementary angles measures 6 degrees less than twice the other. How large are the angles?

20. Flying against the wind, a jet makes a 2,700-mile flight in 5 hours. The return flight takes $4\frac{1}{2}$ hours. Find the speed of the plane in still air and the wind speed.

MATH 1104

Unit 4: Polynomials

TEACHER NOTES

MATERIALS NEEDED FOR LIFEPAC	
Required	Suggested
(none)	(none)

ADDITIONAL LEARNING ACTIVITIES

Section 1: Products and Factoring

1. Show that a polynomial is any expression of the type $a_n x^n + a_{n-1} x^{n-1} + ... + a_2 x^2 + a_1 x + a_0$, where n is a nonnegative integer and $a_n, a_{n-1}, ..., a_2, a_1,$ and a_0 are real-number coefficients. Each $a_i x^i$ is called a *term*. The leading coefficient, a_n, is the coefficient of the term of the highest power. If $a_n \neq 0$, we say the degree of the polynomial is n.

    Show the following examples.

Polynomial	Degree
$5x^3 - 3x^2 + \frac{1}{4}$	3
$7x^2 - \sqrt{3}x + 5$	2
$-4x + \pi$	1
25	0
$0x^2 + 0x + 0$	no degree
0	no degree

2. Have the students do this activity after the preceding teacher-directed activity. Have students state the degree of each of the following polynomials.

    a. $x^5 - x^3 + x^2 + \frac{1}{2}$

    b. $3x - 7$

    c. $3x^2 - 6$

    d. $\frac{1}{2}$

    e. 0

    f. $0x^3 + 0x^2 + 0x + 17$

Section 2: Operations

1. Discuss rational roots. Let $P(x) = a_n x^n + a_{n-1} x^{n-1} + ... + a_1 x + a_0$, where all the coefficients are integers. Consider a rational number denoted by $\frac{c}{d}$, where c and d are relatively prime (have no common factor other than 1 and -1). If $\frac{c}{d}$ is a root of $P(x)$, then c is a factor of a_0 and d is a factor of a_n.

The usefulness of the rational roots theorem is seen in the following example.

Example: Let $P(x) = 3x^4 - 11x^3 + 10x - 4$. Find the rational roots of P(x). If possible, find the other roots.

By the rational roots theorem, if $\frac{c}{d}$, is a root of P(x), then c must be a factor of -4 (a_0) and d must be a factor of 3 (a_n). Thus, the possibilities for c and d are

c. 1, -1, 4, -4, 2, -2;
d. 1, -1, 3, -3.

Then, the resulting possibilities for $\frac{c}{d}$ are

1, -1, $\frac{1}{3}$, -$\frac{1}{3}$, 4, -4, $\frac{4}{3}$, -$\frac{4}{3}$, 2, -2, $\frac{2}{3}$, and -$\frac{2}{3}$.

Of these twelve possibilities, we know that at most, four of them can be roots because P(x) is of degree 4. To find which possibilities are roots, we can use substitution, but synthetic division is usually more efficient.

```
 1 |   3  -  11  +   0  +  10  -   4
                3  -   8  -   8  +   2
       3  -   8  -   8  +   2  -   2
```

```
-1 |   3  -  11  +   0  +  10  -   4
             -   3  +  14  -  14  +   4
       3  -  14  +  14  -   4  +   0
```

Since P(1) = -2, 1 is not a root; and since P(-1) = 0, -1 is a root. Using the results of the second synthetic division, we can express P(x) as

$P(x) = (x + 1)(3x^3 - 14x^2 + 14x - 4)$.

We now use $3x^3 - 14x^2 + 14x - 4$ and check the other possible roots.

```
 2/3 |   3  -  14  +  14  -   4
                  2  -   8  +   4
         3  -  12  +   6  +   0
```

Since $P(\frac{2}{3}) = 0$, $\frac{2}{3}$ is a root. Again using the results of synthetic division, we can express P(x) as $P(x) = (x + 1)(x - \frac{2}{3})(3x^2 - 12x + 6)$.

Since the factor $3x^2 - 12x + 6$ is quadratic, we can use the quadratic formula to find the other roots, which are $2 + \sqrt{2}$ and $2 - \sqrt{2}$. These roots are irrational numbers. Thus, the rational roots are -1 and $\frac{2}{3}$.

2. Have the students do this activity after the preceding teacher-directed activity. Have the class respond to the following questions.

a. Let $P(x) = 2x^4 - 7x^3 - 35x^2 + 13x + 3$. If $\frac{c}{d}$ is a rational root of P(x), then:

1. What are the possibilities (factors) for c?
2. What are the possibilities (factors) for d?
3. What are the possibilities for $\frac{c}{d}$?
4. Find the rational roots.
5. If possible, find the other roots.

b. Let $P(x) = x^3 + 7x^2 + 4x + 28$. If $\frac{c}{d}$ is a rational root of $P(x)$, then:

1. What are the possibilities (factors) for c?

2. What are the possibilities (factors) for d?

3. What are the possibilities for $\frac{c}{d}$?

4. How can you tell without substitution or synthetic division that no positive roots exist?

5. Find the rational roots of $P(x)$.

6. Find any other existing roots.

Section 3: Variations

1. Discuss the following classification scheme to show the wide variety of functions that occur in mathematics.

All Functions

Algebraic	Nonalgebraic
Rational	(Transcendental)
Polynomials	Exponential
	Logarithmic

Discuss the following ideas, which relate to functions.

a. intervals

b. bounds

c. continuity

d. increasing and decreasing functions

e. horizontal and vertical asymptotes

f. symmetry: odd and even functions

g. composition of functions

2. Have the class graph the function $P(x) = x^3 + 3x^2 - 2x - 6$. To graph the function, have them first find the rational roots by synthetic division. Then have them make a table of function values, using either substitution or synthetic division. Finally, have the students plot the resulting points and connect them with a smooth curve.

Additional Activities

The following activities may be reproduced as student worksheets. The "Using Synthetic Division" activity should be given after the students have done the group activity in Section 2, "Operations."

» MULTIPLYING AND FACTORING POLYNOMIALS

Find the indicated products.

1. $(4x + 7)(4x - 7)$ _____

2. $(5x^2y + 2y)(5x^2y - 2y)$ _____

3. $(4y^2 + 3)(4y^2 - 3)$ _____

4. $(2x + 3 + 5y)(2x + 3 - 5y)$ _____

5. $(-2x^3y^2 + 5t)(2x^3y^2 + 5t)$ _____

6. $(a + b)(a^2 - 2ab + b^2)$ _____

7. $(a^2 + b^2)(a^2 - b^2)$ _____

8. $(3a^2 - b^2)(a^2 + 4ab + b^2)$ _____

9. $(6a + 5)(2a - 7 - 8b)$ _____

10. $(-5a^x + 8b^y)(3a^x + 4b^y)$ _____

Factor these expressions completely.

11. $x^2 + 8x + 12$ _____

12. $6x^2 - 30x - 36$ _____

13. $a^4 - b^4$ _____

14. $9x^2 - 36y^2$ _____

15. $4 - 16y^2$ _____

16. $a^4b^4 - c^4$ _____

17. $m^2 - 9mn + 14n^2$ _____

18. $x^{2n} + 12x^ny^n + 36y^{2n}$ _____

19. $27x^3 - 125y^3$ _____

20. $y^3 - 64$ _____

» USING SYNTHETIC DIVISION

Find only the rational roots of the following polynomials.

1. $x^5 - 32$ _____

2. $x^3 - x^2 - 4x + 4$ _____

3. $x^4 + 2x^3 + 2x^2 - 4x - 8$ _____

4. $x^5 - 5x^4 + 5x^3 + 15x^2 - 36x + 20$ _____

ADDITIONAL ACTIVITIES, SOLUTION KEY

Multiplying and Factoring Polynomials

1. $(4x + 7)4x + (4x + 7)(-7) =$
$16x^2 + 28x − 28x − 49 =$
$16x^2 + 0x − 49 =$
$16x^2 − 49$

2. $(5x^2y + 2y)5x^2y + (5x^2y + 2y)(-2y) =$
$25x^4y^2 + 10x^2y^2 − 10x^2y^2 − 4y^2 =$
$25x^4y^2 + 0x^2y^2 − 4y^2 =$
$25x^4y^2 − 4y^2$

3. $(4y^2 + 3)4y^2 + (4y^2 + 3)(-3) =$
$16y^4 + 12y^2 − 12y^2 − 9 =$
$16y^4 + 0y^2 − 9 =$
$16y^4 − 9$

4.
$\begin{array}{r} 2x + 5y + 3 \\ \underline{2x − 5y + 3} \\ 4x^2 + 10xy + 6x \\ -10xy \quad − 25y^2 − 15y \\ \underline{\quad 6x \quad + 15y + 9} \\ 4x^2 \quad + 12x − 25y^2 \quad + 9 = \\ 4x^2 + 12x − 25y^2 + 9 \end{array}$

5. $(-2x^3y^2 + 5t)2x^3y^2 + (-2x^3y^2 + 5t)5t =$
$-4x^6y^4 + 10x^3y^2t − 10x^3y^2t + 25t^2 =$
$-4x^6y^4 + 0x^3y^2t + 25t^2 =$
$-4x^6y^4 + 25t^2$

6.
$\begin{array}{r} a^2 − 2ab + b^2 \\ \underline{a + b} \\ a^3 − 2a^2b + ab^2 \\ \underline{\quad a^2b − 2ab^2 + b^3} \\ a^3 − a^2b − ab^2 + b^3 \end{array}$

7. $(a^2 + b^2)a^2 − (a^2 + b^2)b^2 =$
$a^4 + a^2b^2 − a^2b^2 − b^4 =$
$a^4 + 0a^2b^2 − b^4 =$
$a^4 − b^4$

8.
$\begin{array}{r} a^2 + 4ab + b^2 \\ \underline{3a^2 − b^2} \\ 3a^4 + 12a^3b + 3a^2b^2 \\ \underline{\quad -a^2b^2 − 4ab^3 − b^4} \\ 3a^4 + 12a^3b + 2a^2b^2 − 4ab^3 − b^4 \end{array}$

9.
$\begin{array}{r} 2a − 8b − 7 \\ \underline{6a + 5} \\ 12a^2 − 48ab − 42a \\ \underline{\quad 10a − 40b − 35} \\ 12a^2 − 48ab − 32a − 40b − 35 \end{array}$

10. $(-5a^x + 8b^y)3a^x + (-5a^x + 8b^y)4b^y =$
$-15a^{2x} + 24a^xb^y − 20a^xb^y + 32b^{2y} =$
$-15a^{2x} + 4a^xb^y + 32b^{2y}$

11. $(x + 2)(x + 6)$

12. $6(x^2 − 5x − 6) =$
$6(x + 1)(x − 6)$

13. $(a^2 + b^2)(a^2 − b^2) =$
$(a^2 + b^2)(a + b)(a − b)$

14. $9(x^2 − 4y^2)$
$9(x + 2y)(x − 2y)$

15. $4(1 − 4y^2) =$
$4(1 + 2y)(1 − 2y)$

16. $(a^2b^2 + c^2)(a^2b^2 − c^2)$
$(a^2b^2 + c^2)(ab + c)(ab − c)$

17. $(m − 2n)(m − 7n)$

18. $(x^n + 6y^n)(x^n + 6y^n) =$
$(x^n + 6y^n)^2$

19. $(3x − 5y)(9x^2 + 15xy + 25y^2)$

20. $(y − 4)(y^2 + 4y + 16)$

Using Synthetic Division

1. c = 1, -1, 2, -2, 4, -4, 8, -8, 16, -16, 32, -32
   d = 1, -1
   $\frac{c}{d}$ = 1, -1, 2, -2, 4, -4, 8, -8, 16, -16, 32, -32

$$\begin{array}{r|rrrrrr} 2 & 1 & 0 & 0 & 0 & 0 & -32 \\ & & 2 & 4 & 8 & 16 & 32 \\ \hline & 1 & 2 & 4 & 8 & 16 & 0 \end{array}$$

Therefore, $x - 2$ is a root of $x^5 - 32$ and is expressed as $(x - 2)(x^4 + 2x^3 + 4x^2 + 8x + 16)$. Now find the roots of $x^4 + 2x^3 + 4x^2 + 8x + 16$.
c = 1, -1, 2, -2, 4, -4, 8, -8, 16, -16
d = 1, -1
$\frac{c}{d}$ = 1, -1, 2, -2, 4, -4, 8, -8, 16, -16
No other rational roots exist, so 2 is the only rational root.

2. c = 1, -1, 2, -2, 4, -4
   d = 1, -1
   $\frac{c}{d}$ = 1, -1, 2, -2, 4, -4

$$\begin{array}{r|rrrr} 1 & 1 & -1 & -4 & 4 \\ & & 1 & 0 & -4 \\ \hline & 1 & 0 & -4 & 0 \end{array}$$

$$\begin{array}{r|rrrr} 2 & 1 & -1 & -4 & 4 \\ & & 2 & 2 & -4 \\ \hline & 1 & 1 & -2 & 0 \end{array}$$

$$\begin{array}{r|rrrr} -2 & 1 & -1 & -4 & 4 \\ & & -2 & 6 & -4 \\ \hline & 1 & -3 & 2 & 0 \end{array}$$

∴ The rational roots are 1, 2, and -2.

3. c = 1, -1, 2, -2, 4, -4, 8, -8
   d = 1, -1
   $\frac{c}{d}$ = 1, -1, 2, -2, 4, -4, 8, -8
No rational roots exist.

4. c = 1, -1, 2, -2, 4, -4, 5, -5, 10, -10, 20, -20
   d = 1, -1
   $\frac{c}{d}$ = 1, -1, 2, -2, 4, -4, 5, -5, 10, -10, 20, -20

$$\begin{array}{r|rrrrr} 1 & 1 & -5 & 5 & 15 & -36 & 20 \\ & & 1 & -4 & 1 & 16 & -20 \\ \hline & 1 & -4 & 1 & 16 & -20 & 0 \end{array}$$

$$\begin{array}{r|rrrrr} 2 & 1 & -5 & 5 & 15 & -36 & 20 \\ & & 2 & -6 & -2 & 26 & -20 \\ \hline & 1 & -3 & -1 & 13 & -10 & 0 \end{array}$$

$$\begin{array}{r|rrrrr} -2 & 1 & -5 & 5 & 15 & -36 & 20 \\ & & -2 & 14 & -38 & 46 & -20 \\ \hline & 1 & -7 & 19 & -23 & 10 & 0 \end{array}$$

∴ The rational roots are 1, 2, and -2.

ANSWER KEY

SECTION 1

1.1 $x^2 \cdot x^5 = x^{2+5} = x^7$

1.2 $a^4 \cdot a^6 = a^{4+6} = a^{10}$

1.3 $(a^4)^5 = a^{4 \cdot 5} = a^{20}$

1.4 $(x^6)^4 = x^{6 \cdot 4} = x^{24}$

1.5 $(x^2y)^3 = (x^2)^3y^3 = x^6y^3$

1.6 $(2a^2b)^4 = 2^4(a^2)^4b^4 = 16a^8b^4$

1.7 $-2x^2y^3 \cdot 14x^2y^3 = -2(14)x^2 \cdot x^2 \cdot y^3 \cdot y^3 = -28x^4y^6$

1.8 $(3x^2y^6)^7 = 3^7(x^2)^7(y^6)^7 = 2{,}187x^{14}y^{42}$

1.9 $a^2b(3a^2 + 4ab^2) = 3a^2 \cdot a^2b + 4a \cdot a^2 \cdot b^2 \cdot b = 3a^4b + 4a^3b^3$

1.10 $3a^n(a^n + a^{n-1}) = 3a^n \cdot a^n + 3a^n \cdot a^{n-1} = 3a^{2n} + 3a^{2n-1}$

1.11 $6xy(\frac{1}{2}x^2 - \frac{1}{3}xy + \frac{1}{6}y^2) =$

$6xy(\frac{1}{2}x^2) + 6xy(-\frac{1}{3}xy) + 6xy(\frac{1}{6}y^2) =$

$6(\frac{1}{2})x \cdot x^2 \cdot y + 6(-\frac{1}{3})x \cdot x \cdot y \cdot y + 6(\frac{1}{6})x \cdot y \cdot y^2 =$

$3x^3y - 2x^2y^2 + xy^3$

1.12 $(a + 3)(a - 2) = a^2 + 3a - 2a - 6 = a^2 + a - 6$

1.13 $(3xy - 1)(4xy + 2) = 12x^2y^2 - 4xy + 6xy - 2 = 12x^2y^2 + 2xy - 2$

1.14 $(2x - 3y)(4x - y) = 8x^2 - 14xy + 3y^2$

1.15 $(ab - 9)(ab + 8) = a^2b^2 - ab - 72$

1.16 $(m^3n + 8)(m^3n - 5) = m^6n^2 + 3m^3n - 40$

1.17 $(3 - c^2d)(4 - 4c^2d) = 12 - 16c^2d + 4c^4d^2$

1.18 $(1 - 7x)(1 + 9x) = 1 + 2x - 63x^2$

1.19 $(3m^3 - \frac{1}{2}y)(3m^3 - \frac{1}{2}y) = 9m^6 - 3m^3y + \frac{1}{4}y^2$

1.20 $(a + b)(a^2 - ab + b^2) =$
$a^3 - \cancel{a^2b} + \cancel{ab^2} + \cancel{ba^2} - \cancel{ab^2} + b^3 = a^3 + b^3$

1.21 $(a - b)(a^2 + ab + b^2) =$
$a^3 + \cancel{a^2b} + \cancel{ab^2} - \cancel{ba^2} - \cancel{ab^2} - b^3 = a^3 - b^3$

1.22 $(x + y + 3)(x + y - 4)$
Let $x + y = a$.
$(a + 3)(a - 4) = a^2 - a - 12 =$
$(x + y)^2 - (x + y) - 12 =$
$x^2 + 2xy + y^2 - x - y - 12$

1.23 $(a + b - c)(a + b + c)$
Let $a + b = x$.
$(x - c)(x + c) = x^2 - c^2 = (a + b)^2 - c^2 =$
$a^2 + 2ab + b^2 - c^2$

1.24 $(x^2 + 2x - 1)(x^2 + 2x + 5)$
Let $x^2 + 2x = a$.
$(a - 1)(a + 5) = a^2 + 4a - 5 =$
$(x^2 + 2x)^2 + 4(x^2 + 2x) - 5 =$
$x^4 + 4x^3 + 4x^2 + 4x^2 + 8x - 5 =$
$x^4 + 4x^3 + 8x^2 + 8x - 5$

1.25 $[4 - (3c - 1)][6 - (3c - 1)]$
Let $x = 3c - 1$.
$(4 - x)(6 - x) = 24 - 10x + x^2 =$
$24 - 10(3c - 1) + (3c - 1)^2 =$
$24 - 30c + 10 + 9c^2 - 6c + 1 =$
$9c^2 - 36c + 35$

1.26 $(3x - 4y - 5z)(4x + 4y + 5z)$
$[3x - (4y + 5z)][4x + (4y + 5z)]$
Let $a = 4y + 5z$.
$(3x - a)(4x + a) = 12x^2 - 4ax + 3ax - a^2 =$
$12x^2 - ax - a^2 =$
$12x^2 - (4y + 5z)x - (4y + 5z)^2 =$
$12x^2 - 4xy - 5xz - (16y^2 + 40yz + 25z^2) =$
$12x^2 - 4xy - 5xz - 16y^2 - 40yz - 25z^2$

1.27 $w^2 + 2xw + x^2$

1.28 $y^2 - 2xy + x^2$

1.29 $(wx - y)(wx - y) = w^2x^2 - 2wxy + y^2$

1.30 $(x + 2y)(x + 2y) = x^2 + 4xy + 4y^2$

1.31 $(4x^3 + 7y^3z^4)(4x^3 + 7y^3z^4) = 16x^6 + 56x^3y^3z^4 + 49y^6z^8$

1.32 $(10^x + 4^y)(10^x + 4^y) = 10^{2x} + 2 \cdot 10^x \cdot 4^y + 4^{2y}$

1.33 $(2x - \frac{1}{2})(2x - \frac{1}{2}) = 4x^2 - 2x + \frac{1}{4}$

1.34 $(0.1x + 0.4y)(0.1x + 0.4y) = 0.01x^2 + 0.08xy + 0.16y^2$

1.35 $(2a^x + \frac{1}{2}b^x)(2a^x + \frac{1}{2}b^x) = 4a^{2x} + 2a^xb^x + \frac{1}{4}b^{2x}$

1.36 $(3x^{2a} - 4y^az^{3a})(3x^{2a} - 4y^az^{3a}) = 9x^{4a} - 24x^{2a}y^az^{3a} + 16y^{2a}z^{6a}$

1.37 $x^2 - 4$

1.38 $4a^2 - 3ax - x^2$

1.39 $y^2 - \frac{1}{9}$

1.40 $b^4 - 64$

1.41 $25c^2 - \frac{4}{9}$

1.42 $x^2 - 0.04$

1.43 $y^{2n} - 25$

1.44 $a^{2x} - b^{2y}$

1.45 $16y^{2a} - 36x^{2b}$

1.46 $a^2 + ab + ac$

$\quad\quad + ab \quad\quad + b^2 + bc$

$\quad\quad\quad\quad - ac \quad - bc - c^2$

$\overline{a^2 + 2ab \quad\quad + b^2 \quad - c^2}$

$= a^2 + 2ab + b^2 - c^2$

1.47 $x^3 - x^2y + xy^2$

$\quad\quad + x^2y - xy^2 + y^3$

$\overline{x^3 \quad\quad\quad\quad + y^3}$

$= x^3 + y^3$

1.48 $x^3 + x^2y + xy^2$

$\quad\quad - x^2y - xy^2 - y^3$

$\overline{x^3 \quad\quad\quad\quad - y^3}$

$= x^3 - y^3$

1.49 $8x^3 + 4x^2y + 2xy^2$

$\quad\quad - 4x^2y - 2xy^2 - y^3$

$\overline{8x^3 \quad\quad\quad\quad - y^3}$

$= 8x^3 - y^3$

1.50 $27a^3 - 18a^2c + 12ac^2$

$\quad\quad + 18a^2c - 12ac^2 + 8c^3$

$\overline{27a^3 \quad\quad\quad\quad + 8c^3}$

$= 27a^3 + 8c^3$

1.51 $64a^6 + 48a^4b^2 + 36a^2b^4$

$\quad\quad - 48a^4b^2 - 36a^2b^4 - 27b^6$

$\overline{64a^6 \quad\quad\quad\quad\quad - 27b^6}$

$= 64a^6 - 27b^6$

1.52 $x^2 - 8x + 16 = (x - 4)(x - 4) = (x - 4)^2$

1.53 $c^2 + 6c + 9 = (c + 3)(c + 3) = (c + 3)^2$

1.54 $16x^2 + 48xy + 36y^2 = 4(4x^2 + 12xy + 9y^2) =$
$4(2x + 3y)(2x + 3y) = 4(2x + 3y)^2$

1.55 $25a^2 - 70a + 49 = (5a - 7)(5a - 7) = (5a - 7)^2$

1.56 $16ax + 4x^2 + 16a^2 = 4(4ax + x^2 + 4a^2) =$
$4(x^2 + 4ax + 4a^2) = 4(x + 2a)^2$

1.57 $25a^2 + 9b^2 + 30ab = 25a^2 + 30ab + 9b^2 =$
$(5a + 3b)(5a + 3b) = (5a + 3b)^2$

1.58 $2x^2 - 16x + 32 = 2(x^2 - 8x + 16) =$
$2(x - 4)(x - 4) = 2(x - 4)^2$

1.59 $5c^2 + 30c + 45 = 5(c^2 + 6c + 9) =$
$5(c + 3)(c + 3) = 5(c + 3)^2$

1.60 $128x^2 + 96xy + 18y^2 = 2(64x^2 + 48xy + 9y^2) =$
$2(8x + 3y)(8x + 3y) = 2(8x + 3y)^2$

1.61 $450a^2 + 242c^2 + 660ac =$
$450a^2 + 660ac + 242c^2 =$
$2(225a^2 + 330ac + 121c^2) =$
$2(15a + 11c)(15a + 11c) =$
$2(15a + 11c)^2$

1.62 $b^2 - 7b + 12 = (b - 4)(b - 3)$

1.63 $a^2 - 9a + 20 = (a - 5)(a - 4)$

1.64 $x^2 - 2x - 24 = (x - 6)(x + 4)$

1.65 $y^2 - 12 - 4y = y^2 - 4y - 12 = (y - 6)(y + 2)$

1.66 $3y^2 + 7y + 4 = (3y + 4)(y + 1)$

1.67 $a^2 - 5a - 6 = (a - 6)(a + 1)$

1.68 $10b^2 + 17b + 3 = (5b + 1)(2b + 3)$

1.69 $y^2 - xy - 56x^2 = (y - 8x)(y + 7x)$

1.70 $13m^2 - 5mn - 8n^2 = (13m + 8n)(m - n)$

1.71 $3y^4 - 2y^2 - 5 = (3y^2 - 5)(y^2 + 1)$

1.72 $a^8 - 12a^4 + 36 = (a^4 - 6)(a^4 - 6) = (a^4 - 6)^2$

1.73 $3m^2 + 2mn - n^2 = (3m - n)(m + n)$

1.74 $2a^2 + 2b^2 - 5ab = 2a^2 - 5ab + 2b^2 =$
$(2a - b)(a - 2b)$

1.75 $4x^2 + 8xy - 60y^2 = 4(x^2 + 2xy - 15y^2) =$
$4(x + 5y)(x - 3y)$

1.76 $9 - 6a - 24a^2 = 3(3 - 2a - 8a^2) =$
$3(3 + 4a)(1 - 2a)$

1.77 $a^2b^2 - 7ab + 10 = (ab - 5)(ab - 2)$

1.78 $x^{2n} + 10x^n + 16 = (x^n)^2 + 10x^n + 16 =$
$(x^n + 8)(x^n + 2) =$

1.79 $y^{2a} - y^a - 20 = (y^a)^2 - y^a - 20 = (y^a - 5)(y^a + 4)$

1.80 $(3x + y)(3x - y)$

1.81 $4(2a + b)(2a - b)$

1.82 $(1 + 2y)(1 - 2y)$

1.83 $(a + c)(a - c)$

1.84 $(x^3 + 6)(x^3 - 6)$

1.85 $(ab + d)(ab - d)$

1.86 $(3x^2y + z^3)(3x^2y - z^3)$

1.87 $4(3xy^3 + 2)(3xy^3 - 2)$

1.88 $0.09(y + 3)(y - 3)$

1.89 $(1 + 10x)(1 - 10x)$

1.90 $(6a^x + b)(6a^x - b)$

1.91 $(\frac{2}{3}x + \frac{6}{7}y)(\frac{2}{3}x - \frac{6}{7}y)$

1.92 $(x - 1)(x^2 + x + 1)$

1.93 $(y - 3)(y^2 + 3y + 9)$

1.94 $(x + y)(x^2 - xy + y^2)$

1.95 $(2y - 3)(4y^2 + 6y + 9)$

1.96 $x^6 - y^6 = (x^3)^2 - (y^3)^2 = (x^3 + y^3)(x^3 - y^3) =$
$(x + y)(x^2 - xy + y^2) = (x - y)(x^2 + xy + y^2)$

1.97 $(xy + z)(x^2y^2 - xyz + z^2)$

1.98 $(x + \frac{1}{2})(x^2 - \frac{1}{2}x + \frac{1}{4})$

1.99 $a^{3y} + 1 = (a^y)^3 + 1 = (a^y + 1)(a^{2y} - a^y + 1)$

1.100 $(\frac{1}{2}x - \frac{1}{3}y)(\frac{1}{4}x^2 + \frac{1}{6}xy + \frac{1}{9}y^2)$

1.101 $(0.1b - 0.2d)(0.01b^2 + 0.02bd + 0.04d^2)$

1.102 $5x^3 + 40y^6 = 5(x^3 + 8y^6) = 5[x^3 + (2y^2)^3] =$
$5(x + 2y^2)(x^2 - 2xy^2 + 4y^4)$

SELF TEST 1

1.01 $x^3 \cdot x^2 = x^{3+2} = x^5$

1.02 $(x^4)^2 = x^{4 \cdot 2} = x^8$

1.03 $(x^3y^5)^3 = (x^{3 \cdot 3})(y^{5 \cdot 3}) = x^9y^{15}$

1.04 $(14x^3y^2z)^4 = 14^4(x^{3 \cdot 4})(y^{2 \cdot 4})(z^4) = 38{,}416x^{12}y^8z^4$

1.05 $3a^3x(4a^2byx^3) = 3 \cdot 4(a^3 \cdot a^2)(by)(x \cdot x^3) =$
$12a^5byx^4$

1.06 $6a^2x(9a^2 + 4byx^2 + 6abx) =$
$6a^2x(9a^2) + 6a^2x(4byx^2) + 6a^2x(6abx) =$
$54a^4x + 24a^2byx^3 + 36a^3bx^2$

1.07 $(2x + 4)(3x + 8) = 6x^2 + 16x + 12x + 32 =$
$6x^2 + 28x + 32$

1.08 $(12x^2 + 7y^3)(4x^2 + 7y^3) =$
$48x^4 + 84x^2y^3 + 28x^2y^3 + 49y^6 =$
$48x^4 + 112x^2y^3 + 49y^6$

1.09 $(2x + a)(3x^2 + b) =$
$6x^3 + 2xb + 3ax^2 + ab$

1.010 $(2x + y)^2 = (2x + y)(2x + y) =$
$4x^2 + 2xy + 2xy + y^2 = 4x^2 + 4xy + y^2$

1.011 $(a + b)(a - b) = a^2 - b^2$

1.012 $(3a^2 - 7xy)(3a^2 + 7xy) = 9a^4 - 49x^2y^2$

1.013 $(r + s)(r^2 - rs + s^2) =$
$r^3 - r^2s + rs^2$
$\underline{\quad\quad + r^2s - rs^2 + s^3}$
$r^3 \quad\quad\quad\quad + s^3$
$= r^3 + s^3$

1.014 $(2a^2 - 8)(4a^4 + 16a^2 + 64) =$
$8a^6 + 32a^4 + 128a^2$
$\underline{\quad\quad - 32a^4 - 128a^2 - 512}$
$8a^6 \quad\quad\quad\quad\quad - 512$
$= 8a^6 - 512$

1.015 $(x + 3)(x + 3) = (x + 3)^2$

1.016 $(4x^2 + 7)(4x^2 + 7) = (4x^2 + 7)^2$

1.017 $(x + 3)(2x + 5)$

1.018 $(3x + 4)(2x - 7)$

1.019 $2(3x^2 + y)(3x^2 + y) = 2(3x^2 + y)^2$

1.020 $(x + r)(x - r)$

1.021 $3(2x^3 + 3y^2)(2x^3 - 3y^2)$

1.022 $(u - v)(u^2 + uv + v^2)$

1.023 $(2r^2 + 3s^4)(4r^4 - 6r^2s^4 + 9s^8)$

1.024 $(4x^2)^3 - (y^2)^3 = (4x^2 - y^2)(16x^4 + 4x^2y^2 + y^4) =$
$(2x + y)(2x - y)(16x^4 + 4x^2y^2 + y^4)$

SECTION 2

2.1 $8x^2 - x - 8$

2.2 $-2.4x^2 - 1.5x - 11.4$

2.3 $-6x^2 + 3xy + 6y^2$

2.4 $-6a + 4b - 4c$

2.5 $4x^2 - 6x + 2$

2.6 $x^4 + x^3 + 4x^2 - 5x$

2.7 $-x^2 + 6x - 19$

2.8 $-3x + 7y - 8z$

2.9 $-1.2x + 4.0z$

2.10 $-5m - 5n - 1$

2.11 $4x^2 - 4x + 3$
$\underline{2x^2 - 6x - 4}$
$2x^2 + 2x + 7$

2.12 $2a^2 + ab - b^2$
$\underline{2a^2 - ab - 2b^2}$
$\quad\quad 2ab + b^2$

2.13

2	−	3	+	12	=	11
-14			−	24	=	-38
		15	−	4	=	11
-12	+	12	−	16	=	-16

2.14

6	−	12	−	7	=	-13
16	+	3	−	6	=	13
-10	−	15	−	1	=	-26

2.15 $5x^2 - 7x + 15$

2.16 $-3a^3 + 5a^2 - 3a + 7$

2.17 $5m^3 \quad\quad + 3mn^2$
$\quad\quad - 7m^2n + mn^2 - n^3$
$\underline{-2m^3 \quad\quad - mn^2}$
$3m^3 - 7m^2n + 3mn^2 - n^3$

2.18 $\frac{1}{3}a + \frac{3}{4}b - \frac{2}{5}c = \frac{4}{12}a + \frac{6}{8}b - \frac{8}{20}c$
$\frac{1}{4}a + b - \frac{1}{4}c = \frac{3}{12}a + \frac{8}{8}b - \frac{5}{20}c$
$\underline{\frac{1}{2}a - \frac{3}{8}b - \frac{1}{10}c = \frac{6}{12}a - \frac{3}{8}b - \frac{2}{20}c}$
$\quad\quad\quad\quad = \frac{13}{12}a + \frac{11}{8}b - \frac{15}{20}c$
$\quad\quad\quad\quad = \frac{13}{12}a + \frac{11}{8}b - \frac{3}{4}c$
$\quad\quad\text{or } 1\frac{1}{12}a + 1\frac{3}{8}b - \frac{3}{4}c$

2.19 $x^2 + 4x - 1$
$\underline{- \quad\quad 3x - 7}$
$x^2 + x + 6$

2.20 $a^3 \quad\quad - 2a$
$\underline{- \quad\quad a^2 + a - 6}$
$a^3 - a^2 - 3a + 6$

2.21 $2a + b$ $a - 9b$

$$\begin{array}{r} 2a + b \\ + a - 9b \\ \hline 3a - 8b \end{array} \qquad \begin{array}{r} 7a - 11b \\ - 3a - 8b \\ \hline 4a - 3b \end{array}$$

$4a - 3b$ is the third side.

2.22 $2y^2$

2.23 $3x^3 + x^2 - 2x$

2.24 $4x - 5$

2.25 $3a - 5$

2.26 $9x^2 - 3a$

2.27

$$\require{enclose}\begin{array}{r} 4y + \frac{1}{2y-1} \\ 2y-1 \enclose{longdiv}{8y^2 - 4y + 1} \\ \underline{8y^2 - 4y } \\ 1 \end{array}$$

2.28

$$\begin{array}{r} 2a + 3 + \frac{6}{a-1} \\ a-1 \enclose{longdiv}{2a^2 + a + 3} \\ \underline{2a^2 - 2a } \\ 3a + 3 \\ \underline{3a - 3} \\ 6 \end{array}$$

2.29

$$\begin{array}{r} 2y - \frac{3}{2} + \frac{11\frac{1}{2}}{2y-3} \\ 2y+3 \enclose{longdiv}{4y^2 + 3y + 7} \\ \underline{4y^2 + 6y } \\ -3y + 7 \\ \underline{-3y - \frac{9}{2}} \\ 11\frac{1}{2} \end{array}$$

2.30

$$\begin{array}{r} 2x^2 + 5x + 2 \\ 3x-2 \enclose{longdiv}{6x^3 + 11x^2 - 4x - 4} \\ \underline{6x^3 - 4x^2 } \\ 15x^2 - 4x \\ \underline{15x^2 - 10x} \\ 6x - 4 \\ \underline{6x - 4} \\ 0 \end{array}$$

2.31

$$\begin{array}{r} 2x + 7 \\ 3x-5 \enclose{longdiv}{6x^2 + 11x - 35} \\ \underline{6x^2 - 10x } \\ 21x - 35 \\ \underline{21x - 35} \\ 0 \end{array}$$

2.32

$$\begin{array}{r} x + 1 + \frac{-3}{x-1} \\ x-1 \enclose{longdiv}{x^2 + 0x - 4} \\ \underline{x^2 - x } \\ x - 4 \\ \underline{x - 1} \\ -3 \end{array}$$

2.33

$$\begin{array}{r} x^2 - x - 1 + \frac{-2}{x-1} \\ x-1 \enclose{longdiv}{x^3 - 2x^2 + 0x - 1} \\ \underline{x^3 - x^2 } \\ -x^2 + 0x \\ \underline{-x^2 + x} \\ -x - 1 \\ \underline{-x + 1} \\ -2 \end{array}$$

2.34

$$\begin{array}{r} y^2 - 2y + 3 \\ y-2 \enclose{longdiv}{y^3 - 4y^2 + 7y - 6} \\ \underline{y^3 - 2y^2 } \\ -2y^2 + 7y \\ \underline{-2y^2 + 4y} \\ 3y - 6 \\ \underline{3y - 6} \\ 0 \end{array}$$

2.35

$$\begin{array}{r} x^2 + xy + y^2 + \frac{2y^3}{x-y} \\ x-y \enclose{longdiv}{x^3 + 0x^2y + 0xy^2 + y^3} \\ \underline{x^3 - x^2y } \\ x^2y + 0xy^2 \\ \underline{x^2y - xy^2} \\ xy^2 + y^3 \\ \underline{xy^2 - y^3} \\ 2y^3 \end{array}$$

2.36

$$\begin{array}{r} a^2 + 2ab + 2b^2 \\ a^2-2ab+2b^2 \enclose{longdiv}{a^4 + 0a^3b + 0a^2b^2 + 0ab^3 + 4b^4} \\ \underline{a^4 - 2a^3b + 2a^2b^2 } \\ 2a^3b - 2a^2b^2 + 0ab^3 \\ \underline{2a^3b - 4a^2b^2 + 4ab^3} \\ 2a^2b^2 - 4ab^3 + 4b^4 \\ \underline{2a^2b^2 - 4ab^3 + 4b^4} \\ 0 \end{array}$$

2.37

$$\begin{array}{r} 3 + 5y + 5y^2 + \frac{3y^3}{1-y} \\ 1-y \enclose{longdiv}{3 + 2y + 0y^2 - 2y^3} \\ \underline{3 - 3y } \\ 5y + 0y^2 \\ \underline{5y - 5y^2} \\ 5y^2 - 2y^3 \\ \underline{5y^2 - 5y^3} \\ 3y^3 \end{array}$$

2.38

$$\begin{array}{r} 3x - y \\ 3x^3+2x^2y-xy^2 \enclose{longdiv}{9x^4 + 3x^3y - 5x^2y^2 + xy^3} \\ \underline{9x^4 + 6x^3y - 3x^2y^2 } \\ -3x^3y - 2x^2y^2 + xy^3 \\ \underline{-3x^3y - 2x^2y^2 + xy^3} \\ 0 \end{array}$$

2.39

$$
\begin{array}{r}
a^n - 9 + \frac{66}{a^n+8} \\
a^n+8 \overline{\smash{\big)}\ a^{2n} - a^n - 6} \\
\underline{a^{2n} + 8a^n} \\
-9a^n - 6 \\
\underline{-9a^n - 72} \\
66
\end{array}
$$

2.40

$$
\begin{array}{r}
x^4 - x^3y + x^2y^2 - xy^3 + y^4 \\
x+y \overline{\smash{\big)}\ x^5 + 0x^4y + 0x^3y^2 + 0x^2y^3 + 0xy^4 - a^{5n}} \\
\underline{x^5 + x^4y} \\
-x^4y + 0x^3y^2 \\
\underline{-x^4y - x^3y^2} \\
x^3y^2 + 0x^2y^3 \\
\underline{x^3y^2 + x^2y^3} \\
-x^2y^3 + 0xy^4 \\
\underline{-x^2y^3 - xy^4} \\
xy^4 + y^5 \\
\underline{xy^4 + y^5} \\
0
\end{array}
$$

2.41

$$
\begin{array}{r}
x^{4n} + x^{3n}a^n + x^{2n}a^{2n} + x^na^{3n} + a^{4n} \\
x^n-a^n \overline{\smash{\big)}\ x^{5n} + 0x^{4n}a^n + 0x^{3n}a^{2n} + 0x^{2n}a^{3n} + 0x^na^{4n} - a^{5n}} \\
\underline{x^{5n} - x^{4n}a^n} \\
x^{4n}a^n + 0x^{3n}a^{2n} \\
\underline{x^{4n}a^n - x^{3n}a^{2n}} \\
x^{3n}a^{2n} + 0x^{2n}a^{3n} \\
\underline{x^{3n}a^{2n} - x^{2n}a^{3n}} \\
x^{2n}a^{3n} + 0x^na^{4n} \\
\underline{x^{2n}a^{3n} - x^na^{4n}} \\
x^na^{4n} - a^{5n} \\
\underline{x^na^{4n} - a^{5n}} \\
0
\end{array}
$$

2.42

$$
\begin{array}{r|rrrr}
1 & 1 & -4 & 4 & -1 \\
& & 1 & -3 & 1 \\
\hline
& 1 & -3 & 1 & 0
\end{array}
$$

$x^2 - 3x + 1$

2.43

$$
\begin{array}{r|rrrr}
2 & 1 & 6 & 3 & 1 \\
& & 2 & 16 & 38 \\
\hline
& 1 & 8 & 19 & 39
\end{array}
$$

$x^2 + 8x + 19 + \frac{39}{x-2}$

2.44

$$
\begin{array}{r|rrrr}
-1 & 1 & -7 & 0 & 8 \\
& & -1 & 8 & -8 \\
\hline
& 1 & -8 & 8 & 0
\end{array}
$$

$x^2 - 8x + 8$

2.45

$$
\begin{array}{r|rrrr}
1 & 1 & -5 & 4 & 7 \\
& & 1 & -4 & 0 \\
\hline
& 1 & -4 & 0 & 7
\end{array}
$$

$x^2 - 4x + \frac{7}{x-1}$

2.46

$$
\begin{array}{r|rrrrr}
-2 & 12 & 17 & 0 & 8 & -40 \\
& & -24 & 14 & -28 & 40 \\
\hline
& 12 & -7 & 14 & -20 & 0
\end{array}
$$

$12x^3 - 7x^2 + 14x - 20$

2.47

$$
\begin{array}{r|rrrrr}
2 & 1 & -3 & 3 & -3 & 6 \\
& & 2 & -2 & 2 & -2 \\
\hline
& 1 & -1 & 1 & -1 & 4
\end{array}
$$

$x^3 - x^2 + x - 1 + \frac{4}{x-2}$

2.48

$$
\begin{array}{r|rrrrrr}
-4 & 1 & 0 & -8 & 24 & 12 & 40 \\
& & -4 & 16 & -32 & 32 & -176 \\
\hline
& 1 & -4 & 8 & -8 & 44 & -136
\end{array}
$$

$x^4 - 4x^3 + 8x^2 - 8x + 44 - \frac{136}{x+4}$

2.49

$$
\begin{array}{r|rrrr}
-2 & 5 & -12 & -36 & -16 \\
& & -10 & 44 & -16 \\
\hline
& 5 & -22 & 8 & -32
\end{array}
$$

$5x^2 - 22x + 8 - \frac{32}{x+2}$

2.50

$$
\begin{array}{r|rrrrr}
3 & 1 & 0 & 0 & 0 & -81 \\
& & 3 & 9 & 27 & 81 \\
\hline
& 1 & 3 & 9 & 27 & 0
\end{array}
$$

$x^3 + 3x^2 + 9x + 27$

2.51

$$
\begin{array}{r|rrrrr}
3 & 1 & 0 & 0 & 0 & 81 \\
& & 3 & 9 & 27 & 81 \\
\hline
& 1 & 3 & 9 & 27 & 162
\end{array}
$$

$x^3 + 3x^2 + 9x + 27 + \frac{162}{x-3}$

SELF TEST 2

2.01 $5x^3 - 4x + 1$

2.02 $5.3x^2 + 11.1x + 0.8$

2.03 $7a^3 \qquad + 14a + 12$

$\underline{-6a^3 + 12a^2 \qquad - 7}$

$a^3 + 12a^2 + 14a + 5$

2.04 $-10x^2 + 6xy + 3y^2$

2.05 $x^5 - 4x^4 + 7x^3 \qquad\qquad + 8$

$9x^3 + 7x^2 \qquad - 10$

$\underline{-2x^5 + 7x^4 \qquad\qquad - 3x + 8}$

$-x^5 + 3x^4 + 16x^3 + 7x^2 - 3x + 6$

2.06 $-2x^2 - 6x + 23$

2.07 $17.0x - 8.2y + 3.1z$

2.08 $5x^2 - 3x + 8$

$\underline{3x^2 - 7x + 4}$

$2x^2 + 4x + 4$

2.09 $4a + 7b - 12c$

$\underline{8a - 9b \qquad + 12d}$

$-4a + 16b - 12c - 12d$

2.010 $8 + 21 - 48 \qquad = -19$

$\underline{16 - 27 \qquad + 60 = 49}$

$-8 + 48 - 48 - 60 = -68$

2.011 $9w^3 - 6w^2 + 3w$

2.012

$$
\begin{array}{r}
3x^2 - 2x + 5 \\
4x-1\overline{)\,12x^3 - 11x^2 + 22x - 5} \\
\underline{12x^3 - 3x^2} \\
-8x^2 + 22x \\
\underline{-8x^2 + 2x} \\
20x - 5 \\
\underline{20x - 5} \\
0
\end{array}
$$

2.013

$$
\begin{array}{r}
2x + 5 + \frac{13}{x-2} \\
x-2\overline{)\,2x^2 + x + 3} \\
\underline{2x^2 - 4x} \\
5x + 3 \\
\underline{5x - 10} \\
13
\end{array}
$$

2.014

$$
\begin{array}{r}
4x^2 + 5x + 15 + \frac{53}{x-3} \\
x-3\overline{)\,4x^3 - 7x^2 + 0x + 8} \\
\underline{4x^3 - 12x^2} \\
5x^2 + 0x \\
\underline{5x^2 - 15x} \\
15x + 8 \\
\underline{15x - 45} \\
53
\end{array}
$$

2.015

$$
\begin{array}{r}
x^2 + 3x - 5 \\
x^2-x+2\overline{)\,x^4 + 2x^3 - 6x^2 + 11x - 10} \\
\underline{x^4 - x^3 + 2x^2} \\
3x^3 - 8x^2 + 11x \\
\underline{3x^3 - 3x^2 + 6x} \\
-5x^2 + 5x - 10 \\
\underline{-5x^2 + 5x - 10} \\
0
\end{array}
$$

2.016

$$
\begin{array}{r}
2y^2 + y - 5 \\
y+1\overline{)\,2y^3 + 3y^2 - 4y - 5} \\
\underline{2y^3 + 2y^2} \\
y^2 - 4y \\
\underline{y^2 + y} \\
-5y - 5 \\
\underline{-5y - 5} \\
0
\end{array}
$$

2.017

$$
\begin{array}{r}
3x^2 - 2x + 5 \\
4x-1\overline{)\,12x^3 - 11x^2 + 22x - 5} \\
\underline{12x^3 - 3x^2} \\
-8x^2 + 22x \\
\underline{-8x^2 + 2x} \\
20x - 5 \\
\underline{20x - 5} \\
0
\end{array}
$$

2.018

$$
\begin{array}{r|rrrr}
1 & 1 & -2 & 0 & -1 \\
& & 1 & -1 & -1 \\
\hline
& 1 & -1 & -1 & -2
\end{array}
$$

$x^2 - x - 1 - \dfrac{2}{x-1}$

2.019

$$
\begin{array}{r|rrrrr}
2 & 1 & 0 & 0 & -10 & 0 & -8 \\
& & 2 & 4 & 8 & -4 & -8 \\
\hline
& 1 & 2 & 4 & -2 & -4 & -16
\end{array}
$$

$x^4 + 2x^3 + 4x^2 - 2x - 4 - \dfrac{16}{x-2}$

2.020

$$
\begin{array}{r|rrrrr}
-3 & 1 & 0 & 0 & 0 & 81 \\
& & -3 & 9 & -27 & 81 \\
\hline
& 1 & -3 & 9 & -27 & 162
\end{array}
$$

$x^3 - 3x^2 + 9x - 27 + \dfrac{162}{x+3}$

2.021 $(4x^3 + 7y^3z^4)(4x^3 + 7y^3z^4) =$
$16x^6 + 56x^3y^3z^4 + 49y^6z^8$

2.022 $(3x^{2a} - 4y^a z^{3a})(3x^{2a} - 4y^a z^{3a}) =$
$9x^{4a} - 24x^{2a}y^a z^{3a} + 16y^{2a}z^{6a}$

2.023 $m^6n^2 + 3m^3n - 40$

2.024 $a^2 + \ \ ab + ac$

$\qquad ab \qquad + b^2 + bc$

$\underline{\qquad\quad - ac \qquad - bc - c^2}$

$a^2 + 2ab \qquad + b^2 \qquad - c^2$

$= a^2 + 2ab + b^2 - c^2$

2.025 $(x - 6)(x + 4)$

2.026 $3(3 - 2a - 8a^2) = 3(3 + 4a)(1 - 2a)$

2.027 $36a^{2x} - 36 =$
$36(a^{2x} - 1) =$
$36(a^x + 1)(a^x - 1)$

2.028 $(x + \frac{1}{2})(x^2 - \frac{1}{2}x + \frac{1}{4})$

SECTION 3

3.1 $\dfrac{c_1}{d_1} = \dfrac{c_2}{d_2}$

$\dfrac{44}{14} = \dfrac{154}{d}$

$44d = 2{,}156$

$d = 49$

3.2 $\dfrac{x_1}{y_1} = \dfrac{x_2}{y_2}$

$\dfrac{7\frac{1}{2}}{10} = \dfrac{x}{4}$

$10x = 30$

$x = 3$

3.3 $\dfrac{t_1}{v_1} = \dfrac{t_2}{v_2}$

$\dfrac{2\frac{4}{7}}{\frac{13}{14}} = \dfrac{2\frac{1}{4}}{v}$

$\dfrac{18}{7}v = \dfrac{9}{4} \cdot \dfrac{13}{14} = \dfrac{117}{56}$

$v = \dfrac{\overset{13}{\cancel{117}}}{\underset{8}{\cancel{56}}} \cdot \dfrac{\overset{1}{\cancel{7}}}{\underset{2}{\cancel{18}}} = \dfrac{13}{16}$

3.4

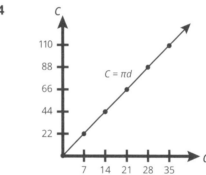

$C = \pi d$

$\dfrac{C}{d} = \pi$

C	22	44	66	88	110
d	7	14	21	28	35

3.5 $\dfrac{V_1}{d_1{}^3} = \dfrac{V_2}{d_2{}^3}$ or $\dfrac{V}{d^3} = c$

3.6 $A = bh$
$c = bh$
No, it is not a direct variation.

3.7 $\dfrac{k_1}{v_1} = \dfrac{k_2}{v_2}$

3.8 $\dfrac{3}{52.08} = \dfrac{5}{x}$

$3x = 260.40$

$x = 86.80$

$86.80 should be paid to 5 men.

3.9 $\dfrac{c_1}{t_1} = \dfrac{c_2}{t_2}$

$\dfrac{.90}{6} = \dfrac{x}{9}$

$6x = 8.10$

$x = 1.35$

$1.35 for 9 minutes

3.10 $\dfrac{d_1}{t_1^2} = \dfrac{d_2}{t_2^2}$

$\dfrac{64}{2^2} = \dfrac{x}{7^2}$

$\dfrac{16\cancel{64}}{1\cancel{4}} = \dfrac{x}{49}$

$x = 16(49) = 784$

784 ft.

3.11 $xy = c$

$x_1y_1 = x_2y_2$

$32x = 132(4) = 528$

$x = \dfrac{528}{32} = 16\frac{1}{2}$

3.12 $x_1y_1 = x_2y_2$

$11(15) = x(3)$

$3x = 165$

$x = 55$

3.13 $v_1p_1 = v_2p_2$

$24(16) = v(30)$

$30v = 384$

$v = 12\frac{4}{5}$ or 12.8 cu. cm

3.14   The factors of 36 are 36, 18, 12, 9, 6, 4, 3, 2, and 1.

$d = rt$

36 mi. = 36 mph(t)

$t = 1$ hr.

The variation is an inverse variation: as one variable increases, the other variable decreases.

$r_1t_1 = r_2t_2$

$36(1) = 18(t)$

$t = 2$ hrs.

$36(1) = 12(t)$

$t = 3$ hrs.

$36(1) = 9(t)$

$t = 4$ hrs.

$36 = 6t$

$t = 6$ hrs.

$36 = 4t$

$t = 9$ hrs.

$36 = 3t$

$t = 12$ hrs.

$36 = 2t$

$t = 18$ hrs.

$36 = 1t$

$t = 36$ hrs.

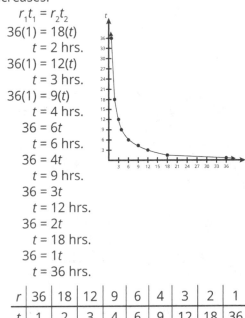

r	36	18	12	9	6	4	3	2	1
t	1	2	3	4	6	9	12	18	36

3.15   direct variation

3.16   inverse variation

3.17   direct variation

3.18   direct variation

3.19   Let v = value

a = age

$va = k$

$v_1a_1 = v_2a_2$

$3,000(2) = v(6)$

$6v = 6,000$

$v = 1,000$

$1,000

3.20   Let g = gravitational attraction (force)

d = distance

$g_1d_1^2 = g_2d_2^2$

$75(8)^2 = g(12)^2$

$4,800 = 144g$

$g = 33\frac{1}{3}$

$33\frac{1}{3}$ lbs. of force

3.21   direct variation

3.22   direct variation

3.23   combined variation

3.24   joint variation

3.25   inverse variation

3.26   direct variation

3.27   combined variation

3.28   combined variation

3.29 $\dfrac{x_1}{y_1} = \dfrac{x_2}{y_2}$

$\dfrac{17\cancel{153}}{1\cancel{9}} = \dfrac{x}{13}$

$x = 17(13) = 221$

3.30 $\dfrac{x_1y_1}{t_1} = \dfrac{x_2y_2}{t_2}$

$\dfrac{6\cancel{12}(25)^5}{\cancel{2}\ \cancel{10}} = \dfrac{\cancel{6}y^2}{\cancel{3}_1}$

$30 = 2y$

$y = 15$

3.31 $\dfrac{Fd^2}{m_1m_2} = c$

3.32 $\dfrac{V_1}{a_1(r_1)^2} = \dfrac{V_2}{a_2(r_2)^2}$

$\dfrac{154}{12(\frac{7}{2})^2} = \dfrac{77}{a(\frac{7}{3})^2}$

$\dfrac{154}{12(\frac{49}{4})} = \dfrac{77}{a(\frac{49}{9})}$

$\dfrac{154a}{147} = \dfrac{77}{1} \cdot \dfrac{9}{49}$

$a = \dfrac{1\cancel{77}}{1} \cdot \dfrac{9}{\cancel{49}_1} \cdot \dfrac{\cancel{147}^3}{\cancel{154}_2}$

$a = \dfrac{27}{2} = 13\frac{1}{2}$

The altitude is $13\frac{1}{2}$ in.

3.33 $\dfrac{t_1n_1}{l_1} = \dfrac{t_2n_2}{l_2}$

$\dfrac{2(8)^2}{25\ \cancel{100}} = \dfrac{t(3)^1}{\cancel{150}\ 50}$

$25t = 200$

$t = 8$

8 days

SELF TEST 3

3.01 a

3.02 b

3.03 b

3.04 a

3.05 c

3.06 d

3.07 a

3.08 b

3.09 a

3.010 c

3.011 $\dfrac{a_1}{b_1} = \dfrac{a_2}{b_2}$

$\dfrac{28}{7} = \dfrac{5}{b}$

$28b = 35$

$b = 1\dfrac{1}{4}$

3.012 $15(18) = 10x$

$x = 27$

3.013 $\dfrac{20.8}{31.2} = \dfrac{p}{15.3}$

$31.2p = 318.24$

$p = 10.2$

3.014 $50(10) = 20y$

$y = 25$

3.015 $\dfrac{w_1 z_1^2}{x_1 y_1} = \dfrac{w_2 z_2^2}{x_2 y_2}$

$\dfrac{280(3)^2}{30(12)} = \dfrac{w(2)^2}{20(10)}$

$\dfrac{\overset{7}{\cancel{28}}\,\overset{3}{\cancel{280}}\overset{}{(9)}}{\underset{1}{\cancel{3}}\,\underset{}{\cancel{30(12)}}} = \dfrac{w\overset{1}{\cancel{(4)}}}{\underset{5}{\cancel{20}}(10)}$

$7 = \dfrac{w}{50}$

$w = 7(50)$

$w = 350$

3.016 $\dfrac{x_1}{y_1 z_1} = \dfrac{x_2}{y_2 z_2}$

$\dfrac{\overset{2}{\cancel{8}}}{\underset{1}{\cancel{4}}(9)} = \dfrac{\overset{8}{\cancel{16}}}{\underset{3}{\cancel{6}}z}$

$\dfrac{2}{9} = \dfrac{8}{3z}$

$2(3z) = 8(9)$

$6z = 72$

$z = \dfrac{72}{6} = 12$

3.017 $\dfrac{V_1}{(r_1)^3} = \dfrac{V_2}{(r_2)^3}$

$\dfrac{1\frac{1}{2}}{6^3} = \dfrac{V}{24^3}$

$\dfrac{\frac{3}{2}}{216} = \dfrac{V}{13{,}824}$

$216V = \dfrac{3}{2}(13{,}824)$

$216V = 20{,}736$

$V = 96 \text{ pints} = 12 \text{ gallons}$

3.018 $r_1 d_1 = r_2 d_2$

$400(24) = r(8)$

$r = 1{,}200 \text{ revolutions}$

3.019 $s_1 A_1 = s_2 A_2$

$55(360) = s(450)$

$s = \dfrac{55(360)}{450}$

$s = 44 \text{ mph}$

3.020 $\dfrac{h_1}{r_1 t_1 (c_1)^2} = \dfrac{h_2}{r_2 t_2 (c_2)^2}$

$\dfrac{1{,}200}{(8)(2)(5)^2} = \dfrac{6{,}000}{r(5)(10)^2}$

$r(5)(10)^2(1{,}200) = (8)(2)(5)^2(6{,}000)$

$r = \dfrac{\overset{2}{\cancel{(8)}}(2)\overset{1}{\cancel{(25)}}\cancel{(6{,}000)}^{\cancel{5}\,1}}{\underset{1}{\cancel{(5)}}\underset{1}{\cancel{(100)}}\cancel{(1{,}200)}_{\cancel{4}\,1}}$

$r = 4 \text{ ohms}$

3.021 $(2x - \tfrac{1}{2})(2x - \tfrac{1}{2}) = 4x^2 - 2x + \tfrac{1}{4}$

3.022 $x^2 - 4$

3.023 $25c^2 - \dfrac{4}{9}$

3.024 $2a^2 - 5ab + 2b^2 = (2a - b)(a - 2b)$

3.025 $(y^a - 5)(y^a + 4)$

3.026 $(2y - 3)(4y^2 + 6y + 9)$

3.027 $4a^2 - b - c^3$

3.028 $2x^3 + 5x^2 + 4x$

3.029

$$
\begin{array}{r}
x^2 + xy + y^2 + \frac{2y^3}{x-y} \\
x - y \overline{\smash{\big)}\ x^3 + 0x^2y + 0xy^2 + y^3} \\
\underline{x^3 - x^2y} \\
x^2y + 0xy^2 \\
\underline{x^2y - xy^2} \\
xy^2 + y^3 \\
\underline{xy^2 - y^3} \\
2y^3
\end{array}
$$

3.030

2	1	-3	3	-3	6
		2	-2	2	-2
	1	-1	1	-1	4

$x^3 - x^2 + x - 1 + \dfrac{4}{x - 2}$

LIFEPAC TEST

1.
$$
\begin{array}{r}
4x^3 + 2x^2 - 4x + \ \ 3 \\
7x^3 - 4x^2 + 7x + \ \ 8 \\
\hline
11x^3 - 2x^2 + 3x + 11
\end{array}
$$

2.
$$
\begin{array}{r}
3a^3 \ \ \ \ \ \ \ \ + 8a - \ \ 6 \\
4a^2 - 9a + 11 \\
\hline
3a^3 + 4a^2 - \ \ a + \ \ 5
\end{array}
$$

3.
$$
\begin{array}{r}
12a^2 + 60a - \ \ 8 \\
16a^2 - 32a + \ \ 9 \\
\hline
-4a^2 + 92a - 17
\end{array}
$$

4. $0.9x^2 + 2.6xy - 2.8$

5. $32x^2 + 68x + 21$

6. $9x^4 - 121$

7. $a^3 - 125$

8.
$$
\begin{array}{r}
2x - \ \ 8 \\
2x + 3 \overline{)\ 4x^2 - \ 10x - 24} \\
\underline{4x^2 + \ \ 6x} \\
-16x - 24 \\
\underline{-16x - 24} \\
0
\end{array}
$$

9.
$$
\begin{array}{r}
5a^2 - \ \ 6a + \ \ 20 + \frac{-175a + 102}{5a^2 + 6a - 9} \\
5a^2 + 6a - 9 \overline{)\ 25a^4 + \ \ 0a^3 + \ 19a^2 - \ \ a - 78} \\
\underline{25a^4 + \ 30a^3 - \ 45a^2} \\
-30a^3 + \ 64a^2 - \ \ \ \ a \\
\underline{-30a^3 - \ 36a^2 + \ 54a} \\
100a^2 - \ \ 55a - 78 \\
\underline{100a^2 + 120a - 180} \\
-175a + 102
\end{array}
$$

10.
$$
\begin{array}{r|rrr}
3 & 3 & 7 & -18 \\
& & 9 & 48 \\
\hline
& 3 & 16 & 30
\end{array}
$$

$3x + 16 + \dfrac{30}{x - 3}$

11. $2a^2(2a^2 + 3ab^2 + b^3)$

12. $(3x + 7)(3x - 4)$

13. $2(3a^2 - 4a - 15) = 2(3a + 5)(a - 3)$

14. $(3a + 4b)(3a + 4b) = (3a + 4b)^2$

15. $(x + 4y)(x - 4y)$

16. $16(x^4 - 4y^8) = 16(x^2 + 2y^4)(x^2 - 2y^4)$

17. $2(7a^2 - 34a + 24) = 2(7a - 6)(a - 4)$

18. $3(4a^2 + 12ab + 9b^2) = 3(2a + 3b)(2a + 3b) = 3(2a + 3b)^2$

19. $(a - b)(a^2 + ab + b^2)$

20. $(2x + 3y^2)(4x^2 - 6xy^2 + 9y^4)$

21. b

22. a

23. d

24.
$$
\frac{x_1}{y_1} = \frac{x_2}{y_2}
$$
$$
\frac{\overset{4}{\cancel{12}}}{\underset{1}{\cancel{3}}} = \frac{x}{9}
$$
$$
x = 4(9)
$$
$$
x = 36
$$

25.
$$
d = rt
$$
$$
r_1 t_1 = r_2 t_2
$$
$$
60(8) = 48(t)
$$
$$
480 = 48t
$$
$$
t = 10 \text{ hours}
$$

ALTERNATE LIFEPAC TEST

1.
$$3x^3 + 2x^2 - 2x + 3$$
$$\underline{7x^3 - 4x^2 + 7x + 8}$$
$$10x^3 - 2x^2 + 5x + 11$$

2.
$$4a^2 + 7a - 5$$
$$\underline{4a^2 - 9a + 11}$$
$$8a^2 - 2a + 6$$

3.
$$12a^2 + 60a - 8$$
$$\underline{15a^2 - 33a + 8}$$
$$-3a^2 + 93a - 16$$

4. $1.9x^2 + 3.6xy - 4.8$

5.
$(7x + 3)(4x + 6) =$
$(7x + 3)4x + (7x + 3)6 =$
$28x^2 + 12x + 42x + 18 =$
$28x^2 + 54x + 18$

6.
$(2x^2 - 9)(2x^2 + 9) =$
$(2x^2 - 9)2x^2 + (2x^2 - 9)9 =$
$4x^4 - 18x^2 + 18x^2 - 81 =$
$4x^4 + 0x^2 - 81 =$
$4x^4 - 81$

7.
$(x - 4)(x^2 + 4x + 16) =$
$x^2 + 4x + 16$
$$\underline{x - 4}$$
$$x^3 + 4x^2 + 16x$$
$$\underline{-4x^2 - 16x - 64}$$
$$x^3 - 64 =$$
$x^3 - 64$

8.
$$\ \ 2x + \ \ \ 3$$
$$2x - 8\overline{)\,4x^2 - 10x - 24}$$
$$\underline{4x^2 - 16x}$$
$$6x - 24$$
$$\underline{6x - 24}$$
$$0$$

9.
$$\ 5a^2 - \ \ 6a + \ \ \ 20 + \frac{-175a + 90}{5a^2 + 6a - 9}$$
$$5a^2 + 6a - 9\overline{)\,25a^4 + \ \ 0a^3 + \ \ 19a^2 - \ \ \ a - \ 90}$$
$$\underline{25a^4 + \ 30a^3 - \ \ 45a^2}$$
$$-30a^3 + \ \ 64a^2 - \ \ \ a$$
$$\underline{-30a^3 - \ \ 36a^2 + \ \ 54a}$$
$$100a^2 - \ \ 55a - \ 90$$
$$\underline{100a^2 + \ 120a - 180}$$
$$-175a + \ 90$$

10.
$$\begin{array}{r|rrr} -4 & 3 & -7 & 19 \\ & & -12 & 76 \\ \hline & 3 & -19 & 95 \end{array}$$

$3x - 19 + \dfrac{95}{x + 4}$

11. $2a^2(3a^2 - 2ab^2 + 4b^3)$

12. $(5x + 8)(3x - 4)$

13. $(2a - 7)(4a + 5)$

14. $(5a + 3b)(5a + 3b) = (5a + 3b)^2$

15. $(3x + a)(3x - a)$

16. $9(9x^8 - y^4) = 9(3x^4 + y^2)(3x^4 - y^2)$

17. $3(2a^2 - 23a + 56) = 3(2a - 7)(a - 8)$

18. $2(a^2 + 4ab + 4b^2) = 2(a + 2b)(a + 2b) = 2(a + 2b)^2$

19. $(a + b)(a^2 - ab + b^2)$

20. $(2x - 3y^2)(4x^2 + 6xy + 9y^4)$

21. a

22. b

23. c

24.
$$\frac{36}{9} = \frac{x}{3}$$
$$\frac{4\,\cancel{36}}{\cancel{9}_{\,1}} = \frac{x}{3}$$
$$x = 12$$

25.
$$d = rt$$
Let r_1 = rate of automobile
t_1 = time of automobile
r_2 = rate of bus
t_2 = time of bus
Since $d_1 = d_2$, $r_1t_1 = r_2t_2$.
$$r_1t_1 = r_2t_2$$
$$48(10) = 60(t)$$
$$480 = 60t$$
$$\tfrac{1}{60}(480) = \tfrac{1}{60}(60t)$$
$$8 = t$$
$$t = 8 \text{ hours}$$

MATH 1104

ALTERNATE LIFEPAC TEST

NAME _____

DATE _____

SCORE _____

Perform the indicated operations. Circle your answer (each answer, 4 points).

1. Find the sum of $3x^3 + 2x^2 - 2x + 3$ and $7x^3 - 4x^2 + 7x + 8$.

2. Add: $4a^2 + 7a - 5$ and $4a^2 - 9a + 11$

3. Subtract $15a^2 - 33a + 8$ from $12a^2 + 60a - 8$.

4. Subtract: $8.3x^2 + 0.9xy + 3.6$
$\underline{6.4x^2 - 2.7xy + 8.4}$

5. Multiply $(7x + 3)(4x + 6)$. _____

6. Multiply $(2x^2 - 9)(2x^2 + 9)$. _____

7. Multiply $(x - 4)(x^2 + 4x + 16)$. _____

8. $2x - 8 \overline{)\, 4x^2 - 10x - 24}$

9. Divide $5a^2 + 6a - 9$ into $25a^4 + 19a^2 - a - 90$.

10. Divide, using synthetic division.

$x + 4 \overline{)\, 3x^2 - 7x + 19}$

Factor completely (each answer, 4 points).

11. $6a^4 - 4a^3b^2 + 8a^2b^3$ _____

12. $15x^2 + 4x - 32$ _____

13. $8a^2 - 18a - 35$ _____

14. $25a^2 + 30ab + 9b^2$ _____

15. $9x^2 - a^2$ _____

16. $81x^8 - 9y^4$ _____

17. $6a^2 - 69a + 168$ _____

18. $2a^2 + 8ab + 8b^2$ _____

19. $a^3 + b^3$ _____

20. $8x^3 - 27y^6$ _____

Write on the blank the letter for the correct answer (each answer, 2 points).

21. _____ $\dfrac{x}{y} = c$

22. _____ $xy = c$

23. _____ $\dfrac{x}{yz} = c$

    a. direct variation
    b. inverse variation
    c. joint variation
    d. combined variation

Solve these problems. Show your work in the space provided, and circle your answer (each answer, 5 points).

24. If x and y vary directly and $x = 36$ when $y = 9$, what will be the value of x when $y = 3$?

25. The rate traveled from Indianapolis to Buffalo by an automobile averages 48 miles per hour. The automobile arrives in Buffalo after ten hours of travel. A bus averages 60 miles per hour. Using the inverse variation relationship, show what the time would be for the bus to complete the same trip.

MATH 1105

Unit 5: Radical Expressions

TEACHER NOTES

MATERIALS NEEDED FOR LIFEPAC	
Required	Suggested
(none)	(none)

ADDITIONAL LEARNING ACTIVITIES

Section 1: Multiplying and Dividing with Fractions

1. Explain that the term *exclusion* as used for a variable in this section is also referred to as *nonsensible replacement* in certain texts. The meanings and methods of handling exclusions by those texts are the same as in this LIFEPAC, i.e., if the resulting value of the variable in question makes the denominator equal to zero, that value may not be used.

2. Have students respond by naming the exclusion values (or nonsensible replacements) for these expressions. Answers are given for the teacher's information.

   a. $\dfrac{x+2}{x-5} \cdot \dfrac{x+3}{x+3}$ Exclusions: $x \neq 5, x \neq -3$

   b. $\dfrac{x+y}{2x^2-1} \cdot \dfrac{x+y}{7x}$ Exclusions: $x \neq \pm\dfrac{\sqrt{2}}{2}, x \neq 0$

   c. $\dfrac{x-2}{x+2} \div \dfrac{x+2}{x+4}$ Exclusions: $x \neq -2, x \neq -4$

   d. $\dfrac{6x^2+4x}{2x^2+4x}$ Exclusions: $x \neq 0, x \neq -2$

   e. $\dfrac{y^2+3y+2}{y^2-1}$ Exclusions: $y \neq \pm 1$

Section 2: Adding and Subtracting Algebraic Fractions

1. Explain that if the denominators of a fractional expression are not like denominators, we may find the equivalent expressions with like denominators and add. If one denominator is the additive inverse of another, we may find a common denominator by multiplying by $\frac{-1}{-1}$.

Section 3: Equations with Fractions

1. Discuss the Fibonacci sequence and compare its derivation with Pascal's Triangle.

    Fibonacci sequence: the first two terms of a sequence are 1 and each succeeding term is the sum of the previous pair of terms as shown.

    ```
    1   1
    1 + 1 = 2
        1 + 2 = 3
            2 + 3 = 5
                3 + 5 = 8
                    5 + 8 = 13
                        and so on
    ```

    Pascal's Triangle: each number within the triangle is found by adding the pair of numbers directly above it at the left and right as shown.

    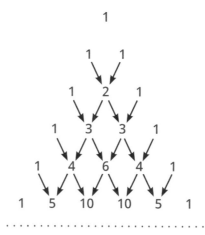

2. Have the students develop the first ten rows of Pascal's Triangle. At the left side of the triangle in a column, have the students number each row. At the right side of the triangle in a column, have the students write the sum of the numbers in each row.

    What kind of sequence is formed by the left-hand column of numbers? What kind of sequence is formed by the right-hand column of numbers?

3. Have the students write the squares of the first eight terms of the Fibonacci sequence. Then have the students add each pair of consecutive squares to make a new sequence. What occurs? Now have the students write the cubes of consecutive terms of the Fibonacci sequence. What occurs?

Additional Activities

The following activities may be reproduced as student worksheets.

» MULTIPLYING AND DIVIDING WITH FRACTIONS

Perform the indicated operations.

1. $\dfrac{x^2 - 2x - 35}{2x^3 - 3x^2} \cdot \dfrac{4x^3 - 9x}{7x - 49}$ _____

2. $\dfrac{r - s}{r + s} \cdot \dfrac{r^2 - s^2}{(r - s)^2}$ _____

3. $\dfrac{m^2 - n^2}{r + s} \div \dfrac{m - n}{r + s}$ _____

4. $\dfrac{a^2 - a - 2}{a^2 - a - 6} \div \dfrac{a^2 - 2a}{2a + a^2}$ _____

5. $\dfrac{(x - y)^2 - z^2}{(x + y)^2 - z^2} \div \dfrac{x - y + z}{x + y - z}$ _____

6. $\dfrac{(a + b)^2 - 9}{(a - b)^2 - 9} \cdot \dfrac{a - b - 3}{a + b + 3}$ _____

7. $\dfrac{x^2 - 7x + 6}{x^2 + 4x - 5} \cdot \dfrac{x^2 + 8x + 15}{x^2 - 4x - 12}$ _____

8. $\dfrac{m + n}{m^2 - n^2} \cdot \dfrac{m^2 + 2mn + n^2}{m^2 - n^2}$ _____

9. $\dfrac{a + b}{x^2 + 2xy + y^2} \div \dfrac{a^2 - b^2}{x^2 - y^2}$ _____

10. $\dfrac{x^2 - 3x - 10}{3x^3 - 12x} \div \dfrac{2x^2 - 5x - 25}{6x^2 + 15x}$ _____

» ADDING AND SUBTRACTING ALGEBRAIC FRACTIONS

1. $\dfrac{1 + \frac{x}{a}}{a - \frac{x^2}{a}}$ _____

2. $\dfrac{\frac{1}{a} + \frac{1}{b}}{\frac{1}{a} - \frac{1}{b}}$ _____

3. $\dfrac{1}{x + 1} - \dfrac{x}{x - 2} + \dfrac{x^2 + 2}{x^2 - x - 2}$ _____

4. $\dfrac{\frac{a - b}{b}}{\frac{a^2 - b^2}{ab}}$ _____

5. $\dfrac{\frac{a^2}{b} + \frac{b^2}{a}}{a^2 - ab + b^2}$ _____

6. $\dfrac{\frac{a}{1 - a} + \frac{1 + a}{a}}{\frac{1 - a}{a} + \frac{a}{1 + a}}$ _____

7. $\dfrac{\frac{1}{x^2} - \frac{1}{y^2}}{\frac{1}{x^2} - \frac{2}{xy} + \frac{1}{y^2}}$ _____

8. $\dfrac{\frac{1}{x} + \frac{1}{y}}{\frac{1}{x^2} - \frac{1}{y^2}}$ _____

9. $\dfrac{\frac{3x}{y^2} - \frac{x}{y}}{1 - \frac{2}{y^2}}$ _____

10. $\dfrac{\frac{x + y}{x}}{\frac{x^2 - y^2}{xy}}$ _____

ADDITIONAL ACTIVITIES, SOLUTION KEY

Multiplying and Dividing Fractions

1. $\dfrac{x^2 - 2x - 35}{2x^3 - 3x^2} \cdot \dfrac{4x^3 - 9x}{7x - 49} =$

$\dfrac{(x + 5)\cancel{(x - 7)}}{{}_x\cancel{x^2}\cancel{(2x - 3)}} \cdot \dfrac{x(2x^2 + 3)\cancel{(2x - 3)}}{7\cancel{(x - 7)}} =$

$\dfrac{(x + 5)(2x^2 + 3)}{7x}$ or $\dfrac{2x^3 + 10x^2 + 3x + 15}{7x}$

2. $\dfrac{r - s}{r + s} \cdot \dfrac{r^2 - s^2}{(r - s)^2} = \dfrac{\cancel{r - s}}{r + s} \cdot \dfrac{(r + s)\cancel{(r - s)}}{\cancel{(r - s)}(r - s)} = 1$

3. $\dfrac{m^2 - n^2}{r + s} \div \dfrac{m - n}{r + s} =$

$\dfrac{(m + n)\cancel{(m - n)}}{\cancel{r + s}} \cdot \dfrac{\cancel{r + s}}{\cancel{m - n}} = m + n$

4. $\dfrac{a^2 - a - 2}{a^2 - a - 6} \div \dfrac{a^2 - 2a}{2a + a^2} =$

$\dfrac{(a + 1)\cancel{(a - 2)}}{\cancel{(a + 2)}(a - 3)} \cdot \dfrac{a\cancel{(2 + a)}}{a\cancel{(a - 2)}} =$

$\dfrac{a + 1}{a - 3}$

5. $\dfrac{(x - y)^2 - z^2}{(x - y)^2 - z^2} \div \dfrac{x - y + z}{x + y - z} =$

$\dfrac{(x - y - z)\cancel{(x - y + z)}}{\cancel{(x + y - z)}(x + y + z)} \cdot \dfrac{\cancel{x + y - z}}{\cancel{x - y + z}} =$

$\dfrac{x - y - z}{x + y + z}$

6. $\dfrac{(a + b)^2 - 9}{(a + b)^2 - 9} \cdot \dfrac{a - b - 3}{a + b + 3} =$

$\dfrac{(a + b + 3)(a + b - 3)}{(a - b + 3)\cancel{(a - b - 3)}} \cdot \dfrac{\cancel{a - b - 3}}{\cancel{a + b + 3}} =$

$\dfrac{a + b - 3}{a - b + 3}$

7. $\dfrac{x^2 - 7x + 6}{x^2 + 4x - 5} \cdot \dfrac{x^2 + 8x + 15}{x^2 - 4x - 12} =$

$\dfrac{\cancel{(x - 1)}(x - 6)}{\cancel{(x - 1)}(x + 5)} \cdot \dfrac{(x + 3)\cancel{(x + 5)}}{(x + 2)\cancel{(x - 6)}} =$

$\dfrac{x + 3}{x + 2}$

8. $\dfrac{m + n}{m^2 - n^2} \cdot \dfrac{m^2 + 2mn + n^2}{m^2 - n^2} =$

$\dfrac{\cancel{m + n}}{\cancel{(m + n)}(m - n)} \cdot \dfrac{\cancel{(m + n)}(m + n)}{\cancel{(m + n)}(m - n)} =$

$\dfrac{m + n}{(m - n)(m - n)} = \dfrac{m + n}{(m - n)^2}$

9. $\dfrac{a + b}{x^2 + 2xy + y^2} \div \dfrac{a^2 - b^2}{x^2 - y^2}$

$\dfrac{\cancel{a + b}}{\cancel{(x + y)}(x + y)} \cdot \dfrac{(x + y)(x - y)}{\cancel{(a + b)}(a - b)} =$

$\dfrac{x - y}{(x + y)(a - b)}$

10. $\dfrac{x^2 - 3x - 10}{3x^3 - 12x} \div \dfrac{2x^2 - 5x - 25}{6x^2 + 15x}$

$\dfrac{(x + 2)\cancel{(x - 5)}}{3x\cancel{(x + 2)}(x - 2)} \cdot \dfrac{3x\cancel{(2x + 5)}}{\cancel{(2x + 5)}\cancel{(x - 5)}} =$

$\dfrac{1}{x - 2}$

Adding and Subtracting Algebraic Fractions

1. The LCD is a.

$$\frac{a[1] + \cancel{a}[\frac{x}{\cancel{a}}]}{a[a] - \cancel{a}[\frac{x^2}{\cancel{a}}]} = \frac{a + x}{a^2 - x^2} =$$

$$\frac{\cancel{a + x}}{\cancel{(a + x)}(a - x)} = \frac{1}{a - x}$$

2. The LCD is ab.

$$\frac{\cancel{a}b[\frac{1}{\cancel{a}}] + a\cancel{b}[\frac{1}{\cancel{b}}]}{\cancel{a}b[\frac{1}{\cancel{a}}] - a\cancel{b}[\frac{1}{\cancel{b}}]} = \frac{b + a}{b - a}$$

3.

$$\frac{1}{x + 1} - \frac{x}{x - 2} + \frac{x^2 + 2}{x^2 - x - 2} =$$

$$\frac{1}{x + 1} - \frac{x}{x - 2} + \frac{x^2 + 2}{(x + 1)(x - 2)} =$$

The LCD is $(x + 1)(x - 2)$.

$$\cancel{(x + 1)}(x - 2)\left[\frac{1}{\cancel{x + 1}}\right] -$$

$$(x + 1)\cancel{(x - 2)}\left[\frac{x}{\cancel{x - 2}}\right] +$$

$$\cancel{(x + 1)}\cancel{(x - 2)}\left[\frac{x^2 + 2}{\cancel{(x + 1)}\cancel{(x - 2)}}\right] =$$

$$x - 2 - x(x + 1) + x^2 + 2 =$$

$$x - 2 - x^2 - x + x^2 + 2 = 0$$

4. The LCD is ab.

$$\frac{a\cancel{b}[\frac{a - b}{\cancel{b}}]}{\cancel{ab}[\frac{a^2 - b^2}{\cancel{ab}}]} = \frac{a(\cancel{a - b})}{(a + b)(\cancel{a - b})} = \frac{a}{a + b}$$

5. The LCD is ab.

$$\frac{a\cancel{b}[\frac{a^2}{\cancel{b}}] + \cancel{a}b[\frac{b^2}{\cancel{a}}]}{ab[a^2 - ab + b^2]} = \frac{a^3 + b^3}{ab(a^2 - ab + b^2)} =$$

$$\frac{(a + b)(\cancel{a^2 - ab + b^2})}{ab(\cancel{a^2 - ab + b^2})} = \frac{a + b}{ab}$$

6. The LCD is $a(1 + a)(1 - a)$.

$$\frac{a}{1 - a} = a(1 + a)\cancel{(1 - a)}\left[\frac{a}{\cancel{1 - a}}\right] = a^2(1 + a)$$

$$\frac{1 + a}{a} = \cancel{a}(1 + a)(1 - a)\left[\frac{1 + a}{\cancel{a}}\right] = (1 + a)^2(1 - a)$$

$$\frac{1 - a}{a} = \cancel{a}(1 + a)(1 - a)\left[\frac{1 - a}{\cancel{a}}\right] = (1 + a)(1 - a)^2$$

$$\frac{a}{1 + a} = a\cancel{(1 + a)}(1 - a)\left[\frac{a}{\cancel{1 + a}}\right] = a^2(1 - a)$$

$$\frac{a^2(1 + a) + (1 + a)^2(1 - a)}{(1 + a)(1 - a)^2 + a^2(1 - a)} =$$

$$\frac{a^2 + a^3 + (1 + 2a + a^2)(1 - a)}{(1 + a)(1 - 2a + a^2) + a^2 - a^3} =$$

$$\frac{a^2 + a^3 + 1 + a - \cancel{a^2} - \cancel{a^3}}{1 - a - \cancel{a^2} + \cancel{a^3} + \cancel{a^2} - \cancel{a^3}} = \frac{1 + a}{1 - a}$$

7. The LCD is x^2y^2.

$$\frac{x^2y^2[\frac{1}{\cancel{x^2}}] - x^2y^2[\frac{1}{\cancel{y^2}}]}{x^2y^2[\frac{1}{\cancel{x^2}}] - x^2y^2[\frac{2}{\cancel{xy}}] + x^2y^2[\frac{1}{\cancel{y^2}}]} =$$

$$\frac{y^2 - x^2}{y^2 - 2xy + x^2} = \frac{(y + x)(\cancel{y - x})}{(y - x)(\cancel{y - x})} =$$

$$\frac{y + x}{y - x} \quad \text{or} \quad \frac{x + y}{-x + y}$$

8. The LCD is x^2y^2.

$$\frac{x^2y^2[\frac{1}{\cancel{x}}] - x^2y^2[\frac{1}{\cancel{y}}]}{x^2y^2[\frac{1}{\cancel{x^2}}] - x^2y^2[\frac{1}{\cancel{y^2}}]} = \frac{xy^2 + x^2y}{y^2 - x^2} =$$

$$\frac{xy(\cancel{y + x})}{(\cancel{y + x})(y - x)} = \frac{xy}{y - x} \quad \text{or} \quad \frac{xy}{-x + y}$$

9. The LCD is y^2.

$$\frac{y^2[\frac{3x}{\cancel{y^2}}] - y^2[\frac{x}{\cancel{y}}]}{y^2[1] - y^2[\frac{2}{\cancel{y^2}}]} = \frac{3x + xy}{y^2 - 2}$$

10. The LCD is xy.

$$\frac{xy[\frac{x + y}{\cancel{x}}]}{\cancel{xy}[\frac{x^2 - y^2}{\cancel{xy}}]} = \frac{y(x + y)}{(\cancel{x + y})(x - y)} = \frac{y}{x - y}$$

ANSWER KEY

SECTION 1

1.1   1

1.2 $1 \cdot 2 = 2$

1.3 $\frac{1}{2^2} = \frac{1}{4}$

1.4 $\frac{4}{2(1)} = \frac{4}{2} = 2$

1.5 $\frac{1}{2^4} \cdot 1 = \frac{1}{16}$

1.6   1

1.7 $10^{-2} = \frac{1}{10^2} = \frac{1}{100}$ or   0.01

1.8 $\frac{1}{2^2} + \frac{1}{5^2} = \frac{1}{4} + \frac{1}{25} = \frac{25}{100} + \frac{4}{100} = \frac{29}{100}$

1.9 $1 \cdot \frac{1}{10^4} = \frac{1}{10{,}000}$ or   0.0001

1.10 $\frac{1}{1+1} = \frac{1}{2}, x \neq 0$

1.11 $\frac{1}{a^4}$

1.12 $\frac{2}{1} = 2$

1.13 $3a^2(\frac{1}{b}) = \frac{3a^2}{b}$

1.14 $(\frac{5}{3a^2})^3 = \frac{125}{27a^6}$

1.15 $\frac{\frac{1}{x} \cdot \frac{1}{y^2}}{(\frac{1}{z})^3} = \frac{z^3}{xy^2}$

1.16 $(\frac{1}{6a^2})^4 = \frac{1}{1{,}296a^8}$

1.17 $\frac{2b^2}{5a^4}$

1.18 $3(\frac{1}{x+y}) = \frac{3}{(x+y)^2}$

1.19 $a^{6n-3n} = a^{3n}$

1.20 $a^{4n}b^{5n}$

1.21 $5^3a^{9n} = 125a^{9n}$

1.22 $\frac{b^{x+5}}{b^x} \cdot \frac{c}{c} = b^{x+5-x} \cdot 1 = b^5$

1.23 $\frac{x^{2n+10}}{y^2}$

1.24 $3^0 = 1$

1.25 $2(2)^0(3)^{-2}$

       $= 2(2)^0(\frac{1}{3^2})$

       $= 2(1)\frac{1}{9}$

       $= \frac{2}{9}$

1.26 $2^{-2} \cdot 3^{-2}$

       $= \frac{1}{2^2} \cdot \frac{1}{3^2}$

       $= \frac{1}{4} \cdot \frac{1}{9}$

       $= \frac{1}{36}$

1.27   1

1.28 $3(2)^{-1} + 2(3)^{-1}$

       $= 3(\frac{1}{2}) + 2(\frac{1}{3})$

       $= \frac{3}{2} + \frac{2}{3}$

       $= \frac{9}{6} + \frac{4}{6}$

       $= \frac{13}{6}$ or $2\frac{1}{6}$

1.29 $2^{-3} \cdot 3^{-3}$

       $= \frac{1}{2^3} \cdot \frac{1}{3^3}$

       $= \frac{1}{8} \cdot \frac{1}{27}$

       $= \frac{1}{216}$

1.30 $2^{-3} + 3^{-3}$

       $= \frac{1}{2^3} + \frac{1}{3^3}$

       $= \frac{1}{8} + \frac{1}{27}$

       $= \frac{27}{216} + \frac{8}{216}$

       $= \frac{35}{216}$

1.31 $(2+3)^{-3}$

       $= 5^{-3}$

       $= \frac{1}{5^3}$

       $= \frac{1}{125}$

1.32 $\frac{1}{6}$

1.33 $\frac{1}{3}$

1.34 $\frac{7}{9}$

1.35 $\frac{7}{8}$

1.36 $\frac{2}{7}$

1.37 $\frac{5}{6}$

1.38 $\frac{7}{10}$

1.39 $\frac{27}{9}\cdot\frac{c^4}{c^7}\cdot\frac{d^5}{d^4}=\frac{3d}{c^3}$; $c \neq 0, d \neq 0$

1.40 $\frac{a}{a}\cdot\frac{b^2}{b^2}\cdot\frac{x}{y}=\frac{x}{y}$; $a \neq 0, b \neq 0, y \neq 0$

1.41 $-\frac{12}{9}\cdot\frac{m^7}{m^2}\cdot\frac{t^5}{t^3}=-\frac{4m^5t^2}{3}$; $m \neq 0, t \neq 0$

1.42 $\frac{36}{15}\cdot\frac{x^5}{x^5}\cdot\frac{y^8}{y^7}\cdot\frac{z^{10}}{z^2}=\frac{12yz^8}{5}$; $x \neq 0, y \neq 0, z \neq 0$

1.43 $\frac{17}{51}\cdot\frac{x^5}{x^7}\cdot\frac{y^2}{y^3}\cdot\frac{z^3}{z}=\frac{z^2}{3x^2y}$; $x \neq 0, y \neq 0, z \neq 0$

1.44 $\frac{m\cancel{(a^2+4)}}{\cancel{a^2+4}}=m$; no restrictions

1.45 $\frac{\cancel{(2x+1)}(2x-1)}{2\cancel{(2x+1)}}=\frac{2x-1}{2}$; $x \neq -\frac{1}{2}$

1.46 $\frac{4y}{8y+24}=\frac{\cancel{4}y}{\cancel{4}(2y+6)}=\frac{y}{2y+6}$; $y \neq -3$

1.47 $\frac{\cancel{(7a+2)}(2a-5)}{\cancel{(7a+2)}(a-5)}=\frac{2a-5}{a-5}$; $a \neq 5, -\frac{2}{7}$

1.48 $\frac{y^2(y-3)+(y-3)}{(y+3)(y-3)}=\frac{\cancel{(y-3)}+(y^2+1)}{(y+3)\cancel{(y-3)}}=\frac{y^2+1}{y+3}$; $y \neq 3, -3$

1.49 $\frac{a(1-a^3)}{a^2+a+1}=\frac{a(1-a)\cancel{(1+a+a^2)}}{\cancel{a^2+a+1}}=a(1-a)$;
no restrictions

1.50 $\frac{x(y+z)+a(y+z)}{(y+z)(y^2-yz+z^2)}=\frac{\cancel{(y+z)}(x+a)}{\cancel{(y+z)}(y^2-yz+z^2)}=\frac{x+a}{y^2-yz+z^2}$;
y and z cannot both be 0.

1.51 $\frac{-2(x^2y^3z)(x-z^2)}{3xy^4z(z-x)}=\frac{-2x(x-z^2)}{3y(z-x)}$; $x \neq 0, y \neq 0, z \neq 0, z \neq x$

1.52 $\frac{(y-1)^3}{(y-1)^2(-1)^2}=y-1$; $y \neq 1$

1.53 $\frac{(y^3+3)(2y^3-1)}{(1+2y^3)(1-2y^3)}=\frac{y^3+3}{1+2y^3}$

1.54 $\frac{(x-y)^2-a^2}{(y+a)^2-x^2}=\frac{(x-y+a)\overset{-1}{\cancel{(x-y-a)}}}{(y+a+x)\cancel{(y+a-x)}}=\frac{y-x-a}{y+a+x}$

1.55 $\frac{(x-y)^5}{(x-y)^3}=(x-y)^2$ or $x^2-2xy+y^2$

1.56 $\frac{(x^2+1)^2(3x-1)^2(9x)-(3x-1)^3 4x(x^2+1)}{(x^2+1)^4}=$

$\frac{(x^2+1)[(x^2+1)(3x-1)^2(9x)-(3x-1)^3(4x)]}{(x^2+1)^4}=$

$\frac{(x^2+1)(3x-1)^2(9x)-(3x-1)^3(4x)}{(x^2+1)^3}=$

$\frac{9x(x^2+1)(3x-1)^2-4x(3x-1)^3}{(x^2+1)^3}$

1.57 $\frac{\overset{1}{\cancel{2}}}{\underset{1}{\cancel{5}}}\cdot\frac{\overset{1}{\cancel{5}}}{\underset{6}{\cancel{12}}}=\frac{1}{6}$

1.58 $\frac{\overset{1}{\cancel{2}}}{\underset{1}{\cancel{3}}}\cdot\frac{\cancel{5}}{8}\cdot\frac{\overset{1}{\cancel{3}}}{\underset{1}{\cancel{10}}}=\frac{1}{8}$

1.59 $\frac{11}{4}\cdot\frac{\overset{3}{\cancel{9}}}{8}\cdot\frac{23}{\underset{2}{\cancel{6}}}=\frac{759}{64}$ or $11\frac{55}{64}$

1.60 $\frac{\overset{1}{\cancel{33}}\cdot 6\cdot\overset{2}{\cancel{14}}}{\underset{1}{\cancel{231}}}=\frac{12}{1}=12$

1.61 $\frac{\overset{1}{\cancel{6a^2}}}{\underset{1}{\cancel{5b^2}}}\cdot\frac{\overset{3b}{\cancel{45b^3}}}{\underset{a}{\cancel{18a^3}}}=\frac{3b}{a}$; $a \neq 0, b \neq 0$

1.62 $\frac{4\cancel{x^3}}{\cancel{3}}\cdot\frac{\overset{3}{\cancel{9}}\cdot 9\cdot 9}{\cancel{x^3}}=972$; $x \neq 0$

1.63 $\frac{\overset{x}{\cancel{3x^2}}}{1}\cdot\frac{3x-6}{\underset{1}{\cancel{3x}}}=3x^2-6x$; $x \neq 0$

1.64 $\frac{\overset{1}{\cancel{x-y}}}{(x+1)\underset{1}{\cancel{(x-1)}}}\cdot\frac{\overset{1}{\cancel{x-1}}}{(x+y)\underset{1}{\cancel{(x-y)}}}=\frac{1}{(x+1)(x+y)}$;
$x \neq -1, x \neq 1, y \neq x$

1.65 $\frac{\overset{a}{\cancel{a^2}}\overset{1}{\cancel{(a+b)}}}{\underset{1}{\cancel{5a}}}\cdot\frac{\overset{5}{\cancel{25}}}{3\underset{1}{\cancel{(b+a)}}}=\frac{5a}{3}$; $a \neq 0, a \neq -b$

1.66 $\frac{\overset{x}{\cancel{2x^3}}}{1}\cdot\frac{1}{\underset{1}{\cancel{7y}}}\cdot\frac{\overset{y}{\cancel{14y^2}}}{\underset{4}{\cancel{16x^2}}}=\frac{xy}{4}$; $x \neq 0, y \neq 0$

1.67 $\frac{\overset{1}{\cancel{a}}\overset{1}{\cancel{(a-6)}}}{\underset{1}{\cancel{a-6}}}\cdot\frac{a+3}{\underset{1}{\cancel{a}}}=a+3$; $a \neq 0, 6$

1.68 $\frac{\overset{1}{\cancel{(b-5)}}(b+2)}{\underset{(b-2)}{\cancel{(b-2)^2}}}\cdot\frac{\overset{1}{\cancel{b-2}}}{\underset{1}{\cancel{b-5}}}=\frac{b+2}{b-2}$; $b \neq 2, 5$

1.69 $\frac{\overset{1}{\cancel{x}}}{\underset{1}{\cancel{x-y}}}\cdot\frac{\overset{-1}{\cancel{y-x}}}{\underset{1}{\cancel{x}}}=-1$; $x \neq 0, x \neq y$

1.70 $\frac{(a+1)(a^2-a+1)}{2a(a+2)}\cdot\frac{3(a^2-a+1)}{4(a+2)^2}=\frac{3(a+1)(a^2-a+1)}{8a(a+2)^3}$

1.71 $\frac{(2x-y)\overset{1}{\cancel{(2x+y)}}}{\underset{1}{\cancel{(4x+3y)}}(2x+y)}\cdot\frac{\overset{1}{\cancel{(4x+3y)}}\overset{1}{\cancel{(x-3y)}}}{\cancel{(2x+y)}\underset{1}{\cancel{(x-3y)}}}=\frac{2x-y}{2x+y}$

1.72 $\frac{\overset{1}{\cancel{(3a-1)}}\overset{1}{\cancel{(a-4)}}}{\underset{1}{\cancel{(3a-1)}}(3a-1)}\cdot\frac{7\overset{1}{\cancel{(4+a)}}}{\underset{1}{\cancel{(a+4)}}\underset{1}{\cancel{(a-4)}}}=\frac{7}{3a-1}$

1.73 $\frac{\overset{1}{\cancel{x}}\overset{1}{\cancel{(x-4)}}}{\underset{1}{\cancel{x}}(x+2)}\cdot\frac{1}{(x-5)\underset{1}{\cancel{(x-4)}}(x-5)(x+2)}=\frac{1}{(x+2)^2(x-5)^2}$

1.74 $\frac{(x-y+z)\overset{-1}{\cancel{(x-y-z)}}}{\underset{1}{\cancel{(x+y+z)}}(x+y-z)}\cdot\frac{\overset{1}{\cancel{x+y+z}}}{\underset{1}{\cancel{z+y-x}}}=\frac{-x+y-z}{x+y-z}$

1.75 $\frac{3(4a^2-1)}{2}\cdot\frac{1}{(2a+1)^2}\cdot\frac{2a+1}{6}=$

$\frac{\overset{1}{\cancel{3}}\overset{1}{\cancel{(2a+1)}}(2a-1)}{2}\cdot\frac{1}{\underset{2a+1}{\cancel{(2a+1)^2}}}\cdot\frac{\overset{1}{\cancel{2a+1}}}{\underset{2}{\cancel{6}}}=\frac{2a-1}{4}$

1.76 $\frac{5}{\underset{1}{\cancel{6}}}\cdot\frac{\overset{2}{\cancel{12}}}{7}=\frac{10}{7}$ or $1\frac{3}{7}$

1.77 $\frac{34}{3}\div\frac{17}{6}=\frac{\overset{2}{\cancel{34}}}{\underset{1}{\cancel{3}}}\times\frac{\overset{2}{\cancel{6}}}{\underset{1}{\cancel{17}}}=4$

1.78 $\frac{7}{\underset{1}{\cancel{8}}}\left(\frac{9}{10}\cdot\frac{\overset{1}{\cancel{8}}}{5}\right)=\frac{63}{50}$ or $1\frac{13}{50}$

1.79 $\frac{\overset{1}{\cancel{14a^2}}}{\underset{1}{\cancel{10b^2}}}\cdot\frac{\overset{1}{\cancel{15b^2}}}{\underset{1}{\cancel{21a^2}}}=1$

1.80 $\frac{\overset{x}{\cancel{7x^3}}}{\underset{1}{\cancel{3}}}\cdot\frac{\overset{1}{\cancel{6}}}{\underset{1}{\cancel{14x^2}}}=\frac{x}{1}=x$

1.81 $\frac{\overset{1}{\cancel{(x+2)}}(x-2)}{\underset{1}{\cancel{2}}}\cdot\frac{\overset{6}{\cancel{12}}}{\underset{1}{\cancel{x+2}}}=\frac{6(x-2)}{1}=6x-12$

1.82 $\dfrac{(a-1)(a-1)}{6} \cdot \dfrac{1}{(a+1)(a-1)} = \dfrac{a-1}{6(a+1)}$

1.83 $\dfrac{(x+2y)(x^2-2xy+4y^2)}{2\,14} \cdot \dfrac{3\,21}{(x+2y)^2} = \dfrac{3(x^2-2xy+4y^2)}{2(x+2y)}$

1.84 $\dfrac{(a+3)^2}{a\,3} \cdot \dfrac{(a+3)(a-3)}{5} = \dfrac{(a+3)^3}{5}$

1.85 $\dfrac{(z+y)(z-y)}{(a+b)(a-b)} \cdot \dfrac{a-b}{z+y} = \dfrac{(z-y)}{(a+b)}$

1.86 $\dfrac{8}{2x+3y} \cdot \dfrac{(2x+3y)(2x-3y)}{2\,10} = \dfrac{2x-3y}{2}$

1.87 $\dfrac{(x-2)(x^2+2x+4)}{x^2+2x+4} \cdot \dfrac{1}{(x+2)(x-2)} = \dfrac{1}{x+2}$

1.88 $\dfrac{(a-2)(a+1)}{(a-3)(a+2)} \cdot \dfrac{a(2+a)}{a(a-2)} = \dfrac{a+1}{a-3}$

1.89 $\dfrac{2p}{(2p+1)(2p-1)} \cdot \dfrac{3(2p+1)}{6p^3} = \dfrac{1}{p^2(2p-1)}$

1.90 $\dfrac{8}{(3+a)(3-a)} \cdot \dfrac{(a-3)(a-3)}{a(a-3)(a+2)} = \dfrac{-2}{(a+3)(a+2)}$

1.91 $\dfrac{(x-y)(x-y)(x-y)}{(y+z)(y^2-yz+z^2)} \cdot \dfrac{y^2-yz+z^2}{(x-y)(x-y)} = \dfrac{(x-y)}{(y+z)}$

1.92 $\dfrac{x(y+z)}{z(x-z)} \cdot \dfrac{y(x-z)}{z(x+y)} \cdot \dfrac{x(x+y)}{y(y+z)} = \dfrac{x^2}{z^2}$

1.93 $\dfrac{(3y+4x)(3y-4x)}{(5y+x)(y-x)} \cdot \dfrac{3(y+x)}{(4y-7x)(3y+4x)} \cdot \dfrac{(4y-7x)(5y-x)}{4x-3y} =$

$\dfrac{-3(y+x)(5y-x)}{(5y+x)(y-x)}$

1.94 $\dfrac{(a-9)(a+2)}{4a^3} \cdot \dfrac{2a^2(a-2)}{(a-9)(a+5)} \cdot \dfrac{(a+5)(a-2)}{(a-2)(a-2)} = \dfrac{a+2}{2a}$

1.95 $\dfrac{(x+2y)(x-2y)}{x+2y} \cdot \dfrac{1}{(x+2y)^2} \cdot \dfrac{x+2y}{2x} = \dfrac{x-2y}{2x(x+2y)}$

SELF TEST 1

1.01 $\dfrac{\frac{1}{x^2} \cdot 1 \cdot z^2}{xy} = \dfrac{z^2}{xy \cdot x^2} = \dfrac{z^2}{x^3 y}$

1.02 $3 \cdot 2^{-3} a^2 b^3 c^5 x^{-4} y^{-3} z^{-1}$

1.03 $1 \cdot 18x^2 y = 18x^2 y$

1.04 $\dfrac{8x^3(x)(z^5)}{6y^2(y)(z^4)} = \dfrac{8x^4 z^5}{6y^3 z^4} = \dfrac{4x^4 z}{3y^3}$

1.05 $\dfrac{2^2 \cdot 3^{-3}}{2^{-1} \cdot 3} = \dfrac{2^2 \cdot 2^1}{3^3 \cdot 3} = \dfrac{4 \cdot 2}{27 \cdot 3} = \dfrac{8}{81}$

1.06 $3x^3; \; x \neq 0$

1.07 $\dfrac{4ab(2bx)}{4ab(a-2b)} = \dfrac{2bx}{a-2b}; \; a \neq 0, \; b \neq 0, \; a \neq b$

1.08 $\dfrac{(3a-1)(9a^2+3a+1)}{(3a-1)(3a-1)} = \dfrac{9a^2+3a+1}{3a-1}; \; a \neq \dfrac{1}{3}$

1.09 $\dfrac{x(1+x^3)}{x^2-x+1} = \dfrac{x(1+x)(1-x+x^2)}{x^2-x+1} = x(1+x);$ no restrictions

1.010 $\dfrac{(x-1)(x^2+x+1)}{x(x^2+x+1)} = \dfrac{x-1}{x}; \; x \neq 0$

1.011 $\dfrac{(x+y)(x-y)}{x-y} \cdot \dfrac{2xy}{x(x+y)} = 2y$

1.012 $\dfrac{(2a-3)(3a+2)}{6a^2} \cdot \dfrac{9a^3}{(3a+7)(3a+2)} = \dfrac{3a(2a-3)}{2(3a+7)}$

1.013 $\dfrac{5a}{12bc^2} \cdot \dfrac{18b^2c^2}{15a^2} = \dfrac{b}{2a^2}$

1.014 $\dfrac{a(c-d)}{d} \cdot \dfrac{d(a-b)}{b(d-c)} = \dfrac{-a(a-b)}{b} = \dfrac{a(b-a)}{b}$ or $\dfrac{ab-a^2}{b}$

1.015 $\dfrac{(1-2a)(1+2a+4a^2)}{2a(1-2a)} \cdot \dfrac{a}{a^2(1+2a^2)} = \dfrac{a(1+2a+4a^2)}{2(1+2a^2)}$

1.016 $\dfrac{x^2}{x-1} \cdot \dfrac{y(1-x)}{x^2} = \dfrac{-xy}{1} = -xy$

1.017 $\dfrac{10ab^2}{c^3d} \cdot \dfrac{7c^3d^4}{15ab^3} = \dfrac{14d^3}{3b^2}$

1.018 $\dfrac{(2y+1)(2y-1)}{3y(2y-3)} \cdot \dfrac{(2y-3)(y-1)}{(2y+3)(2y+1)} = \dfrac{(2y-1)(y-1)}{3y(2y+3)}$

1.019 $\dfrac{(y^2+4)(y^2-4)}{y+2} \cdot \dfrac{5}{y^2+4} =$

$\dfrac{(y^2+4)(y+2)(y-2)}{y+2} \cdot \dfrac{5}{y^2+4} =$

$\dfrac{5(y-2)}{1} = 5(y-2)$ or $5y-10$

1.020 $\dfrac{2x^2 y}{6y^3 z} \cdot \dfrac{8x^2 y^2 z^2}{7z^3} \cdot \dfrac{14x^2 y}{9x} =$

$\dfrac{2x^2 y}{6y^3 z} \cdot \dfrac{8x^2 y^2 z^2}{7z^3} \cdot \dfrac{14x^2 y}{9x} =$

$\dfrac{x^2}{3} \cdot \dfrac{8x^2}{z^2} \cdot \dfrac{2xy}{9} = \dfrac{16x^5 y}{27z^2}$

SECTION 2

2.1 $6 = 2 \cdot 3$
$8 = 2^3$
LCD $= 2^3 \cdot 3 = 24$

2.2 $8 = 2^3$
$6 = 2 \cdot 3$
$4 = 2^2$
LCD $= 2^3 \cdot 3 = 24$

2.3 $5 = 5$
$16 = 2^4$
$20 = 2^2 \cdot 5$
LCD $= 2^4 \cdot 5 = 80$

2.4 $xy^2 = x \cdot y^2$
$x^3y = x^3 \cdot y$
LCD $= x^3y^2$

2.5 $7b = 7 \cdot b$
$3c = 3 \cdot c$
$21bc = 3 \cdot 7 \cdot b \cdot c$
LCD $= 3 \cdot 7 \cdot b \cdot c = 21bc$

2.6 $6a - 2b = 2(3a - b)$
$3a - b = 3a - b$
LCD $= 2(3a - b) = 6a - 2b$

2.7 $(a + 1)^2 = (a + 1)^2$
$a + 1 = a + 1$
$(a + 1)^3 = (a + 1)^3$
LCD $= (a + 1)^3$

2.8 $ab^2 = a \cdot b^2$
$2a^2b = 2 \cdot a^2 \cdot b$
LCD $= 2 \cdot a^2 \cdot b^2 = 2a^2b^2$

2.9 $a^2 - 7a + 6 = (a - 6)(a - 1)$
$a^2 - 36 = (a + 6)(a - 6)$
LCD $= (a - 6)(a - 1)(a + 6)$

2.10 $x^2 + 4x + 4 = (x + 2)^2$
$4 - x^2 = (2 + x)(2 - x)$
LCD $= (x + 2)^2(2 - x)$

2.11 $x - 2 = x - 2$
$x - 1 = x - 1$
$x^2 - 7x + 6 = (x - 6)(x - 1)$
LCD $= (x - 2)(x - 1)(x - 6)$

2.12 $x^2 - 5x + 4 = (x - 4)(x - 1)$
$x^2 - 16 = (x + 4)(x - 4)$
LCD $= (x - 4)(x - 1)(x + 4)$

2.13 $x^2 - x - 20 = (x - 5)(x + 4)$
$x^2 - 2x - 15 = (x - 5)(x + 3)$
$x^2 + 7x + 12 = (x + 4)(x + 3)$
LCD $= (x - 5)(x + 4)(x + 3)$

2.14 $x^3 + y^3 = (x + y)(x^2 - xy + y^2)$
$x + y = x + y$
LCD $= (x + y)(x^2 - xy + y^2)$
$= x^3 + y^3$

2.15 $x - 2 = x - 2$
$x^3 - 8 = (x - 2)(x^2 + 2x + 4)$
$5x^2 + 10x + 20 = 5(x^2 + 2x + 4)$
LCD $= 5(x - 2)(x^2 + 2x + 4)$

2.16 a. $\frac{5 \cdot 4}{6 \cdot 4} = \frac{20}{24}$

b. $\frac{3 \cdot 3}{8 \cdot 3} = \frac{9}{24}$

2.17 a. $\frac{7 \cdot 3}{8 \cdot 3} = \frac{21}{24}$

b. $\frac{1 \cdot 4}{6 \cdot 4} = \frac{4}{24}$

c. $\frac{3 \cdot 6}{4 \cdot 6} = \frac{18}{24}$

2.18 a. $\frac{3 \cdot 16}{5 \cdot 16} = \frac{48}{80}$

b. $\frac{5 \cdot 5}{16 \cdot 5} = \frac{25}{80}$

c. $\frac{9 \cdot 4}{20 \cdot 4} = \frac{36}{80}$

2.19 a. $\frac{2 \cdot x^2}{xy^2 \cdot x^2} = \frac{2x^2}{x^3y^2}$

b. $\frac{3 \cdot y}{x^3y \cdot y} = \frac{3y}{x^3y^2}$

2.20 a. $\frac{3 \cdot 3c}{7b \cdot 3c} = \frac{9c}{21bc}$

b. $\frac{5 \cdot 7b}{3c \cdot 7b} = \frac{35b}{21bc}$

c. $\frac{11}{21bc}$

2.21 a. $\frac{5ab}{6a - 2b}$

b. $\frac{2ab \cdot 2}{(3a - b)2} = \frac{4ab}{6a - 2b}$

2.22 a. $\frac{3a(a + 1)}{(a + 1)^2(a + 1)} = \frac{3a(a + 1)}{(a + 1)^3}$

b. $\frac{2a^2(a + 1)^2}{(a + 1)(a + 1)^2} = \frac{2a^2(a + 1)^2}{(a + 1)^3}$

c. $\frac{5a^3}{(a + 1)^3}$

2.23 a. $\frac{(5a + 3b)(2a)}{ab^2(2a)} = \frac{10a^2 + 6ab}{2a^2b^2}$

b. $\frac{(3a + 4b)(b)}{2a^2b(b)} = \frac{3ab + 4b^2}{2a^2b^2}$

2.24 a. $\frac{6(a + 6)}{(a - 6)(a - 1)(a + 6)} = \frac{6a + 36}{(a - 6)(a - 1)(a + 6)}$

b. $\frac{3(a - 1)}{(a + 6)(a - 6)(a - 1)} = \frac{3a - 3}{(a - 6)(a - 1)(a + 6)}$

2.25 a. $\frac{7(2 - x)}{(x + 2)^2(2 - x)} = \frac{14 - 7x}{(x + 2)^2(2 - x)}$

b. $\frac{5(x + 2)}{(2 + x)(2 - x)(x + 2)} = \frac{5x + 10}{(x + 2)^2(2 - x)}$

2.26 a. $\frac{2(x - 1)(x - 6)}{(x - 2)(x - 1)(x - 6)}$

b. $\frac{4(x - 2)(x - 6)}{(x - 2)(x - 1)(x - 6)}$

c. $\frac{3(x - 2)}{(x - 2)(x - 1)(x - 6)}$

2.27 a. $\dfrac{x(x+4)}{(x-4)(x-1)(x+4)} = \dfrac{x^2+4x}{(x-4)(x-1)(x+4)}$

b. $\dfrac{(x+1)(x-1)}{(x+4)(x-4)(x-1)} = \dfrac{x^2-1}{(x-4)(x-1)(x+4)}$

2.28 a. $\dfrac{(x-1)(x+3)}{(x-5)(x+4)(x+3)}$

b. $\dfrac{(x+2)(x+4)}{(x-5)(x+4)(x+3)}$

c. $\dfrac{(x+1)(x-5)}{(x-5)(x+4)(x+3)}$

2.29 a. $\dfrac{x}{x^3+y^3}$

b. $\dfrac{x(x^2-xy+y^2)}{(x+y)(x^2-xy+y^2)} = \dfrac{x^3-x^2y+xy^2}{x^3+y^3}$

2.30 a. $\dfrac{5(2x^2-1)(x^2+2x+4)}{5(x-2)(x^2+2x+4)}$

b. $\dfrac{5(2x)}{5(x-2)(x^2+2x+4)} = \dfrac{10x}{5(x-2)(x^2+2x+4)}$

c. $\dfrac{x-2}{5(x-2)(x^2+2x+4)}$

2.31 $\dfrac{5}{8} - \dfrac{4}{8} = \dfrac{1}{8}$

2.32 $\dfrac{8}{18} + \dfrac{12}{18} - \dfrac{9}{18} = \dfrac{11}{18}$

2.33 $-\dfrac{2}{a}$

2.34 $\dfrac{9a}{12} + \dfrac{8a}{12} - \dfrac{a}{12} = \dfrac{16a}{12} = \dfrac{4a}{3}$

2.35 $\dfrac{3yz}{xyz} + \dfrac{1}{xyz} + \dfrac{2z}{xyz} = \dfrac{3yz+2z+1}{xyz}$

2.36 $\dfrac{15}{6y} + \dfrac{1}{6y} - \dfrac{8}{6y} = \dfrac{8}{6y} = \dfrac{4}{3y}$

2.37 $\dfrac{18y^2}{12x^2y^2} - \dfrac{10xy}{12x^2y^2} + \dfrac{7x^2}{12x^2y^2} = \dfrac{18y^2-10xy+7x^2}{12x^2y^2}$

2.38 $\dfrac{6(8-y)}{6(3y)} + \dfrac{2(y+2)}{2(9y)} - \dfrac{3(2)}{3(6y)} = \dfrac{48-6y}{18y} + \dfrac{2y+4}{18y} - \dfrac{6}{18y} =$

$\dfrac{46-4y}{18y} = \dfrac{^1\cancel{2}(23-2y)}{_9\cancel{18}y} = \dfrac{23-2y}{9y}$

2.39 $\dfrac{5(4+a)}{5(a-3)} + \dfrac{4(a-3)}{5(a-3)} = \dfrac{20+5a}{5(a-3)} + \dfrac{4a-12}{5(a-3)} = \dfrac{9a+8}{5a-15}$

2.40 $\dfrac{(x-y)(x-y)}{(x+y)(x-y)} - \dfrac{(x+y)(x+y)}{(x-y)(x+y)} = \dfrac{x^2-2xy+y^2}{x^2-y^2} - \dfrac{x^2+2xy+y^2}{x^2-y^2}$

$= \dfrac{\cancel{x^2}-2xy+\cancel{y^2}-\cancel{x^2}-2xy-\cancel{y^2}}{x^2-y^2} = \dfrac{-4xy}{x^2-y^2}$

2.41 $\dfrac{(x+2)(x+6)}{(x+4)(x+6)} - \dfrac{(x-1)(x+4)}{(x+6)(x+4)} = \dfrac{x^2-8x+12-(x^2+3x-4)}{(x+6)(x+4)}$

$= \dfrac{\cancel{x^2}+8x+12-\cancel{x^2}-3x+4}{(x+6)(x+4)} = \dfrac{5x+16}{(x+6)(x+4)}$

2.42 $\dfrac{4}{(y+3)(y-3)} + \dfrac{5(y-3)}{(y+3)(y-3)} = \dfrac{4+5y-15}{y^2-9} = \dfrac{5y-11}{y^2-9}$

2.43 $\dfrac{1}{b+1} + \dfrac{b^2+2}{(b-2)(b+1)} - \dfrac{b}{b-2} =$

$\dfrac{1(b-2)}{(b+1)(b-2)} + \dfrac{b^2+2}{(b-2)(b+1)} - \dfrac{b(b+1)}{(b-2)(b+1)} =$

$\dfrac{b-2}{(b+1)(b-2)} + \dfrac{b^2+2}{(b-2)(b+1)} - \dfrac{b^2+b}{(b-2)(b+1)} =$

$\dfrac{\cancel{b}-2+\cancel{b^2}+2-\cancel{b^2}-\cancel{b}}{(b-2)(b+1)} = 0$

2.44 $\dfrac{a^2-5}{(a-1)(a^2+a+1)} - \dfrac{(a+1)(a-1)}{(a^2+a+1)(a-1)} = \dfrac{a^2-5-(a^2-1)}{a^3-1} =$

$\dfrac{\cancel{a^2}-5-\cancel{a^2}+1}{a^3-1} = \dfrac{-4}{a^3-1}$

2.45 $\dfrac{(3a-b)(b-2a)}{(a+3b)(b-2a)} - \dfrac{(a+2b)(a+3b)}{(b-2a)(a+3b)} =$

$\dfrac{3ab-b^2-6a^2+2ab-(a^2+5ab+6b^2)}{(a+3b)(b-2a)} =$

$\dfrac{3ab-b^2-6a^2+\cancel{2ab}-a^2-\cancel{5ab}-6b^2}{(a+3b)(b-2a)} =$

$\dfrac{-7a^2-7b^2}{(a+3b)(b-2a)}$

2.46 $\dfrac{y}{(y+4)(y-4)} - \dfrac{y+1}{(y-4)(y-1)} =$

$\dfrac{y(y-1)}{(y+4)(y-4)(y-1)} - \dfrac{(y+1)(y+4)}{(y-4)(y-1)(y+4)} =$

$\dfrac{y^2-y-(y^2+5y+4)}{(y-4)(y-1)(y+4)} = \dfrac{\cancel{y^2}-y-\cancel{y^2}-5y-4}{(y-4)(y-1)(y+4)} =$

$\dfrac{-6y-4}{(y-4)(y-1)(y+4)}$ or $\dfrac{-2(3y+2)}{(y-4)(y-1)(y+4)}$

2.47 $\dfrac{x+6}{(x+5)(x+3)} + \dfrac{3x}{x+5} - \dfrac{x-3}{x+3} =$

$\dfrac{x+6}{(x+5)(x+3)} + \dfrac{3x(x+3)}{(x+5)(x+3)} - \dfrac{(x-3)(x+5)}{(x+3)(x+5)} =$

$\dfrac{x+6+3x^2+9x-(x^2+2x-15)}{(x+5)(x+3)} =$

$\dfrac{x+6+3x^2+9x-x^2-2x+15}{(x+5)(x+3)} =$

$\dfrac{2x^2+8x+21}{(x+5)(x+3)}$

2.48 $\dfrac{2x}{(y+x)(y-x)} - \dfrac{x}{y-x} = \dfrac{2x}{(y+x)(y-x)} - \dfrac{x(y+x)}{(y-x)(y+x)} =$

$\dfrac{2x-(xy+x^2)}{(y+x)(y-x)} = \dfrac{2x-xy-x^2}{(y+x)(y-x)}$

2.49 $\dfrac{(2x+y)(x-y)}{(x+y)(x-y)} - \dfrac{(2x-y)(x+y)}{(x-y)(x+y)} - \dfrac{3x^2-y^2}{(x+y)(x-y)} =$

$\dfrac{2x^2-xy-y^2-(2x^2+xy-y^2)-(3x^2-y^2)}{(x+y)(x-y)} =$

$\dfrac{\cancel{2x^2}-xy-\cancel{y^2}-\cancel{2x^2}-xy+\cancel{y^2}-3x^2+y^2}{(x+y)(x-y)} = \dfrac{-3x^2-2xy+y^2}{(x+y)(x-y)} =$

$\dfrac{(-3x+y)\cancel{(x+y)}}{\cancel{(x+y)}(x-y)} = \dfrac{-3x+y}{x-y}$

2.50 $\dfrac{(2a-1)(a+b)(b)}{a(a+b)(b)} - \dfrac{(b+1)(a+b)(a)}{b(a+b)(a)} + \dfrac{(a+b)(ab)}{(a+b)(ab)} =$

$\dfrac{2a^2b+2ab^2-ab-b^2-(a^2b+a^2+ab^2+ab)+a^2b+ab^2}{ab(a+b)} =$

$\dfrac{2a^2b+2ab^2-ab-b^2-\cancel{a^2b}-a^2-\cancel{ab^2}-ab+\cancel{a^2b}+\cancel{ab^2}}{ab(a+b)} =$

$\dfrac{2a^2b+2ab^2-2ab-b^2-a^2}{ab(a+b)}$

2.51 $\dfrac{x-3}{(x-2)(x-1)} - \dfrac{x-2}{(x-3)(x-1)} - \dfrac{x-1}{(x-3)(x-2)} =$

$\dfrac{(x-3)(x-3)}{(x-2)(x-1)(x-3)} - \dfrac{(x-2)(x-2)}{(x-3)(x-1)(x-2)} - \dfrac{(x-1)(x-1)}{(x-3)(x-2)(x-1)} =$

$= \dfrac{x^2-6x+9-(x^2-4x+4)-(x^2-2x+1)}{(x-3)(x-2)(x-1)} =$

$= \dfrac{\cancel{x^2}-6x+9-\cancel{x^2}+4x-4-x^2+2x-1}{(x-3)(x-2)(x-1)} =$

$= \dfrac{-x^2+4}{(x-3)(x-2)(x-1)} = \dfrac{-1(x^2-4)}{(x-3)(x-2)(x-1)} =$

$= \dfrac{-1(x+2)\cancel{(x-2)}}{(x-3)\cancel{(x-2)}(x-1)} = \dfrac{-1(x+2)}{(x-3)(x-1)} = -\dfrac{x+2}{(x-3)(x-1)}$

2.52

$$\frac{x}{(x-y)(x-y)} - \frac{2}{x+y} - \frac{x-3}{(x+y)(x-y)} =$$

$$\frac{x(x+y)}{(x-y)^2(x+y)} - \frac{2(x-y)^2}{(x+y)(x-y)^2} - \frac{(x-3)(x-y)}{(x+y)(x-y)^2} =$$

$$\frac{x^2 + xy - (2x^2 - 4xy + 2y^2) - (x^2 - 3x - xy + 3y)}{(x-y)^2(x+y)} =$$

$$\frac{\cancel{x^2} + xy - 2x^2 + 4xy - 2y^2 - \cancel{x^2} + 3x + xy - 3y}{(x-y)^2(x+y)} =$$

$$\frac{-2x^2 - 2y^2 + 6xy + 3x - 3y}{(x-y)^2(x+y)}$$

2.53

$$\frac{a}{(1-a)(1+a+a^2)} - \frac{2}{a^2+a+1} + \frac{1}{(a+1)(a-1)} =$$

$$\frac{-a}{(a-1)(1+a+a^2)} - \frac{2}{a^2+a+1} + \frac{1}{(a+1)(a-1)} =$$

$$\frac{-a(a+1)}{(a-1)(1+a+a^2)(a+1)} - \frac{2(a+1)(a-1)}{(a^2+a+1)(a+1)(a-1)} +$$

$$\frac{a^2+a+1}{(a^2+a+1)(a+1)(a-1)} = \frac{-a^2 - a - (2a^2 - 2) + a^2 + a + 1}{(a^2+a+1)(a+1)(a-1)} =$$

$$\frac{-\cancel{a^2} - \cancel{a} - 2a^2 + 2 + \cancel{a^2} + \cancel{a} + 1}{(a^2+a+1)(a+1)(a-1)} = \frac{-2a^2+3}{(a^3-1)(a+1)}$$

2.54 $\quad \dfrac{7(25)+12}{25} = \dfrac{187}{25}$

2.55 $\quad \dfrac{x^2}{x} + \dfrac{1}{x} = \dfrac{x^2+1}{x}$

2.56 $\quad \dfrac{ab}{b} - \dfrac{a}{b} = \dfrac{ab-a}{b}$

2.57 $\quad \dfrac{3a}{3a} - \dfrac{2}{3a} = \dfrac{3a-2}{3a}$

2.58 $\quad \dfrac{x(x+y)}{x+y} - \dfrac{x^2}{x+y} = \dfrac{x^2+xy}{x+y} - \dfrac{x^2}{x+y} = \dfrac{xy}{x+y}$

2.59 $\quad \dfrac{2m(m)}{m} - \dfrac{1}{m} = \dfrac{2m^2}{m} - \dfrac{1}{m} = \dfrac{2m^2-1}{m}$

2.60 $\quad \dfrac{a(a^2)}{a^2} + \dfrac{1}{a^2} = \dfrac{a^3}{a^2} + \dfrac{1}{a^2} = \dfrac{a^3+1}{a^2}$

2.61 $\quad \dfrac{2x}{2x} + \dfrac{2x(2x)}{2x} + \dfrac{1}{2x} = \dfrac{2x+4x^2+1}{2x}$

2.62 $\quad \dfrac{x(x^2+y)}{x^2+y} - \dfrac{x^3}{x^2+y} = \dfrac{x^3+xy}{x^2+y} - \dfrac{x^3}{x^2+y} = \dfrac{xy}{x^2+y}$

2.63

$$\frac{2(x^2+4xy+4y^2)}{x^2+4xy+y^2} - \frac{x^2+10xy+7y^2}{x^2+4xy+4y^2} =$$

$$\frac{2x^2+8xy+8y^2}{x^2+4xy+4y^2} - \frac{x^2+10xy+7y^2}{x^2+4xy+4y^2} = \frac{x^2-2xy+y^2}{x^2+4xy+4y^2}$$

2.64 $\quad 2\dfrac{1}{4}$

2.65 $\quad \dfrac{2x}{x} - \dfrac{y}{x} = 2 - \dfrac{y}{x}$

2.66 $\quad \dfrac{8x^3 - 10x^2}{2x+1} =$

$$2x+1 \overline{)\begin{array}{r} 4x^2 - 7x + \frac{7x}{2x+1} \\ 8x^3 - 10x^2 + 0x \\ \underline{8x^3 + 4x^2} \\ -14x^2 + 0x \\ \underline{-14x^2 - 7x} \\ 7x \end{array}}$$

2.67 $\quad \dfrac{x^5 - y^5}{x+y} =$

$$\begin{array}{r} x^4 - x^3 y + x^2 y^2 - xy^3 + y^4 + \frac{-2y^5}{x+y} \\ x+y \overline{)\,x^5 + 0x^4 y + 0x^3 y^2 + 0x^2 y^3 + 0xy^4 - y^5} \\ \underline{x^5 - x^4 y} \\ -x^4 y + 0x^3 y^2 \\ \underline{-x^4 y - x^3 y^2} \\ x^3 y^2 + 0x^2 y^3 \\ \underline{x^3 y^2 + x^2 y^3} \\ -x^2 y^3 + 0xy^4 \\ \underline{-x^2 y^3 - xy^4} \\ xy^4 - y^5 \\ \underline{xy^4 + y^5} \\ -2y^5 \end{array}$$

2.68 $\quad \dfrac{\frac{a+1}{\cancel{a}}\left(\frac{\cancel{a}}{1}\right)}{5\left(\frac{a}{1}\right)} = \dfrac{a+1}{5a}$

2.69 $\quad \dfrac{\left(1+\frac{x}{y}\right)\left(\frac{y^2}{1}\right)}{\left(1+\frac{x^2}{y^2}\right)\left(\frac{y^2}{1}\right)} = \dfrac{y^2+xy}{y^2-x^2} = \dfrac{y\cancel{(y+x)}}{\cancel{(y+x)}(y-x)} = \dfrac{y}{y-x}$

2.70 $\quad \dfrac{\frac{x^2 y}{z^2}\left(\frac{z^2}{1}\right)}{\frac{xy^2}{z^2}\left(\frac{z^2}{1}\right)} = \dfrac{x^2 y}{xy^2} = \dfrac{x}{y}$

2.71

$$\dfrac{\frac{a^3-27}{(a+3)(a-3)}\overset{1}{(a+3)(a-3)}}{\frac{a^2+3a+9}{a+3}\underset{1}{(a+3)}(a-3)} = \dfrac{a^3-27}{(a-3)(a^2+3a+9)}$$

$$= \dfrac{(a-3)(a^2+3a+9)}{(a-3)(a^2+3a+9)}$$

$$= 1$$

2.72

$$\dfrac{\left(\frac{3x+y}{x-y} - 3\right)(x+y)(x-y)}{\left(1 - \frac{x-3y}{x+y}\right)(x+y)(x-y)}$$

$$= \dfrac{(3x+y)(x+y) - 3(x+y)(x-y)}{(x+y)(x-y) - (x-3y)(x-y)}$$

$$= \dfrac{3x^2+4xy+y^2 - 3(x^2-y^2)}{x^2-y^2 - (x^2-4xy+3y^2)}$$

$$= \dfrac{3x^2+4xy+y^2 - 3x^2 + 3y^2}{x^2-y^2 - x^2 + 4xy - 3y^2}$$

$$= \dfrac{4xy+4y^2}{4xy-4y^2}$$

$$= \dfrac{\overset{1}{4y}(x+y)}{\underset{1}{4y}(x-y)}$$

$$= \dfrac{x+y}{x-y}$$

2.73 $\quad \dfrac{\left(\frac{x^3 y^{-2}}{z}\right)\overset{1}{z^2}y^{-4}}{\left(\frac{x^{-2} z^3}{y^4}\right)z^2 y^4} = \dfrac{x^3 y^{-6}}{x^{-2} z^5} = \dfrac{x^5}{y^6 z^5}$

2.74 $\dfrac{(\frac{(x+y)^{-2}}{1\ y^2})x^{-2}y^3}{(\frac{x^3y^{-2}(x+y)^{-1}}{x^2\ _1})x^2y^{-3}} = \dfrac{(x+y)^{-2}x^{-2}}{x^3y^{-5}(x+y)^{-1}} = \dfrac{y^5(x+y)}{x^3(x^2)(x+y)^2}$

$\qquad = \dfrac{y^5}{x^5(x+y)}$ or $\dfrac{y^5}{x^6+x^5y}$

2.75 $(\frac{r}{s} + \frac{s}{s})(\frac{r^2}{s^2r^2} + \frac{s^2r^2}{s^2r^2}) = (\frac{r+s}{s})(\frac{\overset{1}{r^2}(1+s^2)}{s^2r^2\ _1}) =$

$\qquad \dfrac{(r+s)(1+s^2)}{s^3}$

2.76 $(\frac{a^2}{ab} - \frac{b^2}{ab})[\frac{a(a+b)}{a+b} - \frac{a^2}{a+b}] =$

$\qquad (\frac{a^2-b^2}{ab})(\frac{a^2+ab-a^2}{a+b}) = \dfrac{a^2-b^2}{\underset{1}{\cancel{ab}}} \cdot \dfrac{\overset{1}{\cancel{ab}}}{a+b} = \dfrac{\overset{1}{(a+b)}(a-b)}{\underset{1}{a+b}}$

$\qquad = a - b$

2.77 $(\frac{a^2}{ab} + \frac{b^2}{ab})[\frac{a(a^2+b)}{a^2+b} - \frac{a^3}{a^2+b}] = (\frac{a^2+b}{ab})(\frac{a^3+ab-a^3}{a^2+b})$

$\qquad\qquad = \dfrac{\overset{1}{\cancel{a^2+b}}}{\underset{1}{\cancel{ab}}} \cdot \dfrac{\overset{1}{\cancel{ab}}}{\underset{1}{\cancel{a^2+b}}} = 1$

2.78 $[\frac{(2a+5b)(a-b)-15b^2}{a-b}] \div [\frac{2a(a-b)-9ab+15b^2}{a-b}] =$

$\qquad \dfrac{2a^2+3ab-5b^2-15b^2}{a-b} \cdot \dfrac{a-b}{2a^2-2ab-9ab+15b^2} =$

$\qquad \dfrac{2a^2+3ab-20b^2}{a-b} \cdot \dfrac{a-b}{2a^2-11ab+15b^2} =$

$\qquad \dfrac{\overset{1}{(2a-5b)}(a+4b)}{\underset{1}{\cancel{a-b}}} \cdot \dfrac{\overset{1}{\cancel{a-b}}}{\overset{1}{(2a-5b)}(a-3b)} = \dfrac{a+4b}{a-3b}$

2.79 $[\frac{(x+y)(x+y)}{(x-y)(x+y)} - \frac{(x-y)(x-y)}{(x+y)(x-y)} + \frac{4y^2}{(x+y)(x-y)}] \div$

$\qquad (\frac{x-y}{x+y} + \frac{x+y}{x+y}) =$

$\qquad \dfrac{x^2+2xy+y^2-(x^2-2xy+y^2)+4y^2}{(x+y)(x-y)} \div \dfrac{2x}{x+y} =$

$\qquad \dfrac{\cancel{x^2}+2xy+\cancel{y^2}-\cancel{x^2}+2xy-\cancel{y^2}+4y^2}{(x+y)(x-y)} \cdot \dfrac{\overset{1}{\cancel{x+y}}}{2x} =$

$\qquad \dfrac{4xy+4y^2}{x-y} \cdot \dfrac{1}{2x} = \dfrac{\overset{2}{4}y(x+y)}{x-y} \cdot \dfrac{1}{\underset{1}{2x}} = \dfrac{2y(x+y)}{x(x-y)}$ or

$\qquad \dfrac{2xy+2y^2}{x^2-xy}$

SELF TEST 2

2.01 $\dfrac{2^{-2} \cdot 5^0}{2^3 \cdot 5^{-2}} = \dfrac{\frac{1}{2^2} \cdot 1}{2^3 \cdot \frac{1}{5^2}} = \dfrac{5^2}{2^3 \cdot 2^2} = \dfrac{25}{32}$

2.02 $\dfrac{(a+b)\overset{1}{(a-b)}}{\underset{1}{(a-b)}(a^2+ab+b^2)} = \dfrac{a+b}{a^2+ab+b^2}$

2.03 $\dfrac{2\overset{1}{(x+2y)}}{\underset{1}{(x+y)}(x-y)} \cdot \dfrac{x+y}{\underset{1}{(x+2y)}(x+2y)} = \dfrac{2}{(x-y)(x+2y)}$

2.04 $\dfrac{(3x+1)(3x-1)}{(2x+3)\underset{1}{(2x-3)}} \cdot \dfrac{\overset{1}{(2x-3)}(x-3)}{(x+5)(x-2)} = \dfrac{(3x+1)(3x-1)(x-3)}{(2x+3)(x+5)(x-2)}$

2.05 $\quad a^2 + a + 1 = a^2 + a + 1$

$\qquad\quad a - 1 = a - 1$

$\qquad\quad a^3 - 1 = (a-1)(a^2+a+1)$

$\quad$ LCD $= (a-1)(a^2+a+1) = a^3 - 1$

$\quad$ a. $\dfrac{3a^2(a-1)}{(a^2+a+1)(a-1)} = \dfrac{3a^3-3a^2}{a^3-1}$

$\quad$ b. $\dfrac{2a(a^2+a+1)}{(a-1)(a^2+a+1)} = \dfrac{2a^3-2a^2+2a}{a^3-1}$

$\quad$ c. $\dfrac{a^3}{a^3-1}$

$\quad$ d. $a^3 - 1$

2.06 $\quad 51 = 3 \cdot 17$

$\qquad 85 = 5 \cdot 17$

$\quad$ LCD $= 3 \cdot 5 \cdot 17 = 255$

$\quad$ a. $\dfrac{8 \cdot 5}{51 \cdot 5} = \dfrac{40}{255}$

$\quad$ b. $\dfrac{19 \cdot 3}{85 \cdot 3} = \dfrac{57}{255}$

$\quad$ c. 255

2.07 $\quad 12bc^2 = 2^2 \cdot 3 \cdot b \cdot c^2$

$\qquad 18b^2c^2 = 2 \cdot 3^2 \cdot b^2 \cdot c^2$

$\quad$ LCD $= 2^2 \cdot 3^2 \cdot b^2 \cdot c^2 = 36b^2c^2$

$\quad$ a. $\dfrac{11a \cdot 3b}{12bc^2 \cdot 3b} = \dfrac{33ab}{36b^2c^2}$

$\quad$ b. $\dfrac{13a^3 \cdot 2}{18b^2c^2 \cdot 2} = \dfrac{26a^3}{36b^2c^2}$

$\quad$ c. $36b^2c^2$

2.08 $\dfrac{4(a-7)}{4(3)} + \dfrac{2(5a-3)}{2(6)} - \dfrac{3(2a+5)}{3(4)} =$

$\qquad \dfrac{4a-28+10a-6-(6a+15)}{12} =$

$\qquad \dfrac{4a-28+10a-6-6a-15}{12} = \dfrac{8a-49}{12}$

2.09 $\dfrac{2 \cdot b}{ac \cdot b} + \dfrac{1 \cdot c}{ab \cdot c} + \dfrac{3 \cdot a}{bc \cdot a} = \dfrac{2b+c+3a}{abc} = \dfrac{3a+2b+c}{abc}$

2.010 $\dfrac{2(a^2-ab+b^2)}{(a+b)(a^2-ab+b^2)} + \dfrac{2x(a+b)}{(a^2-ab+b^2)(a+b)} =$

$\qquad \dfrac{2a^2-2ab+2b^2+2ax+2bx}{a^3+b^3}$ or $\dfrac{2(a^2-ab+b^2+ax+bx)}{a^3+b^3}$

2.011 $\dfrac{5}{x(x-y)} - \dfrac{5}{y(y-x)} = \dfrac{5}{x(x-y)} + \dfrac{5}{y(x-y)} = \dfrac{5y}{xy(x-y)} +$

$\qquad \dfrac{5x}{xy(x-y)} = \dfrac{5y+5x}{xy(x-y)} = \dfrac{5(x+y)}{xy(x-y)}$

2.012 $\dfrac{(x+y)(x+y)}{(x-y)(x+y)} + \dfrac{x-y}{(x+y)(x-y)} - \dfrac{x^2+y^2}{(x+y)(x-y)} =$

$\dfrac{x^2 + 2xy + y^2 + x - y - x^2 - y^2}{x^2 - y^2} = \dfrac{2xy + x - y}{x^2 - y^2}$

2.013 $\dfrac{2a-1}{2a-3} - \dfrac{2a^2 - 5a + 4}{(4a-5)(2a-3)} - \dfrac{3a-2}{4a-5} =$

$\dfrac{(2a-1)(4a-5)}{(2a-3)(4a-5)} - \dfrac{2a^2 - 5a + 4}{(4a-5)(2a-3)} - \dfrac{(3a-2)(2a-3)}{(4a-5)(2a-3)} =$

$\dfrac{8a^2 - 14a + 5 - (2a^2 - 5a + 4) - (6a^2 - 13a + 6)}{(4a-5)(2a-3)} =$

$\dfrac{8a^2 - 14a + 5 - 2a^2 + 5a - 4 - 6a^2 + 13a - 6}{(4a-5)(2a-3)} =$

$\dfrac{4a-5}{(4a-5)(2a-3)} = \dfrac{1}{2a-3}$

2.014 $\dfrac{1}{a-b} - \dfrac{4}{a-b} - \dfrac{8}{a+b} + \dfrac{11a-5b}{a^2-b^2} =$

$-\dfrac{3}{a-b} - \dfrac{8}{a+b} + \dfrac{11a-5b}{(a+b)(a-b)} =$

$-\dfrac{3(a+b)}{(a-b)(a+b)} - \dfrac{8(a-b)}{(a+b)(a-b)} + \dfrac{11a-5b}{(a+b)(a-b)} =$

$\dfrac{-(3a+3b) - (8a-8b) + 11a - 5b}{(a+b)(a-b)}$

$\dfrac{-3a - 3b - 8a + 8b + 11a - 5b}{(a+b)(a-b)} = 0$

2.015 $\dfrac{y(x^3-y^3)}{x^3-y^3} + \dfrac{2y^3}{x^3-y^3} = \dfrac{x^3y - y^4 + 2y^3}{x^3-y^3} = \dfrac{2y^3 + x^3y - y^4}{x^3-y^3}$

2.016 $\dfrac{(y-1)(y+3)}{y+3} - \dfrac{5}{y+3} = \dfrac{y^2 + 2y - 3 - 5}{y+3} = \dfrac{y^2 + 2y - 8}{y+3}$

2.017 $\dfrac{6a-4}{7a-5} - \dfrac{3(7a-5)}{7a-5} = \dfrac{6a - 4 - (21a-15)}{7a-15} =$

$\dfrac{6a - 4 - 21a + 15}{7a-5} = \dfrac{11 - 15a}{7a-5}$

2.018 $\dfrac{(a+1-\frac{6}{a})\frac{a}{1}}{(a+1-\frac{6}{a})\frac{a}{1}} = \dfrac{a^2+a-6}{a^2-a-2} = \dfrac{(a+3)(a-2)}{(a+1)(a-2)} = \dfrac{a+3}{a+1}$

2.019 $\dfrac{(\frac{m-2}{m+1}+2)(\frac{m+1}{1})}{(1+\frac{1-2m}{m+1})(\frac{m+1}{1})} = \dfrac{m-2+2m+2}{m+1+1+2m} = \dfrac{3m}{3m+2}$

2.020 $\dfrac{(\frac{a+b}{a} - \frac{2a}{b} - \frac{a-b}{b})\frac{ab}{1}}{(\frac{2a-b}{b} - \frac{b}{a})\frac{ab}{1}} = \dfrac{b(a+b) - 2a(a) - a(a-b)}{a(2a-b) - b(b)} =$

$= \dfrac{ab + b^2 - 2a^2 - a^2 + ab}{2a^2 - ab - b^2} = \dfrac{b^2 + 2ab - 3a^2}{2a^2 - ab - b^2}$

$= \dfrac{(b+3a)(b-a)}{(2a+b)(a-b)} = \dfrac{-3a-b}{2a+b}$

SECTION 3

3.1 $\dfrac{x}{2} + 3 + x + 9 = 60$

$x + 6 + 2x + 18 = 120$

$3x + 24 = 120$

$3x = 96$

$x = 32$

Check:

$\dfrac{32}{2} + 3 + 32 + 9 = 60$

$16 + 44 = 60$

$60 = 60$

3.2 $\dfrac{a}{4} + \dfrac{a}{3} = 21$

$12(\dfrac{a}{4}) + 12(\dfrac{a}{3}) = 12(21)$

$3a + 4a = 252$

$7a = 252$

$a = 36$

Check:

$\dfrac{36}{4} + \dfrac{36}{3} = 21$

$9 + 12 = 21$

$21 = 21$

3.3 $\dfrac{3x}{4} + \dfrac{2x}{3} = 51$

$12(\dfrac{3x}{4}) + 12(\dfrac{2x}{3}) = 12(51)$

$9x + 8x = 612$

$17x = 612$

$x = 36$

Check:

$\dfrac{3(36)}{4} + \dfrac{2(36)}{3} = 51$

$\dfrac{108}{4} + \dfrac{72}{3} = 51$

$27 + 24 = 51$

$51 = 51$

3.4 $\dfrac{y}{4} - 1\dfrac{1}{2} = \dfrac{y}{6}$

$12(\dfrac{y}{4}) - 12(\dfrac{3}{2}) = 12(\dfrac{y}{6})$

$3y - 18 = 2y$

$y - 18 = 0$

$y = 18$

Check:

$\dfrac{18}{4} - \dfrac{3}{2} = \dfrac{18}{6}$

$\dfrac{9}{2} - \dfrac{3}{2} = 3$

$3 = 3$

3.5
$$\frac{2x}{3} - \frac{5x}{9} - \frac{x}{6} - \frac{5x}{12} = \frac{13}{2}$$

$$36(\tfrac{2x}{3}) - 36(\tfrac{5x}{9}) - 36(\tfrac{x}{6}) - 36(\tfrac{5x}{12}) = 36(\tfrac{13}{2})$$
$$24x - 20x - 6x - 15x = 234$$
$$-17x = 234$$
$$x = -\tfrac{234}{17} \text{ or } -13\tfrac{13}{17}$$

Check:
$$\frac{2(-\frac{234}{17})}{3} - \frac{5(-\frac{234}{17})}{9} - \frac{-\frac{234}{17}}{6} - \frac{5(-\frac{234}{17})}{12} = \frac{13}{2}$$

$$-\frac{\overset{156}{\cancel{468}}}{\underset{17}{\cancel{51}}} + \frac{\overset{130}{\cancel{1,170}}}{\underset{17}{\cancel{153}}} + \frac{\overset{39}{\cancel{234}}}{\underset{17}{\cancel{102}}} + \frac{\overset{585}{\cancel{1,170}}}{\underset{102}{\cancel{204}}} = \frac{13}{2}$$

$$-\frac{156}{17} + \frac{130}{17} + \frac{39}{17} + \frac{585}{102} = \frac{13}{2}$$

$$\frac{13}{17} + \frac{\overset{195}{\cancel{585}}}{\underset{34}{\cancel{102}}} = \frac{13}{2}$$

$$\frac{26}{34} + \frac{195}{34} = \frac{13}{2}$$

$$\frac{221}{34} = \frac{13}{2}$$

$$\frac{13}{2} = \frac{13}{2}$$

3.6
$$\frac{x-4}{4} + \frac{3x+5}{2} = 12$$

$$4(\tfrac{x-4}{4}) + 4(\tfrac{3x+5}{2}) = 4(12)$$
$$x - 4 + 6x + 10 = 48$$
$$7x + 6 = 48$$
$$7x = 42$$
$$x = 6$$

Check:
$$\frac{6-4}{4} + \frac{3(6)+5}{2} = 12$$

$$\frac{2}{4} + \frac{23}{2} = 12$$

$$\frac{1}{2} + \frac{23}{2} = 12$$

$$\frac{24}{2} = 12$$

$$12 = 12$$

3.7
$$\frac{3a}{10} + 8 = \frac{5(a+8)}{12}$$

$$60(\tfrac{3a}{10}) + 60(8) = 60\tfrac{5(a+8)}{12}$$
$$6(3a) + 60(8) = 5(5a + 40)$$
$$18a + 480 = 25a + 200$$
$$480 = 7a + 200$$
$$280 = 7a$$
$$a = 40$$

Check:
$$\frac{3(40)}{10} + 8 = \frac{5(40+8)}{12}$$

$$\frac{\overset{12}{\cancel{120}}}{\underset{1}{\cancel{10}}} + 8 = \frac{5(\overset{4}{\cancel{48}})}{\underset{1}{\cancel{12}}}$$

$$12 + 8 = 20$$
$$20 = 20$$

3.8
$$\frac{10-x}{2} = \frac{5}{2} + \frac{5-x}{3}$$

$$6(\tfrac{10-x}{2}) = 6(\tfrac{5}{2}) + 6(\tfrac{5-x}{3})$$
$$30 - 3x = 15 + 10 - 2x$$
$$30 = x + 25$$
$$x = 5$$

Check:
$$\frac{10-5}{2} = \frac{5}{2} + \frac{5-5}{3}$$

$$\frac{5}{2} = \frac{5}{2} + 0$$

$$\frac{5}{2} = \frac{5}{2}$$

3.9
$$\frac{3a}{4} = \frac{13}{3} - \frac{a}{3}$$

$$12(\tfrac{3a}{4}) = 12(\tfrac{13}{3}) - 12(\tfrac{a}{3})$$
$$9a = 52 - 4a$$
$$13a = 52$$
$$a = 4$$

Check:
$$\frac{3(4)}{4} = \frac{13}{3} - \frac{4}{3}$$

$$\frac{12}{4} = \frac{13}{3} - \frac{4}{3}$$

$$\frac{12}{4} = \frac{9}{3}$$

$$3 = 3$$

3.10
$$\frac{a-1}{2} = \frac{a+2}{3}$$
$$3a - 3 = 2a + 4 \qquad \text{(cross-multiply)}$$
$$a - 3 = 4$$
$$a = 7$$
Check:
$$\frac{7-1}{2} = \frac{7+2}{3}$$

$$\frac{6}{2} = \frac{9}{3}$$
$$3 = 3$$

3.11
$$\frac{a}{3} - \frac{9}{2} = 2a + 1$$

$$6(\tfrac{a}{3}) - 6(\tfrac{9}{2}) = 6(2a + 1)$$

$$2a - 27 = 12a + 6$$
$$-27 = 10a + 6$$
$$-33 = 10a$$
$$a = -\frac{33}{10}$$

Check:

$$\frac{-\frac{33}{10} - \frac{9}{2}}{3} = 2(-\frac{33}{10}) + 1$$

$$\frac{-\frac{33}{30} - \frac{9}{2}}{} = -\frac{33}{5} + 1$$

$$\frac{-11}{10} - \frac{45}{10} = -\frac{28}{5}$$

$$-\frac{56}{10} = -\frac{28}{5}$$

$$-\frac{28}{5} = -\frac{28}{5}$$

3.12

$$9(\frac{15x}{4} - 2) = 15x - \frac{21}{2}$$

$$4[9(\frac{15x}{4} - 2)] = 4(15x - \frac{21}{2})$$

$$9(15x - 8) = 60x - 42$$

$$135x - 72 = 60x - 42$$

$$75x - 72 = -42$$

$$75x = 30$$

$$x = \frac{30}{75} = \frac{2}{5}$$

Check:

$$9(\frac{15 \cdot \frac{2}{5}}{4} - 2) = 15(\frac{2}{5}) - \frac{21}{2}$$

$$9(\frac{6}{4} - 2) = 3(2) - \frac{21}{2}$$

$$9(\frac{3}{2} - 2) = 6 - \frac{21}{2}$$

$$9(-\frac{1}{2}) = \frac{12}{2} - \frac{21}{2}$$

$$-\frac{9}{2} = -\frac{9}{2}$$

3.13

$$\frac{3x - 1}{3} - \frac{x - 3}{15} = \frac{2x + 3}{2}$$

$$30(\frac{3x - 1}{3}) - 30(\frac{x - 3}{15}) = 30(\frac{2x + 3}{2})$$

$$10(3x - 1) - 2(x - 3) = 15(2x + 3)$$

$$30x - 10 - 2x + 6 = 30x + 45$$

$$28x - 4 = 30x + 45$$

$$-2x - 4 = 45$$

$$-2x = 49$$

$$x = -\frac{49}{2}$$

Check:

$$\frac{3(-\frac{49}{2}) - 1}{3} - \frac{-\frac{49}{2} - 3}{15} = \frac{2(-\frac{49}{2}) + 3}{2}$$

$$\frac{-\frac{147}{2} - 1}{3} + \frac{49 + 6}{30} = \frac{-49 + 3}{2}$$

$$\frac{-147 - 2}{6} + \frac{55}{30} = -\frac{46}{2}$$

$$-\frac{149}{6} + \frac{11}{6} = -\frac{46}{2}$$

$$\frac{-149 + 11}{6} = -23$$

$$-\frac{138}{6} = -23$$

$$-23 = -23$$

3.14

$$20 + \frac{3}{4}(12 - y) = \frac{3}{2}y - 20$$

$$4(20) + 4[\frac{3}{4}(12 - y)] = 4(\frac{3}{2}y) - 4(10)$$

$$80 + 3(12 - y) = 2(3y) - 40$$

$$80 + 36 - 3y = 6y - 40$$

$$116 - 3y = 6y - 40$$

$$156 - 3y = 6y$$

$$156 = 9y$$

$$y = \frac{156}{9} = \frac{52}{3}$$

Check:

$$20 + \frac{3}{4}(12 - \frac{52}{3}) = \frac{3}{2}(\frac{52}{3}) - 10$$

$$20 + 9 - 13 = 26 - 10$$

$$29 - 13 = 16$$

$$16 = 16$$

3.15

$$\frac{3x - 14}{5} - \frac{5x - 6}{5} = \frac{4x + 7}{10} - \frac{5}{2}$$

$$10(\frac{3x - 14}{5}) - 10(\frac{5x - 6}{5}) = 10(\frac{4x + 7}{10}) - 10(\frac{5}{2})$$

$$2(3x - 14) - 2(5x - 6) = 4x + 7 - 5(5)$$

$$6x - 28 - 10x + 12 = 4x + 7 - 25$$

$$-4x - 16 = 4x - 18$$

$$-16 = 8x - 18$$

$$2 = 8x$$

$$x = \frac{1}{4}$$

Check:

$$\frac{3(\frac{1}{4}) - 14}{5} - \frac{5(\frac{1}{4}) - 6}{5} = \frac{4(\frac{1}{4}) + 7}{10} - \frac{5}{2}$$

$$\frac{\frac{3}{4} - \frac{56}{4}}{\frac{20}{4}} - \frac{\frac{5}{4} - \frac{24}{4}}{\frac{20}{4}} = \frac{1 + 7}{10} - \frac{5}{2}$$

$$\frac{3 - 56}{20} - \frac{5 - 24}{20} = \frac{8}{10} - \frac{5}{2}$$

$$\frac{-53}{20} - (\frac{-19}{20}) = \frac{8}{10} - \frac{25}{10}$$

$$\frac{-53}{20} + \frac{19}{20} = -\frac{17}{10}$$

$$-\frac{34}{20} = -\frac{17}{10}$$

$$-\frac{17}{10} = -\frac{17}{10}$$

3.16

$$\frac{5}{a} + \frac{1}{2} = \frac{6}{a}$$

$$LCD = 2a$$

$$2a(\frac{5}{a}) + 2a(\frac{1}{2}) = 2a(\frac{6}{a})$$

$$10 + a = 12$$

$$a = 2$$

Check:

$$\frac{5}{2} + \frac{1}{2} = \frac{6}{2}$$

$$\frac{6}{2} = \frac{6}{2}$$

3.17

$$\frac{1}{y-2} = \frac{2}{y+1}$$

$$\text{LCD} = (y-2)(y+1)$$

$$1(y+1) = 2(y-2)$$

$$y+1 = 2y-4$$

$$y+5 = 2y$$

$$5 = y$$

Check:

$$\frac{1}{5-2} = \frac{2}{5+1}$$

$$\frac{1}{3} = \frac{2}{6}$$

$$\frac{1}{3} = \frac{1}{3}$$

3.18

$$\frac{5}{2x+6} - 2 = \frac{1-8x}{4x}$$

$$\frac{5}{2(x+3)} - 2 = \frac{1-8x}{4x}$$

$$\text{LCD} = 4x(x+3)$$

$$\frac{5\cancel{(4x)}(x+3)}{\cancel{2(x+3)}} - 2(4x)(x+3) = \frac{(1-8x)\cancel{(4x)}(x+3)}{\cancel{4x}}$$

$$10x - 8x^2 - 24x = 3 - 23x - 8x^2$$

$$-14x = 3 - 23x$$

$$9x = 3$$

$$x = \frac{1}{3}$$

Check:

$$\frac{5}{2\left(\frac{1}{3}\right)+6} - 2 = \frac{1-8\left(\frac{1}{3}\right)}{\frac{4}{3}}$$

$$\frac{5}{\frac{2}{3}+6} - 2 = \frac{1-\frac{8}{3}}{\frac{4}{3}}$$

$$\frac{\frac{15}{3}}{\frac{2}{3}+\frac{18}{3}} - 2 = \frac{\frac{3}{3}-\frac{8}{3}}{\frac{4}{3}}$$

$$\frac{15}{2+18} - 2 = \frac{3-8}{4}$$

$$\frac{3}{4} - 2 = -\frac{5}{4}$$

$$-\frac{5}{4} = -\frac{5}{4}$$

3.19

$$\frac{1}{2} = \frac{14}{6x-2} - \frac{6}{3x-1}$$

$$\frac{1}{2} = \frac{14}{2(3x-1)} - \frac{6}{3x-1}$$

$$\text{LCD} = 2(3x-1)$$

$$1(3x-1) = 14 - 2(6)$$

$$3x-1 = 14-12$$

$$3x = 3$$

$$x = 1$$

Check:

$$\frac{1}{2} = \frac{14}{4} - \frac{6}{2}$$

$$\frac{1}{2} = \frac{7}{2} - \frac{6}{2}$$

$$\frac{1}{2} = \frac{1}{2}$$

3.20

$$\frac{5y}{y-1} + \frac{4y^2+13}{y^2-y} = \frac{y+4}{y}$$

$$\text{LCD} = y(y-1)$$

$$\frac{5y(y)}{(y-1)y} + \frac{4y^2+13}{y(y-1)} = \frac{(y+4)(y-1)}{y(y-1)}$$

$$5y^2 + 4y^2 + 13 = y^2 + 3y - 4$$

$$9y^2 + 13 = y^2 + 3y - 4$$

$$8y^2 + 13 = 3y - 4$$

$$8y^2 - 3y + 13 = -4$$

$$8y^2 - 3y + 17 = 0$$

$$y = \frac{3 \pm \sqrt{(-3)^2 - 4(8)(17)}}{2(8)}$$

$$y = \frac{3 \pm \sqrt{9 - 544}}{16}$$

∴ No real-number solution exists.

3.21

$$\frac{2a-2}{a-3} - \frac{a-3}{a-2} = \frac{a^2-8a+27}{a^2-5a+6}$$

$$\text{LCD} = (a-3)(a-2)$$

$$(2a-2)(a-2) - (a-3)^2 = a^2 - 8a + 27$$

$$2a^2 - 6a + 4 - (a^2 - 6a + 9) = a^2 - 8a + 27$$

$$\cancel{2a^2} - \cancel{6a} + 4 - \cancel{a^2} + \cancel{6a} - 9 = \cancel{a^2} - 8a + 27$$

$$-5 = -8a + 27$$

$$8a - 5 = 27$$

$$8a = 32$$

$$a = 4$$

Check:

$$\frac{2(4)-2}{4-3} - \frac{4-3}{4-2} = \frac{4^2-8(4)+27}{4^2-5(4)+6}$$

$$\frac{8-2}{1} - \frac{1}{2} = \frac{16-32+27}{16-20+6}$$

$$6 - \frac{1}{2} = \frac{11}{2}$$

$$\frac{11}{2} = \frac{11}{2}$$

3.22

$$\frac{1}{a+3} - \frac{4}{a-3} = \frac{2a}{a^2-9}$$

$$\frac{1}{(a+3)} - \frac{4}{(a-3)} = \frac{2a}{(a+3)(a-3)}$$

$$\text{LCD} = (a+3)(a-3)$$

$$1(a-3) - 4(a+3) = 2a$$

$$a - 3 - 4a - 12 = 2a$$

$$-3a - 15 = 2a$$

$$-5a - 15 = 0$$

$$-5a = 15$$

$$a = -3$$

Check:

$$\frac{1}{-3+3} - \frac{4}{-3-3} = \frac{2(-3)}{3^2-9}$$

$$\frac{1}{0} - \frac{4}{-6} = \frac{-6}{0}$$

∴ $a = -3$ is an extraneous root.

3.23 $\dfrac{4}{3a-5} + \dfrac{3a^2+38a+36}{25a-9a^3} = \dfrac{3}{3a+5}$

$\dfrac{4}{3a-5} + \dfrac{3a^2+38a+36}{a(5-3a)(5+3a)} = \dfrac{3}{3a+5}$

LCD $= a(5-3a)(5+3a)$

$-4a(3a+5) + 3a^2 + 38a + 36 = 3a(5-3a)$

$-12a^2 - 20a + 3a^2 + 38a + 36 = 15a - 9a^2$

$18a + 36 = 15a$

$3a + 36 = 0$

$3a = -36$

$a = -12$

Check:

$\dfrac{4}{3(-12)-5} + \dfrac{3(-12)+38(-12)+36}{25(-12)-9(-12)^3} = \dfrac{3}{3(-12)+5}$

$\dfrac{4}{-41} + \dfrac{3(144)-456+36}{-300-9(-1,728)} = \dfrac{3}{-31}$

$-\dfrac{4}{41} + \dfrac{12}{15,252} = -\dfrac{3}{31}$

$-\dfrac{4}{41} + \dfrac{1}{1,271} = -\dfrac{3}{31}$

$\dfrac{-124+1}{1,271} = -\dfrac{3}{31}$

$\dfrac{-123}{1,271} = -\dfrac{3}{31}$

Cross products are $-3,813 = -3,813$

3.24 $\dfrac{a^2+1}{a^2-1} - \dfrac{2}{a+1} = \dfrac{a}{a-1}$

LCD $= (a+1)(a-1)$

$a^2 + 1 - 2(a-1) = a(a+1)$

$a^2 + 1 - 2a + 2 = a^2 + a$

$-2a + 3 = a$

$-3a + 3 = 0$

$-3a = -3$

$a = 1$

Check:

$\dfrac{1^2+1}{1^2-1} - \dfrac{2}{1+1} = \dfrac{1}{1-1}$

$\dfrac{2}{0} - \dfrac{2}{2} = \dfrac{1}{0}$

∴ $a = 1$ is an extraneous root.

3.25 $\dfrac{2}{a+3} - \dfrac{a^2+3a-10}{a^3+5a^2+6a} = \dfrac{a-4}{a^2+3a}$

$\dfrac{2}{a+3} - \dfrac{a^2+3a-10}{a(a^2+5a+6)} = \dfrac{a-4}{a(a+3)}$

$\dfrac{2}{a+3} - \dfrac{a^2+3a-10}{a(a+2)(a+3)} = \dfrac{a-4}{a(a+3)}$

LCD $= a(a+2)(a+3)$

$2(a)(a+2) - (a^2+3a-10) = (a-4)(a+2)$

$2a^2 + 4a - a^2 - 3a + 10 = a^2 - 2a - 8$

$a + 10 = -2a - 8$

$3a + 10 = -8$

$3a = -18$

$a = -6$

Check:

$\dfrac{2}{-6+3} - \dfrac{(-6)^2+3(-6)-10}{(-6)^3+5(-6)^2+6(-6)} = \dfrac{-6-4}{(-6)^2+3(-6)}$

$\dfrac{2}{-3} - \dfrac{36-18-10}{-216+180-36} = \dfrac{-10}{36-18}$

$-\dfrac{2}{3} - \dfrac{8}{-72} = -\dfrac{10}{18}$

$-\dfrac{2}{3} + \dfrac{1}{9} = -\dfrac{5}{9}$

$-\dfrac{5}{9} = -\dfrac{5}{9}$

3.26 $\dfrac{2}{3} + \dfrac{1}{2\frac{2}{5}} - \dfrac{1}{x} = \dfrac{1}{3} - \dfrac{1}{2\frac{2}{3}}$

$\dfrac{2}{3} + \dfrac{1}{\frac{12}{5}} - \dfrac{1}{x} = \dfrac{1}{3} - \dfrac{1}{\frac{8}{3}}$

$\dfrac{2}{3} + \dfrac{5}{12} - \dfrac{1}{x} = \dfrac{1}{3} - \dfrac{3}{8}$

LCD $= 24x$

$16x + 10x - 24 = 8x - 9x$

$26x - 24 = -x$

$26x = -x + 24$

$27x = 24$

$x = \dfrac{24}{27} = \dfrac{8}{9}$

Check:

$\dfrac{2}{3} + \dfrac{5}{12} - \dfrac{9}{8} = \dfrac{1}{3} - \dfrac{3}{8}$

LCD $= 24$

$\dfrac{16}{24} + \dfrac{10}{24} - \dfrac{27}{24} = \dfrac{8}{24} - \dfrac{9}{24}$

$-\dfrac{1}{24} = -\dfrac{1}{24}$

3.27 $\dfrac{5}{4} = 4\left(\dfrac{1}{12} + \dfrac{1}{x}\right) - \dfrac{1}{2}$

$\dfrac{5}{4} = \dfrac{1}{3} + \dfrac{4}{x} - \dfrac{1}{2}$

LCD $= 12x$

$15x = 4x + 48 - 6x$

$15x = -2x + 48$

$17x = 48$

$x = \dfrac{48}{17}$

Check:

$\dfrac{5}{4} = 4\left(\dfrac{1}{12} + \dfrac{17}{48}\right) - \dfrac{1}{2}$

$\dfrac{5}{4} = \dfrac{16}{48} + \dfrac{68}{48} - \dfrac{24}{48}$

$\dfrac{5}{4} = \dfrac{60}{48}$

$\dfrac{5}{4} = \dfrac{5}{4}$

3.28

$$\frac{1}{y^2 - y - 2} - \frac{2}{y - 2} = \frac{1}{y + 1}$$

$$\frac{1}{(y - 2)(y + 1)} - \frac{2}{y - 2} = \frac{1}{y + 1}$$

$$1 - 2(y + 1) = 1(y - 2)$$
$$1 - 2y - 2 = y - 2$$
$$-2y - 1 = y - 2$$
$$-2y + 1 = y$$
$$1 = 3y$$
$$y = \frac{1}{3}$$

Check:

$$\frac{1}{(\frac{1}{3})^2 - \frac{1}{3} - 2} - \frac{2}{\frac{1}{3} - 2} = \frac{1}{\frac{1}{3} + 1}$$

$$\frac{1}{\frac{1}{9} - \frac{1}{3} - 2} - \frac{2}{\frac{1}{3} - 2} = \frac{1}{\frac{1}{3} + 1}$$

$$\frac{\frac{9}{9}}{\frac{1}{9} - \frac{3}{9} - \frac{18}{9}} - \frac{\frac{6}{3}}{\frac{1}{3} - \frac{6}{3}} = \frac{\frac{3}{3}}{\frac{1}{3} + \frac{3}{3}}$$

$$\frac{9}{1 - 3 - 18} - \frac{6}{1 - 6} = \frac{3}{1 + 3}$$

$$-\frac{9}{20} - \frac{6}{-5} = \frac{3}{4}$$

$$-\frac{9}{20} + \frac{24}{20} = \frac{3}{4}$$

$$\frac{15}{20} = \frac{3}{4}$$

$$\frac{3}{4} = \frac{3}{4}$$

3.29

$$\frac{y - \frac{1}{2}}{3} - \frac{2y + 2}{2y + 1} = \frac{2y + \frac{1}{2}}{6}$$

$$LCD = 6(2y + 1)$$

$$2(2y + 1)(y - \frac{1}{2}) - (12y + 12) = (2y + \frac{1}{2})(2y + 1)$$

$$4y^2 - 1 - 12y - 12 = 4y^2 + 3y + \frac{1}{2}$$

$$-12y - 13 = 3y + \frac{1}{2}$$

$$-15y - 13 = \frac{1}{2}$$

$$-15y = \frac{27}{2}$$

$$y = \frac{27}{2} \cdot (-\frac{1}{15}) = -\frac{9}{10}$$

Check:

$$\frac{-\frac{9}{10} - \frac{1}{2}}{3} - \frac{2(-\frac{9}{10}) + 2}{2(-\frac{9}{10}) + 1} = \frac{2(-\frac{9}{10}) + \frac{1}{2}}{6}$$

$$\frac{-\frac{9}{10} - \frac{5}{10}}{\frac{30}{10}} - \frac{-\frac{18}{10} + \frac{20}{10}}{-\frac{18}{10} + \frac{10}{10}} = \frac{-\frac{18}{10} + \frac{5}{10}}{\frac{60}{10}}$$

$$\frac{-9 - 5}{30} - \frac{-18 + 20}{-18 + 10} = \frac{-18 + 5}{60}$$

$$-\frac{14}{30} - \frac{2}{-8} = \frac{-13}{60}$$

$$-\frac{28}{60} + \frac{15}{60} = -\frac{13}{60}$$

$$-\frac{13}{60} = -\frac{13}{60}$$

3.30

$$a - \frac{3a - 6}{6} = \frac{3a + 2}{3}$$

$$LCD = 6$$
$$6a - (3a - 6) = 2(3a + 2)$$
$$6a - 3a + 6 = 6a + 4$$
$$-3a = -2$$
$$a = \frac{2}{3}$$

Check:

$$\frac{2}{3} - \frac{3(\frac{2}{3}) - 6}{6} = \frac{3(\frac{2}{3}) + 2}{3}$$

$$\frac{2}{3} - \frac{2 - 6}{6} = \frac{2 + 2}{3}$$

$$\frac{2}{3} - \frac{-4}{6} = \frac{4}{3}$$

$$\frac{2}{3} + \frac{4}{6} = \frac{4}{3}$$

$$\frac{4}{3} = \frac{4}{3}$$

3.31

$$\frac{x - 2}{x + 3} = \frac{3}{8}$$

$$8(x - 2) = 3(x + 3)$$
$$8x - 16 = 3x + 9$$
$$5x - 16 = 9$$
$$5x = 25$$
$$x = 5$$

3.32

$$\frac{2}{x + 1} = \frac{1}{x - 2}$$

$$2(x - 2) = 1(x + 1)$$
$$2x - 4 = x + 1$$
$$x - 4 = 1$$
$$x = 5$$

3.33

$$\frac{2y + 5}{5} = \frac{3y + 11}{4}$$

$$4(2y + 5) = 5(3y + 11)$$
$$8y + 20 = 15y + 55$$
$$-7y + 20 = 55$$
$$-7y = 35$$
$$y = -5$$

3.34

$$\frac{3}{x - 3} = \frac{5}{2x - 7}$$

$$3(2x - 7) = 5(x - 3)$$
$$6x - 21 = 5x - 15$$
$$x - 21 = -15$$
$$x = 6$$

3.35

$$\frac{3}{y + 1} = \frac{5}{y + 3}$$

$$3(y + 3) = 5(y + 1)$$
$$3y + 9 = 5y + 5$$
$$-2y + 9 = 5$$
$$-2y = -4$$
$$y = 2$$

3.36
$$\frac{3x - 1}{9x - 5} = \frac{x + 1}{3x + 1}$$
$$(3x - 1)(3x + 1) = (9x - 5)(x + 1)$$
$$9x^2 - 1 = 9x^2 + 4x - 5$$
$$-1 - 4x = -5$$
$$-4x = -4$$
$$x = 1$$

3.37
$$\frac{6x - 2}{9x} = \frac{2x - 1}{3x + 1}$$
$$(6x - 2)(3x + 1) = 9x(2x - 1)$$
$$18x^2 - 2 = 18x^2 - 9x$$
$$9x = 2$$
$$x = \frac{2}{9}$$

3.38
$$\frac{3}{x^2 + 4x + 4} = \frac{3}{x^2 + 8}$$
$$3(x^2 + 8) = 3(x^2 + 4x + 4)$$
$$3x^2 + 24 = 3x^2 + 12x + 12$$
$$12 = 12x$$
$$x = 1$$

3.39
$$\frac{6y^2 - 2y + 5}{4} = \frac{3y^2 - 2}{2}$$
$$2(6y^2 - 2y + 5) = 4(3y^2 - 2)$$
$$12y^2 - 4y + 10 = 12y^2 - 8$$
$$-4y = -18$$
$$y = \frac{-18}{-4} = \frac{9}{2}$$

3.40
$$\frac{3x - 12}{3x} = \frac{4x^2 - 9}{4x^2 - 16x + 15}$$
$$\frac{\overset{1}{\cancel{3}}(x - 4)}{\underset{1}{\cancel{3}x}} = \frac{(2x + 3)\cancel{(2x - 3)}}{(2x - 5)\cancel{(2x - 3)}}$$
$$(x - 4)(2x - 5) = x(2x + 3)$$
$$2x^2 - 13x + 20 = 2x^2 + 3x$$
$$-16x + 20 = 0$$
$$-16x = -20$$
$$x = \frac{-20}{-16} = \frac{5}{4}$$

SELF TEST 3

3.01
$$\frac{a^4 b^3 \cdot \frac{1}{c^2}}{a^2 \cdot \frac{1}{b} \cdot 1} = \frac{a^4 b^3 \cdot b}{a^2 \cdot c^2} = \frac{a^4 b^4}{a^2 c^2} = \frac{a^2 b^4}{c^2}$$

3.02
$$\frac{2a^2 - 7a - 15}{3a^2 - 8a - 3} \cdot \frac{9a^2 - 1}{4a^2 - 9} \cdot \frac{2a^2 - 9a + 9}{a^2 + 3a - 10} =$$
$$\frac{\overset{1}{\cancel{(2a + 3)}}(a - 5)}{\underset{1}{\cancel{(3a + 1)}}\cancel{(a - 3)}} \cdot \frac{\overset{1}{\cancel{(3a + 1)}}(3a - 1)}{\cancel{(2a + 3)}\underset{1}{\cancel{(2a - 3)}}} \cdot \frac{\overset{1}{\cancel{(2a - 3)}}\overset{1}{\cancel{(a - 3)}}}{(a - 2)(a + 5)} =$$
$$\frac{(a - 5)(3a - 1)}{(a - 2)(a + 5)}$$

3.03 LCD = $x^3 - 1$
$$\frac{3x^2(x - 1)}{(x - 1)(x^2 + x + 1)} - \frac{x^3}{(x - 1)(x^2 + x + 1)} - \frac{2x(x^2 + x + 1)}{(x - 1)(x^2 + x + 1)} =$$
$$\frac{3x^3 - 3x^2 - x^3 - (2x^3 + 2x^2 + 2x)}{(x - 1)(x^2 + x + 1)} =$$
$$\frac{\cancel{2x^3} - 3x^2 - \cancel{2x^3} - 2x^2 - 2x}{x^3 - 1} = \frac{-5x^2 - 2x}{x^3 - 1}$$

3.04
$$\frac{(1 - \frac{2x - 1}{x - 1})(x - 1)(x + 1)}{(1 - \frac{1}{x + 1})(x - 1)(x + 1)} =$$
$$\frac{(x - 1)(x + 1) - (2x - 1)(x + 1)}{(x - 1)(x + 1) - 1(x - 1)} = \frac{x^2 - 1 - (2x^2 + x - 1)}{x^2 - 1 - x + 1} =$$
$$\frac{x^2 - \cancel{1} - 2x^2 - x + \cancel{1}}{x^2 - x} = \frac{-x^2 - x}{x^2 - x} = \frac{\cancel{x}(-x - 1)}{\underset{1}{\cancel{x}}(x - 1)}$$

3.05 b

3.06 a

3.07 c

3.08 LCD = $12(2x + 1)$
$$\frac{2x - 1}{6} = \frac{4x + 1}{12} + \frac{2x + 2}{2x + 1}$$
$$2(2x - 1)(2x + 1) = (4x + 1)(2x + 1) + 12(2x + 2)$$
$$8x^2 - 2 = 8x^2 + 6x + 1 + 24x + 24$$
$$\cancel{8x^2} - 2 = \cancel{8x^2} + 30x + 25$$
$$0 = 30x + 27$$
$$-30x = 27$$
$$x = \frac{27}{-30} = -\frac{9}{10}$$

Check:
$$\frac{2(-\frac{9}{10}) - 1}{6} = \frac{4(-\frac{9}{10}) + 1}{12} + \frac{2(-\frac{9}{10}) + 2}{2(-\frac{9}{10}) + 1}$$

$$\frac{-\frac{9}{5} - 1}{6} = \frac{-\frac{18}{5} + 1}{12} + \frac{-\frac{9}{5} + 2}{-\frac{9}{5} + 1}$$

$$\frac{-\frac{9}{5} - \frac{5}{5}}{\frac{30}{5}} = \frac{-\frac{18}{5} + \frac{5}{5}}{\frac{60}{5}} + \frac{-\frac{9}{5} + \frac{10}{5}}{-\frac{9}{5} + \frac{5}{5}}$$

$$\frac{-9 - 5}{30} = \frac{-18 + 5}{60} + \frac{-9 + 10}{-9 + 5}$$

$$\frac{-14}{30} = \frac{-13}{60} + \frac{1}{-4}$$

$$-\frac{28}{60} = -\frac{13}{60} - \frac{15}{60}$$

$$-\frac{28}{60} = -\frac{28}{60}$$

3.09 LCD = 6

$$\frac{a}{6} - 10 = \frac{a}{3}$$
$$a - 6(10) = 2(a)$$
$$a - 60 = 2a$$
$$-60 = a$$

Check:

$$\frac{-60}{6} - 10 = \frac{-60}{3}$$
$$-10 - 10 = -20$$
$$-20 = -20$$

3.010 LCD = 6

$$\frac{2a}{3} - \frac{3a}{2} = -\frac{5}{2}$$
$$2(2a) - 3(3a) = 3(-5)$$
$$4a - 9a = -15$$
$$-5a = -15$$
$$a = 3$$

Check:

$$\frac{2(3)}{3} - \frac{3(3)}{2} = -\frac{5}{2}$$
$$2 - \frac{9}{2} = -\frac{5}{2}$$
$$\frac{4}{2} - \frac{9}{2} = -\frac{5}{2}$$
$$-\frac{5}{2} = -\frac{5}{2}$$

3.011 LCD = 35

$$\frac{5x}{7} - \frac{7x}{5} = \frac{24}{35}$$
$$5(5x) - 7(7x) = 24$$
$$25x - 49x = 24$$
$$-24x = 24$$
$$x = -1$$

Check:

$$\frac{5(-1)}{7} - \frac{7(-1)}{5} = \frac{24}{35}$$
$$-\frac{5}{7} + \frac{7}{5} = \frac{24}{35}$$
$$-\frac{25}{35} + \frac{49}{35} = \frac{24}{35}$$
$$\frac{24}{35} = \frac{24}{35}$$

3.012 LCD = 20

$$\frac{4a}{5} + \frac{3}{2} - \frac{a}{4} = \frac{7a}{10}$$
$$4(4a) + 10(3) - 5(a) = 2(7a)$$
$$16a + 30 - 5a = 14a$$
$$11a + 30 = 14a$$
$$30 = 3a$$
$$10 = a$$

Check:

$$\frac{4(10)}{5} + \frac{3}{2} - \frac{10}{4} = \frac{7(10)}{10}$$
$$8 + \frac{3}{2} - \frac{5}{2} = 7$$
$$8 - \frac{2}{2} = 7$$
$$8 - 1 = 7$$
$$7 = 7$$

3.013 LCD = 6x

$$\frac{5}{x} - \frac{3}{2x} = \frac{7}{6}$$
$$6(5) - 3(3) = x(7)$$
$$30 - 9 = 7x$$
$$21 = 7x$$
$$3 = x$$

Check:

$$\frac{5}{3} - \frac{3}{2(3)} = \frac{7}{6}$$
$$\frac{5}{3} - \frac{1}{2} = \frac{7}{6}$$
$$\frac{10}{6} - \frac{3}{6} = \frac{7}{6}$$
$$\frac{7}{6} = \frac{7}{6}$$

3.014 LCD = $x(x + 2)(x - 3)$

$$\frac{1}{x} = \frac{3}{x + 2} - \frac{2}{x - 3}$$
$$1(x + 2)(x - 3) = 3(x)(x - 3) - 2(x)(x + 2)$$
$$x^2 - x - 6 = 3x^2 - 9x - 2x^2 - 4x$$
$$-x - 6 = -13x$$
$$12x - 6 = 0$$
$$12x = 6$$
$$x = \frac{6}{12} = \frac{1}{2}$$

Check:

$$\frac{1}{\frac{1}{2}} = \frac{3}{\frac{1}{2} + 2} - \frac{2}{\frac{1}{2} - 3}$$
$$\frac{2}{1} = \frac{3}{\frac{5}{2}} - \frac{2}{-\frac{5}{2}}$$
$$2 = 3(\tfrac{2}{5}) - 2(-\tfrac{2}{5})$$
$$2 = \frac{6}{5} + \frac{4}{5}$$
$$2 = \frac{10}{5}$$
$$2 = 2$$

3.015

$$\frac{2}{2 - y} + \frac{3}{y + 2} = \frac{2y}{y^2 - 4}$$
$$-\frac{2}{y - 2} + \frac{3}{y + 2} = \frac{2y}{(y + 2)(y - 2)}$$

LCD = $(y + 2)(y - 2)$

$$-2(y + 2) + 3(y - 2) = 2y$$
$$-2y - 4 + 3y - 6 = 2y$$
$$y - 10 = 2y$$
$$-10 = y$$

Check:

$$\frac{2}{2 - (-10)} + \frac{3}{-10 + 2} = \frac{2(-10)}{(-10)^2 - 4}$$
$$\frac{2}{2 + 10} + \frac{3}{-8} = \frac{-20}{100 - 4}$$
$$\frac{2}{12} - \frac{3}{8} = -\frac{20}{96}$$
$$\frac{16}{96} - \frac{36}{96} = -\frac{20}{96}$$
$$-\frac{20}{96} = -\frac{20}{96}$$

3.016

$$\frac{3}{1-3x} + \frac{5}{2-x} + \frac{9-2x}{3x^2-7x+2} = 0$$

$$\frac{3}{1-3x} + \frac{5}{2-x} + \frac{9-2x}{(3x-1)(x-2)} = 0$$

LCD = $(3x-1)(x-2)$

$-3(x-2) - 5(3x-1) + 9 - 2x = 0$

$-3x + 6 - 15x + 5 + 9 - 2x = 0$

$-20x + 20 = 0$

$-20x = -20$

$x = 1$

Check:

$$\frac{3}{1-3(1)} + \frac{5}{2-1} + \frac{9-2(1)}{3(1)^2-7(1)+2} = 0$$

$$\frac{3}{1-3} + \frac{5}{1} + \frac{9-2}{3-7+2} = 0$$

$$\frac{3}{-2} + 5 + \frac{7}{-2} = 0$$

$$5 - \frac{10}{2} = 0$$

$$5 - 5 = 0$$

$$0 = 0$$

3.017

$$\frac{7}{a-2} = \frac{2}{3}$$

$3(7) = 2(a-2)$

$21 = 2a - 4$

$25 = 2a$

$$a = \frac{25}{2} \text{ or } 12\frac{1}{2}$$

Check:

$$\frac{7}{\frac{25}{2}-2} = \frac{2}{3}$$

$$\frac{\frac{14}{2}}{\frac{25}{2}-\frac{4}{2}} = \frac{2}{3}$$

$$\frac{14}{25-4} = \frac{2}{3}$$

$$\frac{14}{21} = \frac{2}{3}$$

$$\frac{2}{3} = \frac{2}{3}$$

3.018

$$\frac{2a+5}{5} = \frac{3a+11}{4}$$

$4(2a+5) = 5(3a+11)$

$8a + 20 = 15a + 55$

$-7a + 20 = 55$

$-7a = 35$

$a = -5$

Check:

$$\frac{2(-5)+5}{5} = \frac{3(-5)+11}{4}$$

$$\frac{-10+5}{5} = \frac{-15+11}{4}$$

$$\frac{-5}{5} = \frac{-4}{4}$$

$$-1 = -1$$

3.019

$$\frac{y-1}{y+3} = \frac{y+1}{y+10}$$

$(y-1)(y+10) = (y+3)(y+1)$

$y^2 + 9y - 10 = y^2 + 4y + 3$

$5y - 10 = 3$

$5y = 13$

$$y = \frac{13}{5}$$

Check:

$$\frac{\frac{13}{5}-1}{\frac{13}{5}+3} = \frac{\frac{13}{5}+1}{\frac{13}{5}+10}$$

$$\frac{\frac{13}{5}-\frac{5}{5}}{\frac{13}{5}+\frac{15}{5}} = \frac{\frac{13}{5}+\frac{5}{5}}{\frac{13}{5}+\frac{50}{5}}$$

$$\frac{13-5}{13+15} = \frac{13+5}{13+50}$$

$$\frac{8}{28} = \frac{18}{63}$$

$$\frac{2}{7} = \frac{2}{7}$$

3.020

$$\frac{6x+4}{4x-3} = \frac{3x+2}{2x+5}$$

$(6x+4)(2x+5) = (4x-3)(3x+2)$

$12x^2 + 38x + 20 = 12x^2 - x - 6$

$39x + 20 = -6$

$39x = -26$

$$x = \frac{-26}{39} = -\frac{2}{3}$$

Check:

$$\frac{6(-\frac{2}{3})+4}{4(-\frac{2}{3})-3} = \frac{3(-\frac{2}{3})+2}{2(-\frac{2}{3})+5}$$

$$\frac{-4+4}{-\frac{8}{3}-3} = \frac{-2+2}{-\frac{4}{3}+5}$$

$$\frac{0}{-\frac{8}{3}-3} = \frac{0}{-\frac{4}{3}+5}$$

$$0 = 0$$

SECTION 4

4.1

	r	t	d
First Automobile	$x + 10$	$\dfrac{320}{x + 10}$	320
Second Automobile	x	$\dfrac{240}{x}$	240

$$\frac{320}{x + 10} = \frac{240}{x}$$
$$320(x) = (x + 10)(240)$$
$$320x = 240x + 2{,}400$$
$$80x = 2{,}400$$
$$x = 30 \text{ mph}$$
$$x + 10 = 30 + 10 = 40 \text{ mph}$$

The first automobile travels 40 mph; the second automobile travels 30 mph.

Check:
$$240 \div 30 = 8 \text{ hrs.} \qquad 320 \div 40 = 8 \text{ hrs.}$$
$$30 \times 8 = 240 \text{ mi.} \qquad 40 \times 8 = 320 \text{ mi.}$$

4.2

	r	t	d
Freight Train	30	$\dfrac{x}{30}$	x
Express Train	55	$\dfrac{x + 300}{55}$	$x + 300$

$$\frac{x}{30} = \frac{x + 300}{55}$$
$$x(55) = 30(x + 300)$$
$$55x = 30x + 9{,}000$$
$$25x = 9{,}000$$
$$x = 360$$
$$\frac{360}{30} = \frac{360 + 300}{55}$$
$$\frac{360}{30} = \frac{660}{55}$$
$$12 = 12$$

Check:
$$12 \times 30 = 360 \text{ mi.} \qquad 12 \times 55 = 660 \text{ mi.}$$

The express train will overtake the freight train in 12 hours.

4.3

	r	t	d
With the wind	$180 + x$	$\dfrac{800}{180 + x}$	800
Against the wind	$180 - x$	$\dfrac{640}{180 - x}$	640

$$\frac{800}{180 + x} = \frac{640}{180 - x}$$
$$800(180 - x) = (180 + x)(640)$$
$$144{,}000 - 800x = 115{,}200 + 640x$$
$$28{,}800 - 800x = 640x$$
$$28{,}800 = 1{,}440x$$
$$x = 20 \text{ mph}$$

The wind is blowing at 20 mph.

Check:
$$\frac{800}{180 + 20} = \frac{600}{180 - 20}$$
$$\frac{800}{200} = \frac{640}{160}$$
$$4 = 4$$
$$200 \times 4 = 800 \text{ mi.} \qquad 160 \times 4 = 640 \text{ mi.}$$

4.4

	r	t	d
Upstream	$x - 3$	$\dfrac{36}{x - 3}$	36
Downstream	$x + 3$	$\dfrac{36}{x + 3}$	36

$$\frac{36}{x - 3} = 1 + \frac{36}{x + 3}$$

LCD $= (x - 3)(x + 3)$
$$36(x + 3) = 1(x - 3)(x + 3) + 36(x - 3)$$
$$36x + 108 = x^2 - 9 + 36x - 108$$
$$108 = x^2 - 117$$
$$x^2 = 225$$
$$\sqrt{x^2} = \sqrt{225}$$
$$x = 15 \text{ mph}$$

The speed of the boat in still water is 15 mph.

Check:
$$\frac{36}{15 - 3} = 1 + \frac{36}{15 + 3}$$
$$\frac{36}{12} = 1 + \frac{36}{18}$$
$$3 = 1 + 2$$
$$3 = 3$$

$$\begin{array}{r} 12 \text{ mph} \\ \times\ 3 \text{ hrs.} \\ \hline 36 \text{ mi.} \end{array} \qquad \begin{array}{r} 18 \text{ mph} \\ \times\ 2 \text{ hrs.} \\ \hline 36 \text{ mi.} \end{array}$$

4.5

	r	t	d
With the wind	$120 + x$	$\dfrac{640}{120 + x}$	640
Against the wind	$120 - x$	$\dfrac{320}{120 - x}$	320

$$\frac{640}{120 + x} = \frac{320}{120 - x}$$

$(120 + x)(320) = 640(120 - x)$
$120 + x = 2(120 - x)$
$120 + x = 240 - 2x$
$x = 120 - 2x$
$3x = 120$
$x = 40$ mph

The rate of the wind is 40 mph.
Check:

$$\frac{640}{120 + 40} = \frac{320}{120 - 40}$$

$$\frac{640}{160} = \frac{320}{80}$$

$$4 = 4$$

$160 \times 4 = 640$ mi. $80 \times 4 = 320$ mi.

4.6

	r	t	d
Upstream	$15 - x$	$\dfrac{35}{15 - x}$	35
Downstream	$15 + x$	$\dfrac{140}{15 + x}$	140

$$\frac{35}{15 - x} = \frac{140}{15 + x}$$

$35(15 + x) = (15 - x)(140)$
$525 + 35x = 2{,}100 - 140x$
$35x = 1{,}575 - 140x$
$175x = 1{,}575$
$x = 9$ km/hr.
$15 + x = 15 + 9 = 24$ km/hr.
downstream

The speed of the boat is 24 km/hr. downstream.
Check:

$$\frac{35}{15 - 9} = \frac{140}{15 + 9}$$

$$\frac{35}{6} = \frac{140}{24}$$

$$\frac{35}{6} = \frac{35}{6}$$

4.7

	r	t	d
Joe	8	$\dfrac{x}{8}$	x
Ron	4	$\dfrac{44 - x}{4}$	$44 - x$

$$\frac{x}{8} = \frac{44 - x}{4} + \frac{1}{4}$$

LCD = 8

$x = 2(44 - x) + 2(1)$
$x = 88 - 2x + 2$
$x = 90 - 2x$
$3x = 90$
$x = 30$ miles
$44 - x = 44 - 30 = 14$ miles

Joe travels 30 miles; Ron travels 14 miles.
Check:

$$\frac{30}{8} = \frac{44 - 30}{4} + \frac{1}{4}$$

$$\frac{30}{8} = \frac{14}{4} + \frac{1}{4}$$

$$\frac{15}{4} = \frac{15}{4}$$

$8 \times 3\frac{3}{4} = 30$ mi. $4 \times 3\frac{1}{2} = 14$ mi.

4.8

	r	t	d
Out	4	x	$4x$
Return	2	$1\frac{1}{2} - x$	$3 - 2x$

$4x = 3 - 2x$
$6x = 3$
$x = \dfrac{1}{2}$

Roger paddles 4 kilometers.
Distance paddled $= 4x + 3 - 2x$
$\qquad\qquad\quad = 4(\frac{1}{2}) + 3 - 2(\frac{1}{2})$
$\qquad\qquad\quad = 2 + 3 - 1$
$\qquad\qquad\quad = 4$ kilometers

Check:

$4(\frac{1}{2}) = 3 - 2(\frac{1}{2})$
$\quad 2 = 3 - 1$
$\quad 2 = 2$

4.9

	r	t	d
Downstream	$x + 1.5$	$\dfrac{0.9}{x + 1.5}$	0.9
Upstream	$x - 1.5$	$\dfrac{0.6}{x - 1.5}$	0.6

$$\frac{0.9}{x + 1.5} = \frac{0.6}{x - 1.5}$$
$$\frac{9}{10x + 15} = \frac{6}{10x - 15}$$
$$9(10x - 15) = (10x + 15)(6)$$
$$90x - 135 = 60x + 90$$
$$30x - 135 = 90$$
$$30x = 225$$
$$x = 7.5 \text{ mph}$$

He can swim 7.5 mph in still water.

Check:
$$\frac{0.9}{7.5 + 1.5} = \frac{0.6}{7.5 - 1.5}$$
$$\frac{0.9}{9} = \frac{0.6}{6}$$
$$0.1 = 0.1$$

4.10

	r	t	d
Car	$4x$	$\dfrac{160}{4x}$	160
Motorcycle	$5x$	$\dfrac{160}{5x}$	160

$$\frac{160}{5x} + \frac{1}{2} = \frac{160}{4x}$$
$$\frac{32}{x} + \frac{1}{2} = \frac{40}{x}$$

LCD = $2x$
$$2(32) + x(1) = 2(40)$$
$$64 + x = 80$$
$$x = 16$$
$$4x = 4(16) = 64 \text{ mph}$$
$$5x = 5(16) = 80 \text{ mph}$$

The average rates are 64 mph for the car and 80 mph for the motorcycle.

Check:
$$\frac{160}{5(16)} + \frac{1}{2} = \frac{160}{4(16)}$$
$$\frac{160}{80} + \frac{1}{2} = \frac{160}{64}$$
$$2 + \frac{1}{2} = \frac{160}{64}$$
$$2\frac{1}{2} = \frac{5}{2}$$
$$2\frac{1}{2} = 2\frac{1}{2}$$

64 mph × $2\frac{1}{2}$ hr. = 160 miles
80 mph × 2 hr. = 160 miles

4.11

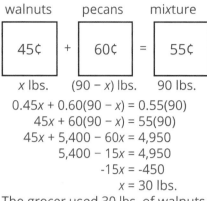

walnuts   pecans   mixture

45¢ + 60¢ = 55¢

x lbs. $(90 - x)$ lbs.   90 lbs.

$$0.45x + 0.60(90 - x) = 0.55(90)$$
$$45x + 60(90 - x) = 55(90)$$
$$45x + 5,400 - 60x = 4,950$$
$$5,400 - 15x = 4,950$$
$$-15x = -450$$
$$x = 30 \text{ lbs.}$$

The grocer used 30 lbs. of walnuts.

Check:
$$0.45(30) + 0.60(90 - 30) = 0.55(90)$$
$$0.45(30) + 0.60(60) = 0.55(90)$$
$$13.50 + 36.00 = 49.50$$
$$49.50 = 49.50$$

4.12

3%   0%   3.6%
butterfat   butterfat   butterfat

☐ − ☐ = ☐

300 lbs. x $300 - x$

$$0.03(300) - 0(x) = 0.036(300 - x)$$
$$30(300) = 36(300 - x)$$
$$9,000 = 10,800 - 36x$$
$$0 = 1,800 - 36x$$
$$36x = 1,800$$
$$x = 50 \text{ lbs.}$$

He must remove 50 lbs. of skimmed milk.

Check:
$$0.03(300) - 0 = 0.036(300 - 50)$$
$$0.03(300) = 0.036(250)$$
$$9.00 = 9.000$$

4.13

7% iodine   0% iodine   4% iodine

☐ + ☐ = ☐

20 oz. x oz. $(20 + x)$ oz.

$$0.07(20) + 0(x) = 0.04(20 + x)$$
$$7(20) = 4(20 + x)$$
$$140 = 80 + 4x$$
$$60 = 4x$$
$$x = 15 \text{ oz.}$$

The druggist must add 15 oz. of alcohol.

Check:
$$0.07(20) + 0(15) = 0.04(20 + 15)$$
$$0.07(20) + 0 = 0.04(35)$$
$$1.40 = 1.40$$

4.14

36¢	+	52¢	=	40¢
x		$300 - x$		300 qts.

$0.36x + 0.52(300 - x) = 0.40(300)$
$36x + 52(300 - x) = 40(300)$
$36x + 15{,}600 - 52x = 12{,}000$
$15{,}600 - 16x = 12{,}000$
$-16x = -3{,}600$
$x = 225$
$300 - x = 300 - 225 = 75$

He should mix 225 qts. of 36¢ oil with 75 qts. of 52¢ oil.

Check:
$0.36(225) + 0.52(300 - 225) = 0.40(300)$
$0.36(225) + 0.52(75) = 0.40(300)$
$81 + 39 = 120$
$120 = 120$

4.15

20%	−	0%	=	40%
40		x		$40 - x$

$0.20(40) - 0(x) = 0.40(40 - x)$
$20(40) = 40(40 - x)$
$800 = 1{,}600 - 40x$
$40x + 800 = 1{,}600$
$40x = 800$
$x = 20$

20 qts. of water have evaporated.

Check:
$0.20(40) = 0.40(40 - 20)$
$0.20(40) = 0.40(20)$
$8.00 = 8.00$

4.16

$0.50	+	$0.80	=	$0.75
x lbs.		$(30 - x)$ lbs.		30 lbs.

$0.50(x) + 0.80(30 - x) = 0.75(30)$
$50x + 80(30 - x) = 75(30)$
$50x + 2{,}400 - 80x = 2{,}250$
$2{,}400 - 30x = 2{,}250$
$-30x = -150$
$x = 5$
$30 - x = 30 - 5 = 25$

He should use 5 lbs. of 50¢ seeds and 25 lbs. of 80¢ seeds.

Check:
$0.50(5) + 0.80(30 - 5) = 0.75(30)$
$0.50(5) + 0.80(25) = 0.75(30)$
$2.50 + 20.00 = 22.50$
$22.50 = 22.50$

4.17

10% solution	+	100% salt	=	25% solution
50 lbs.		x lbs.		$(50 + x)$ lbs.

$0.10(50) + 1.00(x) = 0.25(50 + x)$
$5 + x = 12.50 + 0.25x$
$500 + 100x = 1{,}250 + 25x$
$500 + 75x = 1{,}250$
$75x = 750$
$x = 10$ lbs.

10 lbs. of salt must be added.

Check:
$0.10(50) + 1.00(10) = 0.25(50 + 10)$
$0.10(50) + 1.00(10) = 0.25(60)$
$5 + 10 = 15$
$15 = 15$

4.18

16%	+	100%	=	18%
$820 - x$		x		820

$0.16(820 - x) + 1.00(x) = 0.18(820)$
$16(820 - x) + 1.00(x) = 18(820)$
$13{,}120 - 16x + 100x = 14{,}760$
$13{,}120 + 84x = 14{,}760$
$84x = 1{,}640$
$x \doteq 19.5$

19.5 lbs. of tin should be added.

Check:
$0.16(820 - 19.5) + 1.00(19.5) = 0.18(820)$
$0.16(800.5) + 1.00(19.5) = 0.18(820)$
$128.08 + 19.5 = 147.60$
$147.60 = 147.60$

4.19

70 ounces of silver	+	x ounces of silver	+	96% of silver
80 ounces		x		$80 + x$

$\frac{1}{5} \div 5 = \frac{1}{25}$ gold
$\frac{24}{25} = 96\%$ silver
$70 + x = 0.96(80 + x)$
$7{,}000 + 100x = 96(80 + x)$
$7{,}000 + 100x = 7{,}680 + 96x$
$100x = 680 + 96x$
$4x = 680$
$x = 170$

170 ounces of silver must be added.

Check:
$70 + 170 = 0.96(80 + 170)$
$70 + 170 = 0.96(250)$
$240 = 240.00$

4.20 Let x = value per lb. of the mixture

$$\underset{u \text{ lbs.}}{\boxed{}}^{v\text{¢}} + \underset{w \text{ lbs.}}{\boxed{}}^{x\text{¢}} + \underset{y \text{ lbs.}}{\boxed{}}^{z\text{¢}} = (u + w + y) \text{ lbs.} \cdot x$$

$u \cdot v + w \cdot x + y \cdot z$ = value of total mixture

$uv + wx + yz = (u + w + y) \cdot x$

$\dfrac{uv + wx + yz}{u + w + y}$ = value per lb.

The value is $\dfrac{uv + wx + yz}{u + w + y}$ cents per lb.

4.21   5 min. = time for Ted to mow lawn

15 min. = time for Galen to mow lawn

x = time for Ted and Galen to mow lawn together

$\frac{1}{5}$ = part of lawn mowed by Ted in one minute

$\frac{1}{15}$ = part of lawn mowed by Galen in one minute

$x(\frac{1}{5}) + x(\frac{1}{15}) = 1$

LCD = 15

$$3x + x = 15$$
$$4x = 15$$
$$x = \frac{15}{4} = 3\frac{3}{4} \text{ minutes}$$

The job would take $3\frac{3}{4}$ minutes.

Check:

$$\overset{3}{\cancel{\frac{15}{4}}}(\frac{1}{\cancel{5}}) + \overset{1}{\cancel{\frac{15}{4}}}(\frac{1}{\cancel{15}}) = 1$$
$$\frac{3}{4} + \frac{1}{4} = 1$$
$$1 = 1$$

4.22   5 days = time for Mr. Boll to pick a bale of cotton

x days = time for his son to pick a bale of cotton

3 days = time for both working together to pick a bale of cotton

$\frac{1}{5}$ = part of job done by Mr. Boll in one day

$\frac{1}{x}$ = part of job done by his son in one day

$3(\frac{1}{5}) + 3(\frac{1}{x}) = 1$

LCD = $5x$

$$3x + 15 = 5x$$
$$15 = 2x$$
$$x = \frac{15}{2} = 7\frac{1}{2} \text{ days}$$

The son would take $7\frac{1}{2}$ days.

Check:

$$\frac{3}{5} + \frac{3}{\frac{15}{2}} = 1$$
$$\frac{3}{5} + \frac{6}{15} = 1$$
$$\frac{9}{15} + \frac{6}{15} = 1$$
$$1 = 1$$

4.23   24 min. = time for first pipe to fill the tank

8 min. = time for second pipe to fill the tank

12 min. = time for third pipe to fill the tank

x min. = time for all pipes together to fill the tank

$\frac{1}{24}$ = part of tank filled by first pipe in one minute

$\frac{1}{8}$ = part of tank filled by second pipe in one minute

$\frac{1}{12}$ = part of tank filled by third pipe in one minute

$x(\frac{1}{24}) + x(\frac{1}{8}) + x(\frac{1}{12}) = 1$

LCD = 24

$$x + 3x + 2x = 24$$
$$6x = 24$$
$$x = 4 \text{ min.}$$

The tank will be filled in 4 minutes.

Check:

$$4(\frac{1}{24}) + 4(\frac{1}{8}) + 4(\frac{1}{12}) = 1$$
$$\frac{1}{6} + \frac{1}{2} + \frac{1}{3} = 1$$
$$\frac{1}{6} + \frac{3}{6} + \frac{2}{6} = 1$$
$$\frac{6}{6} = 1$$
$$1 = 1$$

4.24   12 days = time for Tom to do the job alone

10 days = time for Dick to do the job alone

x days = time for Harry to to the job alone

4 days = the time for them to to the job together

$\frac{1}{12}$ = the part of the job done by Tom alone in one day

$\frac{1}{10}$ = the part of the job done by Dick alone in one day

$\frac{1}{x}$ = the part of the job done by Harry alone in one day

$4(\frac{1}{12}) + 4(\frac{1}{10}) + 4(\frac{1}{x}) = 1$

LCD = $60x$

$$20x + 24x + 240 = 60x$$
$$44x + 240 = 60x$$
$$240 = 16x$$
$$x = 15 \text{ days}$$

Harry will take 15 days.

Check:

$$\frac{1}{3} + \frac{2}{5} + \frac{4}{15} = 1$$
$$\frac{5}{15} + \frac{6}{15} + \frac{4}{15} = 1$$
$$\frac{15}{15} = 1$$
$$1 = 1$$

4.25 6 hrs. = time required for pipe to drain the cistern

4 hrs. = time required for first pipe to fill the cistern

5 hrs. = time required for second pipe to fill the cistern

x hrs. = time required for the cistern to be filled if all pipes are running

$\frac{1}{6}$ = the part of the cistern drained by the pipe in one hour

$\frac{1}{4}$ = the part of the cistern filled by the first pipe in one hour

$\frac{1}{5}$ = the part of the cistern filled by the second pipe in one hour

$\frac{1}{x}$ = the part of the cistern filled by all three pipes together

$\frac{x}{4} + \frac{x}{5} - \frac{x}{6} = 1$

LCD = 60

$15x + 12x - 10x = 60$

$17x = 60$

$x = \frac{60}{17} = 3\frac{9}{17}$ hrs.

The cistern will be filled in $3\frac{9}{17}$ hrs.

Check:

$\overset{15}{\cancel{\frac{60}{17}}}\left(\frac{1}{\underset{1}{\cancel{4}}}\right) + \overset{12}{\cancel{\frac{60}{17}}}\left(\frac{1}{\underset{1}{\cancel{5}}}\right) - \overset{10}{\cancel{\frac{60}{17}}}\left(\frac{1}{\underset{1}{\cancel{6}}}\right) = 1$

$\frac{15}{17} + \frac{12}{17} - \frac{10}{17} = 1$

$\frac{17}{17} = 1$

$1 = 1$

4.26 12 hrs. = time required to fill the pool with Doe's hoses

30 hrs. = time required to fill the pool with Jones's hose

x hrs. = time required to fill the pool with both families' hoses

$\frac{1}{12}$ = part of the pool filled by Doe's hoses in one hour

$\frac{1}{30}$ = part of the pool filled by Jones's hose in one hour

$\frac{1}{x}$ = part of the pool filled by both families' hoses in one hour

$\frac{x}{12} + \frac{x}{30} = 1$

LCD = 60

$5x + 2x = 60$

$7x = 60$

$x = \frac{60}{7} = 8\frac{4}{7}$ hrs.

The pool will be filled in $8\frac{4}{7}$ hrs.

Check:

$\frac{\frac{60}{7}}{12} + \frac{\frac{60}{7}}{30} = 1$

$\frac{60}{84} + \frac{60}{210} = 1$

$\frac{5}{7} + \frac{2}{7} = 1$

$\frac{7}{7} = 1$

$1 = 1$

4.27 3 hrs. = time for Jim Roller to paint the room

4 hrs. = time for John Brush to paint the room

x hrs. = time for both to paint the room

$\frac{1}{3}$ = the part of the room painted by Jim Roller in one hour

$\frac{1}{4}$ = the part of the room painted by John Brush in one hour

$\frac{1}{x}$ = the part of the room painted by both in one hour

$\frac{x}{3} + \frac{x}{4} = 1$

LCD = 12

$4x + 3x = 12$

$7x = 12$

$x = \frac{12}{7} = 1\frac{5}{7}$ hrs.

Check:

$\frac{\frac{12}{7}}{3} + \frac{\frac{12}{7}}{4} = 1$

$\frac{12}{21} + \frac{12}{28} = 1$

$\frac{4}{7} + \frac{3}{7} = 1$

$\frac{7}{7} = 1$

$1 = 1$

4.28 18 hrs. = time for John to type the entire manuscript

x hrs. = time for Laura to type the entire manuscript

$\frac{1}{18}$ = part of manuscript typed by John in one hour

$\frac{1}{x}$ = part of manuscript typed by Laura in one hour

$\frac{2}{18} + \frac{2}{x} = \frac{1}{3}$

$\frac{1}{9} + \frac{2}{x} = \frac{1}{3}$

LCD = $9x$

$x + 18 = 3x$

$18 = 2x$

$x = 9$ hrs.

Laura would take 9 hrs. to type the manuscript.

Check:

$\frac{2}{18} + \frac{2}{9} = \frac{1}{3}$

$\frac{1}{9} + \frac{2}{9} = \frac{1}{3}$

$\frac{3}{9} = \frac{1}{3}$

$\frac{1}{3} = \frac{1}{3}$

4.29 12 hrs. = time for the farmer to seed the corn field

x hrs. = time for the son to seed the corn field

3 hrs. = time for farmer and son to seed the field together

$\frac{1}{12}$ = part of field seeded by farmer in one hour

$\frac{1}{x}$ = part of field seeded by son in one hour

$\frac{1}{3}$ = part of field seeded by both in one hour

$\frac{3}{12} + \frac{3}{x} = 1$

$\frac{1}{4} + \frac{3}{x} = 1$

LCD = $4x$

$x + 12 = 4x$

$12 = 3x$

$x = 4$ hrs.

The son could seed the field in 4 hours.

Check:

$\frac{3}{12} + \frac{3}{4} = 1$

$\frac{1}{4} + \frac{3}{4} = 1$

$\frac{4}{4} = 1$

$1 = 1$

4.30 8 hrs. = time for an experienced plumber to finish a house

12 hrs. = time for an inexperienced plumber to finish a house

x hrs. = time for all 5 plumbers to finish the house

$\frac{1}{8}$ = part of house finished by an experienced plumber in one hour

$\frac{1}{12}$ = part of house finished by an inexperienced plumber in one hour

$\frac{1}{x}$ = part of house finished by all 5 plumbers in one hour

$2(\frac{x}{8}) + 3(\frac{x}{12}) = 1$

$\frac{x}{4} + \frac{x}{4} = 1$

LCD = 4

$x + x = 4$

$2x = 4$

$x = 2$ hrs.

The men will take 2 hours to do the job (if they stay out of one another's way!).

Check:

$2(\frac{2}{8}) + 3(\frac{2}{12}) = 1$

$\frac{4}{8} + \frac{6}{12} = 1$

$\frac{1}{2} + \frac{1}{2} = 1$

$1 = 1$

SELF TEST 4

4.01 $\frac{3^{-2} \cdot 4^2}{3^0 \cdot 4^3} = \frac{\frac{1}{3^2} \cdot 4^2 \cdot}{1 \cdot 4^3} = \frac{4^2}{3^2 \cdot 4^3}$

$\frac{1}{3^2 \cdot 4} = \frac{1}{9 \cdot 4} = \frac{1}{36}$

4.02 $\frac{\cancel{y}\cancel{xy}(x - \cancel{y})(x - y)}{3 \cancel{3x}(x - \cancel{y})} = \frac{y(x - y)}{3} = \frac{xy - y^2}{3}$

4.03 $\frac{a^2 - b^2}{x^2 - y^2} \cdot \frac{(x + y)^2}{a - b} = \frac{(a + b)(\cancel{a - b})}{(\cancel{x + y})(x - y)} \cdot \frac{(\cancel{x + y})(x + y)}{\cancel{a - b}} = \frac{(a + b)(x + y)}{x - y}$

4.04 LCD = $(y - 1)(y - 2)(y - 3)$

$\frac{(y - 3)(y - 3)}{(y - 1)(y - 2)(y - 3)} - \frac{(y - 4)(y - 2)}{(y - 1)(y - 2)(y - 3)} =$

$\frac{y^2 - 6y + 9 - (y^2 - 6y + 8)}{(y - 1)(y - 2)(y - 3)} = \frac{\cancel{y^2} - \cancel{6y} + 9 - \cancel{y^2} - \cancel{6y} - 8}{(y - 1)(y - 2)(y - 3)} =$

$\frac{1}{(y - 1)(y - 2)(y - 3)}$

4.05 $\frac{(5 + \frac{5}{x-1})\frac{x-1}{1}}{(\frac{5}{x-1})\frac{x-1}{1}} = \frac{5(x - 1) + 5}{5} = \frac{x - 1 + 1}{1} = x$

4.06 LCD = $42y$

$42y[\frac{3(y + 7)}{7y}] - 42y(\frac{4y - 7}{6}) =$

$42y(\frac{7y + 10}{3y}) - 42y(\frac{2(7y - 1)}{21})$

$6[3(y + 7)] - 7y(4y - 7) =$

$14(7y + 10) - 2y[2(7y - 1)]$

$18(y + 7) - 7y(4y - 7) =$

$14(7y + 10) - 4y(7y - 1)$

$18y + 126 - \cancel{28y^2} + 49y = 98y + 140 - \cancel{28y^2} + 4y$

$67y + 126 = 102y + 140$

$-35y + 126 = 140$

$-35y = 14$

$y = \frac{14}{-35} = -\frac{2}{5}$

4.07 $\frac{y + 10}{y + 3} = \frac{y + 1}{y - 1}$

$(y + 10)(y - 1) = (y + 3)(y + 1)$

$\cancel{y^2} + 9y - 10 = \cancel{y^2} + 4y + 3$

$5y - 10 = 3$

$5y = 13$

$y = \frac{13}{5}$ or $2\frac{3}{5}$

4.08

	r	t	d
Airplane	$\frac{x}{2}$	2	x
Automobile	$\frac{x}{10}$	10	x

The airplane traveled from 11 a.m. to 1 p.m. = 2 hours.
The automobile traveled from 3 a.m. to 1 p.m. = 10 hours.

$\frac{x}{2} = \frac{x}{10} + 200$

LCD = 10

$\qquad 5(x) = x + 10(200)$
$\qquad 5x = x + 2{,}000$
$\qquad 4x = 2{,}000$
$\qquad x = 500$
$\qquad \frac{x}{10} = \frac{500}{10} = 50$ mph

The automobile is traveling at 50 mph.

Check:

$\qquad \frac{500}{2} = \frac{500}{10} + 200$
$\qquad 250 = 50 + 200$
$\qquad 250 = 250$

4.09

$$\boxed{10\%} \;+\; \boxed{40\%} \;=\; \boxed{25\%}$$

x oz. $(10 - x)$ oz.   10 oz.

$\qquad 0.10(x) + 0.40(10 - x) = 0.25(10)$
$\qquad 10(x) + 40(10 - x) = 25(10)$
$\qquad 10x + 400 - 40x = 250$
$\qquad -30x + 400 = 250$
$\qquad -30x = -150$
$\qquad x = 5$ oz.
$\qquad 10 - x = 10 - 5 = 5$ oz.

The druggist should use 5 ounces of each.

Check:
$\qquad 0.10(5) + 0.40(10 - 5) = 0.25(10)$
$\qquad 0.10(5) + 0.40(5) = 0.25(10)$
$\qquad 0.5 + 2 = 2.5$
$\qquad 2.5 = 2.5$

4.010

x = the time for Mrs. Jones to can her tomatoes
$x + 6$ = the time for Mrs. Jones's daughter to can the tomatoes
$\frac{x + 6}{3}$ = the time for them to can the tomatoes working together
$\frac{1}{x}$ = the part of the tomatoes canned by Mrs. Jones in one hour
$\frac{1}{x + 6}$ = the part of the tomatoes canned by Mrs. Jones's daughter in one hour

$$\frac{x + 6}{3}\left(\frac{1}{x}\right) + \frac{\overset{1}{\cancel{x + 6}}}{3}\left(\frac{1}{\cancel{x + 6}}\right) = 1$$

$$\frac{x + 6}{3x} + \frac{1}{3} = 1$$

LCD = 3x

$\qquad x + 6 + x = 3x$
$\qquad 2x + 6 = 3x$
$\qquad x = 6$ hours

Mrs. Jones would take 6 hours.

Check:

$$\frac{6 + 6}{3}\left(\frac{1}{6}\right) + \frac{6 + 6}{3}\left(\frac{1}{6 + 6}\right) = 1$$

$$\frac{12}{3}\left(\frac{1}{6}\right) + \frac{12}{3}\left(\frac{1}{12}\right) = 1$$

$$\frac{2}{3} + \frac{1}{3} = 1$$

$$\frac{3}{3} = 1$$

$$1 = 1$$

LIFEPAC TEST

1. $\dfrac{36 \cdot \frac{1}{x^4} \cdot y^2 \cdot 1}{5x^2 \cdot \frac{1}{y^3} \cdot \frac{1}{z^2}} = \dfrac{36y^2 \cdot y^3 \cdot z^2}{5x^2 \cdot x^4} = \dfrac{36y^5z^2}{5x^6}$

2. $\dfrac{\overset{2x}{18x^3y^8(x-y)(x-y)}}{\underset{9y^2}{81x^2y^{10}(y-x)(y-x)}} = \dfrac{2x}{9y^2}$

3. $\dfrac{\overset{1}{(a-3)}\overset{1}{(a+6)}}{\underset{1}{(a-2)}\underset{1}{(a-3)}} \cdot \dfrac{5\overset{1}{(a-2)}}{\underset{1}{(a+6)}(a-6)} = \dfrac{5}{a-6}$

4. $\dfrac{p^2 - q^2}{p + q} \cdot \dfrac{p - q}{p + q} = \dfrac{\overset{1}{(p+q)}(p-q)}{\underset{1}{p+q}} \cdot \dfrac{p-q}{p+q} =$

$\dfrac{(p-q)^2}{p+q}$ or $\dfrac{p^2 - 2pq + q^2}{p+q}$

5. $\dfrac{2y^2 - 7y - 15}{3y^2 - 8y - 3} \cdot \dfrac{9y^2 - 1}{4y^2 - 9} \cdot \dfrac{2y^2 - 9y + 9}{y^2 + 3y - 10} =$

$\dfrac{\overset{1}{(2y+3)}(y-5)}{\underset{1}{(3y+1)}\underset{1}{(y-3)}} \cdot \dfrac{\overset{1}{(3y+1)}(3y-1)}{\underset{1}{(2y+3)}\underset{1}{(2y-3)}} \cdot \dfrac{\overset{1}{(y-3)}\overset{1}{(2y-3)}}{(y+5)(y-2)} =$

$\dfrac{(y-5)(3y-1)}{(y+5)(y-2)}$

6. $\quad (a+1)^2 = (a+1)(a+1)$
$\quad (a-1)^2 = (a-1)(a-1)$
$\quad a^2 - 1 = (a+1)(a-1)$
$\text{LCD} = (a+1)(a+1)$
$\quad (a-1)(a-1) = (a+1)^2(a-1)^2$

7. $\text{LCD} = 105$
$105(\frac{y}{3}) + 105(\frac{y}{7}) + 105(\frac{y}{5}) = \frac{35y}{105} + \frac{15y}{105} + \frac{21y}{105} = \frac{71y}{105}$

8. $\dfrac{1}{a-b} + \dfrac{4}{b-a} - \dfrac{8}{a+b} - \dfrac{11a - 5b}{(b+a)(b-a)} =$

$\dfrac{1}{a-b} - \dfrac{4}{a-b} - \dfrac{8}{a+b} - \dfrac{5b - 11a}{(a+b)(a-b)}$

$\text{LCD} = (a+b)(a-b)$

$\dfrac{1(a+b) - 4(a+b) - 8(a-b) - (5b - 11a)}{(a+b)(a-b)} =$

$\dfrac{a + b - 4a - 4b - 8a + 8b - 5b + 11a}{a^2 - b^2} = \dfrac{0}{a^2 - b^2} = 0$

9. $\text{LCD} = x - y$
$\dfrac{(-x-y)(x-y)}{x-y} + \dfrac{x^2 + y^2}{x-y} = \dfrac{-(x+y)(x-y)}{x-y} + \dfrac{x^2 + y^2}{x-y} =$

$\dfrac{-(x^2 - y^2) + x^2 + y^2}{x-y} = \dfrac{-x^2 + y^2 + x^2 + y^2}{x-y} = \dfrac{2y^2}{x-y}$

10. $\dfrac{(1 + \frac{a}{b})\frac{b^2}{1}}{(1 - \frac{a^2}{b^2})\frac{b^2}{1}} = \dfrac{b^2 + ab}{b^2 - a^2} = \dfrac{b\overset{1}{(b+a)}}{\underset{1}{(b+a)}(b-a)} = \dfrac{b}{b-a}$

11. $\text{LCD} = 6$
$\quad a - 6(10) = 2(a)$
$\quad a - 60 = 2a$
$\quad -60 = a$

12. $\text{LCD} = 12$
$12[\frac{2}{3}(y + 2)] - 12[\frac{5}{6}(y - 1)] = 12[\frac{5}{4}(y - 3)] - 12(4)$
$4[2(y + 2)] - 2[5(y - 1)] = 3[5(y - 3)] - 12(4)$
$8y + 16 - 10y + 10 = 15y - 45 - 48$
$-2y + 26 = 15y - 93$
$-17y + 26 = -93$
$-17y = -119$
$y = 7$

13. $\text{LCD} = 20x$
$20x(\frac{1}{4}) + 20x(\frac{1}{x}) = 20x(\frac{1}{5}) - 20x(\frac{3}{x})$
$5x + 20 = 4x - 60$
$x + 20 = -60$
$x = -80$

14. $\dfrac{2}{2-x} + \dfrac{3}{x+2} = \dfrac{2x}{(x+2)(x-2)}$
$-\dfrac{2}{x-2} + \dfrac{3}{x+2} = \dfrac{2x}{(x+2)(x-2)}$
$\text{LCD} = (x+2)(x-2)$
$-2(x + 2) + 3(x - 2) = 2x$
$-2x - 4 + 3x - 6 = 2x$
$x - 10 = 2x$
$-10 = x$

15. $\dfrac{2x + 5}{2x + 3} = \dfrac{x + 3}{x - 1}$

$(2x + 5)(x - 1) = (2x + 3)(x + 3)$
$2x^2 + 3x - 5 = 2x^2 + 9x + 9$
$-6x - 5 = 9$
$-6x = 14$
$x = \dfrac{14}{-6} = -\dfrac{7}{3}$

16.

	r	t	d
original trip	50 mph	$\frac{x}{50}$	x
réturn trip	40 mph	$\frac{x}{40}$	x
round trip	45 mph	$\frac{2x}{45}$	$2x$

$\dfrac{x}{50} + \dfrac{x}{40} = \dfrac{2x}{45} + \dfrac{1}{2}$
$\text{LCD} = 1{,}800$
$1{,}800(\frac{x}{50}) + 1{,}800(\frac{x}{40}) = 1{,}800(\frac{2x}{45}) + 1{,}800(\frac{1}{2})$
$36x + 45x = 80x + 900$
$81x = 80x + 900$
$x = 900 \text{ miles}$

The distance from Town X to Town Y is 900 miles.

Check:
$\dfrac{900}{50} + \dfrac{900}{40} = \dfrac{2(900)}{45} + \dfrac{1}{2}$
$18 + 22.5 = 40 + \dfrac{1}{2}$
$40.5 = 40.5$

17.

$$\boxed{42¢} + \boxed{32¢} = \boxed{36¢}$$

x $\quad$ $200 - x$ $\quad$ 200

$$0.42(x) + 0.32(200 - x) = 0.36(200)$$
$$42(x) + 32(200 - x) = 36(200)$$
$$42x + 6{,}400 - 32x = 7{,}200$$
$$10x + 6{,}400 = 7{,}200$$
$$10x = 800$$
$$x = 80 \text{ liters}$$

80 liters of orange juice should be added.

Check:
$$0.42(80) + 0.32(200 - 80) = 0.36(200)$$
$$0.42(80) + 0.32(120) = 0.36(200)$$
$$33.6 + 38.4 = 72$$
$$72.0 = 72$$

18. $\quad 7\frac{1}{2}$ hrs. = time for first pipe to fill tank

$\quad 10$ hrs. = time for second pipe to fill tank

$\quad x$ = time for first pipe to finish

$\dfrac{1}{7\frac{1}{2}}$ = part of tank filled by first pipe in one hour

$\dfrac{1}{10}$ = part of tank filled by second pipe in one hour

$$x\left(\frac{1}{7\frac{1}{2}}\right) + 8\left(\frac{1}{10}\right) = 1$$

$$x\left(\frac{1}{\frac{15}{2}}\right) + \frac{8}{10} = 1$$

$$\frac{2x}{15} + \frac{4}{5} = 1$$

LCD = 15

$$2x + 12 = 15$$
$$2x = 3$$
$$x = \frac{3}{2} = 1\frac{1}{2} \text{ hrs.}$$

The first pipe would take $1\frac{1}{2}$ hours to finish filling the tank.

Check:
$$\frac{3}{2}\left(\frac{2}{15}\right) + 8\left(\frac{1}{10}\right) = 1$$

$$\frac{1}{5} + \frac{4}{5} = 1$$

$$\frac{5}{5} = 1$$

$$1 = 1$$

ALTERNATE LIFEPAC TEST

1. $\dfrac{49x^{-3}y^3z^{-4}}{8x^4y^{-2}z^0} = \dfrac{49}{8}x^{-3-4}y^{3-(-2)}z^{-4-0} = \dfrac{49}{8}x^{-7}y^5z^{-4} = \dfrac{49y^5}{8x^7z^4}$

2. $\dfrac{63x^4y^9(x-y)^3}{84x^2y^{12}(y-x)^3} = \dfrac{\overset{3}{\cancel{63}}\overset{x^2}{\cancel{x^4}}\overset{}{\cancel{y^9}}\overset{-1}{\cancel{(x-y)^3}}}{\underset{4}{\cancel{84}}\underset{}{\cancel{x^2}}\underset{y^3}{\cancel{y^{12}}}\underset{}{\cancel{(y-x)^3}}} = -\dfrac{3x^2}{4y^3}$

3. $\dfrac{a^2-b^2}{a+b} \cdot \dfrac{a-b}{a+b} = \dfrac{(a+b)(a-b)}{\cancel{a+b}} \cdot \dfrac{a-b}{a+b} = \dfrac{(a-b)^2}{a+b}$

4. $\dfrac{x^2+3x-18}{x^2-3x} \div \dfrac{x^2-5x+6}{5x-10} =$

$\dfrac{\cancel{(x-3)}(x+6)}{x\cancel{(x-3)}} \cdot \dfrac{5\cancel{(x-2)}}{\cancel{(x-2)}(x-3)} = \dfrac{5(x+6)}{x(x-3)}$

5. $\dfrac{7}{x^2-1} = \dfrac{7}{(x+1)(x-1)}$

$\dfrac{3}{x^2+2x+1} = \dfrac{3}{(x+1)(x+1)}$

$\dfrac{3}{(x-1)^2} = \dfrac{3}{(x-1)(x-1)}$

LCD $= (x+1)(x-1)(x+1)(x-1) =$
$(x+1)^2(x-1)^2$

6. $\dfrac{x^2-16}{x^2+4x} \cdot \dfrac{x^2+2x+1}{x^2-3x-4} \div \dfrac{x^2-2x-3}{x^2-x} =$

$\dfrac{\cancel{(x+4)}(x-4)}{x\cancel{(x+4)}} \cdot \dfrac{\cancel{(x+1)}\cancel{(x+1)}}{\cancel{(x+1)}\cancel{(x-4)}} \cdot \dfrac{\cancel{x}(x-1)}{\cancel{(x+1)}(x-3)} = \dfrac{(x-1)}{(y-3)}$

7. LCD $= 8 \cdot 5 \cdot 3 = 120$

$\dfrac{x}{8} + \dfrac{x}{5} + \dfrac{x}{3} = \dfrac{120}{120}\left(\dfrac{x}{8}\right) + \dfrac{120}{120}\left(\dfrac{x}{5}\right) + \dfrac{120}{120}\left(\dfrac{x}{3}\right) =$

$\dfrac{15x}{120} + \dfrac{24x}{120} + \dfrac{40x}{120} = \dfrac{15x+24x+40x}{120} = \dfrac{79x}{120}$

8. $\dfrac{4}{x-y} + \dfrac{1}{y-x} - \dfrac{9x+6y}{y^2-x^2} - \dfrac{8}{x+y} =$

$\dfrac{4}{x-y} - \dfrac{1}{x-y} + \dfrac{9x+6y}{x^2-y^2} - \dfrac{8}{x+y}$

$x-y = x-y$
$x^2-y^2 = (x+y)(x-y)$
$x+y = x+y$
LCD $= (x+y)(x-y)$

$\dfrac{x+y}{(x+y)}\left[\dfrac{4}{x-y}\right] - \dfrac{x+y}{x+y}\left[\dfrac{1}{x-y}\right] +$

$\dfrac{9x+6y}{(x+y)(x-y)} - \dfrac{x-y}{x-y}\left[\dfrac{8}{x+y}\right] =$

$\dfrac{4x+4y}{(x+y)(x-y)} - \dfrac{x+y}{(x+y)(x-y)} +$

$\dfrac{9x+6y}{(x+y)(x-y)} - \dfrac{8x-8y}{(x+y)(x-y)} =$

$\dfrac{4x+4y-x-y+9x+6y-8x+8y}{(x+y)(x-y)} =$

$\dfrac{(4x-x+9x-8x)+(4y-y+6y+8y)}{(x+y)(x-y)} =$

$\dfrac{4x+17y}{(x+y)(x-y)} = \dfrac{4x+17y}{x^2-y^2}$

9. $\dfrac{x^2+y^2}{x-y} - x - y = \dfrac{x^2+y^2}{x-y} - (x+y)$

LCD is $x - y$.

$\dfrac{x^2+y^2}{x-y} - \dfrac{x-y}{x-y}[x+y] =$

$\dfrac{x^2+y^2}{x-y} - \dfrac{x^2-y^2}{x-y} =$

$\dfrac{x^2+y^2-x^2+y^2}{x-y} = \dfrac{2y^2}{x-y}$

10. LCD is y^2.

$\dfrac{\frac{y^2}{y^2}[y] + \frac{27}{y^2}}{\frac{y}{y}\left[\frac{9}{y}\right] + \frac{y^2}{y^2}[y] + \frac{y^2}{y^2}[6]} = \dfrac{\frac{y^3}{y^2} + \frac{27}{y^2}}{\frac{9y}{y^2} + \frac{y^3}{y^2} + \frac{6y^2}{y^2}} = \dfrac{y^3+27}{9y+y^3+6y^2} =$

$\dfrac{(y+3)(y^2-3y+9)}{y(y^2+6y+9)} = \dfrac{(y+3)(y^2-3y+9)}{y\cancel{(y+3)}(y+3)} = \dfrac{y^2-3y+9}{y(y+3)}$

11. The LCD is 35.

$\overset{5}{\cancel{35}}\left[\dfrac{5x}{\cancel{7}}\right] - \overset{7}{\cancel{35}}\left[\dfrac{7x}{\cancel{5}}\right] = 35\left[\dfrac{24}{\cancel{35}}\right]$

$25x - 49x = 24$

$-24x = 24$

$-\dfrac{1}{24}(-24x) = -\dfrac{1}{24}(24)$

$x = -1$

12. The LCD is $42a$.

$\overset{6}{\cancel{42a}}\left[\dfrac{3(a+7)}{\cancel{7a}}\right] - \overset{7}{\cancel{42a}}\left[\dfrac{4a-7}{\cancel{6}}\right] =$

$\overset{14}{\cancel{42a}}\left[\dfrac{7a+10}{\cancel{3a}}\right] - \overset{2}{\cancel{42a}}\left[\dfrac{2(7a-1)}{\cancel{21}}\right]$

$18a + 126 - 28a^2 + 49a = 98a + 140 - 28a^2 + 4a$

$-\cancel{28a^2} + 67a + 126 = -\cancel{28a^2} + 102a + 140$

$67a + 126 - 126 = 102a + 140 - 126$

$67a = 102a + 14$

$67a - 102a = 102a - 102a + 14$

$-35a = 14$

$-\dfrac{1}{35}(-35a) = -\dfrac{1}{35}(14)$

$a = -\dfrac{14}{35} = -\dfrac{2}{5}$

13. The LCD is $20x$.

$\overset{5}{\cancel{20x}}\left[\dfrac{3}{\cancel{4}}\right] + 20x\left[\dfrac{1}{\cancel{x}}\right] = \overset{4}{\cancel{20x}}\left[\dfrac{2}{\cancel{5}}\right] - 20x\left[\dfrac{1}{\cancel{x}}\right]$

$15x + 20 = 8x - 20$

$15x + 20 - 20 = 8x - 20 - 20$

$15x = 8x - 40$

$15x - 8x = 8x - 8x - 40$

$7x = -40$

$\dfrac{1}{7}(7x) = \dfrac{1}{7}(-40)$

$x = -\dfrac{40}{7}$ or $-5\dfrac{5}{7}$

14. $\dfrac{3}{3-x}+\dfrac{2}{x+3}=\dfrac{2x}{x^2-9}-$

$\dfrac{3}{x-3}+\dfrac{2}{x+3}=\dfrac{2x}{(x+3)(x-3)}$

The LCD is $(x+3)(x-3)$.

$(x+3)(x-3)\left[\dfrac{-3}{x-3}\right]+(x+3)(x-3)\left[\dfrac{2}{x+3}\right]=$

$(x+3)(x-3)\left[\dfrac{2x}{(x+3)(x-3)}\right]$

$-3x-9+2x-6=2x$

$-x-15=2x$

$-x-15+15=2x+15$

$-x=2x+15$

$-x-2x=2x-2x+15$

$-3x=15$

$-\dfrac{1}{3}(-3x)=-\dfrac{1}{3}(15)$

$x=-5$

15. $\dfrac{x+3}{2x-5}=\dfrac{x+4}{2x-7}$

The LCD is $(2x-5)(2x-7)$.

$(2x-5)(2x-7)\left[\dfrac{x+3}{2x-5}\right]=(2x-5)(2x-7)\left[\dfrac{x+4}{2x-7}\right]$

$(2x-7)(x+3)=(2x-5)(x+4)$

$2x^2-x-21=2x^2+3x-20$

$-x-21+21=3x-20+21$

$-x=3x+1$

$-x-3x=3x-3x+1$

$-4x=1$

$-\dfrac{1}{4}(-4x)=-\dfrac{1}{4}(1)$

$x=-\dfrac{1}{4}$

16.

	r	t	d
first	x	$\dfrac{120}{x}$	120
second	$x+10$	$\dfrac{160}{x+10}$	160

$\dfrac{120}{x}=\dfrac{160}{x+10}$

$(x+10)120=160x$

$120x+1{,}200=160x$

$120x+1{,}200-1{,}200=160x-1{,}200$

$120x=160x-1{,}200$

$120x-160x=160x-160x-1{,}200$

$-40x=-1{,}200$

$-\dfrac{1}{40}(-40x)=-\dfrac{1}{40}(-1{,}200)$

$x=30$

The average rate on the first trip was 30 mph.

17.

90¢		70¢		85¢
$\square$	+	$\square$	=	$\square$
x		10		$x+10$

$0.90x+7.00=0.85(x+10)$

$90x+700=85x+850$

$90x+700-700=85x+850-700$

$90x=85x+150$

$90x-85x=85x-85x+150$

$5x=150$

$\dfrac{1}{5}\cdot5x=\dfrac{1}{5}\cdot150$

$x=30$

30 lbs. of 90¢ candy must be added.

18. 2 hrs. = time for Mr. Wallace to paint the fence

6 hrs. = time for Greg to paint the fence

$\dfrac{1}{2}$ = part done by Mr. Wallace in 1 hour

x hrs. = time for Greg to finish the job

$\dfrac{1}{2}+\dfrac{x}{6}=1$

The LCD is 6.

$6\left[\dfrac{1}{2}\right]+6\left[\dfrac{x}{6}\right]=6[1]$

$3+x=6$

$3-3+x=6-3$

$x=3$

Greg required 3 hrs. to finish the job.

MATH 1105
ALTERNATE LIFEPAC TEST

NAME _____

DATE _____

SCORE _____

Complete these items (each answer, 3 points).

1. Write using only positive exponents: $\dfrac{49x^{-3}y^3z^{-4}}{8x^4y^{-2}z^0}$ _____

2. Reduce to lowest terms: $\dfrac{63x^4y^9(x-y)^3}{84x^2y^{12}\,(y-x)^3}$ _____

3. Multiply: $\dfrac{a^2-b^2}{a+b} \cdot \dfrac{a-b}{a+b}$ _____

4. Divide: $\dfrac{x^2+3x-18}{x^2-3x} \div \dfrac{x^2-5x+6}{5x-10}$ _____

5. Find the lowest common denominator for $\dfrac{7}{x^2-1}, \dfrac{3}{x^2+2x+1}$, and $\dfrac{3}{(x-1)^2}$. _____

6. Simplify: $\dfrac{x^2-16}{x^2+4x} \cdot \dfrac{x^2+2x+1}{x^2-3x-4} \div \dfrac{x^2-2x-3}{x^2-x}$ _____

Simplify (each answer, 3 points).

7. $\dfrac{x}{8}+\dfrac{x}{5}+\dfrac{x}{3}$ _____

8. $\dfrac{4}{x-y}+\dfrac{1}{y-x}-\dfrac{9x+6y}{y^2-x^2}-\dfrac{8}{x+y}$ _____

9. $\dfrac{x^2+y^2}{x-y}-x-y$ _____

10. $\dfrac{y+\frac{27}{y^2}}{\frac{9}{y}+y+6}$ _____

Solve (each answer, 4 points).

11. $\dfrac{5x}{7} - \dfrac{7x}{5} = \dfrac{24}{35}$

_____

12. $\dfrac{3(a+7)}{7a} - \dfrac{4a-7}{6} = \dfrac{7a+10}{3a} - \dfrac{2(7a-1)}{21}$

_____

13. $\dfrac{3}{4} + \dfrac{1}{x} = \dfrac{2}{5} - \dfrac{1}{x}$

_____

14. $\dfrac{3}{3-x} + \dfrac{2}{x+3} = \dfrac{2x}{x^2-9}$

_____

15. $\dfrac{x+3}{2x-5} = \dfrac{x+4}{2x-7}$

_____

Solve each of the following word problems, showing all four steps (each problem, 5 points).

16. A car traveled 120 miles at a certain average rate. By increasing its average rate by 10 mph, it traveled 160 miles in the same time it traveled the 120-mile trip. Find its average rate on the first trip.

17. How many pounds of candy worth 90 cents per pound must be mixed with 10 pounds of candy worth 70 cents per pound to produce a mixture that can be sold for 85 cents per pound?

18. Mr. Wallace can paint a fence in 2 hours. His son, Greg, can paint the fence in 6 hours. Mr. Wallace painted alone for 1 hour and stopped working. How many hours did Greg require to finish the job?

MATH 1106

Unit 6: Real Numbers

TEACHER NOTES

MATERIALS NEEDED FOR LIFEPAC	
Required	Suggested
(none)	(none)

ADDITIONAL LEARNING ACTIVITIES

Section 1: Real Numbers

1. Stress to the class the necessity of always checking possible solutions in the original equation when using the principle of powers.

    Example: Solve $x - 5 = \sqrt{x + 7}$
    $(x - 5)^2 = (\sqrt{x + 7})^2$
    $x^2 - 10x + 25 = x + 7$
    $x^2 - 11x + 18 = 0$
    $(x - 9)(x - 2) = 0$
    $x = 9$ or $x = 2$

    Checks: For 9: $x - 5 = \sqrt{x + 7}$
    $9 - 5 = \sqrt{9 + 7}$
    $4 = 4$; 9 checks.

    For 2: $x - 5 = \sqrt{x + 7}$
    $2 - 5 = \sqrt{2 + 7}$
    $-3 \neq 3$; 2 does not check. Therefore, the only solution is 9.

2. Point out that while we normally rationalize the denominator with a fraction containing radicals, we might also want to rationalize the numerator occasionally.

    Example: Simplify $\dfrac{\sqrt{x + h} - \sqrt{x}}{h}$

    $$\frac{\sqrt{x + h} - \sqrt{x}}{h} = \frac{(\sqrt{x + h} - \sqrt{x})(\sqrt{x + h} + \sqrt{x})}{h(\sqrt{x + h} + \sqrt{x})}$$

    Then simplify as usual.

3. Have the class indicate how they would rationalize the following radical expressions.

    Examples:
    a. $\dfrac{1}{\sqrt{3} - \sqrt{5}}$

    b. $\dfrac{\sqrt{3} + \sqrt{2}}{3}$

    c. $\dfrac{\sqrt{x} - 5}{\sqrt{x} + 2}$

    d. $\dfrac{\sqrt{x} - \sqrt{5}}{\sqrt{x} + \sqrt{5}}$

4. Have the class simplify the following radical expressions by indicating a single-radical expression (an expression with only one radical).

Example 1: $\sqrt[3]{2}\sqrt{5}$

Convert both radicals to cube roots.

$$\sqrt[3]{2}\sqrt{5} = \sqrt[3]{2}\sqrt[3]{125} = \sqrt[3]{250}$$

Example 2: $\dfrac{a^{\frac{1}{6}}b^{\frac{2}{3}}}{a^{\frac{1}{3}}b^{\frac{5}{6}}} = \dfrac{\sqrt[6]{a}\sqrt[3]{b^2}}{\sqrt[3]{a}\sqrt[6]{b^5}}$

Convert each radical to a sixth root.

$$\frac{\sqrt[6]{a}\sqrt[3]{b^2}}{\sqrt[3]{a}\sqrt[6]{b^5}} = \frac{\sqrt[6]{a}\sqrt[6]{b^4}}{\sqrt[6]{a^2}\sqrt[6]{b^5}} = \frac{\sqrt[6]{ab^4}}{\sqrt[6]{a^2b^5}}$$

Rationalize the denominator.

$$\frac{\left(\sqrt[6]{ab^4}\right)\left(\sqrt[6]{a^4b}\right)}{\left(\sqrt[6]{a^2b^5}\right)\left(\sqrt[6]{a^4b}\right)} = \frac{\sqrt[6]{a^5b^5}}{\sqrt[6]{a^6b^6}} = \frac{\sqrt[6]{a^5b^5}}{ab}$$

a. $a^{\frac{1}{2}}b^{-\frac{1}{2}}c^{\frac{5}{6}}$

b. $\dfrac{a^{\frac{1}{4}}b^{\frac{3}{8}}}{a^{\frac{1}{2}}b^{\frac{1}{8}}}$

c. $\sqrt[4]{7}\sqrt{3}$

d. $\dfrac{\sqrt[4]{(x+2)^3}\sqrt[5]{x+2}}{\sqrt{x+2}}$

Section 2: Quadratic Equations

Section 3: Quadratic Formula

1. Inform the class of the theorem by which one may determine the nature of the solution of each quadratic equation.

   a. If $b^2 - 4ac = 0$, then $ax^2 + bx + a = 0$ has just one real-number solution;

   b. If $b^2 - 4ac > 0$, then $ax^2 + bx + c = 0$ has two real-number solutions; and

   c. If $b^2 - 4ac < 0$, then $ax^2 + bx + c = 0$ has no real-number solution.

2. Discuss the conjugate of a complex number, e.g., the conjugate of $a + bi$ is $a - bi$.

3. Demonstrate the use of fractional notation as a useful means for dividing complex numbers.

Example: Divide $4 + 5i$ by $1 + 4i$.

$$\frac{4+5i}{1+4i} = \frac{(4+5i)(1-4i)}{(1+4i)(1-4i)} =$$

$$\frac{4-11i-20i^2}{1-16i^2} = \frac{4-11i+20}{1+16} =$$

$$\frac{24-11i}{17} \text{ or } \frac{24}{17} - \frac{11i}{17}$$

4. This activity should be done after the preceding teacher-directed Activity 1 has been discussed with the class. Have the class respond as to the nature of the solution to each of the following equations. They are not to be solved. Answers are given in parentheses for the teacher's information.

    a. $9x^2 - 12x + 4 = 0$ (one real-number solution)

    b. $x^2 + 5x + 8 = 0$ (no real-number solutions)

    c. $x^2 + 5x + 6 = 0$ (two real-number solutions)

    d. $x^2 - 2x + 10 = 0$ (no real-number solutions)

    e. $4x^2 - 4\sqrt{3}x + 3 = 0$ (one real-number solution)

    f. $9x^2 - 6x = 0$ (two real-number solutions)

5. Have the class respond by giving the conjugate of each of the following numbers.

a. $7 + 2i$	b. $6 - 4i$	c. $-5i + 9$
d. $3i + 8$	e. $-3 - 6i$	f. $8i - 1$

ADDITIONAL ACTIVITIES

The following activities may be reproduced as student worksheets.

» USING THE DISCRIMINANT

In each of the following equations determine k such that each equation has:
      a. one real-number solution;
      b. two real-number solutions; and
      c. no real-number solution.

1. $x^2 + 3x + k = 0$

2. $kx^2 - 4x + 1 = 0$

3. $x^2 + x = 1 - k$

4. $x^2 + x + k = 0$

5. $x^2 - x + 3x + k = 0$

» IMAGINARY NUMBERS

Simplify each of the following problems, leaving imaginary answers in *i* form.

1. $(1 + 3i) \div (3 + 2i)$ _____

2. $(2 + i) \div (3 - 2i)$ _____

3. $\dfrac{5 + \sqrt{-9}}{3 + \sqrt{-25}}$ _____

4. $(2 + i)(6 - 5i)$ _____

5. $(4 + i)^2$ _____

6. $5(2 - 7i)$ _____

7. $8(5 + i)$ _____

8. $(\sqrt{-3})(\sqrt{-10})$ _____

9. $\left(\dfrac{4 + \sqrt{-9}}{4}\right)\left(\dfrac{4 - \sqrt{-9}}{4}\right)$ _____

10. $(-\sqrt{-7} + 2\sqrt{-14})^2$ _____

11. $3\sqrt{-8} \cdot 4\sqrt{-6}$ _____

12. $\dfrac{3}{8i}$ _____

13. $\dfrac{4}{12i^2}$ _____

14. $i^{10} + 1$ _____

15. $i^8 + 2i$ _____

16. $(8 + 10i) + (2 - 5i)$ _____

17. $(6 - 3i) - (12 + 15i)$ _____

Find the reciprocal of each of the following problems and express it in the form of *a* + *bi*.

18. $3 + 4i$ _____

19. $2 - 7i$ _____

20. $6 + 5i$ _____

ADDITIONAL ACTIVITIES, SOLUTION KEY

Using the Discriminant

In each of these problems,
  (a) $b^2 - 4ac$ must equal 0,
  (b) $b^2 - 4ac$ must be a perfect square, and
  (c) $b^2 - 4ac$ must be a number which is not a
  perfect square.

1. $x^2 + 3x + k = 0$
$a = 1, b = 3, c = k$

a. $b^2 - 4ac = 0$
$3^2 - 4(1)(k) = 0$
$9 - 4k = 0$
$-4k = -9$ (subtract 9 from both sides)
$k = \frac{9}{4}$ (divide both sides by -4)

b. $b^2 - 4ac$ is a perfect square
Examples:
$9 - 4k = 1^2$
$9 - 4k = 1$
$-4k = -8$ (subtract 9 from both sides)
$k = 2$ (divide both sides by -4)

$9 - 4k = 2^2$
$9 - 4k = 4$
$-4k = -5$ (subtract 9 from both sides)
$k = \frac{5}{4}$ (divide both sides by -4)

$9 - 4k = 3^2$
$9 - 4k = 9$
$-4k = 0$ (subtract 9 from both sides)
$k = 0$ (divide both sides by -4)

c. $b^2 - 4ac$ is not a perfect square
Examples:
$9 - 4k = 2$
$-4k = -7$ (subtract 9 from both sides)
$k = \frac{7}{4}$ (divide both sides by -4)

$9 - 4k = 3$
$-4k = -6$ (subtract 9 from both sides)
$k = \frac{3}{2}$ (divide both sides by -4)

$9 - 4k = 5$
$-4k = -4$ (subtract 9 from both sides)
$k = 1$ (divide both sides by -4)

2. $kx^2 - 4x + 1 = 0$
$a = k, b = -4, c = 1$

a. $b^2 - 4ac = 0$
$(-4)^2 - 4(k)(1) = 0$
$16 - 4k = 0$
$-4k = -16$
$k = 4$

b. $b^2 - 4ac$ is a perfect square
Examples:
$16 - 4k = 1^2$
$16 - 4k = 1$
$-4k = -15$
$k = \frac{15}{4}$

$16 - 4k = 2^2$
$16 - 4k = 4$
$-4k = -12$
$k = 3$

$16 - 4k = 3^2$
$16 - 4k = 9$
$-4k = -7$
$k = \frac{7}{4}$

c. $b^2 - 4ac$ is not a perfect square
Examples:
$16 - 4k = 2$
$-4k = -14$
$k = \frac{7}{2}$

$16 - 4k = 3$
$-4k = -13$
$k = \frac{13}{4}$

$16 - 4k = 5$
$-4k = -11$
$k = \frac{11}{4}$

3. $x^2 + x = 1 - k$
$x^2 + x - (1 - k) = 0$
$a = 1, b = 1, c = -(1 - k)$

a. $b^2 - 4ac = 0$
$1^2 - 4(1)[-(1 - k)] = 0$
$1 - 4(-1 + k) = 0$
$1 + 4 - 4k = 0$
$5 - 4k = 0$
$-4k = -5$
$k = \frac{5}{4}$

b. $b^2 - 4ac$ is a perfect square
Examples:
$5 - 4k = 1^2$
$5 - 4k = 1$
$-4k = -4$
$k = 1$

$5 - 4k = 2^2$
$5 - 4k = 4$
$-4k = -1$
$k = \frac{1}{4}$

$5 - 4k = 3^2$
$5 - 4k = 9$
$-4k = 4$
$k = -1$

c. $b^2 - 4ac$ is not a perfect square

Examples:

$5 - 4k = 2$
$-4k = -3$
$k = \dfrac{3}{4}$

$5 - 4k = 3$
$-4k = -2$
$k = \dfrac{1}{2}$

$5 - 4k = 5$
$-4k = 0$
$k = 0$

4. $x^2 + x + k = 0$
$a = 1, b = 1, c = k$

a. $b^2 - 4ac = 0$
$1^2 - 4(1)(k) = 0$
$1 - 4k = 0$
$-4k = -1$
$k = \dfrac{1}{4}$

b. $b^2 - 4ac$ is a perfect square

Examples:

$1 - 4k = 1^2$
$1 - 4k = 1$
$-4k = 0$
$k = 0$

$1 - 4k = 2^2$
$1 - 4k = 4$
$-4k = 3$
$k = -\dfrac{3}{4}$

$1 - 4k = 3^2$
$1 - 4k = 9$
$-4k = 8$
$k = -2$

c. $b^2 - 4ac$ is not a perfect square

Examples:

$1 - 4k = 2$
$-4k = 1$
$k = -\dfrac{1}{4}$

$1 - 4k = 3$
$-4k = 2$
$k = -\dfrac{1}{2}$

$1 - 4k = 5$
$-4k = 4$
$k = -1$

5. $x^2 - x + 3x + k = 0$
$x^2 + 2x + k = 0$
$a = 1, b = 2, c = k$

a. $b^2 - 4ac = 0$
$2^2 - 4(1)(k) = 0$
$4 - 4k = 0$
$-4k = -4$
$k = 1$

b. $b^2 - 4ac$ is a perfect square

Examples:

$4 - 4k = 1^2$
$4 - 4k = 1$
$-4k = -3$
$k = \dfrac{3}{4}$

$4 - 4k = 2^2$
$4 - 4k = 4$
$-4k = 0$
$k = 0$

$4 - 4k = 3^2$
$4 - 4k = 9$
$-4k = 5$
$k = -\dfrac{5}{4}$

c. $b^2 - 4ac$ is not a perfect square

Examples:

$4 - 4k = 2$
$-4k = -2$
$k = \dfrac{1}{2}$

$4 - 4k = 3$
$-4k = -1$
$k = \dfrac{1}{4}$

$4 - 4k = 5$
$-4k = 1$
$k = -\dfrac{1}{4}$

Imaginary Numbers

1. $\dfrac{1 + 3i}{3 + 2i} = \dfrac{(1 + 3i)(3 - 2i)}{(3 + 2i)(3 - 2i)} = \dfrac{3 + 7i - 6i^2}{9 - 4i^2} = \dfrac{3 + 7i + 6}{9 + 4} = \dfrac{9 + 7i}{13}$

2. $\dfrac{2 + i}{3 - 2i} = \dfrac{(2 + i)(3 + 2i)}{(3 - 2i)(3 + 2i)} = \dfrac{6 + 7i + 2i^2}{9 - 4i^2} = \dfrac{6 + 7i - 2}{9 + 4} = \dfrac{4 + 7i}{13}$

3. $\dfrac{5 + \sqrt{-9}}{3 + \sqrt{-25}} = \dfrac{5 + 3i}{3 + 5i} = \dfrac{(5 + 3i)(3 - 5i)}{(3 + 5i)(3 - 5i)} =$

$\dfrac{15 - 16i - 15i^2}{9 - 25i^2} = \dfrac{15 - 16i + 15}{9 + 25} = \dfrac{30 - 16i}{34} =$

$\dfrac{15 - 8i}{17}$

4. $(2 + i)(6 - 5i) =$
$12 - 4i - 5i^2 =$
$12 - 4i + 5 = 17 - 4i$

5. $(4 + i)^2 = (4 + i)(4 + i) =$
$16 + 8i + i^2 =$
$16 + 8i - 1 = 15 + 8i$

6. $10 - 35i$

7. $40 + 8i$

8. $(\sqrt{-3})(\sqrt{-10}) = (i\sqrt{3})(i\sqrt{10}) =$
$i^2\sqrt{30} = -1\sqrt{30} = -\sqrt{30}$

9. $\left(\dfrac{4 + \sqrt{-9}}{4}\right)\left(\dfrac{4 - \sqrt{-9}}{4}\right) = \left(\dfrac{4 + 3i}{4}\right)\left(\dfrac{4 - 3i}{4}\right) =$

$\dfrac{16 - 9i^2}{16} = \dfrac{16 + 9}{16} = \dfrac{25}{16}$

10. $(-\sqrt{7} + 2\sqrt{-14})^2 =$
$(-i\sqrt{7} + 2i\sqrt{14})^2 =$
$(-i\sqrt{7} + 2i\sqrt{14})(-i\sqrt{7} + 2i\sqrt{14}) =$
$i^2\sqrt{49} - 4i^2\sqrt{98} + 4i^2\sqrt{196} =$
$-1\sqrt{49} + 4\sqrt{98} - 4\sqrt{196} =$
$-7 + 4(7\sqrt{2}) - 4(14) =$
$-7 + 28\sqrt{2} - 56 =$
$-63 + 28\sqrt{2}$

11. $3\sqrt{-8} \cdot 4\sqrt{-6} = 3i\sqrt{8} \cdot 4i\sqrt{6} =$
$12i^2\sqrt{48} = -12\sqrt{48} = -12(4\sqrt{3})$
$-48\sqrt{3}$

12. $\dfrac{3}{8i} = \dfrac{(3)(i)}{(8i)(i)} = \dfrac{3i}{8i^2} = \dfrac{3i}{-8} = -\dfrac{3}{8}i$

13. $\dfrac{4}{12i^2} = \dfrac{4}{-12} = -\dfrac{1}{3}$

14. $i^{10} + 1 = -1 + 1 = 0$

15. $1 + 2i$

16. $10 + 5i$

17. $(6 - 3i) - (12 + 15i) =$
$6 - 3i - 12 - 15i =$
$-6 - 18i$

18. The reciprocal of $3 + 4i$ is $\dfrac{1}{3 + 4i} = \dfrac{1}{3} + \dfrac{1}{4}i$,

where $a = \dfrac{1}{3}$ and $b = \dfrac{1}{4}$.

19. The reciprocal of $2 - 7i$ is $\dfrac{1}{2 - 7i} = \dfrac{1}{2} - \dfrac{1}{7}i$,

where $a = \dfrac{1}{2}$ and $b = -\dfrac{1}{7}$.

20. The reciprocal of $6 + 5i$ is $\dfrac{1}{6 + 5i} = \dfrac{1}{6} + \dfrac{1}{5}i$,

where $a = \dfrac{1}{6}$ and $b = \dfrac{1}{5}$.

ANSWER KEY

SECTION 1

1.1 rational
1.2 irrational
1.3 irrational
1.4 irrational
1.5 rational
1.6 rational
1.7 irrational
1.8 rational
1.9 irrational
1.10 irrational
1.11 $\dfrac{225}{1,000} = \dfrac{9}{40}$

1.12 $\dfrac{625}{1,000} = \dfrac{5}{8}$

1.13 $-\dfrac{66\frac{2}{3}}{100} = -\dfrac{200}{300} = -\dfrac{2}{3}$

1.14 Let $0.888... = x$
$$10x = 8.888...$$
$$\underline{\quad x = 0.888...}$$
$$9x = 8$$
$$x = \dfrac{8}{9}$$

1.15 Let $3.143143... = x$
$$1,000x = 3,143.143...$$
$$\underline{\quad x = \qquad 3.143...}$$
$$999x = 3,140$$
$$x = -\dfrac{3,140}{999}$$

1.16 index
1.17 radicand
1.18 radical sign
1.19 radical
1.20 principal
1.21 $x^{3/5}$
1.22 $y^{2/2}$ or y^1 or y
1.23 $a^{1/3}$
1.24 $x^{5/4}$
1.25 $b^{1/2}$
1.26 $\sqrt[5]{y^3}$
1.27 $\sqrt{x^5}$
1.28 $\sqrt{b}$
1.29 $\sqrt{q^3}$
1.30 $\sqrt[5]{s^6}$
1.31 $\sqrt[3]{-27^2} = (-3)^2 = 9$
1.32 $\sqrt{81} = 9$
1.33 $\sqrt[3]{(\frac{27}{8})^4} = (\frac{3}{2})^4 = \dfrac{81}{16}$ or $5\frac{1}{16}$
1.34 $\sqrt{25^5} = 5^5 = 3{,}125$

1.35 $(\sqrt[3]{0.125})^2 = (0.5)^2 = 0.25$
1.36 $\sqrt[3]{3}\,\sqrt[3]{16} = \sqrt[3]{48}$
$$= \sqrt[3]{8 \cdot 6}$$
$$= 2\sqrt[3]{6}$$
1.37 $\sqrt{3} \cdot 2\sqrt{2} = 2\sqrt{6}$
1.38 $\sqrt{6}\sqrt{8} = \sqrt{48}$
$$= \sqrt{16 \cdot 3}$$
$$= 4\sqrt{3}$$
1.39 $\sqrt[4]{5x} \cdot \sqrt[4]{2x} = \sqrt[4]{10x^2}$
1.40 $\sqrt[3]{-64} = \sqrt[3]{(-4)^3} = -4$
1.41 $\sqrt[4]{a^3b} \cdot \sqrt[4]{ab^2} = \sqrt[4]{a^4b^3} = a\sqrt[4]{b^3}$
1.42 $5\sqrt[3]{4} \cdot 2\sqrt[3]{2} = 10\sqrt[3]{8}$
$$= 10 \cdot 2$$
$$= 20$$
1.43 $\sqrt[4]{x^3y} \cdot \sqrt[4]{xy^2} = \sqrt[4]{x^4y^3} = x\sqrt[4]{y^3}$
1.44 $\dfrac{\sqrt{6}}{\sqrt{3}} = \sqrt{\dfrac{6}{3}} = \sqrt{2}$
1.45 $\sqrt[3]{54} \div \sqrt[3]{2} = \dfrac{\sqrt[3]{54}}{\sqrt[3]{2}} = \sqrt[3]{\dfrac{54}{2}} = \sqrt[3]{27} = 3$
1.46 $\dfrac{6\sqrt[4]{3}}{5\sqrt[4]{243}} = (\frac{6}{5})\sqrt[4]{\dfrac{3}{243}} = (\frac{6}{5})\sqrt[4]{\dfrac{1}{81}} = \dfrac{\overset{2}{\cancel{6}}}{5} \cdot \dfrac{1}{\underset{1}{\cancel{3}}} = \dfrac{2}{5}$
1.47 $\sqrt[4]{a^9} \div \sqrt[4]{a} = \sqrt[4]{\dfrac{a^9}{a}} = \sqrt[4]{a^8} = \sqrt[4]{(a^2)^4} = a^2$
1.48 $\sqrt[3]{\dfrac{3}{4}} = \sqrt[3]{\dfrac{3 \cdot 2}{4 \cdot 2}} = \sqrt[3]{\dfrac{6}{8}} = \dfrac{\sqrt[3]{6}}{\sqrt[3]{8}} = \dfrac{\sqrt[3]{6}}{2}$
1.49 $(4\sqrt{2})^2 = 16(\sqrt{2})^2 = 32$
1.50 $(\sqrt[3]{5a^2})^3 = 5a^2$
1.51 $\sqrt[n]{a^2} \cdot \sqrt[n]{a^{n-2}} = \sqrt[n]{a^{2+n-2}} = \sqrt[n]{a^n} = a,\ n > 0$
1.52 $\sqrt{3}(3\sqrt{3} - \sqrt{2}) = 3\sqrt{3}\sqrt{3} - \sqrt{3}\sqrt{2}$
$$= 3 \cdot 3 - \sqrt{6}$$
$$= 9 - \sqrt{6}$$
1.53 $2\sqrt[3]{(x-y)^2}\,\sqrt[3]{x-y} = 2\sqrt[3]{(x-y)^3}$
$$= 2(x-y) \text{ or } 2x - 2y$$
1.54 $(2\sqrt{5a} - 3\sqrt{3})(3\sqrt{5a} + \sqrt{2})$
$$= 6 \cdot 5a - 9\sqrt{3}\sqrt{5a} + 2\sqrt{5a}\sqrt{2} - 3\sqrt{3}\sqrt{2}$$
$$= 30a - 9\sqrt{15a} + 2\sqrt{10a} - 3\sqrt{6}$$
1.55 $(7 - \sqrt{x})^2 = 49 - 14\sqrt{x} + x$
1.56 $(\sqrt[3]{2} + \sqrt{3})^2 = (\sqrt[3]{2})^2 + 2\sqrt[3]{2}\sqrt{3} + (\sqrt{3})^2$
$$= \sqrt[3]{4} + 2\sqrt[3]{2}\sqrt{3} + 3$$
1.57 $(\sqrt{x+y} + \sqrt{x-y}) \cdot (\sqrt{x+y} - \sqrt{x-y})$
$$= (\sqrt{x+y})^2 - (\sqrt{x-y})^2 = x + y - (x - y)$$
$$= \cancel{x} + y - \cancel{x} + y$$
$$= 2y,\ x > y$$

1.58 $(5 - \sqrt[3]{4})(5 + \sqrt[3]{4})$
$= 25 - (\sqrt[3]{4})^2 = 25 - \sqrt[3]{16}$
$= 25 - 2\sqrt[3]{2}$

1.59 $\dfrac{\frac{\sqrt{2}+1}{3}(\frac{3\sqrt{5}}{1})}{\frac{6}{\sqrt{5}}(\frac{3\sqrt{5}}{1})} = \dfrac{\sqrt{5}(\sqrt{2}+1)}{18} = \dfrac{\sqrt{15}}{18}$

1.60 $\sqrt{5} - a$

1.61 $x + \sqrt{2}$

1.62 $\sqrt{8} + \sqrt{9}$

1.63 $2x^2 - \sqrt{3}$

1.64 $a + \sqrt{a-1}$

1.65 $\sqrt{x} - 2\sqrt{b}$

1.66 $\dfrac{5(4 + \sqrt{3})}{(4 - \sqrt{3})(4 + \sqrt{3})} = \dfrac{20 + 5\sqrt{3}}{16 - 3} = \dfrac{20 + 5\sqrt{3}}{13}$

1.67 $\dfrac{12(\sqrt{7} - 2)}{(\sqrt{7} + 2)(\sqrt{7} - 2)} = \dfrac{12\sqrt{7} - 24}{7 - 4} = \dfrac{12\sqrt{7} - 24}{3} = $
$4\sqrt{7} - 8$

1.68 $\dfrac{6(\sqrt{2} + \sqrt{3})}{(\sqrt{2} - \sqrt{3})(\sqrt{2} + \sqrt{3})} = \dfrac{6\sqrt{2} + 6\sqrt{3}}{2 - 3} = \dfrac{6\sqrt{2} + 6\sqrt{3}}{-1} = $
$-6\sqrt{2} - 6\sqrt{3}$

1.69 $\dfrac{5\sqrt{6}\sqrt{5}}{\sqrt{5}\sqrt{5}} = \dfrac{5\sqrt{30}}{5} = \sqrt{30}$

1.70 $\dfrac{(3\sqrt{2} - 2\sqrt{3})(3\sqrt{2} - 2\sqrt{3})}{(3\sqrt{2} + 2\sqrt{3})(3\sqrt{2} - 2\sqrt{3})} = \dfrac{18 - 12\sqrt{6} + 12}{18 - 12} = $
$\dfrac{30 - 12\sqrt{6}}{6} = 5 - 2\sqrt{6}$

1.71 $\dfrac{(\sqrt{a} + 2\sqrt{y})(\sqrt{a} + 2\sqrt{y})}{(\sqrt{a} - 2\sqrt{y})(\sqrt{a} + 2\sqrt{y})} = \dfrac{a + 4\sqrt{ay} + 4y}{a - 4y}$

1.72 $\dfrac{\sqrt{6}(\sqrt{5} + \sqrt{3})}{(\sqrt{5} - \sqrt{3})(\sqrt{5} + \sqrt{3})} = \dfrac{\sqrt{30} + \sqrt{18}}{5 - 3} = \dfrac{\sqrt{30} + 3\sqrt{2}}{2}$

1.73 $\dfrac{(2\sqrt{x} - 3\sqrt{y})(\sqrt{x} - \sqrt{y})}{(\sqrt{x} + \sqrt{y})(\sqrt{x} - \sqrt{y})} = \dfrac{2x - 5\sqrt{xy} + 3y}{x - y}$

1.74 $\dfrac{(3\sqrt{6} + 5\sqrt{2})(4\sqrt{6} + 3\sqrt{2})}{(4\sqrt{6} - 3\sqrt{2})(4\sqrt{6} + 3\sqrt{2})} = \dfrac{72 + 29\sqrt{12} + 30}{96 - 18} = $
$\dfrac{102 + 58\sqrt{3}}{78} = \dfrac{51 + 29\sqrt{3}}{39}$

1.75 $\dfrac{(\sqrt{a+1} - 2)(\sqrt{a+1} - 2)}{(\sqrt{a+1} + 2)(\sqrt{a+1} - 2)} = \dfrac{a + 1 - 4\sqrt{a+1} + 4}{a + 1 - 4} = $
$\dfrac{5 + a - 4\sqrt{a+1}}{a - 3}$

1.76 $\sqrt{x} = 7$
$(\sqrt{x})^2 = 7^2$
$x = 49$
Check:
$\sqrt{4} = 7$
$7 = 7$

1.77 $\sqrt{x - 5} = 4$
$(\sqrt{x - 5})^2 = 4^2$
$x - 5 = 16$
$x = 21$
Check:
$\sqrt{21 - 5} = 4$
$\sqrt{16} = 4$
$4 = 4$

1.78 $\sqrt{x - 1} + 4 = 0$
$\sqrt{x - 1} = -4$
$(\sqrt{x - 1})^2 = (-4)^2$
$x - 1 = 16$
$x = 17$
Check:
$\sqrt{17 - 1} + 4 = 0$
$\sqrt{16} + 4 = 0$
$4 + 4 = 0$
$8 \neq 0$
$\therefore$ This equation has no roots.

1.79 $\sqrt{x} + 1 = 7 - 2\sqrt{x}$
$3\sqrt{x} + 1 = 7$
$3\sqrt{x} = 6$
$\sqrt{x} = 2$
$(\sqrt{x})^2 = 2^2$
$x = 4$
Check:
$\sqrt{4} + 1 = 7 - 2\sqrt{4}$
$2 + 1 = 7 - 4$
$3 = 3$

1.80 $\sqrt{4x} = 2\sqrt{2x - 3}$
$(\sqrt{4x})^2 = (2\sqrt{2x - 3})^2$
$4x = 4(2x - 3)$
$4x = 8x - 12$
$-4x = -12$
$x = 3$
Check:
$\sqrt{4(3)} = 2\sqrt{2(3) - 3}$
$\sqrt{12} = 2\sqrt{6 - 3}$
$2\sqrt{3} = 2\sqrt{3}$

1.81 $\sqrt[3]{x - 5} - 2 = 0$
$\sqrt[3]{x - 5} = 2$
$(\sqrt[3]{x - 5})^3 = 2^3$
$x - 5 = 8$
$x = 13$
Check:
$\sqrt[3]{13 - 5} - 2 = 0$
$\sqrt[3]{8} - 2 = 0$
$2 - 2 = 0$
$0 = 0$

1.82
$$\sqrt{2y - 5} = \sqrt{2y + 6}$$
$$(\sqrt{2y - 5})^2 = (\sqrt{2y + 6})^2$$
$$2\cancel{y} - 5 = 2\cancel{y} + 6$$
$$-5 \neq 6$$
∴ This equation has no roots.

1.83
$$2\sqrt{5x - 4} - 3 = -11$$
$$2\sqrt{5x - 4} = -8$$
$$\sqrt{5x - 4} = -4$$
$$(\sqrt{5x - 4})^2 = (-4)^2$$
$$5x - 4 = 16$$
$$5x = 20$$
$$x = 4$$

Check:
$$2\sqrt{5(4) - 4} - 3 = -11$$
$$2\sqrt{20 - 4} - 3 = -11$$
$$2\sqrt{16} - 3 = -11$$
$$8 - 3 = -11$$
$$-5 \neq -11$$
∴ This equation has no roots.

1.84
$$x - 8 = -\sqrt{x^2 - 8}$$
$$(x - 8)^2 = (-\sqrt{x^2 - 8})^2$$
$$\cancel{x^2} - 16x + 64 = \cancel{x^2} - 8$$
$$-16x = -72$$
$$x = \frac{-72}{-16} = \frac{9}{2} \text{ or } 4\frac{1}{2}$$

Check:
$$-3\frac{1}{2} - 8 = -\sqrt{(\frac{9}{2})^2 - 8}$$
$$-3\frac{1}{2} = -\sqrt{\frac{81}{4} - \frac{32}{4}}$$
$$-3\frac{1}{2} = -\sqrt{\frac{49}{4}}$$
$$-3\frac{1}{2} = -\frac{7}{2}$$

1.85
$$\sqrt{y} - \sqrt{7} = \sqrt{y + 7}$$
$$(\sqrt{y} - \sqrt{7})^2 = (\sqrt{y + 7})^2$$
$$\cancel{y} - 2\sqrt{7y} + 7 = \cancel{y} + 7$$
$$-2\sqrt{7y} = 0$$
$$\sqrt{7y} = 0$$
$$(\sqrt{7y})^2 = 0^2$$
$$7y = 0$$
$$y = 0$$

Check:
$$\sqrt{0} - \sqrt{7} = \sqrt{0 + 7}$$
$$-\sqrt{7} \neq \sqrt{7}$$
∴ This equation has no roots.

1.86
$$-\sqrt{6x + 1} - 5 = -7 - \sqrt{3x + 1}$$
$$-\sqrt{6x + 1} = -2 - \sqrt{3x + 1}$$
$$(-\sqrt{6x + 1})^2 = (-2 - \sqrt{3x + 1})^2$$
$$6x + 1 = 4 + 4\sqrt{3x + 1} + 3x + 1$$
$$6x + 1 = 5 + 4\sqrt{3x + 1} + 3x$$
$$3x + 1 = 5 + 4\sqrt{3x + 1}$$
$$3x - 4 = 4\sqrt{3x + 1}$$
$$(3x - 4)^2 = (4\sqrt{3x + 1})^2$$
$$9x^2 - 24x + 16 = 16(3x + 1)$$
$$9x^2 - 24x + \cancel{16} = 48x + \cancel{16}$$
$$9x^2 - 72x = 0$$
$$9x(x - 8) = 0$$
$$9x = 0 \text{ or } x - 8 = 0$$
$$x = 0 \qquad x = 8$$

Check:
$$-\sqrt{6(0) + 1} - 5 = -7 - \sqrt{3(0) + 1}$$
$$-1 - 5 = -7 - 1$$
$$-6 \neq -8$$
or
$$-\sqrt{6(8) + 1} - 5 = -7 - \sqrt{3(8) + 1}$$
$$-\sqrt{48 + 1} - 5 = -7 - \sqrt{24 + 1}$$
$$-\sqrt{49} - 5 = -7 - \sqrt{25}$$
$$-7 - 5 = -7 - 5$$
$$-12 = -12$$
∴ $x = 8$

1.87
$$\sqrt{4x + 5} - \sqrt{x - 1} = \sqrt{x + 4}$$
$$\sqrt{4x + 5} = \sqrt{x - 1} + \sqrt{x + 4}$$
$$(\sqrt{4x + 5})^2 = (\sqrt{x - 1} + \sqrt{x + 4})^2$$
$$4x + 5 = x - 1 + 2\sqrt{(x - 1)(x + 4)} + x + 4$$
$$4x + 5 = 2x + 3 + 2\sqrt{x^2 + 3x - 4}$$
$$2x + 5 = 3 + 2\sqrt{x^2 + 3x - 4}$$
$$2x + 2 = 2\sqrt{x^2 + 3x - 4}$$
$$x + 1 = \sqrt{x^2 + 3x - 4}$$
$$(x + 1)^2 = (\sqrt{x^2 + 3x - 4})^2$$
$$\cancel{x^2} + 2x + 1 = \cancel{x^2} + 3x - 4$$
$$-x + 1 = -4$$
$$-x = -5$$
$$x = 5$$

Check:
$$\sqrt{4(5) + 5} - \sqrt{5 - 1} = \sqrt{5 + 4}$$
$$\sqrt{20 + 5} - \sqrt{4} = \sqrt{9}$$
$$\sqrt{25} - \sqrt{4} = \sqrt{9}$$
$$5 - 2 = 3$$
$$3 = 3$$

1.88 $\dfrac{\sqrt{x}+7}{\sqrt{x}+1} = \dfrac{\sqrt{x}+7}{\sqrt{x}-1}$

Cross-multiply:

$$(\sqrt{x}+7)(\sqrt{x}-1) = (\sqrt{x}+1)(\sqrt{x}+1)$$
$$\cancel{x}+6\sqrt{x}-7 = \cancel{x}+2\sqrt{x}+1$$
$$4\sqrt{x}-7 = 1$$
$$4\sqrt{x} = 8$$
$$\sqrt{x} = 2$$
$$(\sqrt{x})^2 = 2^2$$
$$x = 4$$

Check:

$$\dfrac{\sqrt{4}+7}{\sqrt{4}+1} = \dfrac{\sqrt{4}+1}{\sqrt{4}-1}$$
$$\dfrac{2+7}{2+1} = \dfrac{2+1}{2-1}$$
$$\dfrac{9}{3} = \dfrac{3}{1}$$
$$3 = 3$$

1.89 $\sqrt{12x-23} = \sqrt{3x-11} + \sqrt{3x}$
$$(\sqrt{12x-23})^2 = (\sqrt{3x-11}+\sqrt{3x})^2$$
$$12x-23 = 3x-11 + 2\sqrt{3x}\cdot\sqrt{3x-11} + 3x$$
$$12x-23 = 6x-11 + 2\sqrt{9x^2-33x}$$
$$6x-23 = -11 + 2\sqrt{9x^2-33x}$$
$$6x-12 = 2\sqrt{9x^2-33x}$$
$$3x-6 = \sqrt{9x^2-33x}$$
$$(3x-6)^2 = \sqrt{9x^2-33x}^2$$
$$\cancel{9x^2}-36x+36 = \cancel{9x^2}-33x$$
$$-3x+36 = 0$$
$$-3x = -36$$
$$x = 12$$

Check:
$$\sqrt{12(12)-23} = \sqrt{3(12)-11} + \sqrt{3(12)}$$
$$\sqrt{144-23} = \sqrt{36-11} + \sqrt{36}$$
$$\sqrt{121} = \sqrt{25} + \sqrt{36}$$
$$11 = 5+6$$
$$11 = 11$$

1.90 $\sqrt{x-2} - \sqrt{2x} = \sqrt{x+2}$
$$\sqrt{x-2} = \sqrt{x+2} + \sqrt{2x}$$
$$\sqrt{x-2} - \sqrt{x+2} = \sqrt{2x}$$
$$(\sqrt{x-2} - \sqrt{x+2})^2 = (\sqrt{2x})^2$$
$$x-\cancel{2} - 2\sqrt{x+2}\cdot\sqrt{x-2} + x+\cancel{2} = 2x$$
$$\cancel{2x} - 2\sqrt{x^2-4} = \cancel{2x}$$
$$-2\sqrt{x^2-4} = 0$$
$$\sqrt{x^2-4} = 0$$
$$(\sqrt{x^2-4})^2 = 0^2$$
$$x^2-4 = 0$$
$$x^2 = 4$$
$$\sqrt{x^2} = \sqrt{4}$$
$$x = 2$$

Check:
$$\sqrt{2-2} - \sqrt{2(2)} = \sqrt{2+2}$$
$$\sqrt{0} - \sqrt{4} = \sqrt{4}$$
$$-2 \neq 2$$

∴ This equation has no roots.

SELF TEST 1

1.01 rational
1.02 irrational
1.03 irrational
1.04 rational

1.05 Let $0.1313\ldots = x$
$$100x = 13.1313\ldots$$
$$\underline{\quad x = 0.1313\ldots}$$
$$99x = 13$$
$$x = \dfrac{13}{99}$$

1.06 $4x^{3/2}$
1.07 $y^{2/3}$
1.08 $6x^{2/5}y^{1/5}$

1.09 $\sqrt[3]{\left(\dfrac{64}{27}\right)^2} = \left(\dfrac{4}{3}\right)^2 = \dfrac{16}{9}$

1.010 $\sqrt[3]{\left(\dfrac{-27}{8}\right)^4} = \left(\dfrac{-3}{2}\right)^4 = \dfrac{81}{16}$

1.011 $\dfrac{1}{3}(3\sqrt[3]{3}) = \sqrt[3]{3}$

1.012 $\sqrt[3]{24} = \sqrt[3]{8}\sqrt[3]{3} = 2\sqrt[3]{3}$

1.013 $\dfrac{\sqrt{25}}{\sqrt{128}} = \dfrac{5}{\sqrt{2}\sqrt{64}} = \dfrac{5}{8\sqrt{2}} = \dfrac{5\sqrt{2}}{8\sqrt{2}(\sqrt{2})} = \dfrac{5\sqrt{2}}{\sqrt{16}}$

1.014 $2\sqrt{4}\sqrt{5} + 8\sqrt{9}\sqrt{5} - \sqrt{16}\sqrt{5}$
$$= 4\sqrt{5} + 24\sqrt{5} - 4\sqrt{5}$$
$$= 24\sqrt{5}$$

1.015 $\sqrt[3]{8x^3} = 2x$

1.016 $6\sqrt[3]{24} = 6\sqrt[3]{8}\sqrt[3]{3} = 12\sqrt[3]{3}$

1.017 $3\sqrt[3]{-27}\sqrt[3]{2} + \dfrac{3}{2}\sqrt[3]{-125}\sqrt[3]{2} + 4\sqrt[3]{-8}\sqrt[3]{2}$

$$= -9\sqrt[3]{2} - \dfrac{15}{2}\sqrt[3]{2} - 8\sqrt[3]{2} = -24\dfrac{1}{2}\sqrt[3]{2}$$

1.018 $4x + 12\sqrt{xy} + 9y$

1.019 $\dfrac{2\sqrt[3]{25}}{3\sqrt[3]{5}\sqrt[3]{25}} = \dfrac{2\sqrt[3]{25}}{3\sqrt[3]{125}} = \dfrac{2\sqrt[3]{25}}{15}$

1.020 $\dfrac{(\sqrt{5}+\sqrt{3})(\sqrt{3}+\sqrt{5})}{(\sqrt{3}-\sqrt{5})(\sqrt{3}+\sqrt{5})} = \dfrac{\sqrt{15}+\sqrt{9}+\sqrt{25}+\sqrt{15}}{3-5} =$

$$\dfrac{\sqrt{15}+3+5+\sqrt{15}}{-2} = \dfrac{8+2\sqrt{15}}{-2} = -4-\sqrt{15}$$

1.021 $\sqrt{x}+5 = 9$
$$\sqrt{x} = 4$$
$$(\sqrt{x})^2 = 4^2$$
$$x = 16$$

Check:
$$\sqrt{16}+5 = 9$$
$$4+5 = 9$$
$$9 = 9$$

1.022
$$3 + \sqrt{x + 2} = 11$$
$$\sqrt{x + 2} = 8$$
$$(\sqrt{x + 2})^2 = 8^2$$
$$x + 2 = 64$$
$$x = 62$$

Check:
$$3 + \sqrt{62 + 2} = 11$$
$$3 + \sqrt{64} = 11$$
$$3 + 8 = 11$$
$$11 = 11$$

1.023
$$\sqrt{x + 3} = \sqrt{2x - 3}$$
$$(\sqrt{x + 3})^2 = (\sqrt{2x - 3})^2$$
$$x + 3 = 2x - 3$$
$$-x + 3 = -3$$
$$-x = -6$$
$$x = 6$$

Check:
$$\sqrt{6 + 3} = \sqrt{2(6) - 3}$$
$$\sqrt{9} = \sqrt{12 - 3}$$
$$\sqrt{9} = \sqrt{9}$$
$$3 = 3$$

1.024
$$\sqrt{3x + 4} = 1 + \sqrt{3x - 11}$$
$$(\sqrt{3x + 4})^2 = (1 + \sqrt{3x - 11})^2$$
$$3x + 4 = 1 + 2\sqrt{3x - 11} + 3x - 11$$
$$\cancel{3x} + 4 = \cancel{3x} - 10 + 2\sqrt{3x - 11}$$
$$14 = 2\sqrt{3x - 11}$$
$$7 = \sqrt{3x - 11}$$
$$7^2 = (\sqrt{3x - 11})^2$$
$$49 = 3x - 11$$
$$60 = 3x$$
$$20 = x$$

Check:
$$\sqrt{3(20) + 4} = 1 + \sqrt{3(20) - 11}$$
$$\sqrt{60 + 4} = 1 + \sqrt{60 - 11}$$
$$\sqrt{64} = 1 + \sqrt{49}$$
$$8 = 1 + 7$$
$$8 = 8$$

1.025
$$2\sqrt{x + 2} - \sqrt{x - 3} = \sqrt{x + 9}$$
$$2\sqrt{x + 2} = \sqrt{x + 9} + \sqrt{x - 3}$$
$$(2\sqrt{x + 2})^2 = (\sqrt{x + 9} + \sqrt{x - 3})^2$$
$$4(x + 2) = x + 9 + 2\sqrt{x - 3}\sqrt{x + 9} + x - 3$$
$$4x + 8 = 2x + 6 + 2\sqrt{x^2 + 6x - 27}$$
$$2x + 8 = 6 + 2\sqrt{x^2 + 6x - 27}$$
$$2x + 2 = 2\sqrt{x^2 + 6x - 27}$$
$$x + 1 = \sqrt{x^2 + 6x - 27}$$
$$(x + 1)^2 = (\sqrt{x^2 + 6x - 27})^2$$
$$\cancel{x^2} + 2x + 1 = \cancel{x^2} + 6x - 27$$
$$-4x + 1 = -27$$
$$-4x = -28$$
$$x = 7$$

Check:
$$2\sqrt{7 + 2} - \sqrt{7 - 3} = \sqrt{7 + 9}$$
$$2\sqrt{9} - \sqrt{4} = \sqrt{16}$$
$$6 - 2 = 4$$
$$4 = 4$$

SECTION 2

2.1
$$x^2 = 144$$
$$\sqrt{x^2} = \pm\sqrt{144}$$
$$x = \pm 12$$

Check:
$$12^2 = 144$$
$$(-12)^2 = 144$$

2.2
$$16y^2 = 49$$
$$\sqrt{16y^2} = \pm\sqrt{49}$$
$$4y = \pm 7$$
$$y = \pm\frac{7}{4}$$

Check:
$$16\left(\frac{7}{4}\right)^2 = 49$$
$$16\left(\frac{49}{16}\right) = 49$$
$$49 = 49$$

$$16\left(-\frac{7}{4}\right)^2 = 49$$
$$16\left(\frac{49}{16}\right) = 49$$
$$49 = 49$$

2.3
$$7x^2 = 49$$
$$x^2 = 7$$
$$\sqrt{x^2} = \pm\sqrt{7}$$
$$x = \pm\sqrt{7}$$

Check:
$$7(\sqrt{7})^2 = 49$$
$$7 \cdot 7 = 49$$
$$49 = 49$$

$$7(-\sqrt{7})^2 = 49$$
$$7 \cdot 7 = 49$$
$$49 = 49$$

2.4
$$6x^2 + 1 = 13$$
$$6x^2 = 12$$
$$x^2 = 2$$
$$\sqrt{x^2} = \pm\sqrt{2}$$
$$x = \pm\sqrt{2}$$

Check:
$$6(\sqrt{2})^2 + 1 = 13$$
$$6(2) + 1 = 13$$
$$12 + 1 = 13$$
$$13 = 13$$

$$6(-\sqrt{2})^2 + 1 = 13$$
$$6(2) + 1 = 13$$
$$12 + 1 = 13$$
$$13 = 13$$

2.5
$$5a^2 - 55 = 90$$
$$5a^2 = 145$$
$$a^2 = 29$$
$$\sqrt{a^2} = \pm\sqrt{29}$$
$$a = \pm\sqrt{29}$$

Check:
$$5(\sqrt{29})^2 - 55 = 90$$
$$5(29) - 55 = 90$$
$$145 - 55 = 90$$
$$90 = 90$$

$$5(-\sqrt{29})^2 - 55 = 90$$
$$5(29) - 55 = 90$$
$$145 - 55 = 90$$
$$90 = 90$$

2.6
$$3x^2 + 2 = 11 - x^2$$
$$4x^2 + 2 = 11$$
$$4x^2 = 9$$
$$x^2 = \frac{9}{4}$$
$$\sqrt{x^2} = \pm\sqrt{\frac{9}{4}}$$
$$x = \pm\frac{3}{2}$$

Check:
$$3(\pm\frac{3}{2})^2 + 2 = 11 - (\pm\frac{3}{2})^2$$
$$3(\frac{9}{4}) + 2 = 11 - \frac{9}{4}$$
$$\frac{27}{4} + \frac{8}{4} = \frac{44}{4} - \frac{9}{4}$$
$$\frac{35}{4} = \frac{35}{4}$$

2.7
$$8x^2 - 24 = 3x^2 - 9$$
$$5x^2 - 24 = -9$$
$$5x^2 = 15$$
$$x^2 = 3$$
$$\sqrt{x^2} = \pm\sqrt{3}$$
$$x = \pm\sqrt{3}$$

Check:
$$8(\pm\sqrt{3})^2 - 24 = 3(\pm\sqrt{3})^2 - 9$$
$$8 \cdot 3 - 24 = 3 \cdot 3 - 9$$
$$24 - 24 = 9 - 9$$
$$0 = 0$$

2.8
$$0.2x^2 + 1.2 = 3.4$$
$$2x^2 + 12 = 34$$
$$2x^2 = 22$$
$$x^2 = 11$$
$$\sqrt{x^2} = \pm\sqrt{11}$$
$$x = \pm\sqrt{11}$$

Check:
$$0.2(\pm\sqrt{11})^2 + 1.2 = 3.4$$
$$0.2(11) + 1.2 = 3.4$$
$$2.2 + 1.2 = 3.4$$
$$3.4 = 3.4$$

2.9
$$(x + 3)(x - 3) = 16 - 2x^2$$
$$x^2 - 9 = 16 - 2x^2$$
$$3x^2 - 9 = 16$$
$$3x^2 = 25$$
$$x^2 = \frac{25}{3}$$
$$\sqrt{x^2} = \pm\sqrt{\frac{25}{3}}$$
$$x = \pm\frac{5}{\sqrt{3}} = \pm\frac{5\sqrt{3}}{3}$$

Check:
$$(\pm\frac{5\sqrt{3}}{3} + 3)(\pm\frac{5\sqrt{3}}{3} - 3) = 16 - 2(\pm\frac{5\sqrt{3}}{3})^2$$
$$\frac{25 \cdot 3}{9} - 9 = 16 - 2(\frac{25 \cdot 3}{9})$$
$$\frac{25}{3} - \frac{27}{3} = \frac{48}{3} - 2(\frac{25}{3})$$
$$-\frac{2}{3} = \frac{48}{3} - \frac{50}{3}$$
$$-\frac{2}{3} = -\frac{2}{3}$$

2.10
$$\frac{4}{x^2 - 7} = 1$$
$$x^2 - 7 = 4 \qquad \text{(cross-multiply)}$$
$$x^2 = 11$$
$$\sqrt{x^2} = \pm\sqrt{11}$$
$$x = \pm\sqrt{11}$$

Check:
$$\frac{4}{(\pm\sqrt{11})^2 - 7} = 1$$
$$\frac{4}{11 - 7} = 1$$
$$\frac{4}{4} = 1$$
$$1 = 1$$

2.11
$$(2x - 1)(3x + 2) = x + 292$$
$$6x^2 + \cancel{x} - 2 = \cancel{x} + 292$$
$$6x^2 = 294$$
$$x^2 = 49$$
$$\sqrt{x^2} = \pm\sqrt{49}$$
$$x = \pm 7$$

Check:
$$(2 \cdot 7 - 1)(3 \cdot 7 + 2) = 7 + 292$$
$$(14 - 1)(21 + 2) = 7 + 292$$
$$13(23) = 299$$
$$299 = 299$$

$$[2(-7) - 1][3(-7) + 2] = -7 + 292$$
$$(-14 - 1)(-21 + 2) = -7 + 292$$
$$-15(-19) = 285$$
$$285 = 285$$

2.12
$$5y^2 + 500 = 844.45$$
$$5y^2 = 344.45$$
$$y^2 = 68.89$$
$$y^2 = \frac{6,889}{100}$$
$$\sqrt{y^2} = \pm\sqrt{\frac{6,889}{100}}$$
$$y = \pm\frac{83}{10} = \pm 8.3$$

Check:
$$5(\pm\tfrac{83}{10})^2 + 500 = 844.45$$
$$5(\tfrac{6,889}{100}) + 500 = 844.45$$
$$5(68.89) + 500 = 844.45$$
$$344.45 + 500 = 844.45$$
$$844.45 = 844.45$$

2.13 $-12x$

2.14 16

2.15 $7x^2$

2.16
$$2x^2 - 6 = 0$$
$$2x(x - 3) = 0$$
$$2x = 0 \qquad x - 3 = 0$$
$$x = 0 \qquad x = 3$$

Check:
$$2(0)^2 - 6 \cdot 0 = 0$$
$$0 - 0 = 0$$
$$2 \cdot 3^2 - 6 \cdot 3 = 0$$
$$2 \cdot 9 - 6 \cdot 3 = 0$$
$$18 - 18 = 0$$
$$0 = 0$$

2.17
$$x^2 + 8x + 12 = 0$$
$$(x + 6)(x + 2) = 0$$
$$x + 6 = 0 \qquad x + 2 = 0$$
$$x = -6 \qquad x = -2$$

Check:
$$(-6)^2 + 8(-6) + 12 = 0$$
$$36 - 48 + 12 = 0$$
$$48 - 48 = 0$$
$$0 = 0$$
$$(-2)^2 + 8(-2) + 12 = 0$$
$$4 - 16 + 12 = 0$$
$$16 - 16 = 0$$
$$0 = 0$$

2.18
$$t^2 + 5t - 24 = 0$$
$$(t + 8)(t - 3) = 0$$
$$t + 8 = 0 \qquad t - 3 = 0$$
$$t = -8 \qquad t = 3$$

Check:
$$(-8)^2 + 5(-8) - 24 = 0$$
$$64 - 40 - 24 = 0$$
$$64 - 64 = 0$$
$$0 = 0$$
$$3^2 + 5(3) - 24 = 0$$
$$9 + 15 - 24 = 0$$
$$24 - 24 = 0$$
$$0 = 0$$

2.19
$$2t^2 - t = 10$$
$$2t^2 - t - 10 = 0$$
$$(2t - 5)(t + 2) = 0$$
$$2t - 5 = 0 \qquad t + 2 = 0$$
$$2t = 5 \qquad t = -2$$
$$t = \frac{5}{2}$$

Check:
$$2(\tfrac{5}{2})^2 - \tfrac{5}{2} = 10$$
$$\overset{1}{2}(\frac{25}{\underset{2}{\cancel{4}}}) - \frac{5}{2} = 10$$
$$\frac{25}{2} - \frac{5}{2} = 10$$
$$\frac{20}{2} = 10$$
$$10 = 10$$
$$2(-2)^2 - (-2) = 10$$
$$2 \cdot 4 + 2 = 10$$
$$8 + 2 = 10$$
$$10 = 10$$

2.20
$$x - 6 = -x^2$$
$$x^2 + x - 6 = 0$$
$$(x + 3)(x - 2) = 0$$
$$x + 3 = 0 \qquad x - 2 = 0$$
$$x = -3 \qquad x = 2$$

Check:
$$-3 - 6 = -(-3)^2$$
$$-9 = -9$$
$$2 - 6 = -(2)^2$$
$$-4 = -4$$

2.21
$$2x^2 - 11x + 5 = 0$$
$$(2x - 1)(x - 5) = 0$$
$$2x - 1 = 0 \qquad x - 5 = 0$$
$$2x = 1 \qquad x = 5$$
$$x = \frac{1}{2}$$

Check:
$$2(\tfrac{1}{2})^2 - 11(\tfrac{1}{2}) + 5 = 0$$
$$2(\tfrac{1}{4}) - \tfrac{11}{2} + 5 = 0$$
$$\frac{1}{2} - \frac{11}{2} + 5 = 0$$
$$-\frac{10}{2} + 5 = 0$$
$$-5 + 5 = 0$$
$$0 = 0$$
$$2(5)^2 - 11(5) + 5 = 0$$
$$2(25) - 11(5) + 5 = 0$$
$$50 - 55 + 5 = 0$$
$$-5 + 5 = 0$$
$$0 = 0$$

2.22
$$10t^2 - 29t = -10$$
$$10t^2 - 29t + 10 = 0$$
$$(2t - 5)(5t - 2) = 0$$

$2t - 5 = 0$	$5t - 2 = 0$
$2t = 5$	$5t = 2$
$t = \frac{5}{2}$	$t = \frac{2}{5}$

Check:
$$10(\tfrac{5}{2})^2 - 29(\tfrac{5}{2}) = -10$$
$$10(\tfrac{25}{4}) - 29(\tfrac{5}{2}) = -10$$
$$\frac{125}{2} - \frac{145}{2} = -10$$
$$-\frac{20}{2} = -10$$
$$-10 = -10$$

$$10(\tfrac{2}{5})^2 - 29(\tfrac{2}{5}) = -10$$
$$10(\tfrac{4}{25}) - 29(\tfrac{2}{5}) = -10$$
$$\frac{8}{5} - \frac{58}{5} = -10$$
$$-\frac{50}{5} = -10$$
$$-10 = -10$$

2.23
$$4x^2 - 36 = 0$$
$$(2x + 6)(2x - 6) = 0$$

$2x + 6 = 0$	$2x - 6 = 0$
$2x = -6$	$2x = 6$
$x = -3$	$x = 3$

Check:
$$4(-3)^2 - 36 = 0$$
$$4(9) - 36 = 0$$
$$36 - 36 = 0$$
$$0 = 0$$

$$4(3)^2 - 36 = 0$$
$$4 \cdot 9 - 36 = 0$$
$$36 - 36 = 0$$
$$0 = 0$$

2.24
$$2(a - 2) = -\frac{a - 1}{a - 4}$$
$$2a - 4 = -\frac{a - 1}{a - 4}$$
$$(2a - 4)(a - 4) = -a + 1 \quad \text{(cross-multiply)}$$
$$2a^2 - 12a + 16 = -a + 1$$
$$2a^2 - 11a + 16 = 1$$
$$2a^2 - 11a + 15 = 0$$
$$(2a - 5)(a - 3) = 0$$

$2a - 5 = 0$	$a - 3 = 0$
$2a = 5$	$a = 3$
$a = \frac{5}{2}$	

Check:
$$2(\tfrac{5}{2} - 2) = -\frac{\tfrac{5}{2} - 1}{\tfrac{5}{2} - 4}$$
$$5 - 4 = -\frac{5 - 2}{5 - 8}$$
$$1 = -\frac{3}{-3}$$
$$1 = 1$$

$$2(3 - 2) = -\frac{3 - 1}{3 - 4}$$
$$2 = -\frac{2}{-1}$$
$$2 = 2$$

2.25
$$2(3a^2 - 1) - 6a = 5$$
$$6a^2 - 2 - 6a = 5$$
$$6a^2 - 11a - 2 = 0$$
$$(6a + 1)(a - 2) = 0$$

$6a + 1 = 0$	$a - 2 = 0$
$6a = -1$	$a = 2$
$a = -\frac{1}{6}$	

Check:
$$2[3(-\tfrac{1}{6})^2 - 1] - 6(-\tfrac{1}{6}) = 5(-\tfrac{1}{6})$$
$$2(\tfrac{3}{36} - 1) - 6(-\tfrac{1}{6}) = 5(-\tfrac{1}{6})$$
$$\frac{1}{6} - 2 + 1 = -\frac{5}{6}$$
$$\frac{1}{6} - 1 = -\frac{5}{6}$$
$$-\frac{5}{6} = -\frac{5}{6}$$

$$2[3(2)^2 - 1] - 6(2) = 5(2)$$
$$2(12 - 1) - 12 = 10$$
$$2(11) - 12 = 10$$
$$22 - 12 = 10$$
$$10 = 10$$

2.26
$$\frac{1}{2} \cdot 8 = 4$$
$$4^2 = 16$$

2.27
$$\frac{1}{2} \cdot 18 = 9$$
$$9^2 = 81$$

2.28
$$\frac{1}{2} \cdot 5 = \frac{5}{2}$$
$$(\tfrac{5}{2})^2 = \frac{25}{4}$$

2.29
$$\frac{1}{2} \cdot 7 = \frac{7}{2}$$
$$(\tfrac{7}{2})^2 = \frac{49}{4}$$

2.30
$$\frac{1}{2} \cdot \frac{1}{2} = \frac{1}{4}$$
$$(\tfrac{1}{4})^2 = \frac{1}{16}$$

2.31 $\frac{1}{2} \cdot \frac{2}{3} = \frac{1}{3}$

$(\frac{1}{3})^2 = \frac{1}{9}$

2.32 $0.5 \cdot 0.1 = 0.05$
$(0.05)^2 = 0.0025$

2.33 $y^2 - 12y = -27$
$\frac{1}{2} \cdot 12 = 6$
$6^2 = 36$
$y^2 - 12y + 36 = -27 + 36$
$(y - 6)^2 = 9$
$\sqrt{(y - 6)^2} = \pm\sqrt{9}$
$y - 6 = \pm 3$

$y - 6 = 3 \qquad y - 6 = -3$
$y = 9 \qquad y = 3$

Check:
$9^2 - 12(9) = -27$
$81 - 108 = -27$
$-27 = -27$

$3^2 - 12(3) = -27$
$9 - 36 = -27$
$-27 = -27$

2.34 $x^2 + 8x + 7 = 0$
$x^2 + 8x = -7$
$\frac{1}{2}(8) = 4$
$4^2 = 16$
$x^2 + 8x + 16 = -7 + 16$
$(x + 4)^2 = 9$
$\sqrt{(x + 4)^2} = \pm\sqrt{9}$
$x + 4 = \pm 3$

$x + 4 = 3 \qquad x + 4 = -3$
$x = -1 \qquad x = -7$

Check:
$(-1)^2 + 8(-1) + 7 = 0$
$1 - 8 + 7 = 0$
$-7 + 7 = 0$
$0 = 0$

$(-7)^2 + 8(-7) + 7 = 0$
$49 - 56 + 7 = 0$
$-7 + 7 = 0$
$0 = 0$

2.35 $x^2 + 4x = 32$
$\frac{1}{2} \cdot 4 = 2$
$2^2 = 4$
$x^2 + 4x + 4 = 32 + 4$
$(x + 2)^2 = 36$
$\sqrt{(x + 2)^2} = \pm\sqrt{36}$
$x + 2 = \pm 6$

$x + 2 = 6 \qquad x + 2 = -6$
$x = 4 \qquad x = -8$

Check:
$4^2 + 4(4) = 32$
$16 + 16 = 32$
$32 = 32$

$(-8)^2 + 4(-8) = 32$
$64 - 32 = 32$
$32 = 32$

2.36 $c^2 + 11c = 12$
$\frac{1}{2} \cdot 11 = \frac{11}{2}$
$(\frac{11}{2})^2 = \frac{121}{4}$
$c^2 + 11c + \frac{121}{4} = 12 + \frac{121}{4}$
$(c + \frac{11}{2})^2 = \frac{169}{4}$
$\sqrt{(c + \frac{11}{2})^2} = \pm\sqrt{\frac{169}{4}}$
$c + \frac{11}{2} = \pm\frac{13}{2}$

$c + \frac{11}{2} = \frac{13}{2} \qquad c + \frac{11}{2} = -\frac{13}{2}$
$c = \frac{2}{2} = 1 \qquad c = -\frac{24}{2} = -12$

Check:
$1^2 + 11(1) = 12$
$1 + 11 = 12$
$12 = 12$

$(-12)^2 + 11(-12) = 12$
$144 - 132 = 12$
$12 = 12$

2.37 $x^2 + 3x = 28$
$\frac{1}{2} \cdot 3 = \frac{3}{2}$
$(\frac{3}{2})^2 = \frac{9}{4}$
$x^2 + 3x + \frac{9}{4} = 28 + \frac{9}{4}$
$(x + \frac{3}{2})^2 = \frac{121}{4}$
$\sqrt{(x + \frac{3}{2})^2} = \pm\sqrt{\frac{121}{4}}$
$x + \frac{3}{2} = \pm\frac{11}{2}$

$x + \frac{3}{2} = \frac{11}{2} \qquad x + \frac{3}{2} = -\frac{11}{2}$
$x = \frac{8}{2} = 4 \qquad x = -\frac{14}{2} = -7$

Check:
$4^2 + 3(4) = 28$
$16 + 12 = 28$
$28 = 28$

$(-7)^2 + 3(-7) = 28$
$49 - 21 = 28$
$28 = 28$

2.38

$$x^2 - x = 42$$
$$\frac{1}{2} \cdot 1 = \frac{1}{2}$$
$$(\frac{1}{2})^2 = \frac{1}{4}$$
$$x^2 - x + \frac{1}{4} = 42 + \frac{1}{4}$$
$$(x - \frac{1}{2})^2 = \frac{169}{4}$$
$$\sqrt{(x - \frac{1}{2})^2} = \pm\sqrt{\frac{169}{4}}$$
$$x - \frac{1}{2} = \pm\frac{13}{2}$$

$$x - \frac{1}{2} = \frac{13}{2} \qquad x - \frac{1}{2} = -\frac{13}{2}$$
$$x = \frac{14}{2} = 7 \qquad x = -\frac{12}{2} = -6$$

Check:
$$7^2 - 7 = 42$$
$$49 - 7 = 42$$
$$42 = 42$$

$$(-6)^2 - (-6) = 42$$
$$36 + 6 = 42$$
$$42 = 42$$

2.39

$$y^2 + 36 = 13y$$
$$\frac{1}{2} \cdot 13 = \frac{13}{2}$$
$$(\frac{13}{2})^2 = \frac{169}{4}$$
$$y^2 - 13y + \frac{169}{4} = -\frac{144}{4} + \frac{169}{4}$$
$$(y - \frac{13}{2})^2 = \frac{25}{4}$$
$$\sqrt{(y - \frac{13}{2})^2} = \pm\sqrt{\frac{25}{4}}$$
$$y - \frac{13}{2} = \pm\frac{5}{2}$$

$$y - \frac{13}{2} = \frac{5}{2} \qquad y - \frac{13}{2} = -\frac{5}{2}$$
$$y = \frac{18}{2} = 9 \qquad y = \frac{8}{2} = 4$$

Check:
$$9^2 + 36 = 13(9)$$
$$81 + 36 = 13(9)$$
$$117 = 117$$

$$4^2 + 36 = 13(4)$$
$$16 + 36 = 13(4)$$
$$52 = 52$$

2.40

$$6m^2 + 5m - 3 = 0$$
$$6m^2 + 5m = 3$$
$$m^2 + \frac{5}{6}m = \frac{1}{2}$$
$$\frac{1}{2} \cdot \frac{5}{6} = \frac{5}{12}$$
$$(\frac{5}{12})^2 = \frac{25}{144}$$
$$m^2 + \frac{5}{6}m + \frac{25}{144} = \frac{72}{144} + \frac{25}{144}$$
$$(m + \frac{5}{12})^2 = \frac{97}{144}$$
$$\sqrt{(m + \frac{5}{12})^2} = \pm\sqrt{\frac{97}{144}}$$
$$m + \frac{5}{12} = \pm\frac{\sqrt{97}}{12}$$

$$m + \frac{5}{12} = \frac{\sqrt{97}}{12} \qquad m + \frac{5}{12} = -\frac{\sqrt{97}}{12}$$
$$m = \frac{-5 + \sqrt{97}}{12} \qquad m = \frac{-5 - \sqrt{97}}{12}$$
$$m = \frac{-5 \pm \sqrt{97}}{12}$$

Check:
$$6(\frac{-5 + \sqrt{97}}{12})^2 + 5(\frac{-5 + \sqrt{97}}{12}) - 3 = 0$$
$$\overset{1}{6}(\frac{25 - 10\sqrt{97} + 97}{\underset{24}{144}}) + \frac{-25 + 5\sqrt{97}}{12} - 3 = 0$$
$$\frac{122 - 10\sqrt{97}}{24} + \frac{-25 + 5\sqrt{97}}{12} - 3 = 0$$
$$\frac{61}{12} - \frac{5\sqrt{97}}{12} - \frac{25}{12} + \frac{5\sqrt{97}}{12} - 3 = 0$$
$$\frac{36}{12} - 3 = 0$$
$$3 - 3 = 0$$
$$0 = 0$$

$$6(\frac{-5 - \sqrt{97}}{12})^2 + 5(\frac{-5 - \sqrt{97}}{12}) - 3 = 0$$
$$\overset{1}{6}(\frac{25 + 10\sqrt{97} + 97}{\underset{24}{144}}) + \frac{-25 - 5\sqrt{97}}{12} - 3 = 0$$
$$\frac{122 + 10\sqrt{97}}{24} + \frac{-25 - 5\sqrt{97}}{12} - 3 = 0$$
$$\frac{61}{12} + \frac{5\sqrt{97}}{12} - \frac{25}{12} - \frac{5\sqrt{97}}{12} - 3 = 0$$
$$\frac{36}{12} - 3 = 0$$
$$3 - 3 = 0$$
$$0 = 0$$

2.41

$$2x^2 - 8x + 5 = 0$$
$$2x^2 - 8x = -5$$
$$x^2 - 4x = -\frac{5}{2}$$
$$\frac{1}{2} \cdot 4 = 2$$
$$2^2 = 4$$
$$x^2 - 4x + 4 = -\frac{5}{2} + \frac{8}{2}$$
$$(x - 2)^2 = \frac{3}{2}$$
$$\sqrt{(x - 2)^2} = \pm\sqrt{\frac{3}{2}}$$
$$x - 2 = \pm\frac{\sqrt{6}}{2}$$
$$x = 2 \pm\frac{\sqrt{6}}{2}$$

Check:

$$2(2 + \tfrac{\sqrt{6}}{2})^2 - 8(2 + \tfrac{\sqrt{6}}{2}) + 5 = 0$$
$$2(4 + 2\sqrt{6} + \tfrac{3}{2}) - 16 - 4\sqrt{6} + 5 = 0$$
$$8 + 4\sqrt{6} + 3 - 16 - 4\sqrt{6} + 5 = 0$$
$$0 = 0$$
$$2(2 - \tfrac{\sqrt{6}}{2})2 - 8(2 - \tfrac{\sqrt{6}}{2}) + 5 = 0$$
$$2(4 - 2\sqrt{6} + \tfrac{3}{2}) - 16 + 4\sqrt{6} + 5 = 0$$
$$8 - 4\sqrt{6} + 3 - 16 + 4\sqrt{6} + 5 = 0$$
$$0 = 0$$

2.42
$$5x^2 - 2x - 2 = 0$$
$$5x^2 - 2x = 2$$
$$x^2 - \tfrac{2}{5}x = \tfrac{2}{5}$$
$$\tfrac{1}{2} \cdot \tfrac{2}{5} = \tfrac{1}{5}$$
$$(\tfrac{1}{5})^2 = \tfrac{1}{25}$$
$$x^2 - \tfrac{2}{5}x + \tfrac{1}{25} = \tfrac{10}{25} + \tfrac{1}{25}$$
$$(x - \tfrac{1}{5})^2 = \tfrac{11}{25}$$
$$\sqrt{(x - \tfrac{1}{5})^2} = \pm\sqrt{\tfrac{11}{25}}$$
$$x - \tfrac{1}{5} = \pm\tfrac{\sqrt{11}}{5}$$
$$x = \tfrac{1 \pm \sqrt{11}}{5}$$

Check:

$$5(\tfrac{1 + \sqrt{11}}{5})^2 - 2(\tfrac{1 + \sqrt{11}}{5}) - 2 = 0$$
$$\tfrac{\overset{1}{\cancel{5}}(1 + 2\sqrt{11} + 11)}{\underset{5}{\cancel{25}}} - \tfrac{2}{5} - \tfrac{2\sqrt{11}}{5} - 2 = 0$$
$$\tfrac{1}{5} + \tfrac{2\sqrt{11}}{5} + \tfrac{11}{5} - \tfrac{2}{5} - \tfrac{2\sqrt{11}}{5} - 2 = 0$$
$$\tfrac{10}{5} - 2 = 0$$
$$2 - 2 = 0$$
$$0 = 0$$
$$5(\tfrac{1 - \sqrt{11}}{5})^2 - 2(\tfrac{1 - \sqrt{11}}{5}) - 2 = 0$$
$$\tfrac{\overset{1}{\cancel{5}}(1 - 2\sqrt{11} + 11)}{\underset{5}{\cancel{25}}} - \tfrac{2}{5} + \tfrac{2\sqrt{11}}{5} - 2 = 0$$
$$\tfrac{1}{5} - \tfrac{2\sqrt{11}}{5} + \tfrac{11}{5} - \tfrac{2}{5} + \tfrac{2\sqrt{11}}{5} - 2 = 0$$
$$\tfrac{10}{5} - 2 = 0$$
$$2 - 2 = 0$$
$$0 = 0$$

SELF TEST 2

2.01 Let $0.41666... = x$
$$10x = 4.1666...$$
$$\underline{x = 0.4166...}$$
$$9x = 3.75$$
$$x = \tfrac{3.75}{9} = \tfrac{375}{900} = \tfrac{5}{12}$$

2.02 $x^{3/2}y^{1/3}$

2.03 $\dfrac{\sqrt{32}}{\sqrt{5}} = \dfrac{\sqrt{32}}{\sqrt{5}}\dfrac{\sqrt{5}}{\sqrt{5}} = \dfrac{\sqrt{160}}{5} = \dfrac{4\sqrt{10}}{5}$

2.04 $\dfrac{7}{3 - \sqrt{2}} \cdot \dfrac{3 + \sqrt{2}}{3 + \sqrt{2}} =$
$$\dfrac{21 + 7\sqrt{2}}{9 - 2} = \dfrac{21 + 7\sqrt{2}}{7} = 3 + \sqrt{2}$$

2.05
$$\sqrt{x - 2} - 4 = 0$$
$$\sqrt{x - 2} = 4$$
$$(\sqrt{x - 2})^2 = 4^2$$
$$x - 2 = 16$$
$$x = 18$$

Check:
$$\sqrt{18 - 2} - 4 = 0$$
$$\sqrt{16} - 4 = 0$$
$$4 - 4 = 0$$
$$0 = 0$$

2.06
$$y^2 = 36$$
$$\sqrt{y^2} = \pm\sqrt{36}$$
$$y = \pm 6$$

Check:
$$(\pm 6)^2 = 36$$
$$36 = 36$$

2.07
$$x^2 - 81 = 0$$
$$x^2 = 81$$
$$\sqrt{x^2} = \pm\sqrt{81}$$
$$x = \pm 9$$

Check:
$$(\pm 9)^2 - 81 = 0$$
$$81 - 81 = 0$$
$$0 = 0$$

2.08
$$3x^2 = 147$$
$$x^2 = 49$$
$$\sqrt{x^2} = \pm\sqrt{49}$$
$$x = \pm 7$$

Check:
$$3(\pm 7)^2 = 147$$
$$3(49) = 147$$
$$147 = 147$$

2.09

$$(x - 8)^2 = 48$$
$$\sqrt{(x - 8)^2} = \pm\sqrt{48}$$
$$x - 8 = \pm 4\sqrt{3}$$
$$x = 8 \pm 4\sqrt{3}$$

Check:
$$(8 + 4\sqrt{3} - 8)^2 = 48$$
$$(4\sqrt{3})^2 = 48$$
$$48 = 48$$

$$(8 - 4\sqrt{3} - 8)^2 = 48$$
$$(-4\sqrt{3})^2 = 48$$
$$48 = 48$$

2.010

$$2(x + 7)^2 = 64$$
$$(x + 7)^2 = 32$$
$$\sqrt{(x + 7)^2} = \pm\sqrt{32}$$
$$x + 7 = \pm 4\sqrt{2}$$
$$x = -7 \pm 4\sqrt{2}$$

Check:
$$2(-7 + 4\sqrt{2} + 7)^2 = 64$$
$$2(4\sqrt{2})^2 = 64$$
$$2(32) = 64$$
$$64 = 64$$

$$2(-7 - 4\sqrt{2} + 7)^2 = 64$$
$$2(-4\sqrt{2})^2 = 64$$
$$2(32) = 64$$
$$64 = 64$$

2.011

$$x^2 - 49 = 0$$
$$(x + 7)(x - 7) = 0$$

$x + 7 = 0$	$x - 7 = 0$
$x = -7$	$x = 7$

Check:

$(-7)^2 - 49 = 0$	$7^2 - 49 = 0$
$49 - 49 = 0$	$49 - 49 = 0$
$0 = 0$	$0 = 0$

2.012

$$x^2 + 6x = -9$$
$$x^2 + 6x + 9 = 0$$
$$(x + 3)(x + 3) = 0$$
$$x + 3 = 0$$
$$x = -3 \;\text{(double root)}$$

Check:
$$(-3)^2 + 6(-3) = -9$$
$$9 - 18 = -9$$
$$-9 = -9$$

2.013

$$y^2 + 7y = 18$$
$$y^2 + 7y - 18 = 0$$
$$(y + 9)(y - 2) = 0$$

$y + 9 = 0$	$y - 2 = 0$
$y = -9$	$y = 2$

Check:

$(-9)^2 + 7(-9) = 18$	$2^2 + 7(2) = 18$
$81 - 63 = 18$	$4 + 14 = 18$
$18 = 18$	$18 = 18$

2.014

$$2x^2 - 7x - 15 = 0$$
$$(2x + 3)(x - 5) = 0$$

$2x + 3 = 0$	$x - 5 = 0$
$2x = -3$	$x = 5$
$x = -\dfrac{3}{2}$	

Check:
$$2(-\tfrac{3}{2})^2 - 7(-\tfrac{3}{2}) - 15 = 0$$
$${}^1\!\!\!\; 2(\tfrac{9}{4}_2) + \tfrac{21}{2} - 15 = 0$$
$$\frac{30}{2} - 15 = 0$$
$$15 - 15 = 0$$
$$0 = 0$$

$$2(5)^2 - 7(5) - 15 = 0$$
$$2(25) - 7(5) - 15 = 0$$
$$50 - 35 - 15 = 0$$
$$50 - 50 = 0$$
$$0 = 0$$

2.015

$$\frac{1}{x - 4} + 1 = \frac{14}{x + 2}$$
$$\text{LCD} = (x - 4)(x + 2)$$
$$1(x + 2) + (x - 4)(x + 2) = 14(x - 4)$$
$$x + 2 + x^2 - 2x - 8 = 14x - 56$$
$$x^2 - x - 6 = 14x - 56$$
$$x^2 - 15x - 6 = -56$$
$$x^2 - 15x + 50 = 0$$
$$(x - 5)(x - 10) = 0$$

$x - 5 = 0$	$x - 10 = 0$
$x = 5$	$x = 10$

Check:
$$\frac{1}{5 - 4} + 1 = \frac{14}{5 + 2}$$
$$\frac{1}{1} + 1 = \frac{14}{7}$$
$$2 = 2$$

$$\frac{1}{10 - 4} + 1 = \frac{14}{10 + 2}$$
$$\frac{1}{6} + 6 = \frac{14}{12}$$
$$\frac{7}{6} = \frac{7}{6}$$

2.016

$$y^2 + 2y = 48$$
$$\frac{1}{2} \cdot 2 = 1$$
$$1^2 = 1$$
$$y^2 + 2y + 1 = 48 + 1$$
$$(y + 1)^2 = 49$$
$$\sqrt{(y + 1)^2} = \pm\sqrt{49}$$
$$y + 1 = \pm 7$$

$y + 1 = 7$	$y + 1 = -7$
$y = 6$	$y = -8$

Check:

$6^2 + 2(6) = 48$	$(-8)^2 + 2(-8) = 48$
$36 + 12 = 48$	$64 - 16 = 48$
$48 = 48$	$48 = 48$

2.017
$$2x^2 + 4x - 30 = 0$$
$$2x^2 + 4x = 30$$
$$x^2 + 2x = 15$$
$$\frac{1}{2} \cdot 2 = 1$$
$$1^2 = 1$$
$$x^2 + 2x + 1 = 15 + 1$$
$$(x + 1)^2 = 16$$
$$\sqrt{(x + 1)^2} = \pm\sqrt{16}$$
$$x + 1 = \pm 4$$

$$x + 1 = 4 \qquad\qquad x + 1 = \text{-}4$$
$$x = 3 \qquad\qquad\quad x = \text{-}5$$

Check:
$$2(3)^2 + 4(3) - 30 = 0$$
$$2(9) + 4(3) - 30 = 0$$
$$18 + 12 - 30 = 0$$
$$30 - 30 = 0$$
$$2(\text{-}5)^2 + 4(\text{-}5) - 30 = 0$$
$$2(25) + 4(\text{-}5) - 30 = 0$$
$$50 - 20 - 30 = 0$$
$$50 - 50 = 0$$
$$0 = 0$$

2.018
$$\frac{1}{x-1} - \frac{1}{x} = \frac{1}{6}$$
$$\text{LCD} = 6x(x - 1)$$
$$1(6x) - 1(6)(x - 1) = 1(x)(x - 1)$$
$$\cancel{6x} - \cancel{6x} + 6 = x^2 - x$$
$$6 = x^2 - x$$
$$0 = x^2 - x - 6$$
$$0 = (x - 3)(x + 2)$$

$$x - 3 = 0 \qquad\qquad x + 2 = 0$$
$$x = 3 \qquad\qquad\quad x = \text{-}2$$

Check:
$$\frac{1}{3-1} - \frac{1}{3} = \frac{1}{6}$$
$$\frac{1}{2} - \frac{1}{3} = \frac{1}{6}$$
$$\frac{3}{6} - \frac{2}{6} = \frac{1}{6}$$
$$\frac{1}{6} = \frac{1}{6}$$

$$\frac{1}{\text{-}2-1} - \frac{1}{\text{-}2} = \frac{1}{6}$$
$$\text{-}\frac{1}{3} + \frac{1}{2} = \frac{1}{6}$$
$$\text{-}\frac{2}{6} + \frac{3}{6} = \frac{1}{6}$$
$$\frac{1}{6} = \frac{1}{6}$$

2.019
$$y^2 - 5y = 3$$
$$\frac{1}{2} \cdot 5 = \frac{5}{2}$$
$$\left(\frac{5}{2}\right)^2 = \frac{25}{4}$$
$$y^2 - 5y + \frac{25}{4} = 3 + \frac{25}{4}$$
$$\left(y - \frac{5}{2}\right)^2 = \frac{37}{4}$$
$$\sqrt{\left(y - \frac{5}{2}\right)^2} = \pm\sqrt{\frac{37}{4}}$$
$$y - \frac{5}{2} = \pm\frac{\sqrt{37}}{2}$$
$$y = \frac{5}{2} \pm \frac{\sqrt{37}}{2}$$
$$y = \frac{5 \pm \sqrt{37}}{2}$$

Check:
$$\left(\frac{5 + \sqrt{37}}{2}\right)^2 - 5\left(\frac{5 + \sqrt{37}}{2}\right) = 3$$
$$\frac{25 + 10\sqrt{37} + 37}{4} - \frac{25 + 5\sqrt{37}}{2} = 3$$
$$\frac{63 + 10\sqrt{37}}{4} - \frac{50 + 10\sqrt{37}}{4} = 3$$
$$\frac{62 + 10\cancel{\sqrt{37}} - 50 - 10\cancel{\sqrt{37}}}{4} = 3$$
$$\frac{12}{4} = 3$$
$$3 = 3$$

$$\left(\frac{5 - \sqrt{37}}{2}\right)^2 - 5\left(\frac{5 - \sqrt{37}}{2}\right) = 3$$
$$\frac{25 - 10\sqrt{37} + 37}{4} - \frac{25 - 5\sqrt{37}}{2} = 3$$
$$\frac{63 - 10\sqrt{37}}{4} - \frac{50 - 10\sqrt{37}}{4} = 3$$
$$\frac{62 - 10\cancel{\sqrt{37}} - 50 + 10\cancel{\sqrt{37}}}{4} = 3$$
$$\frac{12}{4} = 3$$
$$3 = 3$$

2.020
$$\frac{3}{x} = 2\frac{1}{2} - \frac{x}{3}$$
$$\frac{3}{x} = \frac{5}{2} - \frac{x}{3}$$
$$\text{LCD} = 6x$$
$$3(6) = 5(3x) - x(2x)$$
$$18 = 15x - 2x^2$$
$$2x^2 + 18 = 15x$$
$$2x^2 - 15x + 18 = 0$$
$$(2x - 3)(x - 6) = 0$$

$$2x - 3 = 0 \qquad\qquad x - 6 = 0$$
$$2x = 3 \qquad\qquad\quad x = 6$$
$$x = \frac{3}{2}$$

Check:
$$\frac{3}{\frac{3}{2}} = \frac{5}{2} - \frac{\frac{3}{2}}{3} \qquad\qquad \frac{3}{6} = \frac{5}{2} - \frac{6}{3}$$
$$2 = \frac{5}{2} - \frac{1}{2} \qquad\qquad\quad \frac{1}{2} = \frac{5}{2} - 2$$
$$2 = \frac{4}{2} \qquad\qquad\qquad\quad \frac{1}{2} = \frac{1}{2}$$
$$2 = 2$$

SECTION 3

3.1 $3x^2 + 6x - 12 = 0$
$a = 3; b = 6; c = -12$

3.2 $-3m^2 - 10m + 5 = 0$
$a = -3; b = -10; c = 5$

3.3 $17x^2 - 12x + 0 = 0$
$a = 17; b = -12; c = 0$

3.4 $\frac{3x}{4} = \frac{1}{x}$
$3x^2 = 4$ (cross-multiply)
$3x^2 + 0x - 4 = 0$
$a = 3; b = 0; c = -4$

3.5 $\frac{y + 2}{y + 1} + \frac{2y^2 - y + 3}{y^2 - 1} = -\frac{y - 2}{y - 1}$
$LCD = (y + 1)(y - 1)$
$(y + 2)(y - 1) + 2y^2 - y + 3 = (-y + 2)(y + 1)$
$y^2 + \cancel{y} - 2 + 2y^2 - \cancel{y} + 3 = -y^2 + y + 2$
$3y^2 + 1 = -y^2 + y + 2$
$4y^2 + 1 = y + 2$
$4y^2 - y + 1 = 2$
$4y^2 - y - 1 = 0$
$a = 4; b = -1; c = -1$

3.6 $x^2 + 6x - 55 = 0$
$a = 1; b = 6; c = -55$
$x = \frac{-6 \pm \sqrt{6^2 - 4(1)(-55)}}{2(1)}$
$x = \frac{-6 \pm \sqrt{36 + 220}}{2}$
$x = \frac{-6 \pm \sqrt{256}}{2}$
$x = \frac{-6 \pm 16}{2}$
$x = \frac{-6 + 16}{2} = \frac{10}{2} = 5$
$x = \frac{-6 - 16}{2} = \frac{-22}{2} = -11$
$x = 5, -11$

3.7 $8x^2 - 2x - 1 = 0$
$a = 8; b = -2; c = -1$
$x = \frac{2 \pm \sqrt{(-2)^2 - 4(8)(-1)}}{2(8)}$
$x = \frac{2 \pm \sqrt{4 + 32}}{16}$
$x = \frac{2 \pm \sqrt{36}}{16}$
$x = \frac{2 \pm 6}{16}$
$x = \frac{2 + 6}{16} = \frac{8}{16} = \frac{1}{2}$
$x = \frac{2 - 6}{16} = \frac{-4}{16} = -\frac{1}{4}$
$x = \frac{1}{2}, -\frac{1}{4}$

3.8 $x^2 + 6x + 9 = 0$
$a = 1; b = 6; c = 9$
$x = \frac{-6 \pm \sqrt{6^2 - 4(1)(9)}}{2(1)}$
$x = \frac{-6 \pm \sqrt{36 - 36}}{2} = \frac{-6 \pm \sqrt{0}}{2}$
$x = \frac{-6}{2} = -3$

3.9 $8x^2 - 7x + 0 = 0$
$a = 8; b = -7; c = 0$
$x = \frac{7 \pm \sqrt{(-7)^2 - 4(8)(0)}}{2(8)}$
$x = \frac{7 \pm \sqrt{49 - 0}}{16} = \frac{7 \pm 7}{16}$
$x = \frac{7 + 7}{16} = \frac{14}{16} = \frac{7}{8}$
$x = \frac{7 - 7}{16} = 0$
$x = \frac{7}{8}, 0$

3.10 $x^2 - 19x + 34 = 0$
$a = 1; b = -19; c = 34$
$x = \frac{19 \pm \sqrt{(-19)^2 - 4(1)(34)}}{2(1)}$
$x = \frac{19 \pm \sqrt{361 - 136}}{2} = \frac{19 \pm \sqrt{225}}{2}$
$x = \frac{19 \pm 15}{2}$
$x = \frac{19 + 15}{2} = \frac{34}{2} = 17$
$x = \frac{19 - 15}{2} = \frac{4}{2} = 2$
$x = 17, 2$

3.11 $-3x^2 - 10x + 5 = 0$
$a = -3; b = -10; c = 5$
$x = \frac{10 \pm \sqrt{(-10)^2 - 4(-3)(5)}}{2(-3)}$
$x = \frac{10 \pm \sqrt{100 + 60}}{-6} = \frac{10 \pm 4\sqrt{10}}{-6}$
$x = \frac{5 \pm 2\sqrt{10}}{-3}$

3.12 $2x^2 + 5x + 2 = 0$
$a = 2; b = 5; c = 2$
$x = \frac{-5 \pm \sqrt{5^2 - 4(2)(2)}}{2(2)}$
$x = \frac{-5 \pm \sqrt{25 - 16}}{4}$
$x = \frac{-5 \pm \sqrt{9}}{4}$
$x = \frac{-5 \pm 3}{4}$
$x = \frac{-5 + 3}{4} = \frac{-2}{4} = -\frac{1}{2}$
$x = \frac{-5 - 3}{4} = \frac{-8}{4} = -2$
$x = -\frac{1}{2}, -2$

3.13 $3x^2 + 4x - 6 = 0$
$a = 3; b = 4; c = -6$
$x = \frac{-4 \pm \sqrt{4^2 - 4(3)(-6)}}{2(3)}$
$x = \frac{-4 \pm \sqrt{16 + 72}}{6} = \frac{-4 \pm \sqrt{88}}{6}$
$x = \frac{-4 \pm 2\sqrt{22}}{6}$
$x = \frac{-2 \pm \sqrt{22}}{3}$

3.14 $(3 - y)(y + 4) = 3y - 5$
$3y + 12 - y^2 - 4y = 3y - 5$
$-y^2 - y + 12 = 3y - 5$
$-y^2 - 4y + 12 = -5$
$-y^2 - 4y + 17 = 0$
$a = -1; b = -4; c = 17$
$y = \frac{4 \pm \sqrt{(-4)^2 - 4(-1)(17)}}{2(-1)}$
$y = \frac{4 \pm \sqrt{16 + 68}}{-2} = \frac{4 \pm \sqrt{84}}{-2}$
$y = \frac{4 \pm 2\sqrt{21}}{-2}$
$y = -2 \pm \sqrt{21}$

3.15 $\frac{5x - 2}{2} - \frac{19x + 6}{2x} = \frac{3x - 2}{4}$
LCD = $4x$
$2x(5x - 2) - 2(19x + 6) = x(3x - 2)$
$10x^2 - 4x - 38x - 12 = 3x^2 - 2x$
$10x^2 - 42x - 12 = 3x^2 - 2x$
$7x^2 - 42x - 12 = -2x$
$7x^2 - 40x - 12 = 0$
$a = 7; b = -40; c = -12$
$x = \frac{40 \pm \sqrt{(-40)^2 - 4(7)(-12)}}{2(7)}$
$x = \frac{40 \pm \sqrt{1,600 + 336}}{14} = \frac{40 \pm \sqrt{1,936}}{14}$
$x = \frac{40 \pm 44}{14} = \frac{20 \pm 22}{7}$
$x = \frac{20 + 22}{7} = \frac{42}{7} = 6$
$x = \frac{20 - 22}{7} = -\frac{2}{7}$
$x = 6, -\frac{2}{7}$

3.16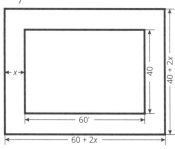
$(60 + 2x)(40 + 2x) = 2(60)(40)$
$2,400 + 120x + 80x + 4x^2 = 4,800$
$4x^2 + 200x + 2,400 = 4,800$

$4x^2 + 200x - 2,400 = 0$
$x^2 + 50x - 600 = 0$
$(x + 60)(x - 10) = 0$
$x + 60 = 0 \quad x - 10 = 0$
$x = -60; \quad x = 10$
(meaningless value)
The width from pool edge to patio edge is 10 feet.
Check:
$(60 + 2 \cdot 10)(40 + 2 \cdot 10) = 4,800$
$(60 + 20)(40 + 20) = 4,800$
$80(60) = 4,800$
$4,800 = 4,800$

3.17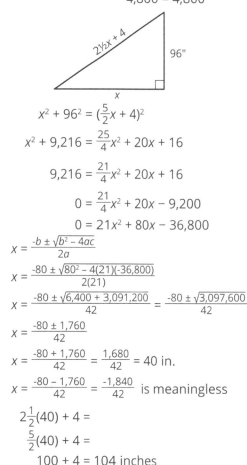
$x^2 + 96^2 = (\frac{5}{2}x + 4)^2$
$x^2 + 9,216 = \frac{25}{4}x^2 + 20x + 16$
$9,216 = \frac{21}{4}x^2 + 20x + 16$
$0 = \frac{21}{4}x^2 + 20x - 9,200$
$0 = 21x^2 + 80x - 36,800$
$x = \frac{-b \pm \sqrt{b^2 - 4ac}}{2a}$
$x = \frac{-80 \pm \sqrt{80^2 - 4(21)(-36,800)}}{2(21)}$
$x = \frac{-80 \pm \sqrt{6,400 + 3,091,200}}{42} = \frac{-80 \pm \sqrt{3,097,600}}{42}$
$x = \frac{-80 \pm 1,760}{42}$
$x = \frac{-80 + 1,760}{42} = \frac{1,680}{42} = 40$ in.
$x = \frac{-80 - 1,760}{42} = \frac{-1,840}{42}$ is meaningless
$2\frac{1}{2}(40) + 4 =$
$\frac{5}{2}(40) + 4 =$
$100 + 4 = 104$ inches
The other leg measures 40 inches; the hypotenuse measures 104 inches.
Check:
$40^2 + 96^2 = (\frac{5}{2} \cdot 40 + 4)^2$
$40^2 + 96^2 = (100 + 4)^2$
$40^2 + 96^2 = 104^2$
$1,600 + 9,216 = 10,816$
$10,816 = 10,816$

3.18 Let x = the first odd integer
$x + 2$ = the second odd integer

$$x(x + 2) = 2{,}115$$
$$x^2 + 2x = 2{,}115$$
$$x^2 + 2x - 2{,}115 = 0$$
$$x = \frac{-b \pm \sqrt{b^2 - 4ac}}{2a}$$
$$x = \frac{-2 \pm \sqrt{2^2 - 4(1)(-2{,}115)}}{2(1)}$$
$$x = \frac{-2 \pm \sqrt{4 + 8{,}460}}{2} = \frac{-2 \pm \sqrt{8{,}464}}{2}$$
$$x = \frac{-2 \pm 92}{2}$$
$$x = -1 \pm 46$$
$$x = -1 + 46 = 45$$
$$x = -1 - 46 = -47$$
$$x + 2 = 45 + 2 = 47$$
$$x + 2 = -47 + 2 = -45$$

The integers are 45 and 47 or -45 and -47.

Check:

$45(45 + 2) = 2{,}115$	$-47(-47 + 2) = 2{,}115$
$45(47) = 2{,}115$	$-47(-45) = 2{,}115$
$2{,}115 = 2{,}115$	$2{,}115 = 2{,}115$

3.19 Let x = the first number
$x + 1$ = the second number

$$x^2 + 23 = (x + 1)^2$$
$$\cancel{x^2} + 23 = \cancel{x^2} + 2x + 1$$
$$22 = 2x$$
$$x = 11$$
$$x + 1 = 11 + 1 = 12$$

The numbers are 11 and 12.

Check:
$$11^2 + 23 = (11 + 1)^2$$
$$121 + 23 = 12^2$$
$$144 = 144$$

3.20

	r	t	d
up	$x - 2$	$\dfrac{12}{x - 2}$	12
return	$x + 2$	$\dfrac{12}{x + 2}$	12

$$\frac{12}{x + 2} + \frac{3}{2} = \frac{12}{x - 2}$$
$$\text{LCD} = 2(x + 2)(x - 2)$$
$$12(2)(x - 2) + 3(x + 2)(x - 2) = 12(2)(x + 2)$$
$$24(x - 2) + 3(x^2 - 4) = 24(x + 2)$$
$$\cancel{24x} - 48 + 3x^2 - 12 = \cancel{24x} + 48$$
$$3x^2 - 60 = 48$$
$$3x^2 = 108$$
$$x^2 = 36$$
$$\sqrt{x^2} = \pm\sqrt{36}$$
$$x = \pm 6$$

The rate of the boat is 6 mph.

Check:
$$\frac{12}{6 + 2} + \frac{3}{2} = \frac{12}{6 - 2}$$
$$\frac{12}{8} + \frac{3}{2} = \frac{12}{4}$$
$$\frac{3}{2} + \frac{3}{2} = 3$$
$$\frac{6}{2} = 3$$
$$3 = 3$$

4 mph	8 mph
× 3 hr.	× 1.5 hr.
12 mi.	12 mi.

3.21

	r	t	d
Loren	x	$\dfrac{200}{x}$	200
Lois	$x - 10$	$\dfrac{100}{x - 10}$	100
Loren	x	$\dfrac{300}{x}$	300

$$\frac{200}{x} + \frac{100}{x - 10} = \frac{1}{2} + \frac{300}{x}$$
$$\text{LCD} = 2x(x - 10)$$
$$200(2)(x - 10) + 100(2x) = 1(x)(x - 10) + 300(2)(x - 10)$$
$$400(x - 10) + 200x = x^2 - 10x + 600(x - 10)$$
$$400x - 4{,}000 + 200x = x^2 - 10x + 600x - 6{,}000$$
$$600x - 4{,}000 = x^2 + 590x - 6{,}000$$
$$-4{,}000 = x^2 - 10x - 6{,}000$$
$$0 = x^2 - 10x - 2{,}000$$
$$0 = (x - 50)(x + 40)$$

$0 = x - 50$	$x + 40 = 0$
$x = 50$ mph	$x = -40$
	is meaningless

Loren drove at 50 mph.

Check:
$$\frac{200}{50} + \frac{100}{50 - 10} = \frac{1}{2} + \frac{300}{50}$$
$$4 + \frac{100}{40} = \frac{1}{2} + 6$$
$$4 + \frac{5}{2} = \frac{1}{2} + 6$$
$$6\frac{1}{2} = 6\frac{1}{2}$$

3.22 Let x = Laura's time to complete the job
$\dfrac{x + 2}{2}$ = Tammy's time to complete the job
$x + 2$ = Jeri's time to complete the job
$1\frac{1}{3}$ hr. = time to do the work together

$$\frac{1\frac{1}{3}}{x} + \frac{1\frac{1}{3}}{\frac{x + 2}{2}} + \frac{1\frac{1}{3}}{x + 2} = 1$$
$$\frac{\frac{4}{3}}{x} + \frac{\frac{4}{3}}{\frac{x + 2}{2}} + \frac{\frac{4}{3}}{x + 2} = 1$$
$$\frac{4}{3x} + \frac{8}{3x + 6} + \frac{4}{3x + 6} = 1$$
$$\text{LCD} = 3x(3x + 6)$$

$4(3x + 6) + 8(3x) + 4(3x) = 1(3x)(3x + 6)$
$12x + 24 + 24x + 12x = 9x^2 + 18x$
$48x + 24 = 9x^2 + 18x$
$24 = 9x^2 - 30x$
$0 = 9x^2 - 30x - 24$
$0 = 3x^2 - 10x - 8$

$x = \dfrac{-b \pm \sqrt{b^2 - 4ac}}{2a}$

$x = \dfrac{10 \pm \sqrt{(-10)^2 - 4(3)(-8)}}{2(3)}$

$x = \dfrac{10 \pm \sqrt{100 + 96}}{6} = \dfrac{10 \pm \sqrt{196}}{6}$

$x = \dfrac{10 \pm 14}{6} = \dfrac{5 \pm 7}{3}$

$x = \dfrac{5 + 7}{3} = \dfrac{12}{3} = 4$ hours

$x = \dfrac{5 - 7}{3} = \dfrac{-2}{3}$ is meaningless

$\dfrac{x + 2}{2} = \dfrac{4 + 2}{2} = \dfrac{6}{2} = 3$ hours

$x + 2 = 4 + 2 = 6$ hours

Laura would take 4 hours, Tammy would take 3 hours, and Jeri would take 6 hours.

Check:

$\dfrac{\frac{4}{3}}{4} + \dfrac{\frac{4}{3}}{\frac{4+2}{2}} + \dfrac{\frac{4}{3}}{4 + 2} = 1$

$\dfrac{\frac{4}{3}}{4} + \dfrac{\frac{4}{3}}{\frac{6}{2}} + \dfrac{\frac{4}{3}}{6} = 1$

$\dfrac{1}{3} + \dfrac{\frac{4}{3}}{3} + \dfrac{\frac{4}{3}}{6} = 1$

$\dfrac{3}{9} + \dfrac{4}{9} + \dfrac{2}{9} = 1$

$\dfrac{9}{9} = 1$

$1 = 1$

3.23 Let x = time required for Ron to frame the cabin

$x - 4$ = time required for Lee to frame the cabin

$4\frac{4}{5}$ = time required for them working together to frame the cabin

$\dfrac{4\frac{4}{5}}{x} + \dfrac{4\frac{4}{5}}{x - 4} = 1$

$\dfrac{\frac{24}{5}}{x} + \dfrac{\frac{24}{5}}{x - 4} = 1$

$\dfrac{24}{5x} + \dfrac{24}{5(x - 4)} = 1$

LCD = $5x(x - 4)$

$24(x - 4) + 24x = 5x(x - 4)$
$24x - 96 + 24x = 5x^2 - 20x$
$48x - 96 = 5x^2 - 20x$
$-96 = 5x^2 - 68x$
$0 = 5x^2 - 68x + 96$

$x = \dfrac{-b \pm \sqrt{b^2 - 4ac}}{2a}$

$x = \dfrac{68 \pm \sqrt{(-68)^2 - 4(5)(96)}}{2(5)}$

$x = \dfrac{68 \pm \sqrt{4,624 - 1,920}}{10} = \dfrac{68 \pm \sqrt{2,704}}{10}$

$x = \dfrac{68 \pm 52}{10}$

$x = \dfrac{68 + 52}{10} = \dfrac{120}{10} = 12$ days

$x = \dfrac{68 - 52}{10} = \dfrac{16}{10} = 1.6$ is meaningless

(does not check)

$x - 4 = 12 - 4 = 8$ days

Ron would take 12 days and Lee would take 8 days.

Check:

$\dfrac{\frac{24}{5}}{12} + \dfrac{\frac{24}{5}}{12 - 4} = 1$

$\dfrac{\frac{24}{5}}{12} + \dfrac{\frac{24}{5}}{8} = 1$

$\dfrac{2}{5} + \dfrac{3}{5} = 1$

$\dfrac{5}{5} = 1$

$1 = 1$

3.24 Let x = cost of shares bought initially

$x - 10$ = cost of shares bought after drop

$\dfrac{2,000}{x} + 10 = \dfrac{2,000}{x - 10}$

LCD = $x(x - 10)$

$2,000(x - 10) + 10x(x - 10) = 2,000x$
$2,000x - 20,000 + 10x^2 - 100x = 2,000x$
$10x^2 + 1,900x - 20,000 = 2,000x$
$10x^2 - 100x - 20,000 = 0$
$x^2 - 10x - 2,000 = 0$
$(x - 50)(x + 40) = 0$

$x - 50 = 0 \qquad\qquad x + 40 = 0$
$x = 50 \qquad\qquad\quad x = -40$ is meaningless

$x - 10 = 50 - 10 = 40$

Each share cost $50, and Ed bought 40 shares.

Check:

$\dfrac{2,000}{50} + 10 = \dfrac{2,000}{50 - 10}$

$40 + 10 = \dfrac{2,000}{40}$

$50 = 50$

```
$    50        $    40         50
×    40        ×    50       - 10
$ 2,000        $ 2,000         40
```

211

3.25 Let x = Mark's age 3 years ago
$x + 12$ = Mark's age in 9 years
$$x^2 = 6(x + 12)$$
$$x^2 = 6x + 72$$
$x^2 - 6x - 72 = 0$
$(x - 12)(x + 6) = 0$
$x - 12 = 0$ $\qquad$ $x + 6 = 0$
$x = 12$ $\qquad$ $x = -6$ is meaningless
$x + 3 = 12 + 3 = 15$ years old now
Mark is 15 years old.
Check:
$$12^2 = 6(12 + 12)$$
$$144 = 6(24)$$
$$144 = 144$$

3.26 $5 + (-11) = -6$
$-\frac{b}{a} = \frac{-6}{1} = -6$
$5(-11) = -55$
$\frac{c}{a} = \frac{-55}{1} = -55$

3.27 $\frac{1}{2} + (-\frac{1}{4}) = \frac{1}{4}$
$-\frac{b}{a} = \frac{-(-2)}{8} = \frac{2}{8} = \frac{1}{4}$
$\frac{1}{2}(-\frac{1}{4}) = -\frac{1}{8}$
$\frac{c}{a} = -\frac{1}{8}$

3.28 $-3 + (-3) = -6$
$-\frac{b}{a} = \frac{-6}{1} = -6$
$(-3)(-3) = 9$
$\frac{c}{a} = \frac{9}{1} = 9$

3.29 $\frac{7}{8} + 0 = \frac{7}{8}$
$-\frac{b}{a} = \frac{-(-7)}{8} = \frac{7}{8}$
$\frac{7}{8}(0) = 0$
$\frac{c}{a} = \frac{0}{8} = 0$

3.30 $17 + 2 = 19$
$-\frac{b}{a} = \frac{-(-19)}{1} = 19$
$17(2) = 34$
$\frac{c}{a} = \frac{34}{1} = 34$

3.31 $\frac{5 + 2\sqrt{10}}{-3} + \frac{5 - 2\sqrt{10}}{-3} = \frac{10}{-3}$
$-\frac{b}{a} = \frac{-(-10)}{-3} = -\frac{10}{3}$
$(\frac{5 + 2\sqrt{10}}{-3})(\frac{5 - 2\sqrt{10}}{-3}) = \frac{25 - 40}{9} = \frac{-15}{9} = -\frac{5}{3}$
$\frac{c}{a} = -\frac{5}{3}$

3.32 $-\frac{1}{2} + (-2) = -\frac{5}{2}$
$-\frac{b}{a} = -\frac{5}{2}$
$-\frac{1}{2}(-2) = 1$
$\frac{c}{a} = \frac{2}{2} = 1$

3.33 $\frac{-2 + \sqrt{22}}{3} + \frac{-2 - \sqrt{22}}{3} = -\frac{4}{3}$
$-\frac{b}{a} = -\frac{4}{3}$
$(\frac{-2 + \sqrt{22}}{3})(\frac{-2 - \sqrt{22}}{3}) = \frac{4 - 22}{9} = \frac{-18}{9} = -2$
$\frac{c}{a} = \frac{-6}{3} = -2$

3.34 $-2 + \sqrt{21} + (-2 - \sqrt{21}) = -4$
$-\frac{b}{a} = \frac{-(-4)}{-1} = -4$
$(-2 + \sqrt{21})(-2 - \sqrt{21}) = 4 - 21 = -17$
$\frac{c}{a} = \frac{17}{-1} = -17$

3.35 $6 + (-\frac{2}{7}) = 5\frac{5}{7}$ or $\frac{40}{7}$
$-\frac{b}{a} = \frac{-(-40)}{7} = \frac{40}{7}$
$6(-\frac{2}{7}) = -\frac{12}{7}$
$\frac{c}{a} = -\frac{12}{7}$

3.36 A $\quad$ $(-4)^2 - 4(1)(4) = 16 - 16 = 0$
3.37 D $\quad$ $(-5)^2 - 4(1)(7) = 25 - 28 = -3$
3.38 C $\quad$ $(-5)^2 - 4(1)(-4) = 25 + 16 = 41$
3.39 D $\quad$ $2^2 - 4(3)(5) = 4 - 60 = -56$
3.40 A $\quad$ $8^2 - 4(16)(1) = 64 - 64 = 0$
3.41 B $\quad$ $9^2 - 4(1)(14) = 81 - 56 = 25$
3.42 C $\quad$ $3x^2 + 0x - 10 = 0$
$\qquad\qquad$ $0^2 - 4(3)(-10) = 0 + 120 = 120$
3.43 B $\quad$ $2x^2 - 3x - 2 = 0$
$\qquad\qquad$ $(-3)^2 - 4(2)(-2) = 9 + 16 = 25$
3.44 C $\quad$ $x^2 + 5x - 2 = 0$
$\qquad\qquad$ $5^2 - 4(1)(-2) = 25 + 8 = 33$
3.45 D $\quad$ $2m^2 - m + 3 = 0$
$\qquad\qquad$ $(-1)^2 - 4(2)(3) = 1 - 24 = -23$
3.46 B $\quad$ $13^2 - 4(6)(6) = 169 - 144 = 25$
3.47 B $\quad$ $(-4)^2 - 4(1)(-21) = 16 + 84 = 100$
3.48 B $\quad$ $7^2 - 4(2)(6) = 49 - 48 = 1$
3.49 D $\quad$ $7x^2 - 5x + 1 = 0$
$\qquad\qquad$ $(-5)^2 - 4(7)(1) = 25 - 28 = -3$
3.50 D $\quad$ $7x^2 - 8x + 3 = 0$
$\qquad\qquad$ $(-8)^2 - 4(7)(3) = 64 - 84 = -20$
3.51 B $\quad$ $5x^2 - 7x + 0 = 0$
$\qquad\qquad$ $(-7)^2 - 4(5)(0) = 49 - 0 = 49$
3.52 C $\quad$ $3x^2 + 7x - 2 = 0$
$\qquad\qquad$ $7^2 - 4(3)(-2) = 49 + 24 = 73$

3.53 A $(-6)^2 - 4(1)(9) = 36 - 36 = 0$

3.54 D $(-6)^2 - 4(1)(12) = 36 - 48 = -12$

3.55 B $2x^2 - 11x - 21 = 0$

   $(-11)^2 - 4(2)(-21) = 121 + 168 = 289$

3.56 $i\sqrt{5}(i\sqrt{7}) = i^2\sqrt{35} = -\sqrt{35}$

3.57 $(i^2)^3 = (-1)^3 = -1$

3.58 $(i^2)^7(i) = (-1)^7(i) = -i$

3.59 $3i\sqrt{24} = 3i\sqrt{4}\sqrt{6} = 6i\sqrt{6}$

3.60 $2i\sqrt{2} \cdot 5i\sqrt{3} = 10i^2\sqrt{6} = -10\sqrt{6}$

3.61 $4 - 3i$

3.62 5

3.63 $-9 - 3i$

3.64 $5i + 4i + 3i = 12i$

3.65 $4i^2(5) = -20$

3.66 $25 - i^2 = 25 + 1 = 26$

3.67 $(-\sqrt{2})^2 + 2(-\sqrt{2})(-\sqrt{3}) + (\sqrt{-3})^2$

   $= 2 + 2i\sqrt{6} + i^2(3) = 2 + 2i\sqrt{6} - 3 = -1 + 2i\sqrt{6}$

3.68 $9 - 25i^2 = 9 + 25 = 34$

3.69 $i\sqrt{\frac{1}{2}} = \frac{i\sqrt{2}}{2}$

3.70 $5 - 6(i^2)^5 i = 5 - 6(-1)i = 5 + 6i$

3.71 $40 - 30i$

3.72 $(i^2)^6 + 1 = 1 + 1 = 2$

3.73 $\frac{(3-4i)(3-4i)}{(3+4i)(3-4i)} = \frac{9 - 24i + 16i^2}{9 - 16i^2} = \frac{9 - 24i - 16}{9 + 16} = \frac{-7 - 24i}{25}$

3.74 $\frac{(2a + i\sqrt{b})(3a + i\sqrt{b})}{(3a - i\sqrt{b})(3a + i\sqrt{b})} = \frac{6a^2 + 5ai\sqrt{b} + i^2 b}{9a^2 - i^2 b} = \frac{6a^2 + 5ai\sqrt{b} - b}{9a^2 + b}$

3.75 $(5 - 2i^2)^2$

   $= 25 - 20i^2 + 4i^4$

   $= 25 + 20 + 4$

   $= 49$

3.76 $\frac{6(i)}{2i(i)} = \frac{6i}{2i^2} = \frac{6i}{-2} = -3i$

3.77 $(4 - 5i\sqrt{6})^2$

   $= 16 - 40i\sqrt{6} + 25i^2(6)$

   $= 16 - 40i\sqrt{6} - 150$

   $= -134 - 40i\sqrt{6}$

3.78 $\frac{4 - i^2(3)}{4} = \frac{4 + 3}{4} = \frac{7}{4}$

3.79 $\frac{(4+i)(3+2i)}{(3-2i)(3+2i)} = \frac{12 + 11i + 2i^2}{9 - 4i^2} = \frac{12 + 11i - 2}{9 + 4} = \frac{10 + 11i}{13}$

3.80 $\frac{(2-2i)(1-3i)}{(1+3i)(1-3i)} = \frac{2 - 8i + 6i^2}{1 - 9i^2} = \frac{2 - 8i - 6}{1 + 9} = \frac{-4 - 8i}{10}$

   $= \frac{-2 - 4i}{5}$

SELF TEST 3

3.01 Let $0.0555\ldots = x$

$$10x = 0.555\ldots$$
$$\underline{x = 0.055\ldots}$$
$$9x = 0.5$$
$$x = \frac{0.5}{9} = \frac{5}{90} = \frac{1}{18}$$

3.02 $\sqrt{3}$

3.03 $12 + \sqrt{5}$

3.04

$$\sqrt{4x + 5} = 3 - \sqrt{2x - 6}$$
$$(\sqrt{4x + 5})^2 = (3 - \sqrt{2x - 6})^2$$
$$4x + 5 = 9 - 6\sqrt{2x - 6} + 2x - 6$$
$$4x + 5 = 3 + 2x - 6\sqrt{2x - 6}$$
$$2x + 5 = 3 - 6\sqrt{2x - 6}$$
$$2x + 2 = -6\sqrt{2x - 6}$$
$$x + 1 = -3\sqrt{2x - 6}$$
$$(x + 1)^2 = (-3\sqrt{2x - 6})^2$$
$$x^2 + 2x + 1 = 9(2x - 6)$$
$$x^2 + 2x + 1 = 18x - 54$$
$$x^2 - 16x + 1 = -54$$
$$x^2 - 16x + 55 = 0$$
$$(x - 11)(x - 5) = 0$$

   $x - 11 = 0$ $\qquad$ $x - 5 = 0$

   $\qquad x = 11$ $\qquad\qquad x = 5$

Check:

$$\sqrt{4(11) + 5} = 3 - \sqrt{2(11) - 6}$$
$$\sqrt{44 + 5} = 3 - \sqrt{22 - 6}$$
$$\sqrt{49} = 3 - \sqrt{16}$$
$$7 = 3 - 4$$
$$7 \neq -1$$

$$\sqrt{4(5) + 5} = 3 - \sqrt{2(5) - 6}$$
$$\sqrt{20 + 5} = 3 - \sqrt{10 - 6}$$
$$\sqrt{25} = 3 - \sqrt{4}$$
$$5 = 3 - 2$$
$$5 \neq 1$$

∴ This equation has no roots.

3.05

$$x^2 + 10x + 25 = 16$$
$$x^2 + 10x + 9 = 0$$
$$(x + 9)(x + 1) = 0$$

   $x + 9 = 0$ $\qquad$ $x + 1 = 0$

   $\qquad x = -9$ $\qquad\qquad x = -1$

Check:

$$(-9)^2 + 10(-9) + 25 = 16$$
$$81 - 90 + 25 = 16$$
$$-9 + 25 = 16$$
$$16 = 16$$
$$(-1)^2 + 10(-1) + 25 = 16$$
$$1 - 10 + 25 = 16$$
$$-9 + 25 = 16$$
$$16 = 16$$

3.06

$$2x^2 - x = 21$$
$$2x^2 - x - 21 = 0$$
$$(2x - 7)(x + 3) = 0$$
$$2x - 7 = 0 \qquad x + 3 = 0$$
$$2x = 7 \qquad x = -3$$
$$x = \frac{7}{2}$$

Check:

$$2(\tfrac{7}{2})^2 - \tfrac{7}{2} = 21$$
$$\overset{1}{2}(\tfrac{49}{\cancel{4}}) - \tfrac{7}{2} = 21$$
$$\underset{2}{}$$
$$\frac{42}{2} = 21$$
$$21 = 21$$

$$2(-3)^2 - (-3) = 21$$
$$2(9) + 3 = 21$$
$$18 + 3 = 21$$
$$21 = 21$$

3.07

$$3x^2 - 12x = 9$$
$$x^2 - 4x = 3$$
$$\frac{1}{2} \cdot 4 = 2$$
$$2^2 = 4$$

$$x^2 - 4x + 4 = 3 + 4$$
$$(x - 2)^2 = 7$$
$$\sqrt{(x + 1)^2} = \pm\sqrt{7}$$
$$x - 2 = \pm\sqrt{7}$$
$$x = 2 \pm \sqrt{7}$$

Check:

$$3(2 + \sqrt{7})^2 - 12(2 + \sqrt{7}) = 9$$
$$3(4 + 4\sqrt{7} + 7) - 24 - 12\sqrt{7} = 9$$
$$12 + \cancel{12\sqrt{7}} + 21 - 24 - \cancel{12\sqrt{7}} = 9$$
$$9 = 9$$

$$3(2 - 17)^2 - 12(2 - \sqrt{7}) = 9$$
$$3(4 - 4\sqrt{7} + 7) - 24 + 12\sqrt{7} = 9$$
$$12 - \cancel{12\sqrt{7}} + 21 - 24 + \cancel{12\sqrt{7}} = 9$$
$$9 = 9$$

3.08

$$3x^2 + 11x - 4 = 0$$
$$a = 3; \; b = 11; \; c = -4$$
$$x = \frac{-11 \pm \sqrt{11^2 - 4(3)(-4)}}{2(3)}$$
$$x = \frac{-11 \pm \sqrt{121 + 48}}{6} = \frac{-11 \pm \sqrt{169}}{6} = \frac{-11 \pm 13}{6}$$
$$x = \frac{-11 + 13}{6} = \frac{2}{6} = \frac{1}{3}$$
$$x = \frac{-11 - 13}{6} = \frac{-24}{6} = -4$$

Check:

$$3(\tfrac{1}{3})^2 + 11(\tfrac{1}{3}) - 4 = 0$$
$$3(\tfrac{1}{9}) + \tfrac{11}{3} - 4 = 0$$
$$\tfrac{1}{3} + \tfrac{11}{3} - 4 = 0$$
$$\frac{12}{3} - 4 = 0$$
$$4 - 4 = 0$$
$$0 = 0$$

$$3(-4)^2 + 11(-4) - 4 = 0$$
$$3(16) - 44 - 4 = 0$$
$$48 - 48 = 0$$
$$0 = 0$$

3.09

$$2x^2 - 7x - 15 = 0$$
$$a = 2; \; b = -7; \; c = -15$$
$$x = \frac{7 \pm \sqrt{(-7)^2 - 4(2)(-15)}}{2(2)}$$
$$x = \frac{7 \pm \sqrt{49 + 120}}{4} = \frac{7 \pm \sqrt{169}}{4} = \frac{7 \pm 13}{4}$$
$$x = \frac{7 + 13}{4} = \frac{20}{4} = 5$$
$$x = \frac{7 - 13}{4} = \frac{-6}{4} = -\frac{3}{2}$$

Check:

$$2(5)^2 - 7(5) = 15$$
$$2(25) - 35 = 15$$
$$50 - 35 = 15$$
$$15 = 15$$

$$2(-\tfrac{3}{2})^2 - 7(-\tfrac{3}{2}) = 15$$
$$\overset{1}{2}(\tfrac{9}{\cancel{4}}) + \tfrac{21}{2} = 15$$
$$\underset{2}{}$$
$$\frac{9}{2} + \frac{21}{2} = 15$$
$$\frac{30}{2} = 15$$
$$15 = 15$$

3.010

$$12 - 2x = x^2 + 5x$$
$$12 = x^2 + 7x$$
$$0 = x^2 + 7x - 12$$
$$a = 1; \; b = 7; \; c = -12$$
$$x = \frac{-7 \pm \sqrt{7^2 - 4(1)(-12)}}{2(1)} = \frac{-7 \pm \sqrt{49 + 48}}{2} = \frac{-7 \pm \sqrt{97}}{2}$$

Check:

$$2(6 - \tfrac{-7 + \sqrt{97}}{2}) = \tfrac{-7 + \sqrt{97}}{2}(\tfrac{-7 + \sqrt{97}}{2} + 5)$$
$$12 - (-7 + \sqrt{97}) = \frac{49 - 14\sqrt{97} + 97}{4} + \frac{-35 + 5\sqrt{97}}{2}$$
$$12 + 7 - \sqrt{97} = \frac{146 - 14\sqrt{97}}{4} + \frac{-70 + 10\sqrt{97}}{4}$$
$$19 - \sqrt{97} = \frac{146 - 14\sqrt{97} - 70 + 10\sqrt{97}}{4}$$
$$76 - 4\sqrt{97} = 76 - 4\sqrt{97}$$

$$2(6 - \tfrac{-7 - \sqrt{97}}{2}) = \tfrac{-7 - \sqrt{97}}{2}(\tfrac{-7 - \sqrt{97}}{2} + 5)$$
$$12 + 7 + \sqrt{97} = \frac{49 + 14\sqrt{97} + 97}{4} + \frac{-35 - 5\sqrt{97}}{2}$$
$$19 + \sqrt{97} = \frac{146 + 14\sqrt{97}}{4} + \frac{-70 - 10\sqrt{97}}{4}$$
$$19 + \sqrt{97} = \frac{146 + 14\sqrt{97} - 70 - 10\sqrt{97}}{4}$$
$$19 + \sqrt{97} = \frac{76 + 4\sqrt{97}}{4}$$
$$76 + 4\sqrt{97} = 76 + 4\sqrt{97}$$

3.011 $x^2 + 4x + 2 = -4$
$x^2 + 4x + 6 = 0$
$a = 1; b = 4; c = 6$
$x = \dfrac{-4 \pm \sqrt{4^2 - 4(1)(6)}}{2(1)}$
$x = \dfrac{-4 \pm \sqrt{16 - 24}}{2}$
$x = \dfrac{-4 \pm \sqrt{-8}}{2}$
$x = \dfrac{-4 \pm 2i\sqrt{2}}{2}$
$x = -2 \pm i\sqrt{2}$
Check:
$(-2 + i\sqrt{2})(-2 + i\sqrt{2} + 4) + 2 = -4$
$(-2 + i\sqrt{2})(2 + i\sqrt{2}) + 2 = -4$
$-4 + i^2(2) + 2 = -4$
$-4 - \cancel{2} + \cancel{2} = -4$
$-4 = -4$

$(-2 - i\sqrt{2})(-2 - i\sqrt{2} + 4) + 2 = -4$
$(-2 - i\sqrt{2})(2 - i\sqrt{2}) + 2 = -4$
$-4 + i^2(2) + 2 = -4$
$-4 - \cancel{2} + \cancel{2} = -4$
$-4 = -4$

3.012 $\dfrac{1}{3} + (-4) = -3\dfrac{2}{3}$ or $-\dfrac{11}{3}$
$-\dfrac{b}{a} = -\dfrac{11}{3}$
$(\dfrac{1}{3})(-4) = -\dfrac{4}{3}$
$\dfrac{c}{a} = -\dfrac{4}{3}$

3.013 $5 + (-\dfrac{3}{2}) = \dfrac{7}{2}$
$-\dfrac{b}{a} = -\dfrac{-7}{2} = \dfrac{7}{2}$
$5(-\dfrac{3}{2}) = -\dfrac{15}{2}$
$\dfrac{c}{a} = -\dfrac{15}{2}$

3.014 $\dfrac{-7 + \sqrt{97}}{2} + \dfrac{-7 - \sqrt{97}}{2} = \dfrac{-14}{2} = -\dfrac{7}{1} = -7$
$-\dfrac{b}{a} = -\dfrac{7}{1} = -7$
$(\dfrac{-7 + \sqrt{97}}{2})(\dfrac{-7 - \sqrt{97}}{2}) = \dfrac{49 - 97}{4} = -\dfrac{48}{4} = -\dfrac{12}{1} = -12$
$\dfrac{c}{a} = -\dfrac{48}{4} = -12$

3.015 $-2 + i\sqrt{2} + (-2 - i\sqrt{2}) = -4$
$-\dfrac{b}{a} = -\dfrac{4}{1} = -4$
$(-2 + i\sqrt{2})(-2 - i\sqrt{2}) = 4 - i^2(2) = 4 + 2 = 6$
$\dfrac{c}{a} = \dfrac{6}{1} = 6$

3.016 C
$(-5)^2 - 4(1)(-3) = 25 + 12 = 37$

3.017 D
$2^2 - 4(1)(5) = 4 - 20 = -16$

3.018 A
$30^2 - 4(9)(25) = 900 - 900 = 0$

3.019 $\dfrac{2\sqrt{3}}{i\sqrt{6}} = \dfrac{2}{i\sqrt{2}} = \dfrac{2(i\sqrt{2})}{i\sqrt{2}(i\sqrt{2})} = \dfrac{2i\sqrt{2}}{2i^2} = \dfrac{2i\sqrt{2}}{-2} = -i\sqrt{2}$

3.020 $(\dfrac{2 + i\sqrt{3}}{2})(\dfrac{2 - i\sqrt{3}}{2}) = \dfrac{4 - i^2(3)}{4} = \dfrac{4 + 3}{4} = \dfrac{7}{4}$ or $1\dfrac{3}{4}$

LIFEPAC TEST

1. false
2. true

   $\sqrt[3]{15} = \sqrt[3]{15}$
3. true
4. false

   $\sqrt{49} \neq -7$
5. false

   $x + 2 = \pm 7$
6. true

   $x^2 - 6x + 8 = (x - 4)(x - 2)$
7. false

   $3x^2 + 7x - 12 = 0$

   $x^2 + \frac{7}{3}x - 4 = 0$

   $x^2 + \frac{7}{3}x = 4$
8. false

   $x = \frac{-b \pm \sqrt{b^2 - 4ac}}{2a}$
9. true
10. true
11. Let $1.2777... = x$

    $10x = 12.777...$

    $\underline{\quad x = 1.277...}$

    $9x = 11.5$

    $x = \frac{11.5}{9} = \frac{115}{90} = \frac{23}{18}$
12. $x^{2/3}$
13. $\frac{1}{4}\cancel{3} \cdot \frac{\sqrt{2}}{\cancel{3}_1} - \frac{\sqrt{2}}{2} - 3\sqrt[3]{2} + 5\sqrt[3]{2}$

    $= \frac{\sqrt{2}}{4} - \frac{2\sqrt{2}}{4} + 2\sqrt[3]{2}$

    $= 2\sqrt[3]{2} - \frac{\sqrt{2}}{4}$
14. $\frac{(2 + \sqrt{5})(2 - \sqrt{3})}{(2 + \sqrt{3})(2 - \sqrt{3})} = \frac{4 + 2\sqrt{5} - 2\sqrt{3} - \sqrt{15}}{4 - 3}$

    $= 4 + 2\sqrt{5} - 2\sqrt{3} - \sqrt{15}$
15. $\frac{(2\sqrt{3} + 5\sqrt{2})(3\sqrt{3} + 2\sqrt{2})}{(3\sqrt{3} - 2\sqrt{2})(3\sqrt{3} + 2\sqrt{2})} = \frac{18 + 19\sqrt{6} + 20}{27 - 8}$

    $= \frac{38 + 19\sqrt{6}}{19}$

    $= 2 + \sqrt{6}$
16. $\sqrt{x - 2} = x - 8$

    $(\sqrt{x - 2})^2 = (x - 8)^2$

    $x - 2 = x^2 - 16x + 64$

    $-2 = x^2 - 17x + 64$

    $0 = x^2 - 17x + 66$

    $0 = (x - 11)(x - 6)$

    $x - 11 = 0 \qquad x - 6 = 0$

    $\qquad x = 11 \qquad\qquad x = 6$

Check:

$\sqrt{11 - 2} = 11 - 8$

$\sqrt{9} = 3$

$3 = 3$

$\sqrt{6 - 2} = 6 - 8$

$\sqrt{4} = -2$

$2 \neq -2$

$\therefore x = 11$

17. $\sqrt{y + 2} - \frac{3}{\sqrt{y + 2}} = -\sqrt{y}$

    $(\sqrt{y + 2})(\sqrt{y + 2}) - \frac{3(\sqrt{y + 2})}{\sqrt{y + 2}} = -\sqrt{y}(\sqrt{y + 2})$

    $y + 2 - 3 = -\sqrt{y^2 + 2y}$

    $y - 1 = -\sqrt{y^2 + 2y}$

    $(y - 1)^2 = (-\sqrt{y^2 + 2y})^2$

    $\cancel{y^2} - 2y + 1 = \cancel{y^2} + 2y$

    $-4y + 1 = 0$

    $-4y = -1$

    $y = \frac{-1}{-4} = \frac{1}{4}$

Check:

$\sqrt{\frac{1}{4} + 2} - \frac{3}{\sqrt{\frac{1}{4} + 2}} = -\sqrt{\frac{1}{4}}$

$\sqrt{\frac{9}{4}} - \frac{3}{\sqrt{\frac{9}{4}}} = -\sqrt{\frac{1}{4}}$

$\frac{3}{2} - \frac{3}{\frac{3}{2}} = -\frac{1}{2}$

$\frac{3}{2} - 2 = -\frac{1}{2}$

$-\frac{1}{2} = -\frac{1}{2}$

18. $(x - 5)^2 = 81$

    $\sqrt{(x - 5)^2} = \pm\sqrt{81}$

    $x - 5 = \pm 9$

    $x - 5 = 9$

    $x = 14$

    $x - 5 = -9$

    $x = -4$

Check:

$(14 - 5)^2 = 81$

$9^2 = 81$

$81 = 81$

$(-4 - 5)^2 = 81$

$(-9)^2 = 81$

$81 = 81$

19.
$$3x^2 + 2 = 11 - x^2$$
$$4x^2 + 2 = 11$$
$$4x^2 - 9 = 0$$
$$(2x + 3)(2x - 3) = 0$$

$2x + 3 = 0$	$2x - 3 = 0$
$2x = -3$	$2x = 3$
$x = -\frac{3}{2}$	$x = \frac{3}{2}$

Check:
$$3(-\tfrac{3}{2})^2 + 2 = 11 - (-\tfrac{3}{2})^2$$
$$3(\tfrac{9}{4}) + 2 = 11 - \tfrac{9}{4}$$
$$\tfrac{27}{4} + \tfrac{8}{4} = \tfrac{44}{4} - \tfrac{9}{4}$$
$$\tfrac{35}{4} = \tfrac{35}{4}$$

$$3(\tfrac{3}{2})^2 + 2 = 11 - (\tfrac{3}{2})^2$$
$$3(\tfrac{9}{4}) + 2 = 11 - \tfrac{9}{4}$$
$$\tfrac{27}{4} + \tfrac{8}{4} = \tfrac{44}{4} - \tfrac{9}{4}$$
$$\tfrac{35}{4} = \tfrac{35}{4}$$

20.
$$2x^2 + x - 6 = 0$$
$$(2x - 3)(x + 2) = 0$$

$2x - 3 = 0$	$x + 2 = 0$
$2x = 3$	$x = -2$
$x = \frac{3}{2}$	

Check:
$$2(\tfrac{3}{2})^2 + \tfrac{3}{2} - 6 = 0$$
$$2(\tfrac{9}{\cancel{6}_2}) + \tfrac{3}{2} - 6 = 0$$
$$\tfrac{12}{2} - 6 = 0$$
$$6 - 6 = 0$$
$$0 = 0$$

$$2(-2)^2 + (-2) - 6 = 0$$
$$2(4) - 2 - 6 = 0$$
$$8 - 8 = 0$$
$$0 = 0$$

21.
$$\frac{x + 4}{4} = \frac{x}{x - 2}$$
$$(x + 4)(x - 2) = 4(x) \qquad \text{(cross-multiply)}$$
$$x^2 + 2x - 8 = 4x$$
$$x^2 - 2x - 8 = 0$$
$$(x - 4)(x + 2) = 0$$

$x - 4 = 0$	$x + 2 = 0$
$x = 4$	$x = -2$

Check:
$$\frac{4 + 4}{4} = \frac{4}{4 - 2} \qquad\qquad \frac{-2 + 4}{4} = \frac{-2}{-2 - 2}$$
$$\frac{8}{4} = \frac{4}{2} \qquad\qquad\quad \frac{2}{4} = \frac{-2}{-4}$$
$$2 = 2 \qquad\qquad\qquad \frac{1}{2} = \frac{1}{2}$$

22.
$$2x^2 - 10x = 32$$
$$x^2 - 5x = 16$$
$$\tfrac{1}{2} \cdot 5 = \tfrac{5}{2}$$
$$(\tfrac{5}{2})^2 = \tfrac{25}{4}$$
$$x^2 - 5x + \tfrac{25}{4} = 16 + \tfrac{25}{4}$$
$$(x - \tfrac{5}{2})^2 = \tfrac{89}{4}$$
$$\sqrt{(x - \tfrac{5}{2})^2} = \pm\sqrt{\tfrac{89}{4}}$$
$$x - \tfrac{5}{2} = \pm\tfrac{\sqrt{89}}{2}$$
$$x = \tfrac{5}{2} \pm \tfrac{\sqrt{89}}{2}$$
$$x = \tfrac{5 \pm \sqrt{89}}{2}$$

Check:
$$2(\tfrac{5 + \sqrt{89}}{2})^2 - 10(\tfrac{5 + \sqrt{89}}{2}) = 32$$
$$\cancel{2}^1(\tfrac{25 + 10\sqrt{89} + 89}{\cancel{4}_2}) - \tfrac{50 + 10\sqrt{89}}{2} = 32$$
$$\tfrac{114 + 10\sqrt{89} - 50 - 10\sqrt{89}}{2} = 32$$
$$\tfrac{64}{2} = 32$$
$$32 = 32$$

$$2(\tfrac{5 - \sqrt{89}}{2})^2 - 10(\tfrac{5 - \sqrt{89}}{2}) = 32$$
$$\cancel{2}^1(\tfrac{25 - 10\sqrt{89} + 89}{\cancel{4}_2}) - \tfrac{50 - 10\sqrt{89}}{2} = 32$$
$$\tfrac{114 - 10\sqrt{89} - 50 + 10\sqrt{89}}{2} = 32$$
$$\tfrac{64}{2} = 32$$
$$32 = 32$$

23.
$$3x^2 - 4x = -2$$
$$x^2 - \tfrac{4}{3}x = -\tfrac{2}{3}$$
$$\tfrac{1}{2} \cdot \tfrac{4}{3} = \tfrac{2}{3}$$
$$(\tfrac{2}{3})^2 = \tfrac{4}{9}$$
$$x^2 - \tfrac{4}{3}x + \tfrac{4}{9} = -\tfrac{2}{3} + \tfrac{4}{9}$$
$$(x - \tfrac{2}{3})^2 = -\tfrac{2}{9}$$
$$\sqrt{(x - \tfrac{2}{3})^2} = \pm\sqrt{-\tfrac{2}{9}}$$
$$x - \tfrac{2}{3} = \pm\tfrac{\sqrt{-2}}{3}$$
$$x - \tfrac{2}{3} = \pm\tfrac{i\sqrt{2}}{3}$$
$$x = \tfrac{2}{3} \pm \tfrac{i\sqrt{2}}{3}$$
$$x = \tfrac{2 \pm i\sqrt{2}}{3}$$

Check:

$$3(\frac{2 + i\sqrt{2}}{3})^2 - 4(\frac{2 + i\sqrt{2}}{3}) = -2$$

$$\cancel{3}^1[\frac{4 + 4i\sqrt{2} + i^2(2)}{\cancel{9}_3}] - \frac{8 + 4i\sqrt{2}}{3} = -2$$

$$\frac{-6}{3} = -2$$

$$-2 = -2$$

$$3(\frac{2 - i\sqrt{2}}{3})^2 - 4(\frac{2 - i\sqrt{2}}{3}) = -2$$

$$\cancel{3}^1[\frac{4 - 4i\sqrt{2} + i^2(2)}{\cancel{9}_3}] - \frac{8 - 4i\sqrt{2}}{3} = -2$$

$$\frac{4 - \cancel{4i\sqrt{2}} - 2 - 8 + \cancel{4i\sqrt{2}}}{3} = -2$$

$$\frac{-6}{3} = -2$$

$$-2 = -2$$

24. $3x^2 - 4x + 3 = 0$

$a = 3; b = -4; c = 3$

$$x = \frac{4 \pm \sqrt{(-4)^2 - 4(3)(3)}}{2(3)} = \frac{4 \pm \sqrt{16 - 36}}{6}$$

$$x = \frac{4 \pm \sqrt{-20}}{6} = \frac{4 \pm 2i\sqrt{5}}{6} = \frac{2 \pm i\sqrt{5}}{3}$$

25. $2x^2 + 7x + 6 = 6$

$2x^2 + 7x = 0$

$2x^2 + 7x + 0 = 0$

$a = 2; b = 7; c = 0$

$$x = \frac{-7 \pm \sqrt{7^2 - 4(2)(0)}}{2(2)}$$

$$x = \frac{-7 \pm \sqrt{49 - 0}}{4}$$

$$x = \frac{-7 \pm 7}{4}$$

$$x = \frac{-7 + 7}{4} = \frac{0}{4} = 0$$

$$x = \frac{-7 - 7}{4} = \frac{-14}{4} = -\frac{7}{2}$$

26. $\frac{2 + i\sqrt{5}}{3} + \frac{2 - i\sqrt{5}}{3} = \frac{4}{3}$

$$-\frac{b}{a} = -\frac{-4}{3} = \frac{4}{3}$$

$$(\frac{2 + i\sqrt{5}}{3})(\frac{2 - i\sqrt{5}}{3}) = \frac{4 - i^2(5)}{9} = \frac{4 + 5}{9} = \frac{9}{9} = 1$$

$$\frac{c}{a} = \frac{3}{3} = 1$$

27. $0 + (-\frac{7}{2}) = -\frac{7}{2}$

$$-\frac{b}{a} = -\frac{7}{2}$$

$$0(-\frac{7}{2}) = 0$$

$$\frac{c}{a} = \frac{0}{2} = 0$$

28. $b^2 - 4ac$

$= (-4)^2 - 4(5)(3) = 16 - 60 = -44$

Since $b^2 - 4ac < 0$, the roots are imaginary.

29. $i\sqrt{15}i\sqrt{4} = i\sqrt{15}(2i) = 2i^2\sqrt{15} = -2\sqrt{15}$

30. $\frac{(3 + 2i)(6 - 5i)}{(6 + 5i)(6 - 5i)} = \frac{18 - 3i - 10i^2}{36 - 25i^2} = \frac{18 - 3i + 10}{36 + 25} = \frac{28 - 3i}{61}$

ALTERNATE LIFEPAC TEST

1. true
2. false

   $\sqrt{-3}\sqrt{-5} = (i\sqrt{3})(i\sqrt{5}) = i^2\sqrt{15} = -\sqrt{15}$
3. false
4. true

   $(\sqrt{x})^2 = y^2; x = 49$
5. true

   $\sqrt{(x + 2)^2} = \sqrt{49}; x + 2 = \pm7$
6. false

   $x^2 - 6x + 8 = 0$

   $(x - 4)(x - 2) = 0$

   $x - 4 = 0$ or $x - 2 = 0$
7. true; divide the equation by 3
8. true
9. false
10. false; $i^4 = 1$ and $-i = -\sqrt{-1}$
11. Let $1.9444... = x$

    $10x = 19.444...$

    $\underline{x = 1.944...}$

    $9x = 17.5$

    $x = \frac{17.5}{9}$ (divide both sides by 9)

    $x = \frac{175}{90}$ or $\frac{35}{18}$
12. $x^{3/5}$
13. $\sqrt[3]{81} - \sqrt[3]{375} + \sqrt{\frac{1}{3}} - \frac{2}{3}\sqrt{\frac{3}{16}}$

    $\sqrt[3]{27}\sqrt[3]{3} - \sqrt[3]{125}\sqrt[3]{3} + \frac{\sqrt{1}}{\sqrt{3}} - \frac{2\sqrt{3}}{3\sqrt{16}} =$

    $3\sqrt[3]{3} - 5\sqrt[3]{3} + \frac{1}{\sqrt{3}} - \frac{2\sqrt{3}}{12} =$

    $-2\sqrt[3]{3} + \frac{\sqrt{3}}{3} - \frac{\sqrt{3}}{6} = -2\sqrt[3]{3} + \frac{2\sqrt{3}}{6} - \frac{\sqrt{3}}{6} =$

    $-2\sqrt[3]{3} + \frac{\sqrt{3}}{6}$
14. $\frac{2 - \sqrt{3}}{2 - \sqrt{5}} = \frac{(2 - \sqrt{3})(2 + \sqrt{5})}{(2 - \sqrt{5})(2 + \sqrt{5})} = \frac{4 + 2\sqrt{5} - 2\sqrt{3} - \sqrt{15}}{4 - 5} =$

    $-(4 + 2\sqrt{5} - 2\sqrt{3} - \sqrt{15}) =$

    $-4 - 2\sqrt{5} + 2\sqrt{3} + \sqrt{15}$
15. $\frac{2\sqrt{2} - 3\sqrt{3}}{5\sqrt{2} + 2\sqrt{3}} = \frac{(2\sqrt{2} - 3\sqrt{3})(5\sqrt{2} - 2\sqrt{3})}{(5\sqrt{2} + 2\sqrt{3})(5\sqrt{2} - 2\sqrt{3})} =$

    $\frac{20 - 4\sqrt{6} - 15\sqrt{6} + 18}{50 - 12} = \frac{38 - 19\sqrt{6}}{38} = \frac{2 - \sqrt{6}}{2}$
16. $\sqrt{-x - 5} = x + 7$

    $(\sqrt{-x - 5})^2 = (x + 7)^2$

    $-x - 5 = x^2 + 14x + 49$

    $0 = x^2 + 15x + 54$ (add $x + 5$ to both sides)

    $0 = (x + 6)(x + 9)$

    $x + 6 = 0$ or $x + 9 = 0$

    $x = -6$ $x = -9$

Check:

$$\sqrt{-(-6) - 5} = -6 + 7$$
$$\sqrt{1} = 1$$
$$1 = 1$$

$$\sqrt{-(-9) - 5} = -9 + 7$$
$$\sqrt{4} = -2$$
$$2 \neq -2$$

$x = -9$ is an extraneous root.
The root is $x = -6$.

17.
$$\sqrt{x - 3} + \frac{5}{\sqrt{x - 3}} = \sqrt{x}$$
$$(\sqrt{x - 3})(\sqrt{x - 3}) + (\sqrt{x - 3})(\frac{5}{\sqrt{x - 3}}) = (\sqrt{x - 3})(\sqrt{x})$$
$$x - 3 + 5 = \sqrt{x^2 - 3x}$$
$$x + 2 = \sqrt{x^2 - 3x}$$
$$(x + 2)^2 = (\sqrt{x^2 - 3x})^2$$
$$x^2 + 4x + 4 = x^2 - 3x$$
$$7x + 4 = 0 \qquad \text{(add } 3x \text{ to both sides)}$$
$$7x = -4$$
$$x = -\frac{4}{7} \qquad \text{(divide both sides by 7)}$$

Check:

$$\sqrt{\frac{-4}{7} - 3} + \frac{5}{\sqrt{\frac{-4}{7} - 3}} = \sqrt{\frac{-4}{7}}$$

$$\sqrt{-\frac{25}{7}} + \frac{5}{\sqrt{-\frac{25}{7}}} = \sqrt{-\frac{4}{7}}$$

$$\frac{5i}{\sqrt{7}} + \frac{5}{\frac{5i}{\sqrt{7}}} = \frac{2i}{\sqrt{7}}$$

$$\frac{5i\sqrt{7}}{7} + \frac{5\sqrt{7}}{5i} = \frac{2\sqrt{-7}}{7}$$

$$\frac{5}{7}\sqrt{-7} - \sqrt{-7} = \frac{2}{7}\sqrt{-7}$$

$$-\frac{2}{7}\sqrt{-7} \neq \frac{2}{7}\sqrt{-7}$$

$x = -\frac{4}{7}$ is an extraneous root; no roots exist.

18.
$$(x - 7)^2 = 36$$
$$\sqrt{(x - 7)^2} = \sqrt{36}$$
$$x - 7 = \pm 6$$
$$x - 7 = 6 \qquad \text{or} \qquad x - 7 = -6$$
$$x = 13 \qquad\qquad x = 1$$

Check:

$$(13 - 7)^2 = 36 \qquad (1 - 7)^2 = 36$$
$$6^2 = 36 \qquad\qquad (-6)^2 = 36$$
$$36 = 36 \qquad\qquad 36 = 36$$

The roots are $x = 13$ and $x = 1$.

19.
$$-2x^2 + 9 = 25 - 3x^2$$
$$x^2 + 9 = 25 \qquad \text{(add } 3x^2 \text{ to both sides)}$$
$$x^2 = 16 \qquad \text{(subtract 9 from both sides)}$$
$$\sqrt{x^2} = \sqrt{16}$$
$$x = \pm 4$$

Check:

$x = 4$:
$$-2(4)^2 + 9 = 25 - 3(4)^2$$
$$-32 + 9 = 25 - 48$$
$$-23 = -23$$

$x = -4$:
$$-2(-4)^2 + 9 = 25 - 3(-4)^2$$
$$-32 + 9 = 25 - 48$$
$$-23 = -23$$

The roots are $x = \pm 4$.

20.
$$7x^2 - 16x - 15 = 0$$
$$(x - 3)(7x + 5) = 0$$
$$x - 3 = 0 \quad \text{or} \quad 7x + 5 = 0$$
$$x = 3 \qquad\qquad 7x = -5$$
$$x = -\frac{5}{7}$$

Check:

$$7(3)^2 - 16(3) - 15 = 0$$
$$63 - 48 - 15 = 0$$
$$0 = 0$$

$$7(-\frac{5}{7})^2 - 16(-\frac{5}{7}) - 15 = 0$$
$$\frac{25}{7} + \frac{80}{7} - 15 = 0$$
$$\frac{105}{7} - 15 = 0$$
$$15 - 15 = 0$$
$$0 = 0$$

The roots are $x = 3$ and $x = -\frac{5}{7}$.

21.
$$\frac{x + 3}{4} = \frac{2}{x - 4}$$
$$(x + 3)(x - 4) = 4(2) \qquad \text{(cross-multiply)}$$
$$x^2 - x - 12 = 8$$
$$x^2 - x - 20 = 0 \qquad \text{(subtract 8 from both sides)}$$
$$(x + 4)(x - 5) = 0$$
$$x + 4 = 0 \qquad \text{or} \qquad x - 5 = 0$$
$$x = -4 \qquad\qquad\qquad x = 5$$

Check:

$$\frac{-4 + 3}{4} = \frac{2}{-4 - 4} \qquad\qquad \frac{5 + 3}{4} = \frac{2}{5 - 4}$$

$$\frac{-1}{4} = \frac{2}{-8} \qquad\qquad \frac{8}{4} = \frac{2}{1}$$

$$-\frac{1}{4} = -\frac{1}{4} \qquad\qquad 2 = 2$$

The roots are $x = -4$ and $x = 5$.

22.

$$7x^2 - 14x = 56$$
$$x^2 - 2x = 8 \quad \text{(divide both sides by 7)}$$
$$x^2 - 2x - 8 = 0 \quad \text{(subtract 8 from both sides)}$$
$$(x + 2)(x - 4) = 0$$
$$x + 2 = 0 \quad \text{or} \quad x - 4 = 0$$
$$x = -2 \qquad\qquad x = 4$$

Check:
$$7(-2)^2 - 14(-2) = 56$$
$$28 + 28 = 56$$
$$56 = 56$$
$$7(4)^2 - 14(4) = 56$$
$$112 - 56 = 56$$
$$56 = 56$$

The roots are $x = -2$ and $x = 4$.

23.

$$2x^2 - 5x = -7$$
$$x^2 - \frac{5}{2}x = -\frac{7}{2} \quad \text{(divide both sides by 2)}$$
$$\frac{1}{2}\left(\frac{5}{2}\right) = \frac{5}{4}$$
$$\left(\frac{5}{4}\right)^2 = \frac{25}{16}$$
$$x^2 - \frac{5}{2}x + \frac{25}{16} = -\frac{7}{2} + \frac{25}{16}$$
$$\left(x - \frac{5}{4}\right)^2 = -\frac{31}{16}$$
$$\sqrt{\left(x - \frac{5}{4}\right)^2} = \sqrt{\frac{-31}{16}}$$
$$x - \frac{5}{4} = \pm\frac{\sqrt{-31}}{\sqrt{16}}$$
$$x = \frac{5}{4} + \frac{i\sqrt{31}}{4} \quad \text{(add } \frac{5}{4} \text{ to both sides)}$$
$$x = \frac{5 \pm i\sqrt{31}}{4}$$

24.

$$x^2 + x + 1 = 0$$
$$a = 1;\ b = 1;\ c = 1$$
$$x = \frac{-b \pm \sqrt{b^2 - 4ac}}{2a}$$
$$x = \frac{-1 \pm \sqrt{1^2 - 4(1)(1)}}{2(1)} = \frac{-1 \pm \sqrt{1 - 4}}{2}$$
$$x = \frac{-1 \pm \sqrt{-3}}{2} = \frac{-1 \pm i\sqrt{3}}{2}$$

25.

$$(2x + 1)(x + 4) = 4$$
$$2x^2 + 9x + 4 = 4$$
$$2x^2 + 9x = 0 \quad \text{(subtract 4 from both sides)}$$
$$a = 2;\ b = 9;\ c = 0$$
$$x = \frac{-b \pm \sqrt{b^2 - 4ac}}{2a}$$
$$x = \frac{-9 \pm \sqrt{9^2 - 4(2)(0)}}{2(2)}$$
$$x = \frac{-9 \pm \sqrt{81 - 0}}{4}$$
$$x = \frac{-9 \pm 9}{4}$$
$$x = \frac{-9 + 9}{4} = \frac{0}{4} = 0 \quad \text{or} \quad x = \frac{-9 - 9}{4} = \frac{-18}{4} = -\frac{9}{2}$$
$$x = 0, -\frac{9}{2}$$

26. Add the roots of Problem 24, which are $\frac{-1 + i\sqrt{3}}{2}$ and $\frac{-1 - i\sqrt{3}}{2}$.

$$\frac{-1 + i\sqrt{3}}{2} + \frac{-1 - i\sqrt{3}}{2} = \frac{-1 + i\sqrt{3} - 1 - i\sqrt{3}}{2} = \frac{-2}{2} = -1$$
$$-\frac{b}{a} = -\frac{1}{1}$$

Multiply the same roots of Problem 24.

$$\left(\frac{-1 + i\sqrt{3}}{2}\right)\left(\frac{-1 - i\sqrt{3}}{2}\right) = \frac{1 - 3i^2}{4} = \frac{1 + 3}{4} = \frac{4}{4} = 1$$
$$\frac{c}{a} = \frac{1}{1}$$

27. Add the roots of Problem 25, which are $-\frac{9}{2}$ and 0.

$$-\frac{9}{2} + 0 = -\frac{9}{2}$$
$$-\frac{b}{a} = -\frac{9}{2}$$

Multiply the same roots of Problem 25.

$$\left(-\frac{9}{2}\right)(0) = 0$$
$$\frac{c}{a} = \frac{0}{2}$$

28.

$$3x^2 - 8x + 5 = 0$$
$$a = 3;\ b = -8;\ c = 5$$
$$b^2 - 4ac = (-8)^2 - 4(3)(5) = 64 - 60 = 4$$

Since 4 is a perfect square, the roots are real.

29.

$$\sqrt{-13}\sqrt{-9} = (i\sqrt{13})(i\sqrt{9}) =$$
$$(i\sqrt{13})(3i) = 3i^2\sqrt{13} =$$
$$-3\sqrt{13}$$

30.

$$\frac{4 - 2i}{5 + 3i} = \frac{(4 - 2i)(5 - 3i)}{(5 + 3i)(5 - 3i)} =$$
$$\frac{20 - 22i + 6i^2}{25 - 9i^2} = \frac{20 - 22i - 6}{25 + 9} =$$
$$\frac{14 - 22i}{34} = \frac{7 - 11i}{17}$$

MATH 1106

ALTERNATE LIFEPAC TEST

NAME _____

DATE _____

SCORE _____

Answer *true* **or** *false* (each answer, 2 points).

1. _____ 0.864864... is a rational number.

2. _____ $\sqrt{-3}\sqrt{-5} = \sqrt{15}$.

3. _____ $8 + \sqrt{3}$ is the conjugate of $\sqrt{3} + 8$.

4. _____ If $\sqrt{x} = 7$, then $x = 49$.

5. _____ If $(x + 2)^2 = 49$, then $x + 2 = \pm 7$.

6. _____ If $x^2 - 6x + 8 = 0$, then $x + 4 = 0$ or $x + 2 = 0$.

7. _____ In the process of completing the square, $3x^2 + 7x - 12 = 0$ becomes $x^2 + \frac{7}{3}x = 4$.

8. _____ $x = \dfrac{-b \pm \sqrt{b^2 - 4ac}}{2a}$

9. _____ $b^2 - 4ac < 0$ means the root is real.

10. _____ $i^4 = -i$

Complete the following items (each answer, 3 points).

11. Write 1.9444... as a fraction. _____

12. Write $\sqrt[5]{x^3}$ using a fractional exponent. _____

13. Simplify $\sqrt[3]{81} + \sqrt[3]{375} + \sqrt{\frac{1}{3}} - \frac{2}{3}\sqrt{\frac{3}{16}}$. _____

Rationalize the denominators (each answer, 3 points).

14. $\dfrac{2 - \sqrt{3}}{2 - \sqrt{5}}$ _____

15. $\dfrac{2\sqrt{2} - 3\sqrt{3}}{5\sqrt{2} + 2\sqrt{3}}$ _____

Solve these equations. Show your work and circle your answer (each answer, 4 points).

16. $\sqrt{-x - 5} = x + 7$

17. $\sqrt{x - 3} + \dfrac{5}{\sqrt{x - 3}} = \sqrt{x}$

18. $(x - 7)^2 = 36$

19. $-2x^2 + 9 = 25 - 3x^2$

20. $7x^2 - 16x - 15 = 0$

21. $\dfrac{x + 3}{4} = \dfrac{2}{x - 4}$

Solve by completing the square. Show your work and circle your answer (each answer, 4 points).

22. $7x^2 - 14x = 56$

23. $2x^2 - 5x = -7$

Solve by using the quadratic formula. Show your work and circle your answer (each answer, 4 points).

24. $x^2 + x + 1 = 0$

25. $(2x + 1)(x + 4) = 4$

26. Show the check of Problem 24 using the sum and product of the roots.

27. Show the check of Problem 25 using the sum and product of the roots.

28. Use the discriminant to tell whether the roots of $3x^2 - 8x + 5 = 0$ are real or imaginary.

Simplify using *i*. Show your work and circle your answer (each answer, 4 points).

29. $\sqrt{-13}\sqrt{-9}$

30. $\dfrac{4 - 2i}{5 + 3i}$

MATH 1107

Unit 7: Quadratic Relations and Systems

TEACHER NOTES

MATERIALS NEEDED FOR LIFEPAC	
Required	Suggested
(none)	• straightedges • graph paper

ADDITIONAL LEARNING ACTIVITIES

Section 1: Distance Formula and Conic Sections

1. For more advanced students, derive in general terms the general formulas for the various conic sections and their elements. Consider cases more general or different from those in the LIFEPAC.

2. Have students graph conic sections based on the preceding teacher-directed activity.

3. Have students write equations for conics using material from the preceding teacher-directed Activity 1.

4. Have students read and report on the history of mathematics as related to the conic sections, including the mathematicians involved, their cultural and religious backgrounds, the early development of analytical geometry, and applications of conic sections.
    Note: This activity may be done in Section 2 also.

5. Have students consult textbooks, journals, and online sources for applications of conic sections, particularly in such fields as aeronautics, navigation, lighting, sound engineering, and astronomy.

Section 2: Conic Sections and Identification

1. Have students identify conic sections based on the preceding teacher-directed Activity 1 in Section 1.

2. Since work in this LIFEPAC is often facilitated by calculating square root, have students learn an algorithm for use with an elementary electronic calculator for finding square root. How does the algorithm relate to the parabola $x^2 = y$ or $x = \pm\sqrt{y}$?
    Note: This activity may also be used in Section 1 or as an independent activity.

3. Have the student investigate the meaning of eccentricity as it relates to determining types of conic sections.
    Note: This activity may also be used in Section 1 or as a group activity.

Section 3: Systems, Inequalities, and Applications

1. Have students graph inequalities of conic sections based on the preceding discussion in teacher-directed Activity 1 in Section 1.

2. Discuss your favorite applications of conic sections.

3. By using a concordance or online resources, students can study the term *circle* as found in the Bible. Does the Bible give a number for the ratio between the circumference and diameter of a circle?
   Note: This activity may also be used in Sections 1 and 2 or as an independent activity.

4. Students may study degenerate conics. A degenerate conic is one in which the intersection of a plane with a cone is not an ellipse, a parabola, a circle, or a hyperbola.
   Note: This activity may also be used in Sections 1 and 2 or as a group activity. A worksheet about graphing degenerate conics is included.

ADDITIONAL ACTIVITY

The following activity may be reproduced as a student worksheet.

» GRAPHING DEGENERATE CONICS

Graph the following degenerate conics.

1. $3x^2 + 4y^2 = 0$

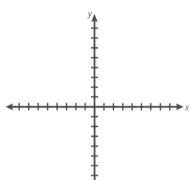

2. $3x^2 + 4y^2 + 6x + 4y + 5 = 0$

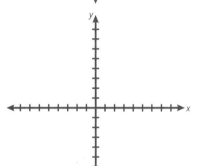

3. $x^2 - 4y^2 = 0$

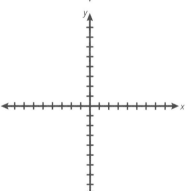

4. $y^2 = 2xy$

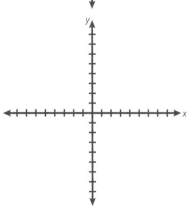

ADDITIONAL ACTIVITY, SOLUTION KEY

1. $3x^2 + 4y^2 = 0$

$\dfrac{3x^2}{12} + \dfrac{4y^2}{12} = \dfrac{0}{12}$

$\dfrac{x^2}{4} + \dfrac{y^2}{3} = 0$

$\dfrac{x^2}{4} = \dfrac{-y^2}{3}$

Since the square of a number cannot be a negative number (except as an imaginary number), the graph is one point (0, 0); the graph is a degenerate ellipse.

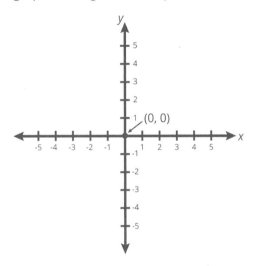

2. $3x^2 + 4y^2 + 6x + 4y + 5 = 0$

$(3x^2 + 6x) + (4y^2 + 4y) = -5$

$3(x^2 + 2x +) + 4(y^2 + y +) = -5$

$3(x^2 + 2x + 1) + 4(y^2 + y + \frac{1}{4}) = -5 + 3 + 1$

$3(x + 1)^2 + 4(y + \frac{1}{2})^2 = -1$

$\dfrac{3(x + 1)^2}{12} + \dfrac{4(y + \frac{1}{2})^2}{12} = -\dfrac{1}{12}$

$\dfrac{(x + 1)^2}{4} + \dfrac{(y + \frac{1}{2})^2}{3} = -\dfrac{1}{12}$

The graph is an imaginary graph; no real roots exist.

3. $x^2 - 4y^2 = 0$

$\dfrac{x^2}{4} - \dfrac{4y^2}{4} = \dfrac{0}{4}$

$\dfrac{x^2}{4} - \dfrac{y^2}{1} = 0$

x	±6	±4	±2	0
y	±3	±2	±1	0

The graph is two intersecting lines, which is a degenerate hyperbola.

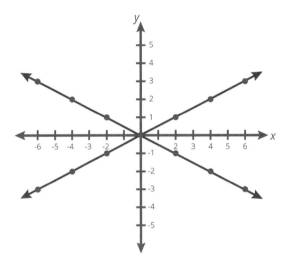

4. $y^2 = 2xy$

x	$-\frac{3}{2}$	-1	$-\frac{1}{2}$	0	$\frac{1}{2}$	1	$\frac{3}{2}$
y	-3	-2	-1	0	1	2	3

The graph approaches a straight line, which is a degenerate parabola.

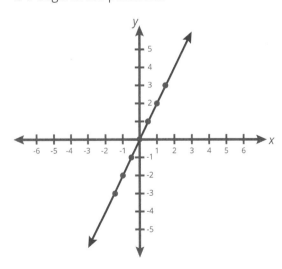

ANSWER KEY

SECTION 1

1.1

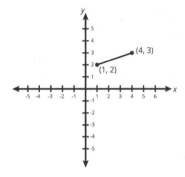

$d = \sqrt{(4-1)^2 + (3-2)^2}$
$= \sqrt{3^2 + 1^2}$
$= \sqrt{9+1}$
$= \sqrt{10}$

1.2

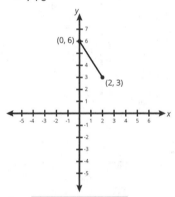

$d = \sqrt{(2-0)^2 + (3-6)^2}$
$= \sqrt{2^2 + (-3)^2}$
$= \sqrt{4+9}$
$= \sqrt{13}$

1.3

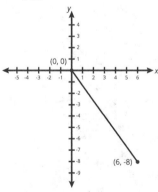

$d = \sqrt{(6-0)^2 + (-8-0)^2}$
$= \sqrt{6^2 + (-8)^2}$
$= \sqrt{36+64}$
$= \sqrt{100}$
$= 10$

1.4

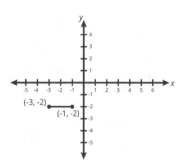

$d = |-3 - (-1)|$
$= |-3 + 1|$
$= |-2|$
$= 2$

1.5

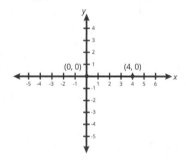

$d = |0 - 4|$
$= |-4|$
$= 4$

1.6

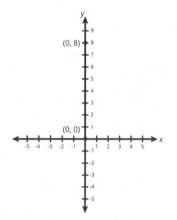

$d = |8 - 0|$
$= |8|$
$= 8$

1.7

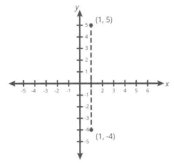

$d = |-4 - 5|$
$\quad = |-9|$
$\quad = 9$

1.8

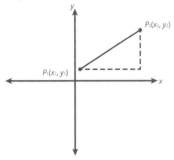

$d = \sqrt{(x_2 - x_1)^2 + (y_2 - y_1)^2}$

1.9

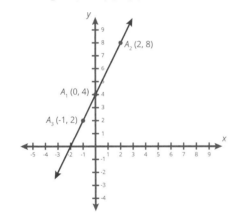

$|A_3A_2| = \sqrt{[2 - (-1)]^2 + (8 - 2)^2}$
$\qquad = \sqrt{3^2 + 6^2}$
$\qquad = \sqrt{9 + 36}$
$\qquad = \sqrt{45}$
$\qquad = 3\sqrt{5}$
$|A_2A_1| = \sqrt{(0 - 2)^2 + (4 - 8)^2}$
$\qquad = \sqrt{(-2)^2 + (-4)^2}$
$\qquad = \sqrt{4 + 16}$
$\qquad = \sqrt{20}$
$\qquad = 2\sqrt{5}$
$|A_3A_1| = \sqrt{(0 - (-1)^2 + (4 - 2)^2}$
$\qquad = \sqrt{1^2 + 2^2}$
$\qquad = \sqrt{1 + 4}$
$\qquad = \sqrt{5}$
$\quad 3\sqrt{5} = 2\sqrt{5} + \sqrt{5}$
$\therefore \ |A_3A_2| = |A_2A_1| + |A_3A_1|$

1.10

Radius = $\sqrt{4}$ = 2
Center: (0, 0)

1.11

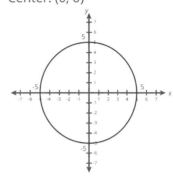

$x^2 + y^2 = 25$
Radius = $\sqrt{25}$ = 5
Center: (0, 0)

1.12

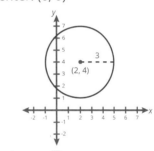

Radius = $\sqrt{9}$ = 3
Center: (2, 4)

1.13

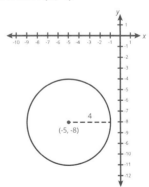

Radius = $\sqrt{16}$ = 4
Center: (-5, -8)

1.14

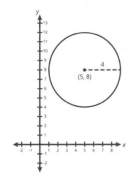

$(x − 5)^2 + (y − 8)^2 = 16$
Radius = $\sqrt{16} = 4$
Center: (5, 8)

1.15

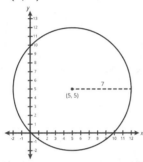

$x^2 − 10x + y^2 − 10y = -1$

$\frac{1}{2} \cdot 10 = 5 \qquad \frac{1}{2} \cdot 10 = 5$

$5^2 = 25 \qquad 5^2 = 25$

$x^2 − 10x + 25 + y^2 − 10y + 25 = -1 + 25 + 25$
$(x − 5)^2 + (y − 5)^2 = 49$
Radius = $\sqrt{49} = 7$
Center: (5, 5)

1.16 $(x − 5)^2 + (y − 6)^2 = 7^2$

1.17

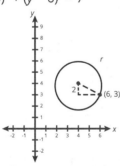

$r = \sqrt{1^2 + 2^2}$
$\quad = \sqrt{1 + 4}$
$\quad = \sqrt{5}$
$(x − 4)^2 + (y − 4)^2 = (\sqrt{5})^2$
$(x − 4)^2 + (y − 4)^2 = 5$

1.18

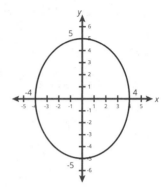

y-intercepts:

$\frac{y^2}{25} = 1$

$y^2 = 25$

$\sqrt{y^2} = \pm\sqrt{25}$

$y = \pm5$

Major intercepts: (0, 5), (0, -5)

x-intercepts:

$\frac{x^2}{16} = 1$

$x^2 = 16$

$\sqrt{x^2} = \pm\sqrt{16}$

$x = \pm4$

Minor intercepts: (4, 0), (-4, 0)
Length of major axis = 2(5) = 10
Length of minor axis = 2(4) = 8

1.19

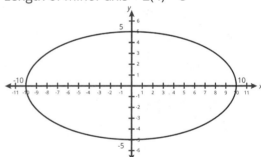

x-intercepts:

$\frac{x^2}{100} = 1$

$x^2 = 100$

$\sqrt{x^2} = \pm\sqrt{100}$

$x = \pm10$

Major intercepts: (10, 0), (-10, 0)

y-intercepts:

$\frac{y^2}{25} = 1$

$y^2 = 25$

$\sqrt{y^2} = \pm\sqrt{25}$

$y = \pm5$

Minor intercepts: (0, 5), (0, -5)
Length of major axis = 2(10) = 20
Length of minor axis = 2(5) = 10

1.20

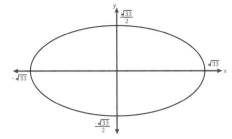

$\frac{x^2}{33} + \frac{4y^2}{33} = 1$

x-intercepts:

$$\frac{x^2}{33} = 1$$
$$x^2 = 33$$
$$\sqrt{x^2} = \pm\sqrt{33}$$
$$x = \pm\sqrt{33}$$

Major intercepts: $(\sqrt{33}, 0)$, $(-\sqrt{33}, 0)$

y-intercepts:

$$\frac{4y^2}{33} = 1$$
$$4y^2 = 33$$
$$y^2 = \frac{33}{4}$$
$$\sqrt{y^2} = \pm\sqrt{\frac{33}{4}}$$
$$y = \pm\frac{\sqrt{33}}{2}$$

Minor intercepts: $(0, \frac{\sqrt{33}}{2})$, $(0, -\frac{\sqrt{33}}{2})$

Length of major axis $= 2\sqrt{33}$

Length of minor axis $= 2\frac{\sqrt{33}}{2} = \sqrt{33}$

1.21

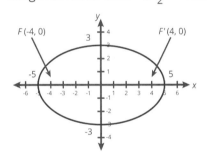

$\frac{9x^2}{225} + \frac{25y^2}{225} = 1$

$\frac{x^2}{25} + \frac{y^2}{9} = 1$

x-intercepts:

$$\frac{x^2}{25} = 1$$
$$x^2 = 25$$
$$\sqrt{x^2} = \pm\sqrt{5}$$
$$x = \pm 5$$

Major intercepts: $(5, 0)$, $(-5, 0)$

y-intercepts:

$$\frac{y^2}{9} = 1$$
$$y^2 = 9$$
$$\sqrt{y^2} = \pm\sqrt{9}$$
$$y = \pm 3$$

Minor intercepts: $(0, 3)$, $(0, -3)$

Length of major axis $= 2(5) = 10$

Length of minor axis $= 2(3) = 6$

$c = \sqrt{a^2 - b^2}$
$\quad = \sqrt{25 - 9}$
$\quad = \sqrt{16}$
$\quad = \pm 4$

Foci are on major axis:

$F(-4, 0)$, $F'(4, 0)$

1.22

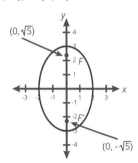

$\frac{9x^2}{36} + \frac{4y^2}{36} = 1$

$\frac{x^2}{4} + \frac{y^2}{9} = 1$

y-intercepts:

$$\frac{y^2}{9} = 1$$
$$y^2 = 9$$
$$\sqrt{y^2} = \pm\sqrt{9}$$
$$y = \pm 3$$

Major intercepts: $(0, 3)$, $(0, -3)$

y-intercepts:

$$\frac{x^2}{4} = 1$$
$$x^2 = 4$$
$$\sqrt{x^2} = \pm\sqrt{4}$$
$$x = \pm 2$$

Minor intercepts: $(2, 0)$, $(-2, 0)$

Length of major axis $= 2(3) = 6$

Length of minor axis $= 2(2) = 4$

$c = \sqrt{a^2 - b^2}$
$\quad = \sqrt{9 - 4}$
$\quad = \sqrt{5}$

Foci are on major axis: $F(0, \sqrt{5})$, $F'(0, -\sqrt{5})$

1.23

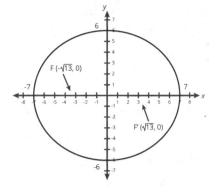

$$\frac{36x^2}{1,764} + \frac{49y^2}{1,764} = 1$$

$$\frac{x^2}{49} + \frac{y^2}{36} = 1$$

x-intercepts:

$$\frac{x^2}{49} = 1$$

$$x^2 = 49$$

$$\sqrt{x^2} = \pm\sqrt{49}$$

$$x = \pm 7$$

Major intercepts: (7, 0), (-7, 0)

y-intercepts:

$$\frac{y^2}{36} = 1$$

$$y^2 = 36$$

$$\sqrt{y^2} = \pm\sqrt{36}$$

$$y = \pm 6$$

Minor intercepts: (0, 6), (0, -6)

Length of major axis = 2(7) = 14

Length of minor axis = 2(6) = 12

$$c = \sqrt{a^2 - b^2}$$

$$= \sqrt{49 - 36}$$

$$= \sqrt{13}$$

Foci are on major axis:

$F(-\sqrt{13}, 0)$, $F'(\sqrt{13}, 0)$

1.24 Major axis is on *x*-axis.

$$\frac{x^2}{5^2} + \frac{y^2}{3^2} = 1$$

$$\frac{x^2}{25} + \frac{y^2}{9} = 1$$

1.25 Major axis is on *y*-axis.

$$\frac{x^2}{2^2} + \frac{y^2}{4^2} = 1$$

$$\frac{x^2}{4} + \frac{y^2}{16} = 1$$

1.26

$$4 = \sqrt{a^2 - 3^2}$$

$$4 = \sqrt{a^2 - 9}$$

$$4^2 = (\sqrt{a^2 - 9})^2$$

$$16 = a^2 - 9$$

$$25 = a^2$$

$$\sqrt{25} = \sqrt{a^2}$$

$$5 = a$$

$$\frac{x^2}{5^2} + \frac{y^2}{3^2} = 1$$

$$\frac{x^2}{25} + \frac{y^2}{9} = 1$$

1.27 $b > a$

$$c = \sqrt{b^2 - a^2}$$

$$6 = \sqrt{8^2 - a^2}$$

$$6 = \sqrt{64 - a^2}$$

$$6^2 = (\sqrt{64 - a^2})^2$$

$$36 = 64 - a^2$$

$$a^2 + 36 = 64$$

$$a^2 = 28$$

$$\sqrt{a^2} = \sqrt{28}$$

$$a = 2\sqrt{7}$$

$$\frac{x^2}{(2\sqrt{7})^2} + \frac{y^2}{8^2} = 1$$

$$\frac{x^2}{28} + \frac{y^2}{64} = 1$$

1.28

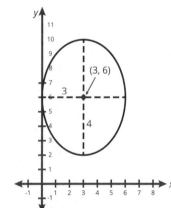

$a = 3, b = 4$

$$\frac{(x - 3)^2}{3^2} + \frac{(y - 6)^2}{4^2} = 1$$

$$\frac{(x - 3)^2}{9} + \frac{(y - 6)^2}{16} = 1$$

SELF TEST 1

1.01

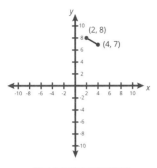

$d = \sqrt{(2-4)^2 + (8-7)^2}$
$= \sqrt{(-2)^2 + 1^2}$
$= \sqrt{4+1}$
$= \sqrt{5}$

1.02

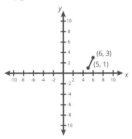

$d = \sqrt{(6-5)^2 + (3-1)^2}$
$= \sqrt{1^2 + 2^2}$
$= \sqrt{1+4}$
$= \sqrt{5}$

1.03

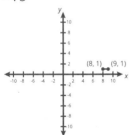

$d = |9-8|$
$= |1|$
$= 1$

1.04

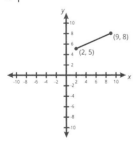

$d = \sqrt{(9-2)^2 + (8-5)^2}$
$= \sqrt{7^2 + 3^2}$
$= \sqrt{49+9}$
$= \sqrt{58}$

1.05

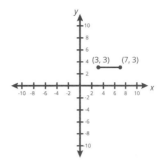

1.06

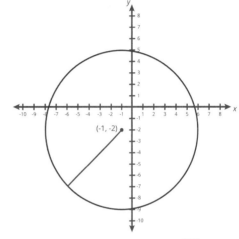

Center: (-1, -2)   Radius = $\sqrt{49}$ = 7

1.07

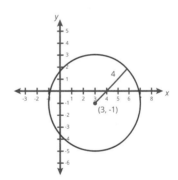

Center: (3, -1)   Radius = $\sqrt{16}$ = 4

1.08

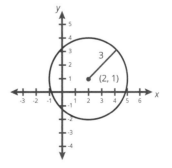

Center: (2, 1)   Radius = $\sqrt{9}$ = 3

1.09

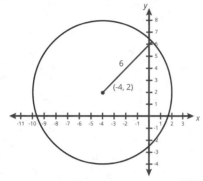

Center: (-4, 2)   Radius = $\sqrt{36}$ = 6

1.010

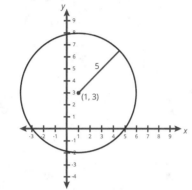

Center: (1, 3)   Radius = $\sqrt{25}$ = 5

1.011

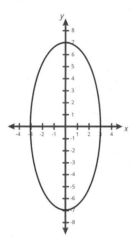

y-intercepts:

$\frac{y^2}{49}$ = 1

y^2 = 49

$\sqrt{y^2}$ = $\pm\sqrt{49}$

y = ±7

Major intercepts: (0, 7) (0, -7)

x-intercepts:

$\frac{x^2}{9}$ = 1

x^2 = 9

$\sqrt{x^2}$ = $\pm\sqrt{9}$

x = ±3

Minor intercepts: (3, 0), (-3, 0)

1.012

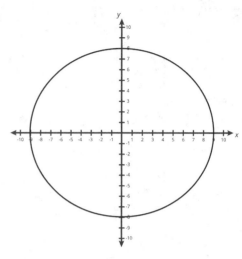

x-intercepts:

$\frac{x^2}{81}$ = 1

x^2 = 81

$\sqrt{x^2}$ = $\pm\sqrt{81}$

x = ±9

Major intercepts: (9, 0), (-9, 0)

y-intercepts:

$\frac{y^2}{64}$ = 1

y^2 = 64

$\sqrt{y^2}$ = $\pm\sqrt{64}$

y = ±8

Minor intercepts: (0, 8), (0, -8)

1.013

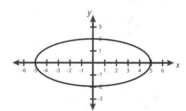

x-intercepts:

$\frac{x^2}{25}$ = 1

x^2 = 25

$\sqrt{x^2}$ = $\pm\sqrt{25}$

x = ±5

Major intercepts: (5, 0), (-5, 0)

y-intercepts:

$\frac{y^2}{4}$ = 1

y^2 = 4

$\sqrt{y^2}$ = $\pm\sqrt{4}$

y = ±2

Minor intercepts: (0, 2), (0, -2)

1.014

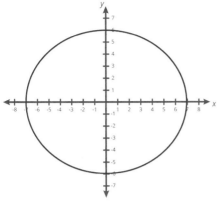

x-intercepts:

$\frac{x^2}{49} = 1$

$x^2 = 49$

$\sqrt{x^2} = \pm\sqrt{49}$

$x = \pm7$

Major intercepts: (7, 0), (-7, 0)

y-intercepts:

$\frac{x^2}{36} = 1$

$y^2 = 36$

$\sqrt{y^2} = \pm\sqrt{36}$

$y = \pm6$

Minor intercepts: (0, 6), (0, -6)

1.015

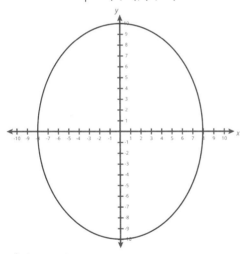

y-intercepts:

$\frac{y^2}{100} = 1$

$y^2 = 100$

$\sqrt{y^2} = \pm\sqrt{100}$

$y = \pm10$

Major intercepts: (0, 10), (0, -10)

x-intercepts:

$\frac{x^2}{64} = 1$

$x^2 = 64$

$\sqrt{x^2} = \pm\sqrt{64}$

$x = \pm8$

Minor intercepts: (8, 0), (-8, 0)

1.016 $(x - 3)^2 + (y - 3)^2 = 2^2$
$(x - 3)^2 + (y - 3)^2 = 4$

1.017 $\frac{x^2}{4^2} + \frac{y^2}{9^2} = 1$

$\frac{x^2}{16} + \frac{y^2}{81} = 1$

1.018 $(x + 2)^2 + (y + 2)^2 = 6^2$
$(x + 2)^2 + (y + 2)^2 = 36$

1.019 $\frac{x^2}{7^2} + \frac{y^2}{5^2} = 1$

$\frac{x^2}{49} + \frac{y^2}{25} = 1$

1.020 $(x - 1)^2 + (y + 5)^2 = 10^2$
$(x - 1)^2 + (y + 5)^2 = 100$

SECTION 2

2.1 through 2.12

Example points are shown; other points are possible.

2.1

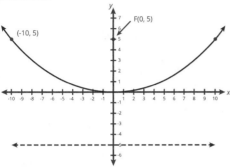

$p > 0$ and the directrix is $y = -5$, so $p = 5$.

From the formula $y = \frac{1}{4p}x^2$, the equation of this parabola is

$y = \frac{1}{4(5)}x^2$ or $y = \frac{1}{20}x^2$.

Another point is (-10, 5):

$y = \frac{1}{20}(-10)$

$y = \frac{1}{20}(100)$

$y = 5$

2.2

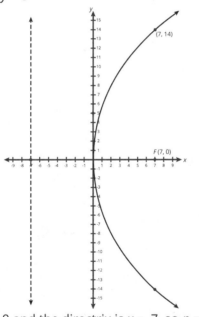

$p > 0$ and the directrix is $x = -7$, so $p = 7$.

From the formula $x = \frac{1}{4p}y^2$, the equation of this parabola is

$x = \frac{1}{4(7)}y^2$ or $x = \frac{1}{28}y^2$.

Another point is (7, 14):

$x = \frac{1}{28}(14)^2$

$x = \frac{1}{28}(196)$

$x = 7$

2.3

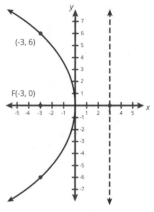

$p > 0$ and the directrix is $x = 3$, so $p = 3$.

From the formula $x = -\frac{1}{4p}y^2$, the equation of this parabola is

$x = -\frac{1}{4(3)}y^2$ or $x = -\frac{1}{12}y^2$

Another point is (-3, 6):

$x = -\frac{1}{12}(6)^2$

$x = -\frac{1}{12}(36)$

$x = -3$

2.4

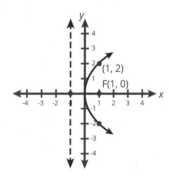

$x - \frac{1}{4(1)}y^2$

$p = 1$

The parabola opens to the right.
The directrix is $x = -p$; $x = -1$.
The focus is $(p, 0) = (1, 0)$.

Another point is (1, 2):

$x = \frac{1}{4}(2)^2$

$x = \frac{1}{4}(4)$

$x = 1$

2.5

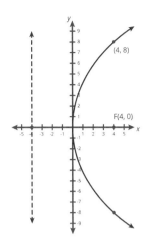

$x = \frac{1}{4(4)}y^2$
$p = 4$
The parabola opens to the right.
The directrix is $x = -p$; $x = -4$
The focus is $(p, 0) = (4, 0)$.
Another point is (4, 8):

$x = \frac{1}{16}(8)^2$
$x = \frac{1}{16}(64)$
$x = 4$

2.6

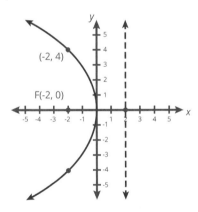

$x = -\frac{1}{4(2)}y^2$
$p = 2$
The parabola opens to the left.
The directrix is $x = p$; $x = 2$.
The focus is $(-p, 0) = (-2, 0)$.
Another point is (-2, 4):

$x = -\frac{1}{8}(4)^2$
$x = -\frac{1}{8}(16)$
$x = -2$

2.7

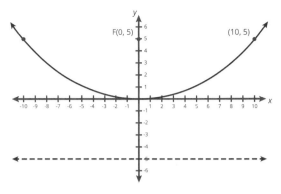

$y = \frac{1}{4(5)}x^2$
$p = 5$
The parabola opens upward.
The directrix is $y = -p$; $y = -5$.
The focus is $(0, p) = (0, 5)$.
Another point is (10, 5):

$y = \frac{1}{20}(10)$
$y = \frac{1}{20}(100)$
$y = 5$

2.8

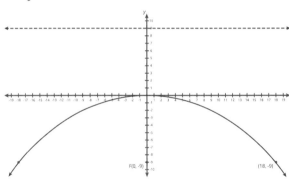

$y = -\frac{1}{36}x^2$
$y = -\frac{1}{4(9)}x^2$
$p = 9$
The parabola opens downward.
The directrix is $y = p$; $y = 9$.
The focus is $(0, -p) = (0, -9)$.
Another point is (18, -9):

$y = -\frac{1}{36}(18)^2$
$y = -\frac{1}{36}(324)$
$y = -9$

2.9

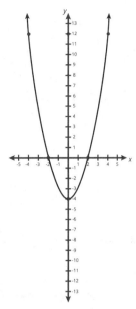

x	±2	±4	0
y	0	12	-4

The graph is a parabola that opens upward.

2.10

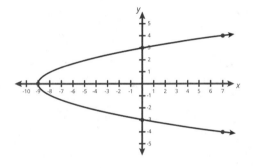

x	0	7	-9
y	±3	±4	0

The graph is a parabola that opens to the right.

2.11

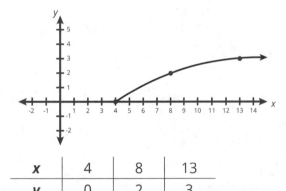

x	4	8	13
y	0	2	3

The graph is the top half of a parabola that opens to the right.

2.12

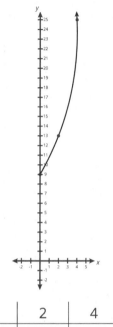

x	0	2	4
y	9	13	25

The graph is the right half of a parabola that opens upward.

2.13

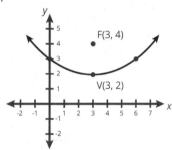

$(y - 2) = \frac{1}{4(2)}(x - 3)^2$

Vertex: (3, 2)

$p = 2$

The parabola opens upward. The axis of symmetry is parallel to the y-axis through 3. The focus is $(h + 0, k + p)$ or $(h, k + p) =$ (3, 2 + 2) = (3, 4).

Another point is $(0, \frac{25}{8})$:

$$y - 2 = \frac{1}{8}(0 - 3)^2$$
$$y - 2 = \frac{1}{8}(9)$$
$$y - 2 = \frac{9}{8}$$
$$y = 2 + \frac{9}{8}$$
$$y = \frac{25}{8}$$

2.14 $y - 3 = \frac{1}{4(4)}(x - 2)^2$

$$y - 3 = \frac{1}{16}(x - 2)^2$$

2.15 $y - 3 = \frac{1}{4(-6)}(x - 4)^2$

$y - 3 = \frac{-1}{24}(x - 4)^2$

2.16 through 2.25

Example points are shown; other points are possible.

2.16

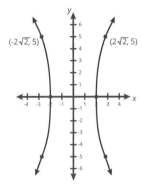

$\frac{x^2}{2^2} - \frac{y^2}{5^2} = 1$

$\frac{x^2}{4} - \frac{y^2}{25} = 1$

Vertices:

$\frac{x^2}{4} = 1$

$x^2 = 4$

$\sqrt{x^2} = \pm\sqrt{4}$

$x = \pm 2$

Vertices: (-2, 0), (2, 0)

Other points:

$y = 5$: $\frac{x^2}{4} - \frac{5^2}{25} = 1$

$\frac{x^2}{4} - \frac{25}{25} = 1$

$\frac{x^2}{4} - 1 = 1$

$\frac{x^2}{4} = 2$

$x^2 = 8$

$\sqrt{x^2} = \pm\sqrt{8}$

$x = \pm 2\sqrt{2}$

Points are (-2√2, 5), (2√2, 5).

2.17

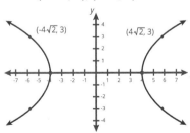

$c^2 = a^2 + b^2$

$5^2 = 4^2 + b^2$

$25 = 16 + b^2$

$9 = b^2$

$\pm\sqrt{9} = \sqrt{b^2}$

$b = \pm 3$

$\frac{x^2}{4^2} - \frac{y^2}{3^2} = 1$

$\frac{x^2}{16} - \frac{y^2}{9} = 1$

Other points:

$y = 3$: $\frac{x^2}{16} - \frac{3^2}{9} = 1$

$\frac{x^2}{16} - \frac{9}{9} = 1$

$\frac{x^2}{16} - 1 = 1$

$\frac{x^2}{16} = 2$

$x^2 = 32$

$\sqrt{x^2} = \pm\sqrt{32}$

$x = \pm 4\sqrt{2}$

Points are (-4√2, 3), (4√2, 3).

2.18

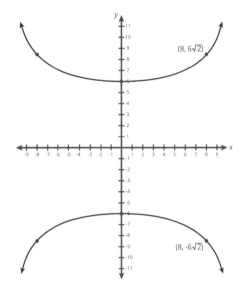

$c^2 = a^2 + b^2$

$10^2 = 6^2 + b^2$

$100 = 36 + b^2$

$64 = b^2$

$\pm\sqrt{64} = \sqrt{b^2}$

$b = \pm 8$

$\frac{y^2}{6^2} - \frac{x^2}{8^2} = 1$

$\frac{y^2}{36} - \frac{x^2}{64} = 1$

Other points:

$x = 8$: $\frac{y^2}{36} - \frac{8^2}{64} = 1$

$\frac{y^2}{36} - \frac{64}{64} = 1$

$\frac{y^2}{36} - 1 = 1$

$\frac{y^2}{36} = 2$

$y^2 = 72$

$\sqrt{y^2} = \pm\sqrt{72}$

$y = \pm 6\sqrt{2}$

Points are (8, -6√2), (8, 6√2).

2.19

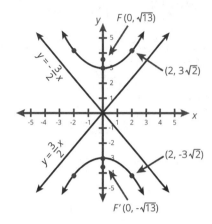

2.20

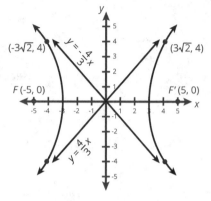

Opens vertically.
Vertices:
$$\frac{y^2}{9} = 1$$
$$y^2 = 9$$
$$\sqrt{y^2} = \pm\sqrt{9}$$
$$y = \pm 3$$
Vertices are (0, 3), (0, -3).
Foci: $c = \sqrt{a^2 + b^2}$
$$= \sqrt{9 + 4}$$
$$= \sqrt{13}$$
Foci are $(0, \sqrt{13})$, $(0, -\sqrt{13})$.
Asymptotes:
$$y = \frac{a}{b}x \text{ and } y = -\frac{a}{b}x$$
$$a = \sqrt{9} = 3$$
$$b = \sqrt{4} = 2$$
$$y = \frac{3}{2}x \text{ and } y = -\frac{3}{2}x$$
Other points:
$x = 2$: $\frac{y^2}{9} - \frac{2^2}{4} = 1$
$$\frac{y^2}{9} - \frac{4}{4} = 1$$
$$\frac{y^2}{9} - 1 = 1$$
$$\frac{y^2}{9} = 2$$
$$y^2 = 18$$
$$\sqrt{y^2} = \pm\sqrt{18}$$
$$y = \pm 3\sqrt{2}$$
Points are $(2, -3\sqrt{2})$, $(2, 3\sqrt{2})$.

Opens horizontally.
Vertices:
$$\frac{x^2}{9} = 1$$
$$x^2 = 1$$
$$\sqrt{x^2} = \pm\sqrt{9}$$
$$x = \pm 3$$
Vertices: (3, 0), (-3, 0)
Foci: $c = \sqrt{a^2 + b^2}$
$$= \sqrt{9 + 16}$$
$$= \sqrt{25}$$
$$= \pm 5$$
Foci are (5, 0), (-5, 0).
Asympotes:
$$y = \frac{b}{a}x \text{ and } y = -\frac{b}{a}x$$
$$a = \sqrt{9} = 3$$
$$b = \sqrt{16} = 4$$
$$y = \frac{4}{3}x \text{ and } y = -\frac{4}{3}x$$
Other points:
$y = 4$: $\frac{x^2}{9} - \frac{4^2}{16} = 1$
$$\frac{x^2}{9} - \frac{16}{16} = 1$$
$$\frac{x^2}{9} - 1 = 1$$
$$\frac{x^2}{9} = 2$$
$$x^2 = 18$$
$$\sqrt{x^2} = \pm\sqrt{18}$$
$$x = \pm 3\sqrt{2}$$
Points are $(-3\sqrt{2}, 4)$, $(3\sqrt{2}, 4)$.

2.21

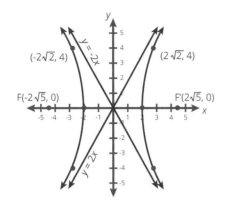

$$\frac{4x^2}{16} - \frac{y^2}{16} = 1$$
$$\frac{x^2}{4} - \frac{y^2}{16} = 1$$

Opens horizontally.

Vertices:

$$\frac{x^2}{4} = 1$$
$$x^2 = 4$$
$$\sqrt{x^2} = \pm\sqrt{4}$$
$$x = \pm 2$$

Vertices: (2, 0), (-2, 0)

Foci: $c = \sqrt{a^2 + b^2}$
$$= \sqrt{4 + 16}$$
$$= \sqrt{20}$$
$$= \pm 2\sqrt{5}$$

Foci are $(2\sqrt{5}, 0)$, $(-2\sqrt{5}, 0)$.

Asymptotes:

$$y = \pm\frac{b}{a}x$$
$$a = \sqrt{4} = 2$$
$$b = \sqrt{16} = 4$$
$$y = \pm\frac{4}{2}x$$
$$y = \pm 2x$$

Other points:

$y = 4$: $\quad \frac{x^2}{4} - \frac{4^2}{16} = 1$
$$\frac{x^2}{4} - \frac{16}{16} = 1$$
$$\frac{x^2}{4} - 1 = 1$$
$$\frac{x^2}{4} = 2$$
$$x^2 = 8$$
$$\sqrt{x^2} = \pm\sqrt{8}$$
$$x = \pm 2\sqrt{2}$$

Points are $(-2\sqrt{2}, 4)$, $(2\sqrt{2}, 4)$.

2.22

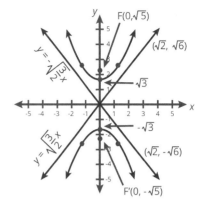

$$\frac{2y^2}{6} - \frac{3x^2}{6} = 1$$
$$\frac{y^2}{3} - \frac{x^2}{2} = 1$$

Opens vertically.

Vertices:

$$\frac{y^2}{3} = 1$$
$$y = 3$$
$$\sqrt{y^2} = \pm\sqrt{3}$$
$$y = \pm\sqrt{3}$$

Vertices are $(0, \sqrt{3})$, $(0, -\sqrt{3})$.

Foci: $c = \sqrt{a^2 + b^2}$
$$= \sqrt{3 + 2}$$
$$= \sqrt{5}$$

Foci are $(0, \sqrt{5})$, $(0, -\sqrt{5})$.

Asymptotes:

$$y = \pm\frac{a}{b}x$$
$$a = \sqrt{3}$$
$$b = \sqrt{2}$$
$$y = \pm\frac{\sqrt{3}}{\sqrt{2}}x$$
$$y = \pm\sqrt{\frac{3}{2}}x$$

Other points:

$x = \sqrt{2}$: $\quad \frac{y^2}{3} - \frac{(\sqrt{2})^2}{2} = 1$
$$\frac{y^2}{3} - \frac{2}{2} = 1$$
$$\frac{y^2}{3} - 1 = 1$$
$$\frac{y^2}{3} = 2$$
$$y^2 = 6$$
$$\sqrt{y^2} = \pm\sqrt{6}$$
$$y = \pm\sqrt{6}$$

Points are $(\sqrt{2}, -\sqrt{6})$, $(\sqrt{2}, \sqrt{6})$.

2.23

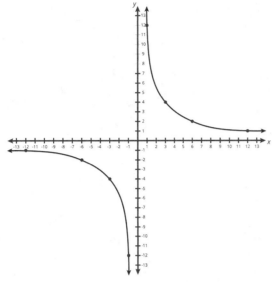

$$y = \frac{12}{x}$$

x	-12	-6	-3	-1	1	3	6	12
y	-1	-2	-4	-12	12	4	2	1

2.24

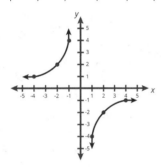

$$x = -\frac{4}{x}$$

x	-4	-2	-1	1	2	4
y	1	2	4	-4	-2	-1

2.25

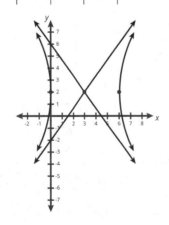

Center: (3, 2)
The hyperbola opens horizontally.

Vertices:
$$\frac{(x-3)^2}{9} = 1$$
$$(x-3)^2 = 9$$
$$x^2 - 6x + 9 = 9$$
$$x^2 - 6x = 0$$
$$x(x-6) = 0$$
$$x = 0 \qquad\qquad x - 6 = 0$$
$$x = 6$$

Vertices: (0, 2), (6, 2)
Asymptotes:
$$(y-k) = \pm\frac{b}{a}(x-h)$$
$$a = \sqrt{9} = 3$$
$$b = \sqrt{16} = 4$$
$$y - 2 = \pm\frac{4}{3}(x-3)$$

2.26

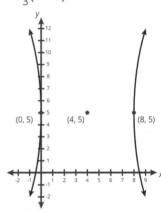

$$\frac{(x-4)^2}{a^2} - \frac{(y-5)^2}{b^2} = 1$$
Let $x = 0$, $y = 5$.
$$\frac{(0-4)^2}{a^2} - \frac{(5-5)^2}{b^2} = 1$$
$$\frac{(-4)^2}{a^2} - \frac{0^2}{b^2} = 1$$
$$\frac{16}{a^2} = 1$$
$$16 = a^2$$
$$\frac{(x-4)^2}{16} - \frac{(y-5)^2}{2^2} = 1$$
$$\frac{(x-4)^2}{16} - \frac{(y-5)^2}{4} = 1$$

2.27

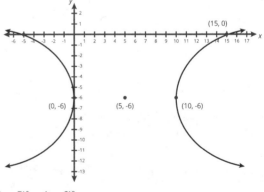

$$\frac{(x-5)^2}{a^2} - \frac{(y+6)^2}{b^2} = 1$$

Let $x = 0$, $y = -6$.

$$\frac{(0-5)^2}{a^2} - \frac{(-6+6)^2}{b^2} = 1$$

$$\frac{(-5)^2}{a^2} - \frac{0^2}{b^2} = 1$$

$$\frac{25}{a^2} = 1$$

$$25 = a^2$$

$$\frac{(x-5)^2}{25} - \frac{(y+6)^2}{b^2} = 1$$

Let $x = 15$, $y = 0$.

$$\frac{(15-5)^2}{25} - \frac{(0-6)^2}{b^2} = 1$$

$$\frac{10^2}{25} - \frac{6^2}{b^2} = 1$$

$$\frac{100}{25} - \frac{36}{b^2} = 1$$

$$4 - \frac{36}{b^2} = 1$$

LCD $= b^2$

$$4b^2 - 36 = b^2$$

$$4b^2 - 36 - b^2 = 0$$

$$3b^2 = 36$$

$$b^2 = 12$$

$$\frac{(x-5)^2}{25} - \frac{(y+6)^2}{12} = 1$$

2.28

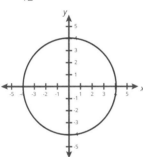

Circle with center $(0, 0)$, radius $= \sqrt{16} = 4$

2.29

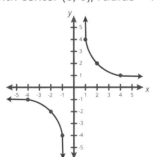

Rectangular hyperbola

$y = \frac{4}{x}$

x	-4	-2	-1	1	2	4
y	-1	-2	-4	4	2	1

2.30

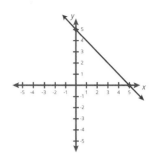

Line

x	0	5
y	5	0

2.31

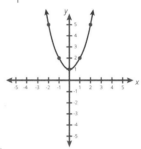

Parabola

x	0	± 1	± 2
y	1	2	5

2.32 Example points are shown; other points are possible.

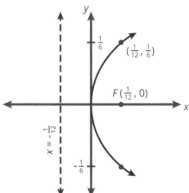

Parabola

$$3y^2 - x = 0$$

$$3y^2 = x$$

$$x = 3y^2$$

$$x = \frac{1}{4(\frac{1}{12})}y^2$$

$p = \frac{1}{12}$

Vertex: $(0, 0)$

Directrix: $x = -p$; $x = -\frac{1}{12}$

Focus: $(p, 0) = (\frac{1}{12}, 0)$

Another point is $(\frac{1}{12}, \frac{1}{6})$:

$$x = \frac{1}{4(\frac{1}{12})}(\frac{1}{6})^2$$

$$x = \frac{1}{\frac{1}{3}}(\frac{1}{36}) = 3(\frac{1}{36}) = \frac{1}{12}$$

2.33

Ellipse

$\frac{x^2}{2} + \frac{2y^2}{2} = 1$

$\frac{x^2}{2} + \frac{y^2}{1} = 1$

x-intercepts:

$\frac{x^2}{2} = 1$

$x^2 = 2$

$\sqrt{x^2} = \pm\sqrt{2}$

$x = \pm\sqrt{2}$

Major intercepts: $(\pm\sqrt{2}, 0)$

y-intercepts:

$\frac{y^2}{1} = 1$

$y^2 = 1$

$\sqrt{y^2} = \pm\sqrt{1}$

$y = \pm 1$

Minor intercepts: $(0, \pm 1)$

2.34

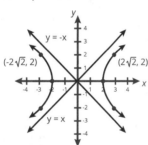

Hyperbola

$\frac{x^2}{4} - \frac{y^2}{4} = 1$

Opens horizontally.

Vertices:

$\frac{x^2}{4} = 1$

$x^2 = 4$

$\sqrt{x^2} = \pm\sqrt{4}$

$x = \pm 2$

Vertices are $(\pm 2, 0)$.

Asymptotes:

$y = \pm\frac{b}{a}x$

$a = \sqrt{4} = 2$

$b = \sqrt{4} = 2$

$y = \pm\frac{2}{2}x$

$y = \pm x$

Other points are $(\pm 2\sqrt{2}, 2)$:

$\frac{x^2}{4} - \frac{2^2}{4} = 1$

$\frac{x^2}{4} - \frac{4}{4} = 1$

$\frac{x^2}{4} - 1 = 1$

$\frac{x^2}{4} = 2$

$x^2 = 8$

$\sqrt{x^2} = \pm\sqrt{8}$

$x = \pm 2\sqrt{2}$

2.35

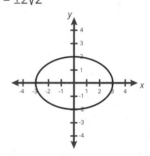

Ellipse

$\frac{4x^2}{36} + \frac{9y^2}{36} = 1$

$\frac{x^2}{9} + \frac{y^2}{4} = 1$

x-intercepts:

$\frac{x^2}{9} = 1$

$x^2 = 9$

$\sqrt{x^2} = \pm\sqrt{9}$

$x = \pm 3$

Major intercepts: $(\pm 3, 0)$

y-intercepts:

$\frac{y^2}{4} = 1$

$y^2 = 4$

$\sqrt{y^2} = \pm\sqrt{4}$

$y = \pm 2$

Minor intercepts: $(0, \pm 2)$

SELF TEST 2

2.01

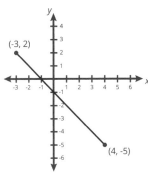

$d = \sqrt{[4-(-3)]^2 + (-5-2)^2}$
$= \sqrt{7^2 + (-7)^2}$
$= \sqrt{49 + 49}$
$= \sqrt{98}$
$= 7\sqrt{2}$

2.02

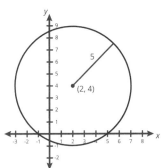

Center: (2, 4)
Radius= $\sqrt{25}$ = 5

2.03

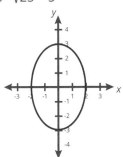

y-intercepts:
$\frac{y^2}{9} = 1$
$y^2 = 9$
$\sqrt{y^2} = \pm\sqrt{9}$
$y = \pm 3$
Major intercepts: (0, ±3)

x-intercepts:
$\frac{x^2}{4} = 1$
$x^2 = 4$
$\sqrt{x^2} = \pm\sqrt{4}$
$x = \pm 2$
Minor intercepts: (±2, 0)

2.04

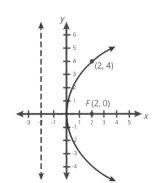

$x = \frac{1}{4(2)}y^2$
$p = 2$
The parabola opens to the right.
Vertex: (0, 0)
Directrix: $x = -p$; $x = -2$
Focus: $(p, 0) = (2, 0)$
Another point is (2, 4):
$x = \frac{1}{8}(4)^2$
$x = \frac{1}{8}(16)$
$x = 2$

2.05

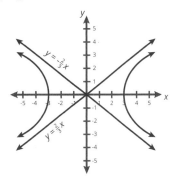

Hyperbola opens horizontally.
Vertices:
$\frac{x^2}{9} = 1$
$x^2 = 9$
$\sqrt{x^2} = \pm\sqrt{9}$
$x = \pm 3$
Vertices are (±3, 0).
Asymptotes:
$y = \pm\frac{b}{a}x$
$a = \sqrt{9} = 3$
$b = \sqrt{4} = 2$
$y = \pm\frac{2}{3}x$

2.06

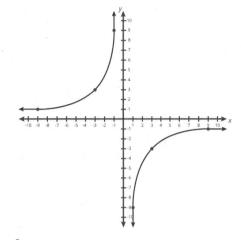

$y = -\dfrac{9}{x}$

x	-9	-3	-1	1	3	9
y	1	3	9	-9	-3	-1

2.07

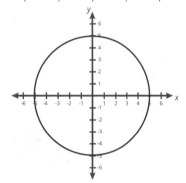

Circle
Center: (0, 0)
Radius = $\sqrt{25}$ = 5

2.08

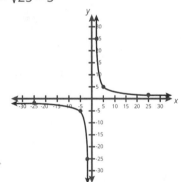

Rectangular Hyperbola
$y = \dfrac{25}{x}$

x	-25	-5	-1	1	5	25
y	-1	-5	-25	25	5	1

Vertices: (5, 5), (-5, -5)
Center: (0, 0)
Asymptotes: x- and y-axes

2.09

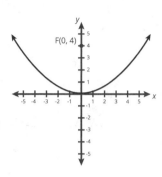

$y = \dfrac{1}{4(4)}x^2$
$p = 4$
Vertex: (0, 0)
The parabola opens upward.
Focus: $(0, p)$ = (0, 4)

2.010

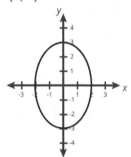

Ellipse
$$\dfrac{9x^2}{36} + \dfrac{4y^2}{36} = 1$$
$$\dfrac{x^2}{4} + \dfrac{y^2}{9} = 1$$

y-intercepts:
$$\dfrac{y^2}{9} = 1$$
$$y^2 = 9$$
$$\sqrt{y^2} = \pm\sqrt{9}$$
$$y = \pm3$$
Major intercepts: (0, ±3)

x-intercepts:
$$\dfrac{x^2}{4} = 1$$
$$x^2 = 4$$
$$\sqrt{x^2} = \pm\sqrt{4}$$
$$x = \pm2$$
Minor intercepts: (±2, 0)
Center: (0, 0)

2.011

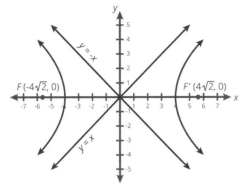

$\frac{x^2}{16} - \frac{y^2}{16} = 1$

Hyperbola opens horizontally.

Vertices:

$\frac{x^2}{16} = 1$

$x^2 = 16$

$\sqrt{x^2} = \pm\sqrt{16}$

$x = \pm 4$

Vertices are (4, 0), (-4, 0)

Center: (0, 0)

Foci: $c = \sqrt{a^2 + b^2}$

$= \sqrt{16 + 16}$

$= \sqrt{32}$

$= \pm 4\sqrt{2}$

Foci are $(4\sqrt{2}, 0)$, $(-4\sqrt{2}, 0)$

Asymptotes:

$y = \pm\frac{b}{a}x$

$a = \sqrt{16} = 4$

$b = \sqrt{16} = 4$

$y = \pm\frac{4}{4}x$

$y = \pm x$

2.012

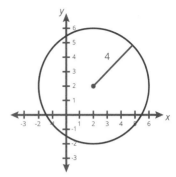

$x^2 - 4x + y^2 - 4y = 8$

$x^2 - 4x + 4 + y^2 - 4y + 4 = 8 + 4 + 4$

$(x - 2)^2 + (y - 2)^2 = 16$

Circle

Center: (2, 2)

Radius $= \sqrt{16} = 4$

2.013 $\frac{x^2}{1^2} + \frac{y^2}{3^2} = 1$

$\frac{x^2}{1} + \frac{y^2}{9} = 1$

2.014 $(x - 1)^2 + (y - 2)^2 = 5^2$

$(x - 1)^2 + (y - 2)^2 = 25$

2.015 $p > 0$ and the directrix is $y = -2$. From the formula $y = \frac{1}{4p}x^2$, the equation of this parabola is

$y = \frac{1}{4(2)}x^2$

$y = \frac{1}{8}x^2$

2.016 $\frac{x^2}{4^2} + \frac{y^2}{1^2} = 1$

$\frac{x^2}{16} + \frac{y^2}{1} = 1$

SECTION 3

3.1

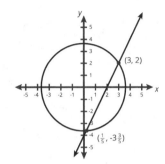

3.2

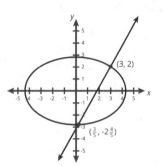

Circle:
Center = (0, 0)
Radius = $\sqrt{13} \doteq 3.6$
Line:

x	0	2
y	-4	0

$$2x - y = 4$$
$$-y = -2x + 4$$
$$y = 2x - 4$$
$$x^2 + y^2 = 13$$
$$x^2 + (2x - 4)^2 = 13$$
$$x^2 + 4x^2 - 16x + 16 = 13$$
$$5x^2 - 16x + 3 = 0$$

$$x = \frac{16 \pm \sqrt{(-16)^2 - 4(5)(3)}}{2(5)} = \frac{16 \pm \sqrt{256 - 60}}{10} = \frac{16 \pm \sqrt{196}}{10}$$
$$= \frac{16 \pm 14}{10}$$
$$x = \frac{16 + 14}{10} = \frac{30}{10} = 3$$
$$x = \frac{16 - 14}{10} = \frac{2}{10} = \frac{1}{5}$$

If $x = 3$:
$$y = 2(3) - 4$$
$$y = 6 - 4$$
$$y = 2$$

If $x = \frac{1}{5}$:
$$y = 2(\tfrac{1}{5}) - 4$$
$$y = \frac{2}{5} - 4$$
$$y = -\frac{18}{5}$$
$$y = -3\tfrac{3}{5}$$

Check the solution, $(\tfrac{1}{5}, -3\tfrac{3}{5})$:

$(\tfrac{1}{5})^2 + (-3\tfrac{3}{5})^2 = 13$ $2(\tfrac{1}{5}) - (-3\tfrac{3}{5}) = 4$

$(\tfrac{1}{5})^2 + (-\tfrac{18}{5})^2 = 13$ $\frac{2}{5} + \frac{18}{5} = 4$

$\frac{1}{25} + \frac{324}{25} = 13$ $\frac{20}{5} = 4$

$\frac{325}{25} = 13$ $4 = 4$

$13 = 13$

The other solution can be checked in a similar manner.

Solution set: $\{(3, 2), (\tfrac{1}{5}, -3\tfrac{3}{5})\}$

Ellipse
$$\frac{4x^2}{72} + \frac{9y^2}{72} = 1$$
$$\frac{x^2}{18} + \frac{y^2}{8} = 1$$
x-intercepts:
$$\frac{x^2}{18} = 1$$
$$x^2 = 18$$
$$\sqrt{x^2} = \pm\sqrt{18}$$
$$x = \pm 3\sqrt{2}$$
Major intercepts: $(\pm 3\sqrt{2}, 0)$
y-intercepts:
$$\frac{y^2}{8} = 1$$
$$y^2 = 8$$
$$\sqrt{y^2} = \pm\sqrt{8}$$
$$y = \pm 2\sqrt{2}$$
Minor intercepts: $(0, \pm 2\sqrt{2})$
Line:

x	0	2
y	-4	0

$$2x - y = 4$$
$$-y = -2x + 4$$
$$y = 2x - 4$$
$$4x^2 + 9y^2 = 72$$
$$4x^2 + 9(2x - 4)^2 = 72$$
$$4x^2 + 9(4x^2 - 16x + 16) = 72$$
$$4x^2 + 36x^2 - 144x + 144 = 72$$
$$40x^2 - 144x + 72 = 0$$
$$5x^2 - 18x + 9 = 0 \quad \text{(divide by 8)}$$

$$x = \frac{18 \pm \sqrt{(-18)^2 - 4(5)(9)}}{2(5)}$$
$$= \frac{18 \pm \sqrt{324 - 180}}{10} = \frac{18 \pm \sqrt{144}}{10} = \frac{18 \pm 12}{10}$$
$$x = \frac{18 + 12}{10} = \frac{30}{10} = 3$$
$$x = \frac{18 - 12}{10} = \frac{6}{10} = \frac{3}{5}$$

If $x = 3$: $y = 2(3) - 4$
$$y = 6 - 4$$
$$y = 2$$

If $x = \frac{3}{5}$: $y = 2(\frac{3}{5}) - 4$

$y = \frac{6}{5} - 4$

$y = -\frac{14}{5}$

$y = -2\frac{4}{5}$

Check of one solution, (3, 2):

$4(3)^2 + 9(2)^2 = 72$	$2(3) - 2 = 4$
$4(9) + 9(4) = 72$	$6 - 2 = 4$
$36 + 36 = 72$	$4 = 4$
$72 = 72$	

The other solution can be checked in a similar manner.

Solution set: $\{(3, 2), (\frac{3}{5}, -2\frac{4}{5})\}$

3.3

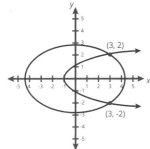

Ellipse:

$\frac{4x^2}{72} + \frac{9y^2}{72} = 1$

$\frac{x^2}{18} + \frac{y^2}{8} = 1$

x-intercepts:

$\frac{x^2}{18} = 1$

$x^2 = 18$

$\sqrt{x^2} = \pm\sqrt{18}$

$x = \pm 3\sqrt{2}$

Major intercepts: $(\pm 3\sqrt{2}, 0)$

y-intercepts:

$\frac{y^2}{8} = 1$

$y^2 = 8$

$\sqrt{y^2} = \pm\sqrt{8}$

$y = \pm 2\sqrt{2}$

Minor intercepts: $(0, \pm 2\sqrt{2})$

Parabola:

$x = y^2 - 1$

x	-1	0	3
y	0	± 1	± 2

$x - y^2 = -1$

$-y^2 = -x - 1$

$y^2 = x + 1$

$4x^2 + 9y^2 = 72$

$4x^2 + 9(x + 1) = 72$

$4x^2 + 9x + 9 = 72$

$4x^2 + 9x - 63 = 0$

$x = \frac{-9 \pm \sqrt{9^2 - 4(4)(-63)}}{2(4)}$

$= \frac{-9 \pm \sqrt{81 + 1{,}008}}{8} = \frac{-9 \pm \sqrt{1{,}089}}{8} = \frac{-9 \pm 33}{8}$

$x = \frac{-9 + 33}{8} = \frac{24}{8} = 3$

$x = \frac{-9 - 33}{8} = \frac{-42}{8} = -\frac{21}{4} = -5\frac{1}{4}$

If $x = 3$: $y^2 = 3 + 1$

$y^2 = 4$

$\sqrt{y^2} = \pm\sqrt{4}$

$y = \pm 2$

If $x = -5\frac{1}{4}$: $y^2 = -5\frac{1}{4} + 1$

$y^2 = -4\frac{1}{4}$; impossible

Check of one solution, (3, 2):

$4(3)^2 + 9(2)^2 = 72$	$3 - 2^2 = -1$
$4(9) + 9(4) = 72$	$3 - 4 = -1$
$36 + 36 = 72$	$-1 = -1$
$72 = 72$	

The other solution, (3, -2), can be checked in a similar manner.

Solution set: $\{(3, 2),(3, -2)\}$

3.4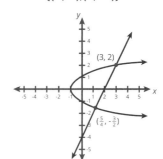

Parabola:

x	-1	0	3
y	0	± 1	± 2

Line:

x	0	2
y	-4	0

$2x - y = 4$

$-y = -2x + 4$

$y = 2x - 4$

$x = y^2 - 1$

$x = (2x - 4)^2 - 1$

$x = 4x^2 - 16x + 16 - 1$

$0 = 4x^2 - 17x + 15$

$x = \frac{17 \pm \sqrt{(-17)^2 - 4(4)(15)}}{2(4)}$

$= \frac{17 \pm \sqrt{289 - 240}}{8} = \frac{17 \pm \sqrt{49}}{8} = \frac{17 \pm 7}{8}$

$x = \frac{17 + 7}{8} = \frac{24}{8} = 3$

$x = \frac{17 - 7}{8} = \frac{10}{8} = \frac{5}{4}$

If $x = 3$: $\quad y = 2(3) - 4$
$\quad\quad\quad\quad\quad y = 6 - 4$
$\quad\quad\quad\quad\quad y = 2$

If $x = \frac{5}{4}$: $\quad y = 2(\frac{5}{4}) - 4$
$\quad\quad\quad\quad\quad y = \frac{5}{2} - 4$
$\quad\quad\quad\quad\quad y = -\frac{3}{2}$

Check of one solution, (3, 2):
$\quad\quad 3 = 2^2 - 1 \quad\quad 2(3) - 2 = 4$
$\quad\quad 3 = 4 - 1 \quad\quad\quad 6 - 2 = 4$
$\quad\quad 3 = 3 \quad\quad\quad\quad\quad 4 = 4$

The other solution can be checked in a similar manner.

Solution set: $\{(3, 2), (\frac{5}{4}, -\frac{3}{2})\}$

3.5

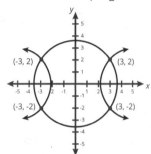

Circle:
Center: (0, 0)
Radius $= \sqrt{13} \doteq 3.6$

Hyperbola:
$\frac{x^2}{5} - \frac{y^2}{5} = 1$
Opens horizontally.
Vertices:
$\quad \frac{x^2}{5} = 1$
$\quad x^2 = 5$
$\quad \sqrt{x^2} = \pm\sqrt{5}$
$\quad x = \pm\sqrt{5}$
Vertices are $(-\sqrt{5}, 0)$, $(\sqrt{5}, 0)$.

$\quad x^2 - y^2 = 5$
$\quad\quad x^2 = y^2 + 5$
$\quad x^2 + y^2 = 13$
$\quad y^2 + 5 + y^2 = 13$
$\quad\quad 2y^2 + 5 = 13$
$\quad\quad\quad 2y^2 = 8$
$\quad\quad\quad\quad y^2 = 4$
$\quad\quad\quad \sqrt{y^2} = \pm\sqrt{4}$
$\quad\quad\quad\quad y = \pm 2$

If $y = 2$: $\quad x^2 = 2^2 + 5$
$\quad\quad\quad\quad x^2 = 4 + 5$
$\quad\quad\quad\quad x^2 = 9$
$\quad\quad\quad \sqrt{x^2} = \pm\sqrt{9}$
$\quad\quad\quad\quad x = \pm 3$

If $y = -2$: $\quad x^2 = (-2)^2 + 5$
$\quad\quad\quad\quad x^2 = 4 + 5$
$\quad\quad\quad\quad x^2 = 9$
$\quad\quad\quad \sqrt{x^2} = \pm\sqrt{9}$
$\quad\quad\quad\quad x = \pm 3$

Check of one solution, (-3, -2):
$\quad (-3)^2 + (-2)^2 = 13 \quad\quad (-3)^2 - (-2)^2 = 5$
$\quad\quad\quad 9 + 4 = 13 \quad\quad\quad\quad\quad 9 - 4 = 5$
$\quad\quad\quad\quad 13 = 13 \quad\quad\quad\quad\quad\quad 5 = 5$

The other solutions can be checked in a similar manner.

Solution set: $\{(3, 2), (3, -2), (-3, 2), (-3, -2)\}$

3.6

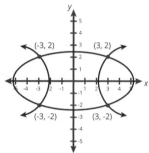

Ellipse:
$\frac{4x^2}{72} + \frac{9y^2}{72} = 1$
$\frac{x^2}{18} + \frac{y^2}{8} = 1$

x-intercepts:
$\quad \frac{x^2}{18} = 1$
$\quad x^2 = 18$
$\quad \sqrt{x^2} = \pm\sqrt{18}$
$\quad\quad x = \pm 3\sqrt{2}$
Major intercepts: $(\pm 3\sqrt{2}, 0)$

y-intercepts:
$\quad \frac{y^2}{8} = 1$
$\quad y^2 = 8$
$\quad \sqrt{y^2} = \pm\sqrt{8}$
$\quad\quad y = \pm 2\sqrt{2}$
Minor intercepts: $(0, \pm 2\sqrt{2})$

Hyperbola:
$\frac{x^2}{5} - \frac{y^2}{5} = 1$
Opens horizontally.
Vertices:
$\quad \frac{x^2}{5} = 1$
$\quad x^2 = 5$
$\quad \sqrt{x^2} = \pm\sqrt{5}$
$\quad x = \pm\sqrt{5}$
Vertices are $(-\sqrt{5}, 0)$, $(\sqrt{5}, 0)$.

$\quad x^2 - y^2 = 5$
$\quad\quad x^2 = y^2 + 5$

$$4x^2 + 9y^2 = 72$$
$$4(y^2 + 5) + 9y^2 = 72$$
$$4y^2 + 20 + 9y^2 = 72$$
$$13y^2 + 20 = 72$$
$$13y^2 = 52$$
$$y^2 = 4$$
$$\sqrt{y^2} = \pm\sqrt{4}$$
$$y = \pm 2$$

If $y = 2$: 　　$x^2 = 2^2 + 5$
$$x^2 = 4 + 5$$
$$x^2 = 9$$
$$\sqrt{x^2} = \pm\sqrt{9}$$
$$x = \pm 3$$

If $y = -2$: 　　$x^2 = (-2)^2 + 5$
$$x^2 = 4 + 5$$
$$x^2 = 9$$
$$\sqrt{x^2} = \pm\sqrt{9}$$
$$x = \pm 3$$

Check of one solution, (-3, 2):

$4(-3)^2 + 9(2)^2 = 72$	$(-3)^2 - 2^2 = 5$
$4(9) + 9(4) = 72$	$9 - 4 = 5$
$36 + 36 = 72$	$5 = 5$
$72 = 72$	

The other solutions can be checked in a similar manner.
Solution set: {(3, 2), (3, -2), (-3, 2), (-3, -2)}

3.7

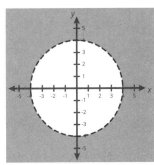

Graph $x^2 + y^2 = 16$.
Circle with center (0, 0) and radius = $\sqrt{16}$ = 4.
Use a dotted path for >.
Check points inside or outside the graph.

Check (0, 0): 　$0^2 + 0^2 \overset{?}{>} 16$
　　　　　　　0 > 16 is false; ∴ the outside of the circle is shaded.

3.8

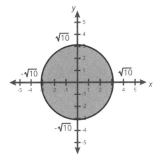

Graph $x^2 + y^2 = 10$.
Circle with center (0, 0) and radius = $\sqrt{10}$.
Use a solid path since the ≤ includes =.
Check points inside or outside the graph.

Check (0, 0): 　　$0^2 + 0^2 \overset{?}{\leq} 10$
　　　　　　　$0 \leq 10$ is true; ∴ the inside of the circle is shaded.

3.9

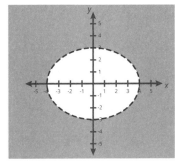

Graph $\frac{x^2}{16} + \frac{y^2}{9} = 1$.
Ellipse with major intercepts (-4, 0) and (4, 0); minor intercepts (0, -3) and (0, 3).
Use a dotted path for >.
Check points inside or outside the graph.

Check (0, 0): 　　$\frac{0^2}{16} + \frac{0^2}{9} \overset{?}{>} 1$
　　　　　　　$0 + 0 \overset{?}{>} 1$
　　　　　　　0 > 1 is false; ∴ the outside of the ellipse is shaded.

3.10

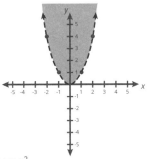

Graph $y = x^2$.

x	0	±1	±2
y	0	1	4

255

Parabola opens up with vertex (0, 0).
Use a dotted path for >.
Check points inside or outside the graph.

Check (0, 1): $1 \overset{?}{>} 0^2$

$1 > 0$ is true; ∴ the inside
of the parabola is shaded.

3.11

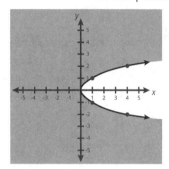

Graph $x = y^2$.

x	0	1	4
y	0	±1	±2

Parabola opens to the right with vertex (0, 0).
Use a solid path since the ≤ includes =.
Check points inside or outside the graph.

Check (1, 0): $1 \overset{?}{\leq} 0^2$

$1 \leq 0$ is false; ∴ the
outside of the graph is
shaded.

3.12

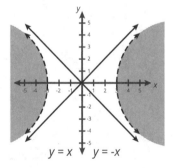

$y = x$ $y = -x$

Graph $x^2 - y^2 = 9$.
$\frac{x^2}{9} - \frac{y^2}{9} = 1$
Hyperbola opens horizontally with vertices
(-3, 0), (3, 0).
Asymptotes are $y = \pm\frac{3}{3}x$; $y = \pm x$.
Use a dotted path for >.
Check points inside or outside the graph.

Check (0, 0): $0^2 - 0^2 \overset{?}{>} 9$

$0 > 9$ is false; ∴
the inside of the
hyperbola is shaded.

3.13 $y = 2,000$
$x = 15$
$y = \frac{k}{x}$
$2,000 = \frac{x}{15}$
$30,000 = k$
$y = \frac{30,000}{x}$

3.14 $y = \frac{30,000}{x}$
$x = 10$
$y = \frac{30,000}{10}$
$y = 3,000$ pounds

3.15 $y = 500$ pounds
$y = \frac{30,000}{x}$
$500 = \frac{30,000}{x}$
$500x = 30,000$
$x = 60$ feet

3.16   Example points are shown; other points are
possible.

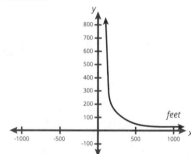

$y = \frac{30,000}{x}, x > 0$

x	100	300	500	1,000
y	300	100	60	30

3.17 $y = kx^2$
$y = 1,000$
$x = 5$
$1,000 = k(5)^2$
$1,000 = 25k$
$\frac{1,000}{25} = k$
$k = 40$
$y = 40x^2$

3.18 $x = 10$
$y = 40x^2$
$y = 40(10)^2$
$y = 40(100)$
$y = 4,000$ pounds

3.19
$$y = 16,000 \text{ pounds}$$
$$y = 40x^2$$
$$16,000 = 40x^2$$
$$\frac{16,000}{40} = x^2$$
$$x^2 = 400$$
$$\sqrt{x^2} = \sqrt{400} \quad \text{(use only the principal square root for length)}$$
$$x = 20 \text{ inches}$$

3.20 Example points are shown; other points are possible.

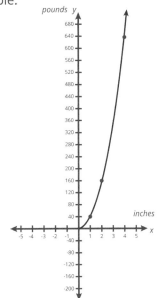

$$y = 40x^2, \ x > 0$$

x	0	1	2	4
y	0	40	160	640

3.21 $y = \frac{10,000}{x}(z + 0.10) - \frac{10,000}{x}(z)$

$= \frac{10,000z + 1,000 - 10,000z}{x}$

$= \frac{1,000}{x}$

a. The z subtracts out.
b. Since the z subtracts out, this means that the original price of fuel before the 10-cent increase does not affect the increase in annual fuel costs.

3.22

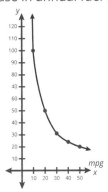

3.23 Not as much difference in increase takes place between 20 mpg and 30 mpg ($16.67 per year) as between 10 mph and 20 mph ($50 per year).

3.24 $x^2 + y^2 = (150,000,000)^2$

3.25

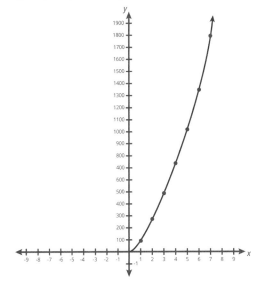

3.26 Parabola: $y = kx^2, \ x > 0$

3.27
$$y = kx^2$$
$$33 = k(1)^2$$
$$33 = k$$
$$y = 33x^2$$

3.28 a. Example:
Let $x = 2$, $y = 130$
Calculated $y = 33(2)^2$
                       $= 33(4)$
                       $= 132$; off by 2

Let $x = 3$, $y = 298$
Calculated $y = 33(3)^2$
                       $= 33(9)$
                       $= 297$; off by 1

The equation does not fit the data exactly. Errors in measurement were probably made.

b. One could use the average of several constants calculated to estimate the coefficient of the x^2.

3.29 $y = \frac{k}{x}$

3.30 $10 = \frac{k}{5}$
$50 = k$

3.31 $25 = \frac{50}{x}$
$25x = 50$
$x = 2$

SELF TEST 3

3.01

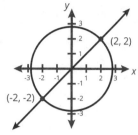

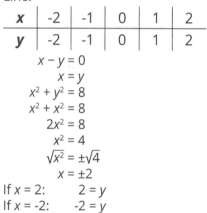

Circle
Center: (0, 0)
Radius = $\sqrt{8}$ = $2\sqrt{2}$
Line:

x	-2	-1	0	1	2
y	-2	-1	0	1	2

$$x - y = 0$$
$$x = y$$
$$x^2 + y^2 = 8$$
$$x^2 + x^2 = 8$$
$$2x^2 = 8$$
$$x^2 = 4$$
$$\sqrt{x^2} = \pm\sqrt{4}$$
$$x = \pm 2$$

If $x = 2$: $2 = y$
If $x = -2$: $-2 = y$

Check of one solution, (2, 2):
$$2^2 + 2^2 = 8$$
$$4 + 4 = 8$$
$$8 = 8$$
$$2 - 2 = 0$$
$$0 = 0$$

The other solution can be checked in a similar manner.
Solution set: {(2, 2), (-2, -2)}

3.02

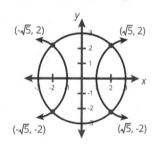

Circle:
Center: (0, 0)
Radius = $\sqrt{9}$ = 3

Hyperbola:
$$\frac{x^2}{1} - \frac{y^2}{1} = 1$$
Hyperbola opens horizontally.

Vertices:
$$\frac{x^2}{1} = 1$$
$$x^2 = 1$$
$$\sqrt{x^2} = \pm\sqrt{1}$$
$$x = \pm 1$$
Vertices are (-1, 0), (1, 0)
$$x^2 - y^2 = 1$$
$$x^2 = y^2 + 1$$
$$x^2 + y^2 = 9$$
$$y^2 + 1 + y^2 = 9$$
$$2y^2 + 1 = 9$$
$$2y^2 = 8$$
$$y^2 = 4$$
$$\sqrt{y^2} = \pm\sqrt{4}$$
$$y = \pm 2$$

If $y = 2$: $x^2 = 2^2 + 1$
$$x^2 = 4 + 1$$
$$x^2 = 5$$
$$\sqrt{x^2} = \pm\sqrt{5}$$
$$x = \pm\sqrt{5}$$

If $y = -2$: $x^2 = (-2)^2 + 1$
$$x^2 = 4 + 1$$
$$x^2 = 5$$
$$\sqrt{x^2} = \pm\sqrt{5}$$
$$x = \pm\sqrt{5}$$

Check of one solution, ($-\sqrt{5}$, 2):
$$(-\sqrt{5})^2 + 2^2 = 9 \qquad (-\sqrt{5})^2 - 2^2 = 1$$
$$5 + 4 = 9 \qquad\qquad 5 - 4 = 1$$
$$9 = 9 \qquad\qquad\quad 1 = 1$$

The other solutions can be checked in a similar manner.
Solution set: {($\sqrt{5}$, 2), ($\sqrt{5}$, -2), ($-\sqrt{5}$, 2), ($-\sqrt{5}$, -2)}

3.03

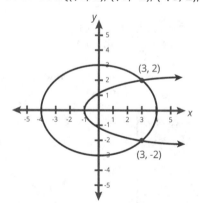

Hyperbola:
$$\frac{4x^2}{72} - \frac{9y^2}{72} = 1$$
$$\frac{x^2}{18} - \frac{y^2}{8} = 1$$

x-intercepts:

$$\frac{x^2}{18} = 1$$
$$x^2 = 18$$
$$\sqrt{x^2} = \pm\sqrt{18}$$
$$x = \pm3\sqrt{2}$$

Major intercepts: ($\pm3\sqrt{2}$, 0)

y-intercepts:

$$\frac{y^2}{8} = 1$$
$$y^2 = 8$$
$$\sqrt{y^2} = \pm\sqrt{8}$$
$$y = \pm2\sqrt{2}$$

Minor intercepts: (0, $\pm2\sqrt{2}$)

Parabola:

$$x = y^2 - 1$$

x	-1	0	3
y	0	±1	±2

$$x - y^2 = -1$$
$$-y^2 = -x - 1$$
$$y^2 = x + 1$$
$$4x^2 + 9y^2 = 72$$
$$4x^2 + 9(x + 1) = 72$$
$$4x^2 + 9x + 9 = 72$$
$$4x^2 + 9x - 63 = 0$$

$$x = \frac{-9 \pm \sqrt{9^2 - 4(4)(-63)}}{2(4)}$$
$$= \frac{-9 \pm \sqrt{81 + 1{,}008}}{8} = \frac{-9 \pm \sqrt{1{,}089}}{8} = \frac{-9 \pm 33}{8}$$
$$x = \frac{-9 + 33}{8} = \frac{24}{8} = 3$$
$$x = \frac{-9 - 33}{8} = \frac{-42}{8} = -\frac{21}{4} = -5\frac{1}{4}$$

If $x = 3$: $\quad y^2 = 3 + 1$
$$y^2 = 4$$
$$\sqrt{y^2} = \pm\sqrt{4}$$
$$y = \pm2$$

If $x = -5\frac{1}{4}$: $\quad y^2 = -5\frac{1}{4} + 1$
$$y^2 = 4\frac{1}{4};\ \text{impossible}$$

Check of one solution, (3, 2):

$4(3)^2 + 9(2)^2 = 72$	$3 - 2^2 = -1$
$4(9) + 9(4) = 72$	$3 - 4 = -1$
$36 + 36 = 72$	$-1 = -1$
$72 = 72$	

The other solution, (3, -2), can be checked in a similar manner.

Solution set: {(3, 2), (3, -2)}

3.04

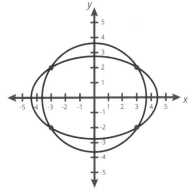

Circle:
Center: (0, 0)
Radius = $\sqrt{13}$

Ellipse:

$$\frac{4x^2}{72} + \frac{9y^2}{72} = 1$$
$$\frac{x^2}{18} + \frac{y^2}{8} = 1$$

x-intercepts:

$$\frac{x^2}{18} = 1$$
$$x^2 = 18$$
$$\sqrt{x^2} = \pm\sqrt{18}$$
$$x = \pm3\sqrt{2}$$

Major intercepts: ($\pm3\sqrt{2}$, 0)

y-intercepts:

$$\frac{y^2}{8} = 1$$
$$y^2 = 8$$
$$\sqrt{y^2} = \pm\sqrt{8}$$
$$y = \pm2\sqrt{2}$$

Minor intercepts: (0, $\pm2\sqrt{2}$)

$$x^2 + y^2 = 13$$
$$x^2 = 13 - y^2$$
$$4x^2 + 9y^2 = 72$$
$$4(13 - y^2) + 9y^2 = 72$$
$$52 - 4y^2 + 9y^2 = 72$$
$$52 + 5y^2 = 72$$
$$5y^2 = 20$$
$$y^2 = 4$$
$$\sqrt{y^2} = \pm\sqrt{4}$$
$$y = \pm2$$

If $y = 2$: $\quad x^2 = 13 - 2^2$
$$x^2 = 13 - 4$$
$$x^2 = 9$$
$$\sqrt{x^2} = \pm\sqrt{9}$$
$$x = \pm3$$

If $y = -2$: $\quad x^2 = 13 - (-2)^2$
$$x^2 = 13 - 4$$
$$x^2 = 9$$

$$\sqrt{x^2} = \pm\sqrt{9}$$
$$x = \pm 3$$

Check of one solution, (-3, 2):

$(-3)^2 + 2^2 = 13$	$4(-3)^2 - 9(2)^2 = 72$
$9 + 4 = 13$	$4(9) + 9(4) = 72$
$13 = 13$	$36 + 36 = 72$
	$72 = 72$

The other solutions can be checked in a similar manner.

Solution set: {(3, 2), (-3, 2), (3, -2), (-3, -2)}

3.05

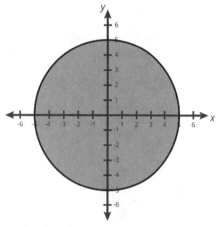

Graph $x^2 + y^2 = 25$.
Circle with center (0, 0) and radius = $\sqrt{25}$ = 5.
Use a solid path since the ≤ includes =.
Check points inside or outside the graph.

Check (0, 0): $0^2 + 0^2 \overset{?}{\le} 25$

$0 \le 25$ is true; ∴ the inside of the circle is shaded.

3.06

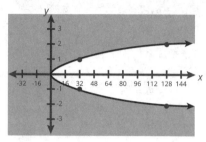

Graph $x = 32y^2$.

x	0	32	128
y	0	±1	±2

Parabola opens to the right with vertex (0, 0).
Use a solid path since the ≤ includes =.
Check points inside or outside the graph.

Check (32, 0): $32 \overset{?}{\le} 32(0)^2$

$32 \le 0$ is false; ∴ the outside of the parabola is shaded.

3.07

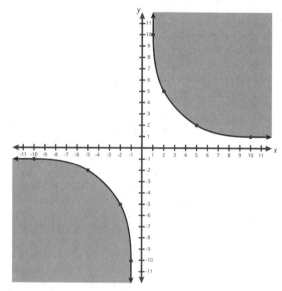

Graph $xy = 10$.

$y = \dfrac{10}{x}$

x	-10	-5	-1	1	5	10
y	-1	-2	-10	10	2	1

Rectangular hyperbola with x- and y-axes as asymptotes.
Use a solid path since the ≥ includes =.
Check points inside or outside the graph.

Check (10, 10): $(10)(10) \overset{?}{\ge} 10$

$100 \ge 0$ is true; ∴ the inside of the hyperbola is shaded.

3.08

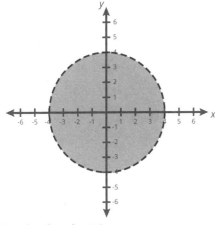

Graph $x^2 + y^2 = 16$.
Circle with center (0, 0) and radius = $\sqrt{16}$ = 4.
Use a dotted path for <.
Check points inside or outside the graph.

Check (0, 0): $0^2 + 0^2 \overset{?}{<} 16$

              0 < 16 is true; ∴ the inside
              of the circle is shaded.

3.09   distance = rate • time
           $300 = xy$

3.010

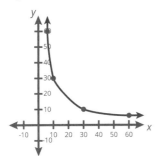

$xy = 300$

$y = \dfrac{300}{x}$

x	5	10	30	60
y	60	30	10	5

3.011 $y = kx$

3.012 $y = kx$
      $40 = k(5)$
      $8 = k$

3.013 $y = kx$
      $8 = 8x$
      $1 = x$

LIFEPAC TEST

1.

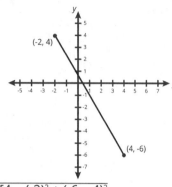

$d = \sqrt{[4 - (-2)^2 + (-6 - 4)^2}$
$\quad = \sqrt{6^2 + (-10)^2}$
$\quad = \sqrt{36 + 100}$
$\quad = \sqrt{136}$
$\quad = 2\sqrt{34}$

2.

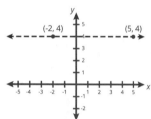

$d = |-2 - 5|$
$\quad = |-7|$
$\quad = 7$

3.

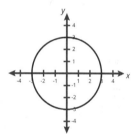

Center: (0, 0)
Radius= $\sqrt{9}$ = 3

4.

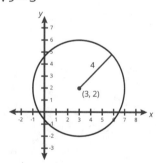

Center: (3, 2)
Radius= $\sqrt{16}$ = 4

5.

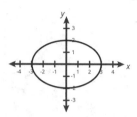

x-intercepts:
$\frac{x^2}{9} = 1$
$x^2 = 9$
$\sqrt{x^2} = \pm\sqrt{9}$
$x = \pm 3$
Major intercepts: (±3, 0)

y-intercepts:
$\frac{y^2}{4} = 1$
$y^2 = 4$
$\sqrt{y^2} = \pm\sqrt{4}$
$y = \pm 2$
Minor intercepts: (0, ±2)

6.

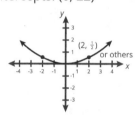

$y = \frac{1}{4(2)}x^2$
The parabola opens upward. Another point is (2, $\frac{1}{2}$):
$y = \frac{1}{8}(2)^2$
$y = \frac{1}{8}(4)$
$y = \frac{1}{2}$

7.

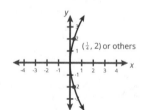

$x = \frac{1}{4(4)}y^2$
The parabola opens to the right. Another point is ($\frac{1}{4}$, 2):
$x = \frac{1}{16}(2)^2$
$x = \frac{1}{16}(4)$
$x = \frac{1}{4}$

8.

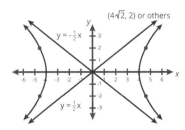

Vertices:

$$\frac{x^2}{16} = 1$$
$$x^2 = 16$$
$$\sqrt{x^2} = \pm\sqrt{16}$$
$$x = \pm 4$$

Vertices are (-4, 0), (4, 0).

Asymptotes:

$$y = \pm\frac{b}{a}x$$
$$a = \sqrt{16} = 4$$
$$b = \sqrt{4} = 2$$
$$y = \pm\frac{2}{4}x$$
$$y = \pm\frac{1}{2}x$$

Other points:

$y = 2$: $\frac{x^2}{16} - \frac{2^2}{4} = 1$

$$\frac{x^2}{16} - \frac{4}{4} = 1$$
$$\frac{x^2}{16} - 1 = 1$$
$$\frac{x^2}{16} = 2$$
$$x^2 = 32$$
$$\sqrt{x^2} = \pm\sqrt{32}$$
$$x = \pm 4\sqrt{2}$$

Points are $(4\sqrt{2}, 2)$, $(-4\sqrt{2}, 2)$.

9.

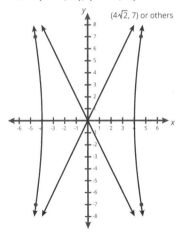

$$\frac{49x^2}{784} - \frac{16y^2}{784} = 1$$
$$\frac{x^2}{16} - \frac{y^2}{49} = 1$$

Vertices:

$$\frac{x^2}{16} = 1$$
$$x^2 = 16$$
$$\sqrt{x^2} = \pm\sqrt{16}$$
$$x = \pm 4$$

Vertices are (±4, 0).

Asymptotes:

$$y = \pm\frac{b}{a}x$$
$$a = \sqrt{16} = 4$$
$$b = \sqrt{49} = 7$$
$$y = \pm\frac{7}{4}x$$

Other points:

$y = 7$: $\frac{x^2}{16} - \frac{7^2}{49} = 1$

$$\frac{x^2}{16} - \frac{49}{49} = 1$$
$$\frac{x^2}{16} - 1 = 1$$
$$\frac{x^2}{16} = 2$$
$$x^2 = 32$$
$$\sqrt{x^2} = \pm\sqrt{32}$$
$$x = \pm 4\sqrt{2}$$

Points are $(-4\sqrt{2}, 7)$, $(4\sqrt{2}, 7)$.

10.

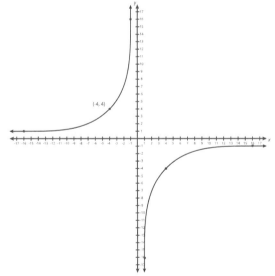

$$y = -\frac{16}{x}$$

x	-16	-4	-1	1	4	16
y	1	4	16	-16	-4	-1

11. $a > b$

$$c = \sqrt{a^2 + b^2}$$
$$= \sqrt{9 - 4}$$
$$= \sqrt{5}$$

Foci: $(\sqrt{5}, 0)$, $(-\sqrt{5}, 0)$

12. $y = \frac{1}{4(2)}x^2$

$p = 2$

Focus = $(0, p) = (0, 2)$

Directrix: $y = -p$; $y = -2$

13. $c = \sqrt{a^2 + b^2}$

$= \sqrt{16 + 4}$

$= \sqrt{20}$

$= 2\sqrt{5}$

Foci: $(-2\sqrt{5}, 0), (2\sqrt{5}, 0)$

Asymptotes:

$y = \pm\frac{b}{a}x$

$a = \sqrt{16} = 4$

$b = \sqrt{4} = 2$

$y = \pm\frac{2}{4}x$

$y = \pm\frac{1}{2}x$

14. $(x - 4)^2 + (y - 4)^2 = 5^2$

$(x - 4)^2 + (y - 4)^2 = 25$

15. $\frac{x^2}{4^2} + \frac{y^2}{1^2} = 1$

$\frac{x^2}{16} + \frac{y^2}{1} = 1$

16. $\frac{x^2}{4^2} - \frac{y^2}{1^2} = 1$

$\frac{x^2}{16} - \frac{y^2}{1} = 1$

17.

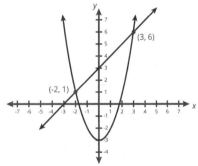

Parabola:

$x^2 - y = 3$

$-y = -x^2 + 3$

$y = x^2 - 3$

x	0	±1	±2
y	-3	-2	1

Line:

x	0	-3
y	3	0

$x - y = -3$

$x = y - 3$

$x^2 - y = 3$

$(y - 3)^2 - y = 3$

$y^2 - 6y + 9 - y = 3$

$y^2 - 7y + 9 = 3$

$y^2 - 7y + 6 = 0$

$(y - 1)(y - 6) = 0$

$y - 1 = 0 \qquad\qquad y - 6 = 0$

$y = 1 \qquad\qquad\quad y = 6$

If $y = 1$: $\quad x = 1 - 3$

$\qquad\qquad\; x = -2$

If $y = 6$: $\quad x = 6 - 3$

$\qquad\qquad\; x = 3$

Check of one solution, (-2, 1):

$(-2)^2 - 1 = 3 \qquad\qquad -2 - 1 = -3$

$\quad 4 - 1 = 3 \qquad\qquad\quad -3 = -3$

$\qquad 3 = 3$

The other solution, (3, 6), can be checked in a similar manner.

Solution set: {(-2, 1), (3, 6)}

18.

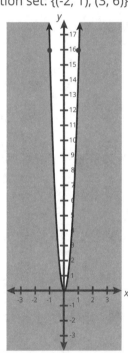

Graph $y = 16x^2$.

x	0	±1	±2
y	0	16	64

Parabola opens upward with vertex (0, 0). Use a solid path since the ≤ includes =. Check points inside or outside the graph.

Check (1, 0): $\quad 0 \overset{?}{\leq} 16(1)^2$

$\qquad\qquad\qquad 0 \leq 16$ is true; ∴ the outside of the parabola is shaded.

19.

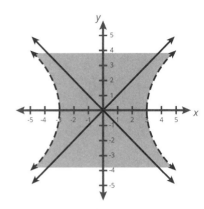

Graph $x^2 - y^2 = 9$.

$\frac{x^2}{9} - \frac{y^2}{9} = 0$

Hyperbola opens horizontally with vertices (±3, 0).

Asymptotes are $y = \pm\frac{3}{3}x$; $y = \pm x$.
Use a dotted path for <.
Check points inside or outside the graph.

Check (0, 0): $0^2 - 0^2 \overset{?}{<} 9$
                 $0 < 9$ is true; ∴ the
                 outside of the hyperbola
                 is shaded.

20. $V = kl$

21. $V = kl$
        $288 = k(12)$
        $\frac{288}{12} = k$
          $k = 24$

22. $V = 24l$
        $V = 24(30)$
        $V = 720$ cu. in.

23. Let height = h
            girth = $2h + 2w$

                $20 = 2h + 2w$
            $20 - 2h = 2w$
            $\frac{20 - 2h}{2} = w$

            $\frac{\overset{1}{\cancel{2}}(10 - h)}{\cancel{2}_1} = w$

            $10 - h = w$

            $hw = k = 24$
            $h(10 - h) = 24$
            $10h - h^2 = 24$
            $-h^2 + 10h - 24 = 0$
            $h^2 - 10h + 24 = 0$
            $(h - 6)(h - 4) = 0$
            $h - 6 = 0$ $h - 4 = 0$
              $h = 6$ $h = 4$
        Height = 6 in. or 4 in.

ALTERNATE LIFEPAC TEST

1.

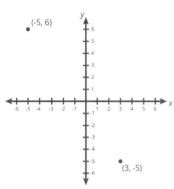

$d = \sqrt{(x_2 - x_1)^2 + (y_2 - y_1)^2}$
$ = \sqrt{[3 - (-5)]^2 + (-5 - 6)^2}$
$ = \sqrt{8^2 + (-11)^2} =$
$ = \sqrt{64 + 121}$
$ = \sqrt{185}$

2.

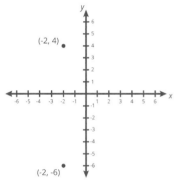

$d = 4 + |-6| = 4 + 6 = 10$

3. $x^2 + y^2 = 16$
        Center = (0, 0)
        $r = 4$

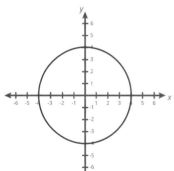

4. $(x - 2)^2 + (y - 3)^2 = 25$
Center = (2, 3)
$r = 5$

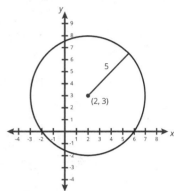

5. To find the y-intercepts, let $x = 0$.
$\frac{y^2}{9} = 1$
$y^2 = 9$
$\sqrt{y^2} = \sqrt{9}$
$y = \pm 3$
The y-intercepts are (0, -3), (0, 3).
To find the x-intercepts, let $y = 0$.
$\frac{x^2}{4} = 1$
$x^2 = 4$
$\sqrt{x^2} = \sqrt{4}$
$x = \pm 2$
The x-intercepts are (-2, 0), (2, 0).

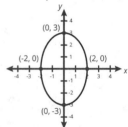

6. $x = \frac{1}{8}y^2$
$x = \frac{1}{4(2)}y^2$
$p = 2$
Focus is (p, 0) = (2, 0)
Directrix is $x = -p$, which is $x = -2$.
To graph the parabola more precisely, graph an extra point such as $(\frac{1}{2}, 2)$.

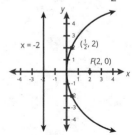

7. $y = \frac{1}{16}x^2$
$y = \frac{1}{4(4)}x^2$
$p = 4$
Focus is (0, p) = (0, 4)
Directrix is $y = -p$, which is $y = -4$.
To graph the parabola more precisely, graph an extra point such as $(2, \frac{1}{4})$.

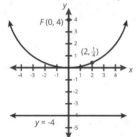

8. $\frac{x^2}{25} - \frac{y^2}{16} = 1$
To find the vertices, let $y = 0$.
$\frac{x^2}{25} = 1$
$x^2 = 25$
$\sqrt{x^2} = \sqrt{25}$
$x = \pm 5$
The vertices are (-5, 0), (5, 0).
The asymptotes are $y = \frac{b}{a}x$ and $y = -\frac{b}{a}x$.
$a = \sqrt{25} = 5$
$b = \sqrt{16} = 4$
The asymptotes are $y = \frac{4}{5}x$ and $y = -\frac{4}{5}x$.

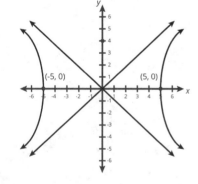

9. $16x^2 - 4y^2 = 64$

$\dfrac{16x^2}{64} - \dfrac{4y^2}{64} = \dfrac{64}{64}$

$\dfrac{x^2}{4} - \dfrac{y^2}{16} = 1$

To find the vertices, let $y = 0$.

$\dfrac{x^2}{4} = 1$

$x^2 = 4$

$\sqrt{x^2} = \sqrt{4}$

$x = \pm 2$

The vertices are (-2, 0), (2, 0).

The asymptotes are $y = \dfrac{b}{a}x$ and $y = -\dfrac{b}{a}x$.

$a = \sqrt{4} = 2$

$b = \sqrt{16} = 4$

The asymptotes are $y = \dfrac{4}{2}x$ and $y = -\dfrac{4}{2}x$ or $y = 2x$ and $y = -2x$.

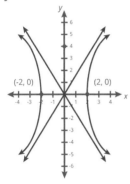

10. $xy = -9$

$y = -\dfrac{9}{x}$ (divide both sides by x)

x	1	-1	3	-3	9	-9
y	-9	9	-3	3	-1	1

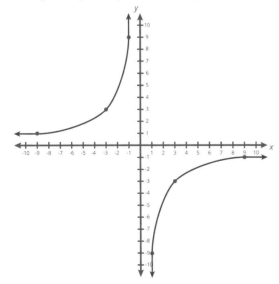

The asymptotes are the x- and y-axes.

11. Since $a^2 > b^2$ (16 > 9), the foci are on the x-axis.

foci = $(-\sqrt{a^2 - b^2}, 0)$ and $(\sqrt{a^2 - b^2}, 0)$

$a^2 = 16, b^2 = 9$

$-\sqrt{a^2 - b^2} = -\sqrt{16 - 9} = -\sqrt{7}$

$\sqrt{a^2 - b^2} = \sqrt{16 - 9} = \sqrt{7}$

Foci: $(-\sqrt{7}, 0), (\sqrt{7}, 0)$

12. $y = \dfrac{1}{24}x^2$

$y = \dfrac{1}{4(6)}x^2$

$p = 6$

Focus = $(0, p) = (0, 6)$

Directrix is $y = -p$, which is $y = -6$.

13. $\dfrac{x^2}{9} - \dfrac{y^2}{4} = 1$

foci = $(-\sqrt{a^2 + b^2}, 0)$ and $(\sqrt{a^2 + b^2}, 0)$

$a^2 = 9, b^2 = 4$

$-\sqrt{a^2 + b^2} = -\sqrt{9 + 4} = -\sqrt{13}$

$\sqrt{a^2 + b^2} = \sqrt{9 + 4} = \sqrt{13}$

Foci: $(-\sqrt{13}, 0), (\sqrt{13}, 0)$

The asymptotes are $y = \dfrac{b}{a}x$ and $y = -\dfrac{b}{a}x$.

$a = \sqrt{9} = 3$

$b = \sqrt{4} = 2$

The asymptotes are $y = \dfrac{2}{3}x$ and $y = -\dfrac{2}{3}x$.

Asymptotes: $y = \pm\dfrac{2}{3}x$

14. $(x - 4)^2 + (y - 5)^2 = 6^2$

$(x - 4)^2 + (y - 5)^2 = 36$

15. $a = 2; a^2 = 4$

$b = 8; b^2 = 64$

$\dfrac{x^2}{4} + \dfrac{y^2}{64} = 1$

16. $a = 6; a^2 = 36$

$b = 5; b^2 = 25$

$\dfrac{y^2}{36} - \dfrac{x^2}{25} = 1$

17. $xy = (-2)(2)$

$xy = -4$

18. $x \geq 8y^2$

x	0	8	8
y	0	1	-1

Try a point within the graph, such as (8, 0), to check the shading.

$x > 8y^2$

$8 > 8(0)^2$

$8 > 0$; true

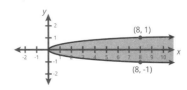

19. $y^2 - x^2 > 4$

$\frac{y^2}{4} - \frac{x^2}{4} > 1$ (divide both sides by 4)

Graph $\frac{y^2}{4} - \frac{x^2}{4} = 1$

To find the y-intercepts, let $x = 0$.

$\frac{y^2}{4} = 1$

$y^2 = 4$

$\sqrt{y^2} = \sqrt{4}$

$y = \pm 2$

The y-intercepts are (0, -2) and (0, 2).

The asymptotes are $y = \frac{a}{b}x$ and $y = -\frac{a}{b}x$.

$a = \sqrt{4} = 2$

$b = \sqrt{4} = 2$

$y = \frac{2}{2}x; y = x$

$y = -\frac{2}{2}x; y = -x$

The asymptotes are $y = \pm x$.

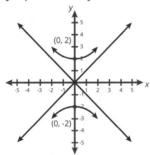

20. $y^2 - x = 3$

x	6	6	-3
y	3	-3	0

The graph is a parabola with vertex (-3, 0), opening to the right.

$2y - 2x = -6$

$y - x = -3$ (divide both sides by 2)

$-x = -3 - y$

$x = y + 3$

x	0	3	6
y	-3	0	3

The graph is a line. Substitute the expression for x ($y + 3$) into the first equation and solve for y.

$y^2 - x = 3$

$y^2 - (y + 3) = 3$

$y^2 - y - 3 = 3$

$y^2 - y - 6 = 0$

$(y + 2)(y - 3) = 0$

$y + 2 = 0$ or $y - 3 = 0$

$y = -2$ $y = 3$

When $y = -2$:

$x = y + 3$

$x = -2 + 3$

$x = 1$

(1, -2)

When $y = 3$:

$x = y + 3$

$x = 3 + 3$

$x = 6$

(6, 3)

The solution set is {(1, -2), (6, 3)}.

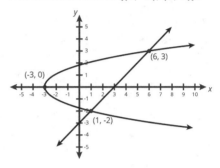

21. $I = \frac{k}{d^2}$

22.

I	I_1	$4I_1$
d	6	d_1

$I_1(6)^2 = 4I_1(d_1)^2$

$I_1(36) = 4I_1(d_1^2)$

$\frac{I_1(36)}{I_1(4)} = \frac{I_1(4)(d_1^2)}{I_1(4)}$ [divide both sides by $I_1(4)$]

$9 = d_1^2$

$\sqrt{9} = \sqrt{d_1^2}$

$3 \text{ ft.} = d_1$

MATH 1107

ALTERNATE LIFEPAC TEST

NAME _____

DATE _____

SCORE _____

Graph and find the distance between the points (each graph, 2 points; each distance, 2 points).

1.   (-5, 6) and (3, -5)

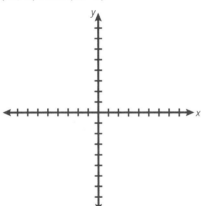

2.   (-2, 4) and (-2, -6)

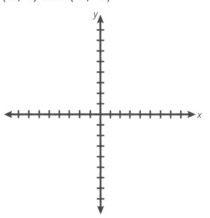

Graph. To graph parabolas and hyperbolas more precisely, graph the asymptotes or an extra point other than a vertex (each graph, 4 points).

3. $x^2 + y^2 = 16$

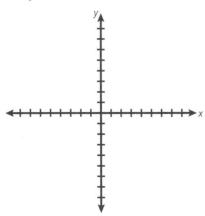

4. $(x - 2)^2 + (y - 3)^2 = 25$

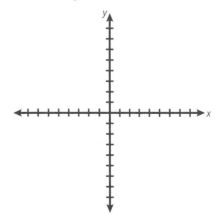

5. $\dfrac{x^2}{4} + \dfrac{y^2}{9} = 1$

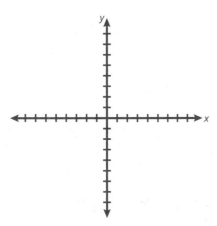

6. $x = \dfrac{1}{8}y^2$

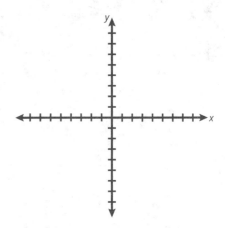

7. $y = \dfrac{1}{16}x^2$

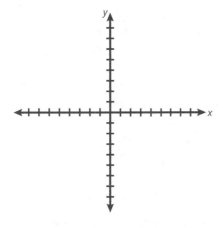

8. $\dfrac{x^2}{25} - \dfrac{y^2}{16} = 1$

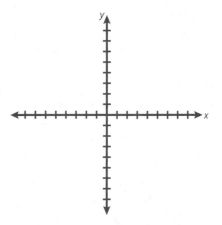

9. $16x^2 - 4y^2 = 64$

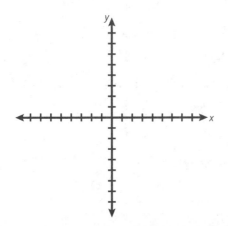

10. $xy = -9$

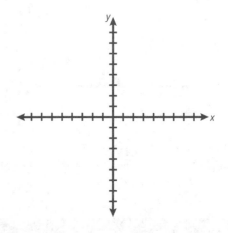

Complete the following items (each answer, 3 points).

11. Give the foci of $\frac{x^2}{16} + \frac{y^2}{9} = 1$.

12. Give the focus and directrix of $y = \frac{1}{24}x^2$.

13. Give the foci and asymptotes of $\frac{x^2}{9} - \frac{y^2}{4} = 1$.

Write the equation of each conic section (each answer, 4 points).

14. Circle with radius 6 and center (4, 5).

15. Ellipse with x-intercepts (2, 0) and (-2, 0) and y-intercepts (0, 8) and (0, -8).

16. Hyperbola with center at (0, 0), with y-intercepts (0, 6) and (0, -6), and with $b = 5$, opening vertically.

17. Hyperbola with x- and y-axes as asymptotes and vertices (-2, 2) and (2, -2).

Graph. To graph parabolas and hyperbolas more precisely, graph the asymptotes or an extra point other than the vertex (each graph, 4 points).

18. $x \geq 8y^2$

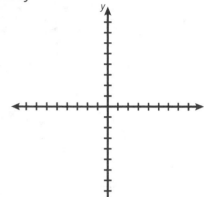

19. $y^2 - x^2 > 4$

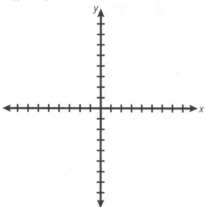

20. Solve the following system by graphing and algebraic methods (graph, 4 points; algebraic solution, 4 points).

$y^2 - x = 3$
$2y - 2x = -6$

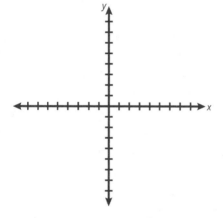

Complete the following items based on the given information (each answer, 3 points).

The amount of illumination (I) on Dick's book varies inversely as the square of the distance (d) from the light.

21. Using k for a constant of proportionality, express the relationship between I and d.

22. The light over Dick's desk is 6 feet away from the desk. How close must Dick hold his book to the light for it to receive four times as much illumination as it would on the desk?

MATH 1108

Unit 8: Exponential Functions

TEACHER NOTES

MATERIALS NEEDED FOR LIFEPAC	
Required	Suggested
(none)	• straightedges • graph paper

ADDITIONAL LEARNING ACTIVITIES

Section 1: Exponential Functions

1. Assist students in learning to use calculators to solve problems in the LIFEPAC. They can also use the calculators to investigate the theorems in the LIFEPAC.

2. Provide interested students with the task of graphing more complex, logarithmic, and exponential functions. Examples are $y = c^{-x}$ (let some $c = e$), $y = c^{ax+b}$ (let some $c = e$), and $y = e^{x^2}$.

3. Have students read and report on the history of mathematics as it is related to exponential functions, logarithms, and matrices, including the mathematicians and scientists involved.
Note: This activity may also be an independent activity.

4. Have the student search the Bible for examples of historical and prophetic treatment of topics related to this LIFEPAC. Examples are rapid rate of growth, large numbers, exponents, and powers.
Note: This activity may also be a group activity.

Section 2: Logarithmic Functions

1. Explain to the class more completely the basic mathematical justification for the linear interpolation procedure based upon similar triangles.

2. Explain to the class the relationship between the linear estimate and the actual logarithmic curve.

3. Help students learn the principles of the slide rule and how these principles depend on logarithms.

4. Have students consult textbooks, journals, or other sources for applications of exponential functions, logarithms, and matrices.
Note: This activity may also be an independent activity.

Section 3: Matrices

1. Provide students with problems in graphing inequalities associated with logarithmic and exponential equations.

2. Teach the class about estimation. You may wish to include numbers that result from approximation, measurement, rounding, significant digits, rules for computing with approximate data, and precision vs. accuracy.

3. Have the students find a matrix A such that $\begin{bmatrix} 1 & 2 \\ 3 & 4 \end{bmatrix} + A = \begin{bmatrix} 9 & 1 \\ 0 & 7 \end{bmatrix}$. Then have the students

find a matrix B such that $\begin{bmatrix} 1 & 2 \\ 3 & 4 \end{bmatrix}(B) = \begin{bmatrix} 9 & 1 \\ 0 & 7 \end{bmatrix}$. The solutions are given for the teacher's information.

Note: This activity may also be an independent activity.

Solution for matrix A:

Let $A = \begin{bmatrix} a & b \\ c & d \end{bmatrix}$.

Then: $1 + a = 9$; $a = 8$
$2 + b = 1$; $b = -1$
$3 + c = 0$; $c = -3$
$4 + d = 7$; $d = 3$

Matrix A is $\begin{bmatrix} 8 & -1 \\ -3 & 3 \end{bmatrix}$.

Solution for matrix B:

Let $B = \begin{bmatrix} a & c \\ b & d \end{bmatrix}$. So $\begin{bmatrix} 1 & 2 \\ 3 & 4 \end{bmatrix}\begin{bmatrix} a & c \\ b & d \end{bmatrix} = \begin{bmatrix} 9 & 1 \\ 0 & 7 \end{bmatrix}$.

$a_{11} = [\ 1\ \ 2\ ][\ a\ \ b\ ] = 1 \cdot a + 2 \cdot b = a + 2b$ $a_{11} = 9$, so $a + 2b = 9$

$a_{12} = [\ 1\ \ 2\ ][\ c\ \ d\ ] = 1 \cdot c + 2 \cdot d = c + 2d$ $a_{12} = 1$, so $c + 2d = 1$

$a_{21} = [\ 3\ \ 4\ ][\ a\ \ b\ ] = 3 \cdot a + 4 \cdot b = 3a + 4b$ $a_{21} = 0$, so $3a + 4b = 0$

$a_{22} = [\ 3\ \ 4\ ][\ c\ \ d\ ] = 3 \cdot c + 4 \cdot d = 3c + 4d$ $a_{22} = 7$, so $3c + 4d = 7$

Solve for a and b.

$a + 2b = 9 \longrightarrow -2a - 4b = -18$ (multiply by -2)
$3a + 4b = 0 \longrightarrow \underline{3a + 4b = \ \ \ 0}$
$ a = -18$

$a + 2b = 9$
$-18 + 2b = 9$
$2b = 27$
$b = \dfrac{27}{2}$

Solve for c and d.

$c + 2d = 1 \longrightarrow -2c - 4d = -2$ (multiply by -2)
$3c + 4d = 7 \longrightarrow \underline{3c + 4d = \ \ 7}$
$ c = 5$

$c + 2d = 1$
$5 + 2d = 1$
$2d = -4$
$d = -2$

Matrix B is $\begin{bmatrix} -18 & 5 \\ \frac{27}{2} & -2 \end{bmatrix}$.

4. The following three equations can be written in matrix form as shown such that $AX = B$. Have the student find matrix X. The solution is given for the teacher's information. *Note:* This activity may also be a group activity.

$$A = \begin{bmatrix} 0.06 & 0.07 & 0.08 \\ 0.06 & 0.07 & -0.08 \\ 1 & 1 & 1 \end{bmatrix}, \quad X = \begin{bmatrix} x_1 \\ x_2 \\ x_3 \end{bmatrix}, \quad B = \begin{bmatrix} 390 \\ 60 \\ 5{,}000 \end{bmatrix}$$

Solution:

$a_{11} = \begin{bmatrix} 0.06 & 0.07 & 0.08 \end{bmatrix}\begin{bmatrix} x_1 & x_2 & x_3 \end{bmatrix} = 390$

$a_{21} = \begin{bmatrix} 0.06 & 0.07 & -0.08 \end{bmatrix}\begin{bmatrix} x_1 & x_2 & x_3 \end{bmatrix} = 60$

$a_{31} = \begin{bmatrix} 1 & 1 & 1 \end{bmatrix}\begin{bmatrix} x_1 & x_2 & x_3 \end{bmatrix} = 5{,}000$

$a_{11} = (0.06)(x_1) + (0.07)(x_2) + (0.08)(x_3) = 390$

$a_{11} = 0.06x_1 + 0.07x_2 + 0.08x_3 = 390$

$a_{11} = 6x_1 + 7x_2 + 8x_3 = 39{,}000$ (multiply by 100)

$a_{21} = (0.06)(x_1) + (0.07)(x_2) + (-0.08)(x_3) = 60$

$a_{21} = 0.06x_1 + 0.07x_2 - 0.08x_3 = 60$

$a_{21} = 6x_1 + 7x_2 - 8x_3 = 6{,}000$ (multiply by 100)

$a_{31} = (1)(x_1) + (1)(x_2) + (1)(x_3) = 5{,}000$

$a_{31} = x_1 + x_2 + x_3 = 5{,}000$

Add a_{11} and a_{21}.

$$\begin{aligned} 6x_1 + 7x_2 + 8x_3 &= 39{,}000 \\ 6x_1 + 7x_2 - 8x_3 &= 6{,}000 \\ \hline 12x_1 + 14x_2 \quad\quad &= 45{,}000 \end{aligned}$$

Add a_{11} and a_{31}.

$$\begin{aligned} 6x_1 + 7x_2 + 8x_3 &= 39{,}000 \\ x_1 + x_2 + x_3 &= 5{,}000 \end{aligned} \quad\longrightarrow\quad \begin{aligned} 6x_1 + 7x_2 + 8x_3 &= 39{,}000 \\ -8x_1 - 8x_2 - 8x_3 &= -40{,}000 \quad \text{(multiply by -8)} \\ \hline -2x_1 - x_2 \quad\quad &= -1{,}000 \end{aligned}$$

Add these two sums and solve for x_1.

$$\begin{aligned} 12x_1 + 14x_2 &= 45{,}000 \\ -2x_1 + x_2 &= -1{,}000 \end{aligned} \quad\longrightarrow\quad \begin{aligned} 12x_1 + 14x_2 &= 45{,}000 \\ -28x_1 - 14x_2 &= -14{,}000 \quad \text{(multiply by 14)} \\ \hline -16x_1 \quad\quad &= 31{,}000 \end{aligned}$$

Add the same two previous sums and solve for x_2.

$$\begin{aligned} 12x_1 + 14x_2 &= 45{,}000 \\ -2x_1 - x_2 &= -1{,}000 \end{aligned} \quad\longrightarrow\quad \begin{aligned} 12x_1 + 14x_2 &= 45{,}000 \\ -12x_1 - 6x_2 &= -6{,}000 \quad \text{(multiply by 6)} \\ \hline 8x_2 &= 39{,}000 \end{aligned}$$

$$x_2 = \frac{39{,}000}{8} = 4{,}875$$

Substitute these values of x_1 and x_2 into the equation for a_{11} and solve for x_3.

$$6x_1 + 7x_2 + 8x_3 = 39{,}000$$
$$(6)(\text{-}1{,}937.5) + (7)(4{,}875) + 8x_3 = 39{,}000$$
$$\text{-}11{,}625 + 34{,}125 + 8x_3 = 39{,}000$$
$$22{,}500 + 8x_3 = 39{,}000$$
$$8x_3 = 39{,}000 - 22{,}500$$
$$8x_3 = 16{,}500$$
$$x_3 = \frac{16{,}500}{8} = 2{,}062.5$$

Therefore, matrix X is $\begin{bmatrix} \text{-}1.937.5 \\ 4{,}875 \\ 2{,}062.5 \end{bmatrix}$

These values of x_1, x_2, and x_3 may be checked by multiplying matrix A by matrix X.

ANSWER KEY

SECTION 1

1.1 $1 + 1 = 2$

1.2 $7^0 = 1$

1.3 $6 \cdot 1 = 6$

1.4 $\dfrac{1}{3^2} = \dfrac{1}{9}$

1.5 $\dfrac{1}{\frac{1}{3^2}} = 3^2 = 9$

1.6 $5^{-2} = \dfrac{1}{5^2} = \dfrac{1}{25}$

1.7 $\dfrac{1}{2^3} + \dfrac{1}{4^2} = \dfrac{1}{8} + \dfrac{1}{16} = \dfrac{2}{16} + \dfrac{1}{16} = \dfrac{3}{16}$

1.8 $4^2 \cdot \dfrac{1}{2^3} = 16 \cdot \dfrac{1}{8} = 2$

1.9 $6^{-2} = \dfrac{1}{6^2} = \dfrac{1}{36}$

1.10 $\dfrac{1}{\frac{1}{2}} = 2$

1.11 $m \cdot \dfrac{1}{n} = \dfrac{m}{n}$

1.12 $\dfrac{1}{(m \cdot n)^1} = \dfrac{1}{mn}$

1.13 $2 \cdot \dfrac{1}{x^3} = \dfrac{2}{x^3}$

1.14 $\dfrac{1}{(2x)^3} = \dfrac{1}{8x^3}$

1.15 $b^{-2-(-3)} = b^{-2+3} = b^1 = b$

1.16 $a^{8-6} = a^2$

1.17 $b^{5+8} = b^{13}$

1.18 $b^{4 \cdot 2} = b^8$

1.19 $\dfrac{2ae^3}{3db}$

1.20 $\dfrac{(3x)^2}{(2x)^2} = \dfrac{9x^2}{3x^2} = \dfrac{9}{4}$

1.21 $\dfrac{2 \cdot \frac{1}{x^2}}{3 \cdot \frac{1}{x^2}} = \dfrac{\frac{2}{x^2}}{\frac{3}{x^2}} = \dfrac{2}{3}$

1.22

x	1	2	3	0	-1	-2	-3	-4	-5
y	2	4	8	1	$\frac{1}{2}$	$\frac{1}{4}$	$\frac{1}{8}$	$\frac{1}{16}$	$\frac{1}{32}$

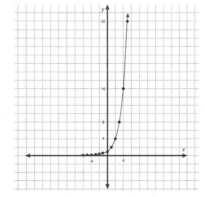

1.23 $\sqrt[4]{16} = 2$

1.24 $\sqrt{-36}$; no real-number answer

1.25 1

1.26 $\sqrt[3]{8^2} = (\sqrt[3]{8})^2 = (2)^2 = 4$

1.27 $\sqrt{(-36)^5} = (\sqrt{-36})^5$; no real-number answer

1.28 $\dfrac{1}{(-25)^{\frac{1}{2}}} = \dfrac{1}{\sqrt{-25}}$; no real-number answer

1.29 $\dfrac{1}{(-27)^{4/3}} = \dfrac{1}{(\sqrt[3]{-27})^4} = \dfrac{1}{(-3)^4} = \dfrac{1}{81}$

1.30 $\dfrac{1}{\frac{4}{9}} = \dfrac{9}{4}$

1.31 $\dfrac{1}{\left(\frac{27}{8}\right)^{2/3}} = \dfrac{1}{\left(\sqrt[3]{\frac{27}{8}}\right)^2} = \dfrac{1}{\left(\frac{3}{2}\right)^2} = \dfrac{1}{\frac{9}{4}} = \dfrac{4}{9}$

1.32 $x^{2/3}$

1.33 $(mn)^{\frac{1}{2}}$

1.34 $(a + b)^{\frac{1}{2}}$

1.35 $\dfrac{1}{\sqrt{2}} \cdot \sqrt{y} = \dfrac{\sqrt{y}}{\sqrt{2}} = \sqrt{\dfrac{y \cdot 2}{2 \cdot 2}} = \dfrac{\sqrt{2y}}{2}$

1.36 $2 \cdot \dfrac{1}{\sqrt{a}} = 2 \cdot \dfrac{1 \cdot \sqrt{a}}{\sqrt{a} \cdot \sqrt{a}} = \dfrac{2\sqrt{a}}{a}$

1.37 $\sqrt[3]{x}\dfrac{1}{\sqrt[3]{y^2}} = \dfrac{\sqrt[3]{x}}{\sqrt[3]{y^2}} = \sqrt[3]{\dfrac{x \cdot y}{y^2 \cdot y}} = \dfrac{\sqrt[3]{xy}}{y}$

1.38 $x^{2/4} = x^{\frac{1}{2}} = \sqrt{x}$

1.39 $(2^2)^{\frac{1}{6}} = 2^{\frac{1}{3}} = \sqrt[3]{2}$

1.40 $(x^2 y^6)^{\frac{1}{8}} = x^{\frac{1}{4}} y^{\frac{3}{4}} = \sqrt[4]{xy^3}$

1.41 $a^{\frac{2m}{m}} = a^2$

1.42 $2^{\frac{1}{2}} \cdot 3^{\frac{1}{3}} = 2^{\frac{3}{6}} \cdot 3^{\frac{2}{6}} = \sqrt[6]{2^3} \cdot \sqrt[6]{3^2} = \sqrt[6]{8 \cdot 9} = \sqrt[6]{72}$

1.43 $3^{\frac{1}{2}} \cdot 2^{\frac{1}{3}} = 3^{\frac{3}{6}} \cdot 2^{\frac{2}{6}} = \sqrt[6]{3^3 \cdot 2^2} = \sqrt[6]{27 \cdot 4} = \sqrt[6]{108}$

1.44 $\dfrac{\sqrt[3]{2}}{\sqrt{2}} = \dfrac{\sqrt[3]{2} \cdot \sqrt{2}}{\sqrt{2} \cdot \sqrt{2}} = \dfrac{\sqrt[3]{2}\sqrt{2}}{2}$

1.45 $4^{\frac{1}{2}} = \sqrt{4} = 2$

1.46 $16^{3/4} = (\sqrt[4]{16})^3 = 2^3 = 8$

1.47 $2^x = 32$
$2^x = 2^5$
$x = 5$

1.48 $2^x = 256$
$2^x = 2^8$
$x = 8$

1.49 $3^x = 81$
$3^x = 3^4$
$x = 4$

1.50 $2^x = \frac{1}{2}$
$2^x = 2^{-1}$
$x = -1$

1.51 $8^x = \frac{1}{2}$
$8^x = 8^{-1}$
$x = -1$

1.52 $3^x = \frac{1}{27}$
$3^x = \frac{1}{3^3} = 3^{-3}$
$x = -3$

1.53 $9^{x-2} = 81$
$9^{x-2} = 9^2$
$x - 2 = 2$
$x = 4$

1.54 $9^x = 27$
$(3^2)^x = 3^3$
$3^{2x} = 3^3$
$2x = 3$
$x = \frac{3}{2}$

1.55 $81^x = 27$
$(3^4)^x = 3^3$
$3^{4x} = 3^3$
$4x = 3$
$x = \frac{3}{4}$

1.56 $2^{-x} = 16$
$2^{-x} = 2^4$
$-x = 4$
$x = -4$

1.57 $27^x = 9$
$(3^3)^x = 3^2$
$3^{3x} = 3^2$
$3x = 2$
$x = \frac{2}{3}$

1.58 $4^x = 0.5$
$(2^2)^x = \frac{1}{2} = 2^{-1}$
$2^{2x} = 2^{-1}$
$2x = -1$
$x = -\frac{1}{2}$

1.59 $16^x = 0.5$
$(2^4)^x = \frac{1}{2} = 2^{-1}$
$2^{4x} = 2^{-1}$
$4x = -1$
$x = -\frac{1}{4}$

1.60

x	-3	-2	-1	0	1	2	3
y	$\frac{1}{27}$	$\frac{1}{9}$	$\frac{1}{3}$	1	3	9	27

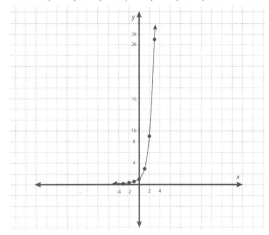

1.61

x	-3	-2	-1	0	1	2	3
y	$\frac{1}{1,000}$	$\frac{1}{100}$	$\frac{1}{10}$	1	10	100	1,000

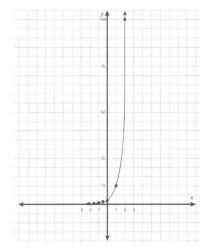

1.62

x	-3	-2	-1	0	1	2	3
y	8	4	2	1	$\frac{1}{2}$	$\frac{1}{4}$	$\frac{1}{8}$

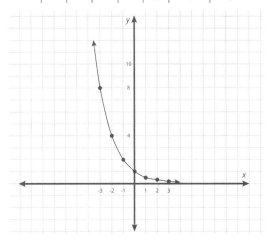

1.63

x	-3	-2	-1	0	1	2	3
y	27	9	3	1	$\frac{1}{3}$	$\frac{1}{9}$	$\frac{1}{27}$

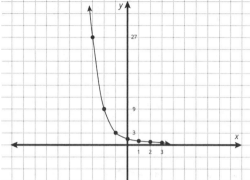

1.64

x	-3	-2	-1	0	1	2	3
y	$\frac{1}{9}$	$\frac{1}{3}$	1	3	9	27	81

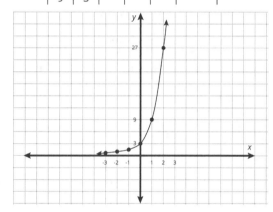

1.65

x	-1	0	1	2
y	$\frac{1}{4}$	1	4	16

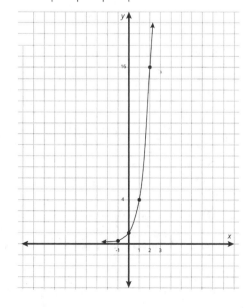

1.66 $y = 1$

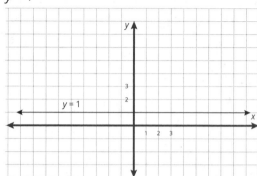

1.67

x	-3	-2	-1	0	1	2	3
y	$-\frac{1}{8}$	$-\frac{1}{4}$	$-\frac{1}{2}$	-1	-2	-4	-8

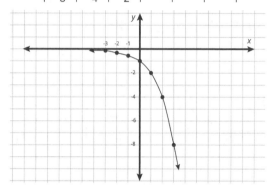

1.68

x	-3	-2	-1	0	1	2	3
y	$\frac{1}{512}$	$\frac{1}{16}$	$\frac{1}{2}$	1	$\frac{1}{2}$	$\frac{1}{16}$	$\frac{1}{512}$

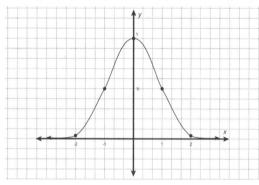

1.69 Let x = length = width = height.
$$x^3 = 27$$
$$\sqrt[3]{x^3} = \sqrt[3]{27}$$
$$x = 3 \text{ ft.}$$
length = width = height = 3 ft.

1.70 1 cu. yd. = $(3)^3$ cu. ft. = 27 cu. ft.

1.71
$$1{,}024 = 16(2)^{n-1}$$
$$2^{10} = 2^4(2)^{n-1}$$
$$2^6 = 2^{n-1} \text{ (divide by } 2^4)$$
$$6 = n - 1$$
$$7 = n$$

1.72 $y = 2^3 = 8$ subsets
Example: $\{a, b, c\}$
Subsets: $\{a\}$, $\{b\}$, $\{c\}$,
$\{a, b\}$, $\{a, c\}$, $\{b, c\}$,
$\{a, b, c\}$, $\{\ \}$

1.73 $1{,}024 = 2^n$
$2^{10} = 2^n$
$n = 10$ elements

1.74   Let y = number of subsets.
Let x = number of elements in original set
$y = 2^x$.

x	0	1	2	3	4
y	1	2	4	8	16

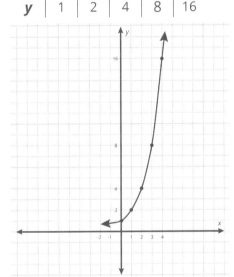

1.75 $n = 4$
$y = 10^4 = 10{,}000$ tags with four numeral
spaces

1.76 $1{,}000{,}000 = 10^n$
$10^6 = 10^n$
$6 = n$
They should use six numeral spaces.

1.77 $y = 3^n$

1.78 $243 = 3^n$
$3^5 = 3^n$
$5 = n$
They need five letter spaces.

1.79 $y = 4^n$
y = number of tags
n = number of spaces (letter spaces plus
blank spaces)

SELF TEST 1

1.01 $3 \cdot 1 = 3$

1.02 $\frac{1}{3} + \frac{1}{2} = \frac{5}{6}$

1.03 $\frac{1}{\frac{1}{3^2}} = 3^2 = 9$

1.04 $\frac{1}{\left(\frac{1}{2}\right)^2} = \frac{1}{\frac{1}{4}} = 4$

1.05 $\frac{1}{(ab)^2}$ or $\frac{1}{a^2b^2}$

1.06 $\frac{x^4}{x^3} = x^{4-3} = x^1 = x$

1.07 $\sqrt{16} = 4$

1.08 $(\sqrt[4]{81})^3 = 3^3 = 27$

1.09 $(\sqrt[5]{-32})^3 = (-2)^3 = -8$

1.010 $\sqrt{-25}$; no real-number solution

1.011 $\frac{1}{(\sqrt[3]{27})^2} = \frac{1}{3^2} = \frac{1}{9}$

1.012 a. 3
b. 9
c. 27
d. 1
e. $\frac{1}{3}$
f. $\frac{1}{9}$
g. $\frac{1}{27}$

1.013 $x^{\frac{3}{4}}$

1.014 $(x^2y^3)^{\frac{1}{6}} = x^{\frac{2}{6}}y^{\frac{3}{6}} = x^{\frac{1}{3}}y^{\frac{1}{2}}$

1.015 $\frac{1}{\sqrt{3}} \cdot \sqrt{x} = \frac{\sqrt{x}}{\sqrt{3}} = \frac{\sqrt{x \cdot 3}}{\sqrt{3 \cdot 3}} = \frac{\sqrt{3x}}{3}$

1.016 $y^{\frac{3}{6}} = y^{\frac{1}{2}} = \sqrt{y}$

1.017 $\sqrt[4]{2^2} = 2^{\frac{2}{4}} = 2^{\frac{1}{2}} = \sqrt{2}$

1.018 $x^{\frac{2}{6}}y^{\frac{6}{6}} = x^{\frac{1}{3}}y = y\sqrt[3]{x}$

1.019 $x^{\frac{3n}{n}} = x^3$

1.020 $\frac{3}{\sqrt{3}} = \frac{3 \cdot \sqrt{3}}{\sqrt{3} \cdot \sqrt{3}} = \frac{3\sqrt{3}}{3} = \sqrt{3}$

1.021 $9^{\frac{1}{2}} = \sqrt{9} = 3$

1.022 $2^x = 2^6$
$x = 6$

1.023 $2^x = 2^{-5}$
$x = -5$

1.024 $(3^2)^x = 3^3$
$3^{2x} = 3^3$
$2x = 3$
$x = \frac{3}{2}$

1.025 $3^{-x} = 3^{-3}$
$-x = -3$
$x = 3$

1.026

x	-3	-2	-1	0	1	2	3
y	$\frac{1}{8}$	$\frac{1}{4}$	$\frac{1}{2}$	1	2	4	8

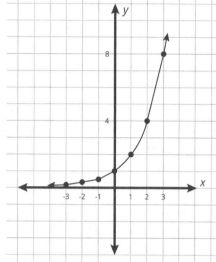

1.027

x	-1	0	1
y	$\frac{1}{9}$	1	9

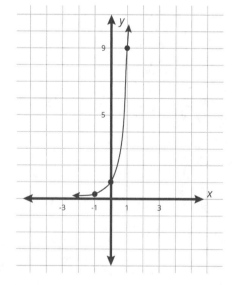

1.028

x	-3	-2	-1	0	1	2	3
y	8	4	2	1	$\frac{1}{2}$	$\frac{1}{4}$	$\frac{1}{8}$

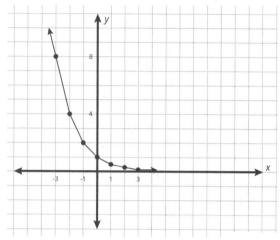

1.029 $100{,}000 = 10^n$
$10^5 = 10^n$
$5 = n$
They need five numeral spaces.

SECTION 2

2.1 $3 = \log_2 8$

2.2 $3 = \log_6 216$

2.3 $0.5 = \log_4 2$

2.4 $-\frac{1}{3} = \log_{125} 5$

2.5 $x = \log_b N$

2.6 $\log_{10} y = x$

2.7 $\log_b y = x$

2.8 $2^4 = 16$

2.9 $3^3 = 27$

2.10 $8^2 = 64$

2.11 $10^{-3} = 0.001$

2.12 $b^x = N$

2.13 $b^x = y$

2.14 $10^x = y$

2.15 Let $x = \log_{10} 1,000$.
   $10^x = 1,000$
   $10^x = 10^3$
   $x = 3$
   $\log_{10} 1,000 = 3$

2.16 Let $x = \log_5 125$.
   $5^x = 125$
   $5^x = 5^3$
   $x = 3$
   $\log_5 125 = 3$

2.17 Let $x = \log_2 32$.
   $2^x = 32$
   $2^x = 2^5$
   $x = 5$
   $\log_2 32 = 5$

2.18 Let $x = \log_{25} 5$.
   $25^x = 5$
   $25^x = 25^{\frac{1}{2}}$
   $x = \frac{1}{2}$
   $\log_{25} 5 = \frac{1}{2}$

2.19 Let $x = \log_{10} 0.1$.
   $10x = 0.1$
   $10x = 10^{-1}$
   $x = -1$
   $\log_{10} 0.1 = -1$

2.20 Let $x = \log_{10} 0.01$.
   $10^x = 0.01$
   $10^x = 10^{-2}$
   $x = -2$
   $\log_{10} 0.01 = -2$

2.21 Let $x = \log_{10} 1$.
   $10^x = 1$
   $10^x = 10^0$
   $x = 0$
   $\log_{10} 1 = 0$

2.22 a. 1
   b. $10^1 = 10$

2.23 a. 0
   b. $10^0 = 1$

2.24 a. -2
   b. $10^{-2} = \frac{1}{10^2} = \frac{1}{100} = 0.01$

2.25 a. -3
   b. $10^{-3} = \frac{1}{10^3} = \frac{1}{1,000} = 0.001$

2.26 a. $\frac{1}{4}$
   b. $10^{\frac{1}{4}} = \sqrt[4]{10}$

2.27 .4082

2.28 .9996

2.29 .0000

2.30 a. 3.50
   b. 3.50

2.31 a. 9.93
   b. 9.93

2.32 .8274

2.33 .6170

2.34 .9991

2.35 4.85

2.36 4.09

2.37 9.86

2.38 $10^x = 4.85$
   $\log_{10} 4.85 = x$
   $x = .6857$

2.39 $10^x = 5.96$
   $\log_{10} 5.96 = x$
   $x = .7752$

2.40 $\log x = .4624$
   $x = 2.90$

2.41 $\log x = .7316$
   $x = 5.39$

2.42 $x = \text{antilog } .9987$
   $x = 9.97$

2.43 $x = 10^{.9294}$
   $\log x = .9294$
   $x = 8.50$

2.44 $x = \log 10^{.3464}$
   $\log x = .3464$
   $x = 2.22$

2.45 0

2.46 1

2.47 0

2.48 1

2.49 $\log_{10} 1,000 =$
   $\log_{10} 10^3 = 3$

2.50 2

2.51 $\log_{10} M - \log_{10} N$

2.52 $\log M + \log N$

2.53 $k \log_{10} M$

2.54 $k \log_{10} 10 = k(1) = k$

2.55 $\log (5)(2) = \log 10$

2.56 $\log 10 - \log y$

2.57 $3 \log N$

2.58 2.54×10^1

2.59 4.723×10^2

2.60 8.49×10^2

2.61 6.5×10^1

2.62 1.789×10^3

2.63 2.1×10^{-1}

2.64 4.8×10^{-1}

2.65 4.1×10^{-2}

2.66 8.72×10^{-2}

2.67 $\log 42.7 = \log 4.27 \times 10^1$
$= \log 4.27 + \log 10^1$
$= .6304 + 1$

2.68 $\log 5{,}340 = \log 5.34 \times 10^3$
$= \log 5.34 + \log 10^3$
$= .7275 + 3$

2.69 $\log 432 = \log 4.32 \times 10^2$
$= \log 4.32 + \log 10^2$
$= .6355 + 2$

2.70 $\log 0.00623 = \log 6.23 \times 10^{-3}$
$= \log 6.23 + \log 10^{-3}$
$= .7945 + (-3)$

2.71 $\log 0.000752 = \log 7.52 \times 10^{-4}$
$= \log 7.52 + \log 10^{-4}$
$= .8762 + (-4)$

2.72 $.9926$

2.73 $\log 0.843 = \log 8.43 \times 10^{-1}$
$= \log 8.43 + \log 10^{-1}$
$= .9258 + (-1)$

2.74 $\log 0.001 = \log 1.00 \times 10^{-3}$
$= \log 1.00 + \log 10^{-3}$
$= .0000 + (-3)$
$= -3$

2.75 $\log 0.01 = \log 1.00 \times 10^{-2}$
$= \log 1.00 + \log 10^{-2}$
$= .0000 + (-2)$
$= -2$

2.76 $\log 0.1 = \log 1.00 \times 10^{-1}$
$= \log 1.00 + \log 10^{-1}$
$= .0000 + (-1)$
$= -1$

2.77 $\log 100 = \log 1.00 \times 10^2$
$= \log 1.00 + \log 10^2$
$= .0000 + 2$
$= 2$

2.78 1

2.79 $9.59 \times 10^1 = 95.9$

2.80 $1.85 \times 10^3 = 1{,}850$

2.81 $3.58 \times 10^{-1} = 0.358$

2.82 $5.46 \times 10^{-4} = 0.000546$

2.83 $8.98 \times 10^{-2} = 0.0898$

2.84 $1 \times 10^{-3} = 0.001$

2.85 $10^5 = 100{,}000$

2.86 1

2.87 $10^{-2} = 0.01$

2.88 $10^3 = 1{,}000$

2.89

x	$\frac{1}{10}$	1	10	100
y	-1	0	1	2

2.90

x	$\frac{1}{2}$	1	2	4	8
y	-1	0	1	2	3

2.91 $y = 2^x$

x	-1	0	1	2	3
y	$\frac{1}{2}$	1	2	4	8

$y = \log_2 x$

x	$\frac{1}{2}$	1	2	4	8
y	-1	0	1	2	3

2.92 Let $N = (36.5)(24.9)$
$\log N = \log 36.5 + \log 24.9$

$\log 36.5 = .5623 + 1$
$\underline{\log 24.9 = .3962 + 1}$
$\log N \quad = .9585 + 2$

$N = $ antilog $(.9585 + 2)$
$N = 908.9$ (estimate) or other answers from 908 to 909

2.93 Let $N = 846 \div 629$.
$\log N = \log 846 - \log 629$

$\log 846 = .9274 + 2$
$\underline{\log 629 = .7987 + 2}$
$\log N \quad = .1287 + 0$

$N = 1.345$ (estimate) or other answers from 1.34 to 1.35

2.94 Let $N = \sqrt[4]{6}$.
$\log N = \log \sqrt[4]{6}$
$\quad = \log 6^{\frac{1}{4}}$
$\quad = \frac{1}{4} \log 6$
$\quad = \frac{1}{4}(.7782)$
$\quad = .19455$

$N = 1.566$ (estimate) or other answers from 1.56 to 1.57

2.95 $2^x = 29$
$\log 2^x = \log 29$
$x(\log 2) = \log 29$
$x = \frac{\log 29}{\log 2} = \frac{1.4624}{.3010} = 4.8585$

2.96 $x = \log_e 2$
$e^x = 2$
$\log e^x = \log 2$
$x(\log e) = \log 2$
$x = \frac{\log 2}{\log e} = \frac{\log 2}{\log 2.72} = \frac{.3010}{.4346} = .6926$

2.97 $x = e^4$
$\log x = \log e^4$
$\log x = 4 \log e = 4 \log 2.72$
$\quad = 4(.4346) = 1.7384$

$x = $ antilog $1.7384 = 54.75$ (estimate) or answers from 54.7 to 54.8

2.98 $2 = 1(1 + 0.05)^n$
$\log 2 = \log (1.05)^n$
$\log 2 = n \log 1.05$
$n = \frac{\log 2}{\log 1.05} = \frac{.3010}{.0212} = 14.20$ years

2.99 $2 = 1(1 + i)^5$
$\log 2 = \log (1 + i)^5$
$\log 2 = 5 \log (1 + i)$
$\log (1 + i) = \frac{\log 2}{5} = \frac{.3010}{5} = .0602$
$1 + i = $ antilog $.0602 = 1.149$
$1 + i = 1.149$
$i = 1.149 - 1$
$i = .149$
$i = 14.9\%$

2.100 $3{,}000 = P(1 + 0.04)^3$
$P = \frac{3{,}000}{(1 + 0.04)^3} = \frac{3{,}000}{(1.04)^3}$
$\quad = \frac{3{,}000}{1.125} \doteq \$2{,}667.00$ rounded to 4 significant digits if four place logs are used to calculate $(1.00)^3$. More accurately, \$2,666.67

2.101 $A = 2{,}000(1 + 0.06)^{19}$
$\quad = 2{,}000(1.06)^{19}$
$\log A = \log 2{,}000 (1.06)^{19}$
$\quad = \log 2{,}000 + \log (1.06)^{19}$
$\quad = \log 2{,}000 + 19 \log 1.06$
$\quad = 3.3010 + 19(.0253)$
$\quad = 3.3010 + .4807$
$\quad = 3.7817$

$A = $ antilog 3.7817
$\quad = \$6{,}049$ rounded to 4 significant digits

2.102 $P = 2{,}000 (1.06)^{19}(1 + 0.08)^{-19}$
$\quad = 2{,}000 (1.06)^{19}(1.08)^{-19}$
$\log P = \log 2{,}000 + 19 \log 1.06 + (-19) \log 1.08$
$\quad = 3.3010 + 19(.0253) - 19(.0334)$
$\quad = 3.1472$

$P = $ antilog $3.1472 \doteq \$1{,}403$
They had less money in real value at the end of the 19 years than they had at the beginning.

2.103 $P = 2{,}000 (1 + 0.08)^{-19}$
$\quad = 2{,}000 (1.08)^{-19}$
$\log P = \log 2{,}000 + \log (1.08)^{-19}$
$\quad = \log 2{,}000 - 19 \log 1.08$
$\quad = 3.3010 - 19(.0334)$
$\quad = 3.3010 - .6346$
$\quad = 2.666$

$P = $ antilog $2.666 = \$463.90$
The better course is to put the money in savings. Better by \$1,403 − 463.90 = \$939.10 in real value.

SELF TEST 2

2.01 $\log_4 16 = 2$
2.02 $\log_a N = b$
2.03 $10^2 = 100$
2.04 $b^x = N$
2.05 1
2.06 0
2.07 $\log_{10} \sqrt{10} = x$
  $10^x = \sqrt{10} = 10^{1/2}$
  $x = \dfrac{1}{2}$
2.08 $\log_5 25 = x$
  $5^x = 25$
  $5^x = 5^2$
  $x = 2$
2.09 .7110
2.010 $\log 26.1 = \log 2.61 \times 10^1$
  $= \log 2.61 + \log 10^1$
  $= .4166 + 1$ or 1.4166
2.011 $\log 0.042 = \log 4.20 \times 10^{-2}$
  $= \log 4.20 + \log 10^{-2}$
  $= .6232 + (-2)$
2.012 2.00
2.013 $4.85 \times 10^2 = 485$
2.014 $4.09 \times 10^{-3} = 0.00409$
2.015 $4.09 \times 10^{-1} = 0.409$
2.016 $10^x = 3$
  $x = \log_{10} 3 = .4771$
2.017 $10^x = \dfrac{1}{100}$
  $10^x = 10^{-2}$
  $x = -2$
2.018 $\log x = 1.4771$
  $x = 3 \times 10^1 = 30$
2.019 $x = 10^{.6020}$
  $\log x = .6020$
  $x = 4$
2.020 2.63×10^1
2.021 4.2×10^{-2}

2.022

x	$\frac{1}{2}$	1	2	4	8
y	-1	0	1	2	3

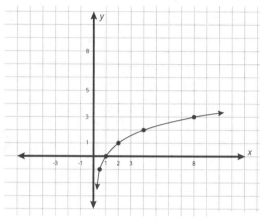

2.023 $\dfrac{1}{(x \cdot y)^3}$ or $\dfrac{1}{x^3 y^3}$
2.024 $\dfrac{a^2}{a^4} = \dfrac{1}{a^2}$
2.025 $(\sqrt[6]{64})^3 = 2^3 = 8$
2.026 $x^{2/6} = x^{1/3}$
2.027 $\dfrac{5}{\sqrt{5}} = \dfrac{5 \cdot \sqrt{5}}{\sqrt{5} \cdot \sqrt{5}} = \dfrac{5 \cdot \sqrt{5}}{5} = \sqrt{5}$

2.028

x	-1	0	1	2	3
y	$\frac{1}{2}$	1	2	4	8

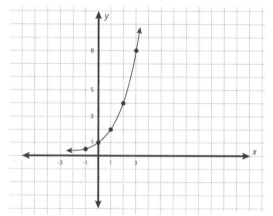

2.029 $4^x = 128$
  $(2^2)^x = 2^7$
  $2^{2x} = 2^7$
  $2x = 7$
  $x = \dfrac{7}{2}$

SECTION 3

3.1   1
3.2   4
3.3   1
3.4   7
3.5   2
3.6   6
3.7   8
3.8   5
3.9   7
3.10   3

3.11

$$\begin{bmatrix} 1 & 2 & 4 \\ 3 & -1 & 6 \end{bmatrix}$$

$$\begin{bmatrix} 1 & 2 & 4 \\ 0 & -7 & -6 \end{bmatrix} \quad \text{-3(row 1) + row 2}$$

$$\begin{bmatrix} 1 & 2 & 4 \\ 0 & 1 & \frac{6}{7} \end{bmatrix} \quad -\frac{1}{7}(\text{row 2})$$

$$\begin{bmatrix} 1 & 0 & \frac{16}{7} \\ 0 & 1 & \frac{6}{7} \end{bmatrix} \quad \text{-2(row 2) + row 1}$$

$x = \frac{16}{7}$
$y = \frac{6}{7}$

Check: $\frac{16}{7} + 2(\frac{6}{7}) = \frac{16 + 12}{7} = \frac{28}{7} = 4$

        $3(\frac{16}{7}) - \frac{6}{7} = \frac{48 - 6}{7} = \frac{42}{7} = 6$

3.12

$$\begin{bmatrix} 1 & 5 & 11 \\ 1 & -1 & 5 \end{bmatrix}$$

$$\begin{bmatrix} 1 & 5 & 11 \\ 0 & -6 & -6 \end{bmatrix} \quad \text{row 2 – row 1}$$

$$\begin{bmatrix} 1 & 5 & 11 \\ 0 & 1 & 1 \end{bmatrix} \quad -\frac{1}{6}(\text{row 2})$$

$$\begin{bmatrix} 1 & 0 & 6 \\ 0 & 1 & 1 \end{bmatrix} \quad \text{-5(row 2) + row 1}$$

$x = 6$
$y = 1$

Check: $6 + 5(1) = 11$
        $6 - 1 = 5$

3.13

$$\begin{bmatrix} 6 & -5 & -25 \\ 8 & 2 & 10 \end{bmatrix}$$

$$\begin{bmatrix} 1 & -\frac{5}{6} & -\frac{25}{6} \\ 8 & 2 & 10 \end{bmatrix} \quad \frac{1}{6}(\text{row 1})$$

$$\begin{bmatrix} 1 & -\frac{5}{6} & -\frac{25}{6} \\ 0 & \frac{52}{6} & \frac{260}{6} \end{bmatrix} \quad \text{row 2 + -8(row 1)}$$

$$\begin{bmatrix} 1 & -\frac{5}{6} & -\frac{25}{6} \\ 0 & 1 & \frac{260}{52} \end{bmatrix} \quad \frac{6}{52}(\text{row 2})$$

$$\begin{bmatrix} 1 & 0 & 0 \\ 0 & 1 & 5 \end{bmatrix} \quad \text{row 1} + \frac{5}{6}(\text{row 2})$$

$x = 0$
$y = 5$

Check: $6(0) - 5(5) = 0 - 25 = -25$
           $8(0) + 2(5) = 0 + 10 = 10$

3.14   Let x = number of nickels.
         Let y = number of dimes.
              $x + y = 30$
          $x(0.05) + y(0.10) = 2.10$

$$\begin{bmatrix} 1 & 1 & 30 \\ 0.05 & 0.10 & 2.10 \end{bmatrix}$$

$$\begin{bmatrix} 1 & 1 & 30 \\ 0 & 0.05 & 0.6 \end{bmatrix} \quad \text{row 2 – 0.05(row 1)}$$

$$\begin{bmatrix} 1 & 1 & 30 \\ 0 & 1 & 12 \end{bmatrix} \quad \frac{1}{0.05}(\text{row 2})$$

$$\begin{bmatrix} 1 & 0 & 18 \\ 0 & 1 & 12 \end{bmatrix} \quad \text{row 1 – row 2}$$

$x = 18$; he had 18 nickels
$y = 12$; he had 12 dimes

Check: $18 + 12 = 30$
         $18(0.05) + 12(0.10) =$
                 $0.9 + 1.2 =$
                 $2.1 = 2.10$

3.15 Let x = the amount loaned at 6%.
Let y = the amount loaned at 9%.

$$x + y = 36{,}000$$
$$0.06x + 0.09y = 0.08(36{,}000)$$

or

$$x + y = 36{,}000$$
$$0.06x + 0.09y = 2{,}880$$

$$\begin{bmatrix} 1 & 1 & 36{,}000 \\ 0.06 & 0.09 & 2{,}880 \end{bmatrix}$$

$$\begin{bmatrix} 1 & 1 & 36{,}000 \\ 0 & 0.03 & 720 \end{bmatrix} \quad \text{row } 2 - 0.06(\text{row } 1)$$

$$\begin{bmatrix} 1 & 1 & 36{,}000 \\ 0 & 1 & 24{,}000 \end{bmatrix} \quad \tfrac{1}{0.03}(\text{row } 2)$$

$$\begin{bmatrix} 1 & 0 & 12{,}000 \\ 0 & 1 & 24{,}000 \end{bmatrix} \quad \text{row } 1 - \text{row } 2$$

The amount loaned at 6% (x) was $12,000.
The amount loaned at 9% (y) was $24,000.

3.16 $[4 \ 3] \times [1 \ 3] = 4 \cdot 1 + 3 \cdot 3 = 13$

3.17 $[4 \ 3] \times [5 \ 4] = 4 \cdot 5 = 3 \cdot 4 = 32$

3.18 $\begin{bmatrix} 3 & 6 \\ 11 & 4 \end{bmatrix}$

3.19 $[5 \ 1 \ 10]$

3.20 $\begin{bmatrix} 15 \\ 3 \\ 9 \end{bmatrix}$

3.21 $a_{11} = [1 \ 2] \times [1 \ 5] = 1 \cdot 1 + 2 \cdot 5 = 11$

$a_{21} = [3 \ 4] \times [1 \ 5] = 3 \cdot 1 + 4 \cdot 5 = 23$

$\begin{bmatrix} 11 \\ 23 \end{bmatrix}$

3.22 $a_{11} = [1 \ 0] \times [1 \ 2] = 1 \cdot 1 + 0 \cdot 2 = 1$

$a_{12} = [1 \ 0] \times [1 \ 3] = 1 \cdot 1 + 0 \cdot 3 = 1$

$a_{13} = [1 \ 0] \times [5 \ 4] = 1 \cdot 5 + 0 \cdot 4 = 5$

$a_{21} = [0 \ 1] \times [1 \ 2] = 0 \cdot 1 + 1 \cdot 2 = 2$

$a_{22} = [0 \ 1] \times [1 \ 3] = 0 \cdot 1 + 1 \cdot 3 = 3$

$a_{23} = [0 \ 1] \times [5 \ 4] = 0 \cdot 5 + 1 \cdot 4 = 4$

$$\begin{bmatrix} 1 & 1 & 5 \\ 2 & 3 & 4 \end{bmatrix}$$

3.23 $a_{11} = [1 \ 4] \times [1 \ 0] = 1 \cdot 1 + 4 \cdot 0 = 1$

$a_{12} = [1 \ 4] \times [0 \ 1] = 1 \cdot 0 + 4 \cdot 1 = 4$

$a_{21} = [5 \ 6] \times [1 \ 0] = 5 \cdot 1 + 6 \cdot 0 = 5$

$a_{22} = [5 \ 6] \times [0 \ 1] = 5 \cdot 0 + 6 \cdot 1 = 6$

$a_{31} = [2 \ 1] \times [1 \ 0] = 2 \cdot 1 + 1 \cdot 0 = 2$

$a_{32} = [2 \ 1] \times [0 \ 1] = 2 \cdot 0 + 1 \cdot 1 = 1$

$$\begin{bmatrix} 1 & 4 \\ 5 & 6 \\ 2 & 1 \end{bmatrix}$$

3.24 Example:
A matrix is a rectangular array of numbers containing abbreviated information. Matrices can be added and multiplied and are used to solve systems of linear equations. Matrices can be used in applications in business, service occupations, computers, and other areas.

3.25 $\begin{bmatrix} 20 & 30 \\ 15 & 5 \\ 5 & 2 \end{bmatrix} \begin{bmatrix} 500 \\ 600 \end{bmatrix}$

$a_{11} = [20 \ 30] \times [500 \ 600]$
$\qquad = 20 \cdot 500 + 30 \cdot 600$
$\qquad = 10{,}000 + 18{,}000 = 28{,}000$

$a_{21} = [15 \ 5] \times [500 \ 600]$
$\qquad = 15 \cdot 500 + 5 \cdot 600$
$\qquad = 7{,}500 + 3{,}000 = 10{,}500$

$a_{31} = [5 \ 2] \times [500 \ 600]$
$\qquad = 5 \cdot 500 + 2 \cdot 600$
$\qquad = 2{,}500 + 1{,}200 = 3{,}700$

Station

$$\begin{matrix} \text{No. 1} \\ \text{No. 2} \\ \text{No. 3} \end{matrix} \begin{bmatrix} 28{,}000 \\ 10{,}500 \\ 3{,}700 \end{bmatrix}$$

The product matrix gives the total sales for each station.

3.26 Let A = [2   1   3]
        quarts carton sacks

$A + 3A$ = [2 1 3] + 3[2 1 3]
       = [2 1 3] + [6 3 9]
       = [8 4 12]

Let B = $\begin{bmatrix} 0.60 \\ 0.70 \\ 0.45 \end{bmatrix}$ per quart
per carton
per sack

AB = [8(0.60) + 4(0.70) + 12(0.45)]
    = [4.8 + 2.8 + 5.4]
    = [13]

Mr. Home spent $13.

3.27 Let A = [0.05   0.06   0.08].

Let B = $\begin{bmatrix} 13{,}000 \\ 12{,}000 \\ 4{,}000 \end{bmatrix}$

AB = [0.05(13,000) + 0.06(12,000) + 0.08(4,000)]
    = [650 + 720 + 320]
    = [$1,690]

Total interest earned is $1,690.

SELF TEST 3

3.01 $\begin{bmatrix} 1 & 3 & 4 \\ 2 & 1 & 8 \end{bmatrix}$

$\begin{bmatrix} 1 & 3 & 4 \\ 0 & -5 & 0 \end{bmatrix}$ row 2 − 2(row 1)

$\begin{bmatrix} 1 & 3 & 4 \\ 0 & 1 & 0 \end{bmatrix}$ $-\frac{1}{5}$(row 2)

$\begin{bmatrix} 1 & 0 & 4 \\ 0 & 1 & 0 \end{bmatrix}$ row 1 − 3(row 2)

$x = 4$
$y = 0$

3.02 $\begin{bmatrix} 2 & 4 & 8 \\ 6 & 3 & -3 \end{bmatrix}$

$\begin{bmatrix} 2 & 4 & 8 \\ 0 & -9 & -27 \end{bmatrix}$ row 2 − 3(row 1)

$\begin{bmatrix} 2 & 4 & 8 \\ 0 & 1 & 3 \end{bmatrix}$ $-\frac{1}{9}$(row 2)

$\begin{bmatrix} 2 & 0 & -4 \\ 0 & 1 & 3 \end{bmatrix}$ row 1 − 4(row 2)

$\begin{bmatrix} 1 & 0 & -2 \\ 0 & 1 & 3 \end{bmatrix}$ $\frac{1}{2}$(row 1)

$x = -2$
$y = 3$

3.03 $\begin{bmatrix} 7 & 9 \\ 12 & 3 \end{bmatrix}$

3.04 a_{11} = [1 4] × [9 1] = 1 • 8 + 4 • 1 = 12

a_{21} = [3 2] × [8 1] = 3 • 8 + 2 • 1 = 26

$\begin{bmatrix} 12 \\ 26 \end{bmatrix}$

3.05 $a_{11} = [4\ 5\ 6] \times [10\ 20\ 30]$

$= 4 \cdot 10 + 5 \cdot 20 + 6 \cdot 30$

$= 40 + 100 + 180 = 320$

$a_{21} = [1\ 2\ 3] \times [10\ 20\ 30]$

$= 1 \cdot 10 + 2 \cdot 20 + 3 \cdot 30$

$= 10 + 40 + 90 = 140$

$$\begin{bmatrix} 320 \\ 140 \end{bmatrix}$$

3.06 $$\begin{bmatrix} 5 & 11 & 14 \\ 8 & 15 & 11 \\ 14 & 10 & 5 \end{bmatrix}$$

3.07   Example:
A matrix is a rectangular array of numbers containing abbreviated information. Matrices can be added and multiplied and are used to solve systems of linear equations. Matrices can be used in applications in business, service occupations, computers, and other areas.

3.08 $\log_b N = x$

3.09 $\log_Q t = P$

3.010 $e^y = x$

3.011 $3^W = Z$

3.012 $\log_{10} 1,000 = \log_{10} 10^3 = 3$

3.013 $\log_{10} \left(\frac{1}{100}\right) = \log_{10} 10^{-2} = -2$

3.014   .6149

3.015   5.51

3.016 $y = \log_2 x$
$2^y = x$

x	$\frac{1}{2}$	1	4	8
y	-1	0	2	3

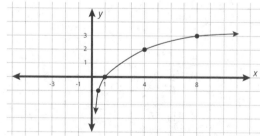

3.017

x	-3	-2	-1	0	1	2
y	27	9	3	1	$\frac{1}{3}$	$\frac{1}{9}$

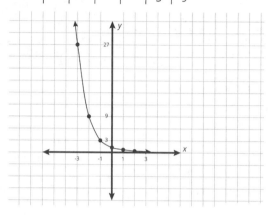

3.018 $\frac{1}{x^4} \cdot x^7 = \frac{x^7}{x^4} = x^3$

3.019 $\frac{\frac{1}{x^4}}{x^7} = \frac{1}{x^4 x^7} = \frac{1}{x^{11}}$

3.020 $\frac{6\sqrt{6}}{\sqrt{6}\sqrt{6}} = \frac{6\sqrt{6}}{6} = \sqrt{6}$

3.021 $(\sqrt[3]{8})^2 = 2^2 = 4$

3.022 $(\sqrt[5]{32})^3 = 2^3 = 8$

3.023 $\frac{1}{\frac{1}{4^2}} = 4^2 = 16$

3.024 $\frac{1}{\left(\frac{1}{8}\right)^{1/3}} = \frac{1}{\sqrt[3]{\frac{1}{8}}} = \frac{1}{\frac{1}{2}} = 2$

3.025 $\frac{y^2}{y^5} = \frac{1}{y^3}$

3.026 $(\sqrt[7]{-128})^3 = (-2)^3 = -8$

3.027 $\sqrt{-8}$; no real-number answer

3.028 $3^{-x} = 243$
$3^{-x} = 3^5$
$-x = 5$
$x = -5$

3.029 $49^x = 7$
$49^x = 49^{1/2}$
$x = \frac{1}{2}$

3.030 $4^x = 1,024$
$4^x = 4^5$
$x = 5$

3.031 $125^x = 5$
$125^x = 125^{1/3}$
$x = \frac{1}{3}$

LIFEPAC TEST

1. $5 \cdot 1 = 5$

2. $4^2 = 16$

3. $\dfrac{1}{(\frac{1}{4})^{1/2}} = \dfrac{1}{\sqrt{\frac{1}{4}}} = \dfrac{1}{\frac{1}{2}} = 2$

4. $\dfrac{1}{(bm)^3}$ or $\dfrac{1}{b^3 m^3}$

5. $\dfrac{y^2}{y^5} = \dfrac{1}{y^3}$

6. $(\sqrt[5]{-243})^3 = (-3)^3 = -27$

7. $\sqrt{-16}$; no real-number answer

8. $(ab)^{1/2}$

9. $x^{2/8} y^{4/8} = x^{1/4} y^{1/2}$

10. $y^{4/8} = y^{1/2} = \sqrt{y}$

11. $(\sqrt[3]{27})^2 = 3^2 = 9$

12. $\dfrac{5}{\sqrt{5}} = \dfrac{5\sqrt{5}}{\sqrt{5}\sqrt{5}} = \dfrac{5\sqrt{5}}{5} = \sqrt{5}$

13. $2^x = 128$
$2^x = 2^7$
$x = 7$

14. $8^x = 256$
$(2^3)^x = 2^8$
$2^{3x} = 2^8$
$3x = 8$
$x = \dfrac{8}{3}$

15. $\log_x P = y$

16. $b^y = M$

17. $x = \log_e e^e$
$e^x = e$
$e^x = e^1$
$x = 1$

18. $x = \log_e 1$
$e^x = 1$
$e^x = e^0$
$x = 0$

19. $x = \log_e \sqrt{e}$
$e^x = \sqrt{e} = e^{1/2}$
$x = \dfrac{1}{2}$

20. $\log 28.9 = \log 2.89 \times 10^1$
$= \log 2.89 + \log 10$
$= .4609 + 1$ or 1.4609

21. $2 \times 10^2 = 200$

22. $\log .0472 = \log 4.72 \times 10^{-2}$
$= \log 4.72 + \log 10^{-2}$
$= .6739 + (-2)$ or $8.6739 - 10$

23. $2.00 \times 10^{-2} = .02$

24. 4.178×10^2

25. 1.73×10^{-2}

26.

x	-1	0	1	2	3
y	$\frac{1}{2}$	1	2	4	8

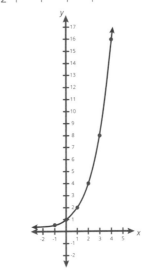

27. $y = \log_2 x$
$2^y = x$

x	$\frac{1}{2}$	1	2	4	8	16
y	-1	0	1	2	3	4

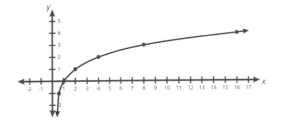

28.

$$\begin{bmatrix} 1 & 4 & 8 \\ 2 & 1 & 9 \end{bmatrix}$$

$$\begin{bmatrix} 1 & 4 & 8 \\ 0 & -7 & -7 \end{bmatrix}$$ row 2 – 2(row 1)

$$\begin{bmatrix} 1 & 4 & 8 \\ 0 & 1 & 1 \end{bmatrix}$$ $-\frac{1}{7}$(row 2)

$$\begin{bmatrix} 1 & 0 & 4 \\ 0 & 1 & 1 \end{bmatrix}$$ row 1 – 4(row 2)

$x = 4$
$y = 1$

29.

$$\begin{bmatrix} 12 \\ 9 \end{bmatrix}$$

30. $a_{11} = [1 \ 8] \times [7 \ 7]$
    $= 1 \cdot 7 + 8 \cdot 7$
    $= 63$

$a_{12} = [1 \ 8] \times [6 \ 4]$
    $= 1 \cdot 6 + 8 \cdot 4$
    $= 38$

$a_{21} = [0 \ 7] \times [7 \ 7]$
    $= 0 \cdot 7 + 7 \cdot 7$
    $= 49$

$a_{22} = [0 \ 7] \times [6 \ 4]$
    $= 0 \cdot 6 + 7 \cdot 4$
    $= 28$

$$\begin{bmatrix} 63 & 38 \\ 49 & 28 \end{bmatrix}$$

ALTERNATE LIFEPAC TEST

1. $(8 \cdot 4)^0 = 32^0 = 1$

2. $\dfrac{1}{4^{-2} \cdot 4^{-3}} = 4^2 \cdot 4^3 = 4^5$

3. $(\tfrac{1}{8})^{-\frac{1}{3}} = \dfrac{1}{\sqrt[3]{\tfrac{1}{8}}} = \dfrac{1}{\tfrac{1}{2}} = 2$

4. $b^{-3}m^{-3} = \dfrac{1}{b^3 m^3}$ or $\dfrac{1}{(bm)^3}$

5. $\dfrac{y^{-6}}{y^{-4}} = \dfrac{y^4}{y^6} = y^{4-6} = y^{-2} = \dfrac{1}{y^2}$

6. $(-128)^{3/7} = (\sqrt[7]{-128})^3 = (-2)^3 = -8$

7. $(-8)^{\frac{1}{2}} = \sqrt{-8}$; no real-number answer

8. $(x + y)^{\frac{1}{2}}$

9. $\sqrt[6]{a^3 b^2} = (a^3 b^2)^{\frac{1}{6}} = a^{3/6} b^{2/6} = a^{\frac{1}{2}} b^{\frac{1}{3}}$

10. $\sqrt[6]{x^3 y^{12}} = (x^3 y^{12})^{\frac{1}{6}} = x^{3/6} y^{12/6} = x^{\frac{1}{2}} y^2 = y^2 \sqrt{x}$

11. $\sqrt[4]{81^2} = (\sqrt[4]{81})^2 = 3^2 = 9$

12. $6 \div \sqrt{12} = \dfrac{6}{\sqrt{12}} = \dfrac{6}{2\sqrt{3}} = \dfrac{3}{\sqrt{3}} = \dfrac{3\sqrt{3}}{\sqrt{3}\sqrt{3}} = \dfrac{3\sqrt{3}}{3} = \sqrt{3}$

13. $3^x = 243$
$3^x = 3^5$
$x = 5$

14. $4^x = 128$
$(2^2)^x = 2^7$
$2x = 7$
$x = \dfrac{7}{2}$

15. $\log_b N = x$

16. $a^y = M$

17. $y = \log_e e^2$
$e^y = e^2$
$y = 2$

18. $y = \log_b 1$
$b^y = 1$
$b^y = 1^0$
$y = 0$

19. $y = \log_{10} 1{,}000$
$10^y = 1{,}000$
$10^y = 10^3$
$y = 3$

20. 1.6243

21. $0.2355 + (-2)$

22. antilog $0.6020 + 2 =$
$4 \cdot 10^2 = 400$

23. antilog $9.7160 - 10 =$
$5.2 \cdot 10^{-1} = 0.52$

24. 1.45×10^{-3}

25. 8.24×10^3

26. $y = 3^x$

y	$\frac{1}{3}$	1	3	9	27
x	-1	0	1	2	3

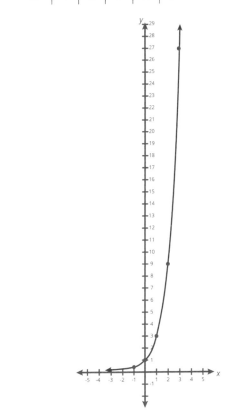

27. $y = \log_3 x$
$x = 3^y$

y	-1	0	1	2	3
x	$\frac{1}{3}$	1	3	9	27

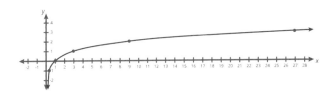

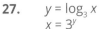

28.

$$\begin{bmatrix} 2 & 8 & 8 \\ 2 & 1 & 9 \end{bmatrix}$$

$$\begin{bmatrix} 1 & 4 & 4 \\ 0 & -7 & 1 \end{bmatrix} \quad \text{row 2 − row 1}$$

$$\begin{bmatrix} 1 & 4 & 4 \\ 0 & 1 & -\frac{1}{7} \end{bmatrix} \quad -\frac{1}{7}(\text{row 2})$$

$$\begin{bmatrix} 1 & 0 & 4\frac{4}{7} \\ 0 & 1 & -\frac{1}{7} \end{bmatrix} \quad \text{row 1 − 4(row 2)}$$

$x = 4\frac{4}{7}$

$y = -\frac{4}{7}$

29.

$$\begin{bmatrix} 9 & 10 \\ 3 & 6 \end{bmatrix}$$

30.

$$\begin{bmatrix} 4 & 7 \\ 2 & 1 \end{bmatrix}\begin{bmatrix} 3 & 1 \\ 1 & 2 \end{bmatrix} =$$

$a_{11} = [4 \ 7] \times [3 \ 1]$

$\quad = 4 \cdot 3 + 7 \cdot 1 = 12 + 7$

$\quad = 19$

$a_{12} = [4 \ 7] \times [1 \ 2]$

$\quad = 4 \cdot 1 + 7 \cdot 2 = 4 + 14$

$\quad = 18$

$a_{21} = [2 \ 1] \times [3 \ 1]$

$\quad = 2 \cdot 3 + 1 \cdot 1 = 6 + 1$

$\quad = 7$

$a_{22} = [2 \ 1] \times [1 \ 2]$

$\quad = 2 \cdot 1 + 1 \cdot 2 = 2 + 2$

$\quad = 4$

$$\begin{bmatrix} 19 & 18 \\ 7 & 4 \end{bmatrix}$$

MATH 1108

ALTERNATE LIFEPAC TEST

NAME _____

DATE _____

SCORE _____

61

76

Use the rules of exponents to evaluate or simplify. Write without negative exponents (each answer, 2 points).

1. $(8 \cdot 4)^0 =$

2. $\dfrac{1}{4^{-2} \cdot 4^{-3}} =$

3. $\left(\dfrac{1}{8}\right)^{-\frac{1}{3}}$

4. $b^{-3}m^{-3}$

5. $\dfrac{y^{-6}}{y^{-4}}$

6. $(-128)^{\frac{3}{7}}$

7. $(-8)^{\frac{1}{2}}$

Express with fractional exponents instead of radicals. Simplify (each answer, 2 points).

8. $\sqrt{x+y}$

9. $\sqrt[6]{a^3 b^2}$

Simplify (each answer, 2 points).

10. $\sqrt[6]{x^3 y^{12}}$

11. $\sqrt[4]{81^2}$

12. $6 \div \sqrt{12}$

Solve (each answer, 3 points).

13. $3^x = 243$

14. $4^x = 128$

Express in logarithmic form. Indicate the base (2 points).

15. $b^x = N$

Express in exponential form (2 points).

16. $\log_a M = y$

Solve for *y* without tables (each answer, 3 points).

17. $y = \log_e e^2$

18. $y = \log_b 1$

19. $y = \log_{10} 1{,}000$

Use the tables of logarithms to calculate (each answer, 2 points).

20. $\log 42.1 =$

21. $\log 0.0172 =$

22. antilog $0.6020 + 2 =$

23. antilog $9.7160 - 10 =$

Express in scientific notation (each answer, 2 points).

24. $0.00145 =$

25. $8{,}240 =$

Graph. Indicate the coordinates of 5 points. Label axes (each graph, 5 points).

26. $y = 3^x$

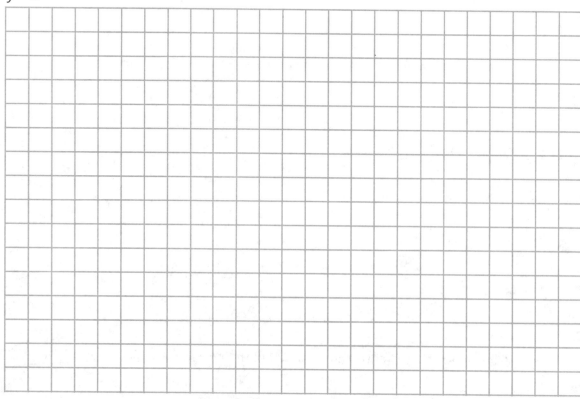

27. $y = \log_3 x$

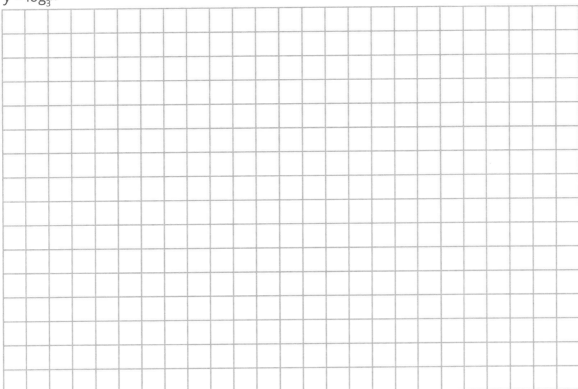

Use matrix methods to solve (5 points).

28. $2x + 8y = 8$
$2x + y = 9$

Perform the following operations on matrices (each answer, 3 points).

29. $\begin{bmatrix} 1 & 3 \\ 2 & 4 \end{bmatrix} + \begin{bmatrix} 8 & 7 \\ 1 & 2 \end{bmatrix} =$

30. $\begin{bmatrix} 4 & 7 \\ 2 & 1 \end{bmatrix} \begin{bmatrix} 3 & 1 \\ 1 & 2 \end{bmatrix} =$

MATH 1109

Unit 9: Counting Principles

TEACHER NOTES

MATERIALS NEEDED FOR LIFEPAC	
Required	Suggested
(none)	• hand-held calculators (for factorials)

ADDITIONAL LEARNING ACTIVITIES

Section 1: Progressions

1. Discuss the harmonic series, how it got its name, and how it differs from both the arithmetic and geometric series.

Section 2: Permutations

1. Allow students to experiment with hand calculators and to observe how factorials grow as they multiply numbers.

2. Copy and complete a table of factorials by finding the values of 1! through 12! You can check your work by finding the value of 13! and comparing with 6,227,020,800.

   Do you think the last digit of every factorial number larger than 4! is 0? Why?

Section 3: Combinations

1. Divide the students into two teams—one team for permutations and the other team for combinations. The teacher then selects various types of objects and the teams must illustrate the use of permutations or combinations with the objects.

Section 4: Probability

1. Use a container and marbles of several colors to demonstrate the difference between drawing with replacement and drawing without replacement in repeated trials.

2. Furnish the class with several sets of dominoes. Split the class into at least four groups and have each group set up a series of five questions about probability with the dominoes. Then each group in turn quizzes the other groups and critiques the answers to their problems.

ADDITIONAL ACTIVITIES

The following activities may be reproduced as student worksheets.

» COMBINATIONS

Suppose you are at a restaurant and like the following items on the menu.

Dinners		Beverages		Desserts	
Hamburger	$10.50	Coffee	$3.00	Hot Fudge Sundae	$5.00
Fried Chicken	$13.00	Cola	$3.00	Apple Pie	$3.00
Shrimp	$15.50	Root Beer	$3.00	Banana Cream Pie	$4.50
Fish and Chips	$19.50	Milk	$3.50	Cheesecake	$7.50
				Fudge Brownie	$4.00

1. If you order dinner and a beverage, without dessert, how many different combinations can you choose from?   _____

2. If you order dinner, a beverage, and a dessert, how many combinations can you choose from?   _____

3. How many choices do you have if you order dinner, a beverage, and a dessert, but decide you do not want seafood?   _____

Suppose you are at the fair. You have a choice of going on any one of 20 rides, eating at any one of 5 snack bars, visiting any one of 4 exhibit buildings, and watching any one of 3 performances.

4. If you go on a ride and visit an exhibit building, how many combinations can you choose from?   _____

5. If you visit an exhibit building and watch a performance, how many choices do you have?   _____

6. If you go on a ride, eat, and watch a performance, how many combinations can you choose from?   _____

7. How many choices do you have if you go on a ride, eat, visit an exhibit building, and watch a performance?   _____

» PROBABILITY

1. Suppose the eight letters of the words *hot cocoa* are written *atcchooo* on individual cards and the cards are then shuffled. If a card is chosen at random, the probability that it will contain the letter *o* is $\frac{3}{8}$. What is the probability that it will contain ...

    a. the letter *c*?   _____

    b. a vowel?   _____

    c. a letter in the word *chocolate*?   _____

    d. a letter in the word *cream*?   _____

2. A piggy bank contains 80 pennies, 25 nickels, 10 dimes, and 5 quarters. The probability is equally likely that any one of the coins will fall out when the bank is turned upside-down and shaken. What is the probability that a coin that falls out of the bank ...

    a. will be a penny?   _____

    b. will be either a nickel or a quarter?   _____

    c. will not be a quarter?   _____

    d. will be at least 10¢?   _____

ADDITIONAL ACTIVITIES, SOLUTION KEY

Combinations

1. Dinner: $C(4, 1) = \frac{4!}{1! \cdot 3!} = \frac{4 \cdot 3 \cdot 2 \cdot 1}{1 \cdot 3 \cdot 2 \cdot 1} = 4$

Beverage: $C(4, 1) = \frac{4!}{1! \cdot 3!} = \frac{4 \cdot 3 \cdot 2 \cdot 1}{1 \cdot 3 \cdot 2 \cdot 1} = 4$

$4 \cdot 4 = 16$ combinations

2. Dinner: $C(4, 1) = \frac{4!}{1! \cdot 3!} = \frac{4 \cdot 3 \cdot 2 \cdot 1}{1 \cdot 3 \cdot 2 \cdot 1} = 4$

Beverage: $C(4, 1) = \frac{4!}{1! \cdot 3!} = \frac{4 \cdot 3 \cdot 2 \cdot 1}{1 \cdot 3 \cdot 2 \cdot 1} = 4$

Dessert: $C(5, 1) = \frac{5!}{1! \cdot 4!} = \frac{5 \cdot 4 \cdot 3 \cdot 2 \cdot 1}{1 \cdot 4 \cdot 3 \cdot 2 \cdot 1} = 5$

$4 \cdot 4 \cdot 5 = 80$ combinations

3. Dinner: $C(2, 1) = \frac{2!}{1! \cdot 1!} = \frac{2 \cdot 1}{1 \cdot 1} = 2$

Beverage: $C(4, 1) = \frac{4!}{1! \cdot 3!} = \frac{4 \cdot 3 \cdot 2 \cdot 1}{1 \cdot 3 \cdot 2 \cdot 1} = 4$

Dessert: $C(5, 1) = \frac{5!}{1! \cdot 4!} = \frac{5 \cdot 4 \cdot 3 \cdot 2 \cdot 1}{1 \cdot 4 \cdot 3 \cdot 2 \cdot 1} = 5$

$2 \cdot 4 \cdot 5 = 40$ combinations

4. Ride: $C(20, 1) = \frac{20!}{1! \cdot 19!} = 20$

Exhibit: $C(4, 1) = \frac{4!}{1! \cdot 3!} = 4$

$20 \cdot 4 = 80$ combinations

5. Exhibit: $C(4, 1) = \frac{4!}{1! \cdot 3!} = 4$

Performance: $C(3, 1) = \frac{3!}{1! \cdot 2!} = 3$

$4 \cdot 3 = 12$ combinations

6. Ride: $C(20, 1) = \frac{20!}{1! \cdot 19!} = 20$

Eat: $C(5, 1) = \frac{5!}{1! \cdot 4!} = 5$

Performance: $C(3, 1) = \frac{3!}{1! \cdot 2!} = 3$

$20 \cdot 5 \cdot 3 = 300$ combinations

7. Ride: $C(20, 1) = \frac{20!}{1! \cdot 19!} = 20$

Eat: $C(5, 1) = \frac{5!}{1! \cdot 4!} = 5$

Exhibit: $C(4, 1) = \frac{4!}{1! \cdot 3!} = 4$

Performance: $C(3, 1) = \frac{3!}{1! \cdot 2!} = 3$

$20 \cdot 5 \cdot 4 \cdot 3 = 1{,}200$ combinations

Probability

1.   a. $p(\text{letter } c) = \frac{2}{8} = \frac{1}{4}$

b. $p(\text{vowel}) = \frac{4}{8} = \frac{1}{2}$

c. $p(\text{letter in } chocolate) = p(\text{letter } c) + p(\text{letter } h) + p(\text{letter } o) + p(\text{letter } l) + p(\text{letter } a) + p(\text{letter } t) + p(\text{letter } e)$

$p(\text{letter } c) = \frac{2}{8} = \frac{1}{4}$

$p(\text{letter } h) = \frac{1}{8}$

$p(\text{letter } o) = \frac{3}{8}$

$p(\text{letter } l) = 0$

$p(\text{letter } a) = \frac{1}{8}$

$p(\text{letter } t) = \frac{1}{8}$

$p(\text{letter } e) = 0$

$p = \frac{1}{4} + \frac{1}{8} + \frac{3}{8} + 0 + \frac{1}{8} + \frac{1}{8} + 0$

$= \frac{2}{8} + \frac{1}{8} + \frac{3}{8} + \frac{1}{8} + \frac{1}{8}$

$= \frac{8}{8} = 1$

d. $p(\text{letter in } cream) = p(\text{letter } c) + p(\text{letter } r) + p(\text{letter } e) + p(\text{letter } a) + p(\text{letter } m)$

$p(\text{letter } c) = \frac{2}{8} = \frac{1}{4}$

$p(\text{letter } r) = 0$

$p(\text{letter } e) = 0$

$p(\text{letter } a) = \frac{1}{8}$

$p(\text{letter } m) = 0$

$p = \frac{1}{4} + 0 + 0 + \frac{1}{8} + 0$

$= \frac{2}{8} + \frac{1}{8} = \frac{3}{8}$

2. The bank contains 120 coins.

a. $p(\text{penny}) = \frac{80}{120} = \frac{2}{3}$

b. $p(\text{nickel or quarter}) = \frac{25}{120} + \frac{5}{120} = \frac{30}{120} = \frac{1}{4}$

c. $p(\text{not quarter}) = 1 - p(\text{quarter})$

$p(\text{quarter}) = \frac{5}{120} = \frac{1}{24}$

$p(\text{not quarter}) = 1 - \frac{1}{24} = \frac{23}{24}$

d. $p(\text{dime or quarter}) = \frac{10}{120} + \frac{5}{120} = \frac{15}{120} = \frac{1}{8}$

ANSWER KEY

SECTION 1

1.1 the positive integers

1.2 an ordering of quantities

1.3 Example:
2, 4, 8, 16, ... 256

1.4 Example:
1, 3, 5, 7, ...

1.5 No first term is written.

1.6 Example:
Both 1, 2, 3, 4, 1, 2, 3, 4, ... and 1, 2, 3, 4, 5, 6, 7, 8, ... have the same first 4 terms.

1.7 Substituting 6 in
$3n + 2 = 3 \cdot 6 + 2 = 18 + 2 = 20$
and 7 in
$3n + 2 = 3 \cdot 7 + 2 = 21 + 2 = 23$

Substituting 6 in
$(a)(-1)^{n+1} = (a)(-1)^{6+1} =$
$(a)(-1)^7 = (a)(-1) = -a$
and 7 in
$(a)(-1)^{n+1} = (a)(-1)^{7+1} =$
$(a)(-1)^8 = (a)(1) = a$

Substituting 6 in
$\frac{1}{n^3} = \frac{1}{6^3} = \frac{1}{216}$
and 7 in
$\frac{1}{n^3} = \frac{1}{7^3} = \frac{1}{343}$

Substituting 6 in
$4^n = 4^6 = 4{,}096$
and 7 in
$4^n = 4^7 = 16{,}384$

1.8 Example:
-2, 2, -2, 2, ...

1.9 a. 2^n
b. $50n$
c. $3a(3 - n)$
d. $(0.1)(-1)^n(n)$
e. $\frac{n+3}{n+2}$

1.10 A series is the sum of the terms of an associated sequence.

1.11 Examples:
a. infinite series:
$1 + 2 + 3 + 4 + ...$
b. finite series:
$2 + 4 + 8 + 18 + ... 256$

1.12 Answers are based on examples in Problem 1.11.
a. $\displaystyle\sum_{n=1}^{\infty} n$ for $1 + 2 + 3 + 4 + ...$

b. $\displaystyle\sum_{n=1}^{8} 2n$ for $2 + 4 + 8 + 16 + ... 256$

1.13 $n = 1$: $\dfrac{1}{2(1) + 1} = \dfrac{1}{3}$

$n = 2$: $\dfrac{2}{2(2) + 1} = \dfrac{2}{5}$

$n = 3$: $\dfrac{3}{2(3) + 1} = \dfrac{3}{7}$

$n = 4$: $\dfrac{4}{2(4) + 1} = \dfrac{4}{9}$

$n = 5$: $\dfrac{5}{2(5) + 1} = \dfrac{5}{11}$

$n = 6$: $\dfrac{6}{2(6) + 1} = \dfrac{6}{13}$

$\dfrac{1}{3} + \dfrac{2}{5} + \dfrac{3}{7} + \dfrac{4}{9} + \dfrac{5}{11} + \dfrac{6}{13}$

1.14 a. arithmetic—common difference is 1
b. geometric—common ratio is $\frac{1}{2}$
c. arithmetic—common difference is 5
d. neither—no common ratio nor difference

1.15 a. arithmetic—common difference is 3
b. neither—no common ratio nor difference
c. geometric—common ratio is $\frac{1}{2}$
d. geometric—common ratio is T

1.16 a. difference
b. ratio

SELF TEST 1

1.01 the positive integers

1.02 an ordering of quantities separated by commas

1.03 the sum of the terms of an associated sequence

1.04 one of the individual quantities of a sequence

1.05 a formula that yields the value of a term when that term's position is substituted in it

1.06 a series that has a common difference between terms

1.07 a series that has a common ratio between terms

1.08 a sequence in which each successive term changes sign

1.09 Example:
2, 4, 8, 16, ... 256

1.010 Example:
3, 6, 9, 12, ...

1.011 Example:
3 + 9 + 27 + 81 + ...

1.012 Example:
3 + 5 + 7 + 9 + ...

1.013 Example:
3, -3, 3, -3, ...

1.014 $2n$

1.015 $2n - 1$

1.016 $\dfrac{n + 1}{n + 2}$

1.017 $3n(-1)^n$

1.018 3^n

1.019 arithmetic—common difference is 7

1.020 geometric—common ratio is 2

1.021 both—common ratio is 1 and common difference is 0

1.022 neither—no common ratio nor difference

1.023 $\displaystyle\sum_{n=1}^{\infty} 3 + 7n$

1.024 $\displaystyle\sum_{n=1}^{\infty} 6$

1.025 $\displaystyle\sum_{n=1}^{4} \dfrac{n}{n+3}$

SECTION 2

2.1 $7! = 7 \cdot 6 \cdot 5 \cdot 4 \cdot 3 \cdot 2 \cdot 1$
$= 42 \cdot 5 \cdot 4 \cdot 3 \cdot 2 \cdot 1$
$= 210 \cdot 4 \cdot 3 \cdot 2 \cdot 1$
$= 840 \cdot 3 \cdot 2 \cdot 1$
$= 2{,}520 \cdot 2 \cdot 1$
$= 5{,}040 \cdot 1$
$= 5{,}040$

2.2 Answers depend on calculator.

2.3 $\dfrac{10! \cdot 4!}{6! \cdot 5!} = \dfrac{\overset{2}{\cancel{10}} \cdot 9 \cdot 8 \cdot 7 \cdot \cancel{6!} \cdot \cancel{4!}}{\cancel{6!} \cdot \cancel{5} \cdot \cancel{4!}} = 2 \cdot 8 \cdot 9 \cdot 7 =$ 1,008

2.4 $9 \cdot 8 \cdot 7! = 9 \cdot 8 \cdot 7 \cdot 6 \cdot 5 \cdot 4 \cdot 3 \cdot 2 \cdot 1$
$= 9!$
$= 362{,}880$

2.5 $\dfrac{0!}{1!} = \dfrac{1}{1} = 1$

2.6

ABC	ABD	ACD	BCD
ACB	ADB	ADC	BDC
BAC	BAD	CAD	CBD
BCA	BDA	CDA	CDB
CAB	DAB	DAC	DBC
CBA	DBA	DCA	DCB

2.7 $P(5, 3) = \dfrac{5!}{(5-3)!} = \dfrac{5!}{2!}$
$= \dfrac{5 \cdot 4 \cdot 3 \cdot \cancel{2!}}{\cancel{2!}} = 5 \cdot 4 \cdot 3 = 60$

2.8 $P(6, 6) = 6! = 720$

2.9 $P(7, 1) = \dfrac{7!}{(7-1)!} = \dfrac{7!}{6!}$
$= \dfrac{7 \cdot \cancel{6} \cdot \cancel{5} \cdot \cancel{4} \cdot \cancel{3} \cdot \cancel{2} \cdot \cancel{1}}{\cancel{6} \cdot \cancel{5} \cdot \cancel{4} \cdot \cancel{3} \cdot \cancel{2} \cdot \cancel{1}} = 7$

2.10 $P(20, 15) = \dfrac{20!}{(20-15)!} = \dfrac{20!}{5!}$

2.11 $P(8, 8) = 8!$ or 40,320

2.12 $P(5, 3) = 60$
The lock has only 60 possibilities. A thief could easily try all 60 possibilities and open the lock.

2.13 $P(11, 11) = 11!$

2.14 $P^c(7, 7) = (7-1)! = 6! = 720$

2.15 $P^c(23, 23) = (23-1)! = 22!$

2.16 Half of the circular permutations of pearls around the neck are obtained by flipping the necklace over before putting it on. Therefore, only half the number of different ways they can be strung exists in relation to the number of ways they can be worn; or
22! divided by 2 = $\dfrac{22!}{2}$.

305

SELF TEST 2

2.01 the product of all the natural numbers from an integer down to 1

2.02 the indicated sum of the terms of an associated sequence

2.03 an ordering of elements of a set

2.04 an ordering of elements in a circle

2.05 $3! \cdot 3! = 3 \cdot 2 \cdot 1 \cdot 3 \cdot 2 \cdot 1 = 6 \cdot 6 = 36$

2.06
$$\sum_{n=1}^{5} 2n + 1$$

$= (2 \cdot 1 + 1) + (2 \cdot 2 + 1) + (2 \cdot 3 + 1) +$
$(2 \cdot 4 + 1) + (2 \cdot 5 + 1)$
$= 3 + 5 + 7 + 9 + 11$
$= 35$

2.07 $\frac{2!}{0!} = \frac{2}{1} = 2$

2.08
$$\sum_{n=1}^{3} 3n$$

$= 3 \cdot 1 + 3 \cdot 2 + 3 \cdot 3$
$= 3 + 6 + 9$
$= 18$

2.09 $\frac{7! \cdot 8! \cdot 3}{5! \cdot 9!} = \frac{7 \cdot 6 \cdot \cancel{5!} \cdot \cancel{8!} \cdot 3}{\cancel{5!} \cdot 9 \cdot \cancel{8!}} = \frac{7 \cdot 6 \cdot 3}{9} = 14$

2.010 $3! + 4! = 3 \cdot 2 \cdot 1 + 4 \cdot 3 \cdot 2 \cdot 1$
$= 6 + 24$
$= 30$

2.011 $5n - 4$

2.012 4

2.013 $p(4, 4) = 4! = 4 \cdot 3 \cdot 2 \cdot 1 = 24$

2.014

WXYZ	*WXZY*	*WYXZ*	*WYZX*	*WZXY*	*WYZX*
XWYZ	*XWZY*	*XYWZ*	*XYZW*	*XZWY*	*XZYW*
YWXZ	*YWZX*	*YXWZ*	*YXZW*	*YZWX*	*YZXW*
ZWXY	*ZWYX*	*ZXWY*	*ZXYW*	*ZYWX*	*ZYXW*

2.015 $P(4, 3) = \frac{4!}{(4 - 3)!} = \frac{4!}{1!} = 24$

2.016

AB	*AC*	*AD*
BA	*BC*	*BD*
CA	*CB*	*CD*
DA	*DB*	*DC*

2.017 $P(n, r) = \frac{n!}{(n - r)!}$

2.018 $P^c(n, n) = (n - 1)!$

2.019 $P(6, 6) = 6! = 720$

2.020 $P(10, 3) = \frac{10!}{(10 - 3)!} = \frac{10!}{7!}$
$= 10 \cdot 9 \cdot 8 = 720$

2.021 Let the family visits be *A*, *B*, and *C*.
Philadelphia:
   A A B B C C
Baltimore:
   B C A C A B
Washington:
   C B C A B A
   1 2 3 4 5 6
$P(3, 3) = 3! = 6$

2.022 $P(15, 4) = \frac{15!}{(15 - 4)!} = \frac{15!}{11!}$
$= 15 \cdot 14 \cdot 13 \cdot 12 = 32,760$

2.023 The first space could be filled in 6 different ways. For each of the 6, the second space could be filled 5 ways. Then the third spot could be filled 4 different ways for each of these 30. Thus the cars could be parked $6 \cdot 5 \cdot 4 = 120$ ways.

2.024 This question is not a circular permutation problem since the semicircle has a beginning and an end. It is treated as a straight permutation problem.
$P(8, 8) = 8! = 40,320$

2.025 $P^c(7, 7) = (7 - 1)! = 6! = 720$

SECTION 3

3.1

abcd	*acde*	*abef*
abce	*acdf*	*bdef*
abcf	*bcde*	*acef*
abde	*bcdf*	*adef*
abdf	*cdef*	*bcef*

3.2 $C(5, 3) = \dfrac{5!}{3!(5-3)!} = \dfrac{5!}{3!2!} = \dfrac{5 \cdot 4 \cdot \cancel{3!}}{\cancel{3!}2!} = \dfrac{5 \cdot 4}{2 \cdot 1} = 10$

3.3 $C(6, 6) = \dfrac{6!}{6!(6-6)!} = \dfrac{6!}{6! \cdot 0!} = \dfrac{6!}{6!} = 1$

3.4 $C(8, 1) = \dfrac{8!}{1!(8-1!)} = \dfrac{8!}{7!} = \dfrac{8 \cdot \cancel{7!}}{\cancel{7!}} = 8$

3.5 $C(7, 3) = \dfrac{7!}{3!(7-3)!} = \dfrac{7!}{3!4!} = \dfrac{7 \cdot \cancel{6} \cdot 5 \cdot \cancel{4!}}{\cancel{3} \cdot \cancel{2} \cdot \cancel{1} \cdot \cancel{4!}} = 7 \cdot 5 = 35$

3.6 $C(20, 18) = \dfrac{20!}{18!(20-18)!} = \dfrac{\overset{10}{\cancel{20}} \cdot 19 \cdot \cancel{18!}}{\cancel{18!}\,\cancel{2!}} = 190$

3.7 $C(20, 2) = \dfrac{20!}{2!(20-2)!} = \dfrac{20!}{2!18!} = \dfrac{\overset{10}{\cancel{20}} \cdot 19 \cdot \cancel{18!}}{\cancel{2} \cdot \cancel{18!}} = 190$

3.8 $C(15, 10) = \dfrac{15!}{10!(15-10)!} = \dfrac{15 \cdot 14 \cdot 13 \cdot 12 \cdot 11 \cdot \cancel{10!}}{\cancel{10!} \cdot 5!}$

$\quad = \dfrac{\overset{3}{\cancel{15}} \cdot \overset{7}{\cancel{14}} \cdot 13 \cdot \cancel{12} \cdot 11}{\cancel{5} \cdot \cancel{4} \cdot \cancel{3} \cdot \cancel{2} \cdot 1} = 3 \cdot 7 \cdot 13 \cdot 11$

$\quad = 21 \cdot 13 \cdot 11 = 3{,}003$

3.9 $C(15, 5) = \dfrac{15!}{5!(15-5)!} = \dfrac{15!}{5! \cdot 10!}$

$\quad = \dfrac{15 \cdot 14 \cdot 13 \cdot 12 \cdot 11 \cdot \cancel{10!}}{5 \cdot 4 \cdot 3 \cdot 2 \cdot 1 \cdot \cancel{10!}}$

$\quad = \dfrac{\overset{3}{\cancel{15}} \cdot \overset{7}{\cancel{14}} \cdot 13 \cdot \cancel{12} \cdot 11}{\cancel{5} \cdot \cancel{4} \cdot \cancel{3} \cdot \cancel{2} \cdot 1} = 3 \cdot 7 \cdot 13 \cdot 11$

$\quad = 3{,}003$

3.10 $C(9, 4) = \dfrac{9!}{4!(9-4)!} = \dfrac{9 \cdot 8 \cdot 7 \cdot 6 \cdot 5!}{4!5!} = \dfrac{9 \cdot \overset{2}{\cancel{8}} \cdot 7 \cdot \cancel{6}}{\cancel{4} \cdot \cancel{3} \cdot \cancel{2} \cdot \cancel{1}}$

$\quad = 9 \cdot 2 \cdot 7 = 126$

3.11 $C(21, 4) = \dfrac{21!}{4!(21-4)!} = \dfrac{\overset{7}{\cancel{21}} \cdot \overset{5}{\cancel{20}} \cdot 19 \cdot \overset{9}{\cancel{18}} \cdot \cancel{17!}}{\cancel{4} \cdot \cancel{3} \cdot \cancel{2} \cdot \cancel{1} \cdot \cancel{17!}}$

$\quad = 7 \cdot 5 \cdot 19 \cdot 9 = 5{,}985$

3.12 $C(7, 5) = \dfrac{7!}{5!(7-5)!} = \dfrac{7 \cdot \cancel{6} \cdot \cancel{5!}}{\cancel{5!} \cdot \cancel{2} \cdot \cancel{1}}\overset{3}{} = 7 \cdot 3 = 21$

3.13 a.

$$
\begin{array}{r}
a + b \\
\times \quad a + b \\
\hline
ab + b^2 \\
a^2 + ab \\
\hline
a^2 + 2ab + b^2 = (a+b)^2 \\
\times \quad a + b \\
\hline
a^2b + 2ab^2 + b^3 \\
a^3 + 2a^2b + ab^2 \\
\hline
a^3 + 3a^2b + 3ab^2 + b^3 = (a+b)^3 \\
\times \quad a + b \\
\hline
a^3b + 3a^2b^2 + 3ab^3 + b^4 \\
a^4 + 3a^3b + 3a^2b^2 + ab^3 \\
\hline
a^4 + 4a^3b + 6a^2b^2 + 4ab^3 + b^4 = (a+b)^4 \\
\times \quad a + b \\
\hline
a^4b + 4a^3b^2 + 6a^2b^3 + 4ab^4 + b^5 \\
a^5 + 4a^4b + 6a^3b^2 + 4a^2b^3 + ab^4 \\
\hline
\end{array}
$$

b. $a^5 + 5a^4b + 10a^3b^2 + 10a^2b^3 + 5ab^4 + b^5 = (a+b)^5$

3.14

$$
\begin{array}{cccccccc}
1 & 7 & 21 & 35 & 35 & 21 & 7 & 1 \\
1 & 8 & 28 & 56 & 70 & 56 & 28 & 8 & 1 \\
1 & 9 & 36 & 84 & 126 & 126 & 84 & 36 & 9 & 1 \\
1 & 10 & 45 & 120 & 210 & 252 & 210 & 120 & 45 & 10 & 1
\end{array}
$$

3.15 The exponents of *a* will decrease and those of *b* will increase; the coefficients will be the 8th row of Pascal's Triangle.

$a^8 + 8a^7b + 28a^6b^2 + 56a^5b^3 + 70a^4b^4 + 56a^3b^5 + 28a^2b^6 + 8ab^7 + b^8$

SELF TEST 3

3.01 a subdivision of a given set of elements

3.02 the coefficients of powers of a binomial, arranged to form a triangle

3.03 an arrangement of quantities separated by commas

3.04 a series that has a common ratio between successive terms

3.05 $C(4, 2) = \dfrac{4!}{2!(4-2)!} = \dfrac{4!}{2!2!} = \dfrac{\cancel{4}^2 \cdot 3 \cdot \cancel{2!}}{\cancel{2} \cdot \cancel{1} \cdot \cancel{2!}} = 2 \cdot 3 = 6$

3.06 $P(4, 2) = \dfrac{4!}{2!} = \dfrac{4 \cdot 3 \cdot \cancel{2!}}{\cancel{2!}} = 4 \cdot 3 = 12$

3.07 Using the ninth row of Pascal's Triangle for the coefficients, $(x + y)^9 = x^9 + 9x^8y + 36x^7y^2 + 84x^6y^3 + 126x^5y^4 + 126x^4y^5 + 84x^3y^6 + 36x^2y^7 + 9xy^8 + y^9$

3.08 $\displaystyle\sum_{n=1}^{4} 2n + 2$

$= (2 \cdot 1 + 2) + (2 \cdot 2 + 2) + (2 \cdot 3 + 2) + (2 \cdot 4 + 2)$
$= 4 + 6 + 8 + 10$
$= 28$

3.09 $C(5, 0) = \dfrac{5!}{0!(5-0)!} = \dfrac{5!}{0!5!} = \dfrac{5!}{1 \cdot 5!} = 1$

3.010 $P(7, 3) = \dfrac{7!}{(7-3)!} = \dfrac{7 \cdot 6 \cdot 5 \cdot \cancel{4!}}{\cancel{4!}} = 210$

3.011 $P(16, 3) = \dfrac{16!}{(16-3)!} = \dfrac{16 \cdot 15 \cdot 14 \cdot \cancel{13!}}{\cancel{13!}} = 3{,}360$

3.012 $C(4, 2) = \dfrac{4!}{2!(4-2)!} = \dfrac{4 \cdot 3 \cdot \cancel{2!}}{2!\cancel{2!}} = \dfrac{12!}{2} = 6$

3.013 $C(5, 3) = \dfrac{5!}{3!(5-3)!} = \dfrac{5 \cdot \cancel{4}^2 \cdot \cancel{3!}}{\cancel{3!} \cdot \cancel{2} \cdot \cancel{1}} = 10$

3.014 $P(5, 4) = \dfrac{5!}{(5-4)!} = \dfrac{5!}{1!} = 5! = 120$

3.015 $C(6, 6) = \dfrac{6!}{6!(6-6)!} = \dfrac{6!}{6!0!} = \dfrac{6!}{6! \cdot 1} = \dfrac{6!}{6!} = 1$

$C(6, 5) = \dfrac{6!}{5!(6-5)!} = \dfrac{6 \cdot \cancel{5!}}{\cancel{5!} \cdot 1} = 6$

$C(6, 4) = \dfrac{6!}{4!(6-4)!} = \dfrac{6!}{4!2!} = \dfrac{\cancel{6}^3 \cdot 5 \cdot \cancel{4!}}{\cancel{4!} \cdot \cancel{2} \cdot \cancel{1}} = 15$

$C(6, 3) = \dfrac{6!}{3!(6-3)!} = \dfrac{6!}{3!3!} = \dfrac{6 \cdot 5 \cdot 4 \cdot \cancel{3!}}{3 \cdot 2 \cdot 1 \cdot \cancel{3!}} = 20$

$C(6, 2) = \dfrac{6!}{2!(6-2)!} = \dfrac{6!}{2!4!} = \dfrac{\cancel{6}^3 \cdot 5 \cdot \cancel{4!}}{\cancel{2} \cdot \cancel{1} \cdot \cancel{4!}} = 15$

$C(6, 1) = \dfrac{6!}{1!(6-1)!} = \dfrac{6 \cdot 5!}{1 \cdot 5!} = 6$

$C(6, 0) = \dfrac{6!}{0!(6-0)!} = \dfrac{6!}{1 \cdot 6!} = \dfrac{6!}{6!} = 1$

$1 + 6 + 15 + 20 + 15 + 6 + 1 = 64$ or 2^6

3.016

PQR	PST
PQS	QRS
PQT	QRT
PRS	QST
PRT	RST

3.017 $\dfrac{n!}{r! \cdot (n-r)!}$

3.018 $(a + b)^n = C(n, 0)a^n + C(n, 1)a^{n-1}b + C(n, 2)a^{n-2}b^2 + \ldots + C(n, n)b^n$

3.019 $C(15, 4) = \dfrac{15!}{4!(15-4)!} = \dfrac{15 \cdot \cancel{14}^7 \cdot 13 \cdot \cancel{12} \cdot \cancel{11!}}{\cancel{4} \cdot \cancel{3} \cdot \cancel{2} \cdot \cancel{1} \cdot \cancel{11!}}$
$= 15 \cdot 7 \cdot 13 = 1{,}365$

3.020 $C(12, 2) = \dfrac{12!}{2!(12-2)!} = \dfrac{\cancel{12}^6 \cdot 11 \cdot \cancel{10!}}{\cancel{2} \cdot \cancel{1} \cdot \cancel{10!}} = 66$

3.021 $P(6, 6) = 6! = 720$

3.022 Since order is significant, the permutation formula would be used.

3.023 $C(20, 3) = \dfrac{20!}{3!(20-3)!} = \dfrac{20 \cdot 19 \cdot \cancel{18}^3 \cdot \cancel{17!}}{\cancel{3} \cdot \cancel{2} \cdot \cancel{1} \cdot \cancel{17!}}$
$= 20 \cdot 19 \cdot 3 = 1{,}140$

3.024 $C(n, r) + C(n, r + 1)$

$= \dfrac{n!}{r!(n-r)!} + \dfrac{n!}{(r+1)!\,(n-(r+1))!}$

$= \dfrac{n!}{r!(n-r)!} + \dfrac{n!}{(r+1)!(n-r-1)!}$

$= \dfrac{(r+1)n! + (n-r)n!}{(r+1)!(n-r)!}$

$= \dfrac{(r+1+n-r)n!}{(r+1)!\,(n-r)!}$

$= \dfrac{(n+1)n!}{(r+1)!\,(n-r)!}$

$= \dfrac{(n+1)!}{(r+1)!\,(n-r)!}$

$= C(n + 1, r + 1)$

3.025 The middle term in a row of Pascal's Triangle has the largest value. Since 6 is exactly halfway between 0 and 12, $C(12, x)$ is maximized when $x = 6$.

SECTION 4

4.1 Example:
   a. 7
   b. 28
   c. 55
   d. 98
   e. In the long run, the number of heads is approximately 50 percent of the tosses.

4.2 Probability is used in random activities that may result in one way or another on any given try.

4.3 An event is made up of one or more outcomes.

4.4 $p(E) = \frac{3}{4}$, $p(\text{not } E) = 1 - p(E) = 1 - \frac{3}{4} = \frac{1}{4}$

4.5 $\frac{500,000,000}{3,000,000,000} = \frac{5}{30} = \frac{1}{6}$

4.6 Since the probability of any particular microchip is equally likely to any other, the probability of selecting the bad one is $\frac{1}{500}$.

4.7 $p(E) = \frac{\text{number of red}}{\text{total number}} = \frac{3}{9} = \frac{1}{3}$;

$p(\text{not } E) = 1 - p(E) = 1 - \frac{1}{3} = \frac{2}{3}$

4.8 a. $p(TT) = \frac{\text{favorable outcomes}}{\text{total outcomes}} = \frac{1}{4}$

   b. $p(HH) = \frac{\text{favorable outcomes}}{\text{total outcomes}} = \frac{1}{4}$

4.9 $p(E) = \frac{\text{no. of black balls}}{\text{no. of balls in urn}} = \frac{x}{x + y}$

4.10 $p(5, 3) = \frac{5!}{(5 - 3)!} = \frac{5!}{2!} = 5 \cdot 4 \cdot 3 = 60$

Since 60 equally likely choices exist, the probability is $\frac{1}{60}$.

4.11 $p(E_1 E_2) = p(E_1) \cdot p(E_2) = \frac{1}{15} \cdot \frac{1}{30} = \frac{1}{450}$

4.12 $p(T) = \frac{1}{2}$; $p(T) = \frac{1}{26}$; $p(T, T) = \frac{1}{4}$

Since these events are independent, the probability is $\frac{1}{2} \cdot \frac{1}{26} \cdot \frac{1}{4} = \frac{1}{208}$.

4.13 $p(E_1 E_2 E_3 E_4 E_5) = p(E_1) \cdot p(E_2) \cdot p(E_3) \cdot p(E_4) \cdot p(E_5)$

$= \frac{1}{6} \cdot \frac{1}{6} \cdot \frac{1}{6} \cdot \frac{1}{6} \cdot \frac{1}{6} = \frac{1}{7,776}$

4.14 a. $p(\text{Every time}) = \frac{1}{10} \cdot \frac{1}{10} \cdot \frac{1}{10} \cdot \frac{1}{10} = \frac{1}{10,000}$

   b. $p(\text{Never}) = \frac{9}{10} \cdot \frac{9}{10} \cdot \frac{9}{10} \cdot \frac{9}{10} = \frac{6,561}{10,000}$

   c. $p(\text{At least once}) = 1 - p(\text{Never})$

   $= 1 - \frac{6,561}{10,000} = \frac{3,439}{10,000}$

   d. $p(\text{Fourth only}) = \frac{9}{10} \cdot \frac{9}{10} \cdot \frac{9}{10} \cdot \frac{1}{10} = \frac{729}{10,000}$

4.15 $p(AB) = p(B) \cdot p(A \mid B)$

$= p(\text{First } i) \cdot p(\text{Second } i \mid \text{First } i)$

$= \frac{4}{11} \cdot \frac{3}{10} = \frac{12}{110} = \frac{6}{55}$

4.16 $0.67 must be 2 quarters, 1 dime, 1 nickel, and 2 pennies.

$p(\text{Nickel first}) \cdot p(\text{Quarter second} \mid \text{Nickel first})$

$= \frac{1}{6} \cdot \frac{2}{5} = \frac{2}{30} = \frac{1}{15}$

SELF TEST 4

4.01 one of the mutually exclusive results of an activity

4.02 a combination of one or more outcomes

4.03 a measure of likelihood of a given result

4.04 compound events whose outcomes do not affect each other

4.05 events involving two or more activities

4.06 probability of one event given that another has occurred

4.07 p(2nd birthday matches first) $= \frac{1}{365}$

4.08 $p(HTH) = p(H) \cdot p(T) \cdot p(H) = \frac{1}{2} \cdot \frac{1}{2} \cdot \frac{1}{2} = \frac{1}{8}$

4.09 Example:
$6 + 8 + 10 + 12 + \ldots + (4 + 2n) + \ldots$

4.010 Two heads and one tail could be HHT, HTH, or THH. Total number of outcomes is $2 \cdot 2 \cdot 2 = 8$; then probability is $\frac{3}{8}$.

4.011 $p(E) = \dfrac{\text{number of red} + \text{number of white}}{\text{total number}} = \frac{3+5}{12} = \frac{8}{12} = \frac{2}{3}$

4.012 AB BA CA AC BC CB

4.013 AB AC BC

4.014 $p(AB) = p(B) \cdot p(A|B)$
$= p(\text{first red}) \cdot p(\text{white}|\text{red})$
$= \frac{3}{12} \cdot \frac{5}{11} = \frac{1}{4} \cdot \frac{5}{11} = \frac{5}{44}$

4.015 $p(\text{certain}) = 1$, $p(E) = \frac{1}{4}$
$p(\text{impossible}) = 0$
$p(\text{compound event}) = 1 \cdot \frac{1}{4} \cdot 0 = 0$

4.016 $p(E) = \frac{50}{5,000} = \frac{1}{100}$
$p(\text{not } E) = 1 - p(E) = 1 - \frac{1}{100} = \frac{99}{100}$
$p(\text{none of 3}) = p(\text{not } E) \cdot p(\text{not } E) \cdot p(\text{not } E)$
$= \frac{99}{100} \cdot \frac{99}{100} \cdot \frac{99}{100} = \frac{970,299}{1,000,000}$

4.017 Use conditional probability. The probability that the first car is number 1 is $\frac{1}{10}$, the probability that the second is number 2 (given that the first is number 1) is $\frac{1}{9}$. Thus the probability that the first two cars are in order is $\frac{1}{10} \cdot \frac{1}{9} = \frac{1}{90}$. Applying the principle to the third car yields $\frac{1}{90} \cdot \frac{1}{8} = \frac{1}{720}$.

4.018 $P(3, 3) = 3! = 6$

4.019 $C(6, 5) = \dfrac{6!}{5!(6-5)!}$
$= \frac{6 \cdot 5!}{5! \cdot 1} = \frac{6}{1} = 6$

4.020 $p(E) = \dfrac{\text{number of outcomes favorable to } E}{\text{total number of outcomes}}$
$= \dfrac{C(11, 3)}{C(21, 3)}$
$= \dfrac{\frac{11!}{3!(11-3)!}}{\frac{21!}{3!(21-3)!}} = \dfrac{\frac{11 \cdot 10 \cdot 9 \cdot 8!}{3 \cdot 2 \cdot 1 \cdot 8!}}{\frac{21 \cdot 20 \cdot 19 \cdot 18!}{3 \cdot 2 \cdot 1 \cdot 18!}} = \dfrac{11 \cdot 5 \cdot 3}{7 \cdot 10 \cdot 19}$
$= \dfrac{11 \cdot 3}{7 \cdot 2 \cdot 19} = \frac{33}{266}$

4.021 These events are independent events, so
$p(E_1 E_2) = p(E_1) \cdot p(E_2) = \frac{4}{8} \cdot \frac{6}{8} = \frac{3}{8}$

4.022 $p(E) = \frac{1}{x}$, $p(\text{not } E) = 1 - \frac{1}{x} = \frac{x}{x} - \frac{1}{x} = \frac{x-1}{x}$
By the multiplication principle: $p(\text{does not occur in } n \text{ repetitions}) = (\frac{x-1}{x})^n$

4.023 No, because $p(E) \cdot p(F) = \frac{1}{2} \cdot \frac{1}{3} = \frac{1}{6} \neq \frac{1}{8}$.

4.024 By conditional probability and the fact that 10 different numbers between 1 and 99 contain a 9, we have
$p(AB) = p(B) \cdot p(A|B) = \frac{10}{100} \cdot \frac{9}{99} = \frac{1}{110}$

4.025 $p(E) = \dfrac{\text{number of outcomes favorable to } E}{\text{total number of outcomes}}$
$= \dfrac{2}{P^C(7, 7)}$
$= \frac{2}{6!} = \frac{2}{720}$
$= \frac{1}{360}$

LIFEPAC TEST

1. $\dfrac{n!}{(n-r)!}$

2. $\dfrac{n!}{r! \cdot (n-r)!}$

3. $\dfrac{P(n,\,r)}{r}$

4. $\dfrac{p(AB)}{p(B)}$

5. Example: 2, -2, 2, -2, …

6. Example: 3, 9, 27, 81, 243, …

7. 2^n

8. $\dfrac{3n}{n+3}$

9. geometric

10. arithmetic

11. neither

12. $P(4,\,4) = 4! = 24$

13. $C(4,\,4) = \dfrac{\cancel{4!}^{4}}{4!(4-4)!} = \dfrac{4!}{4!0!} = 1$

14. $5! = 5 \cdot 4 \cdot 3 \cdot 2 \cdot 1 = 120$

15. $C(7,\,4) = \dfrac{7!}{4!(7-4)!} = \dfrac{7 \cdot \cancel{6} \cdot 5 \cdot \cancel{4!}}{\cancel{4!} \cdot \cancel{3} \cdot 2 \cdot \cancel{1}} = 35$

16. $P^c(5,\,5) = (5-1)! = 4! = 24$

17. $\dfrac{3! + 0!}{2! \cdot 1!} = \dfrac{6+1}{2 \cdot 1} = \dfrac{7}{2}$

18. $P^c(12,\,12) = (12-1)! = 11!$

19. $C(6,\,3) = \dfrac{6!}{3!(6-3)!} = \dfrac{\cancel{6} \cdot 5 \cdot 4 \cdot \cancel{3!}}{\cancel{3} \cdot \cancel{2} \cdot \cancel{1} \cdot \cancel{3!}} = 5 \cdot 4 = 20$

20. $C(50,\,48) = \dfrac{50!}{48!(50-48)!}$

    $= \dfrac{\overset{25}{\cancel{50}} \cdot 49 \cdot \cancel{48!}}{\cancel{48!} \cdot \cancel{2} \cdot \cancel{1}} = 1{,}225$

21. $P^c(8) = (8-1)! = 7!$ or 5,040

22. $p(E) = \dfrac{\text{number of outcomes favorable to } E}{\text{total number of outcomes}}$

    $= \dfrac{7+3+9}{23} = \dfrac{19}{23}$

    or $p(\text{not green}) = 1 - p(\text{green})$

    $= 1 - \dfrac{4}{23} = \dfrac{19}{23}$

23. $p(AB) = p(B) \cdot p(A\,|\,B)$

    $= \dfrac{3}{8} \cdot \dfrac{2}{7} = \dfrac{6}{56} = \dfrac{3}{28}$

24. $P(7,\,4) = \dfrac{7!}{(7-4)!} = \dfrac{7 \cdot 6 \cdot 5 \cdot 4 \cdot 3!}{3!}$

    $= 7 \cdot 6 \cdot 5 \cdot 4 = 840$

25. $C(7,\,4) = \dfrac{7!}{4!(7-4)!} = \dfrac{7 \cdot \cancel{6} \cdot 5 \cdot \cancel{4!}}{\cancel{4!} \cdot \cancel{3} \cdot 2 \cdot \cancel{1}} = 35$

ALTERNATE LIFEPAC TEST

1. $\dfrac{p(AB)}{p(B)}$

2. $\dfrac{n!}{(n-r)!}$

3. $\dfrac{n!}{r! \cdot (n-r)!}$

4. Example: 2 + 5 + 8 + 11 + …

5. Example: 2, 4, 6, 8, 10, …

6. Example: 2 + 4 + 8 + 16 + 32 + …

7. Example: 3, -3, 2, -2, 1, -1, …

8. $4! \cdot 2! = 4 \cdot 3 \cdot 2 \cdot 1 \cdot 2 \cdot 1 = 48$

9. $P(9,\,3) = \dfrac{9!}{6!} = \dfrac{9 \cdot 8 \cdot 7 \cdot 6 \cdot 5 \cdot 4 \cdot 3 \cdot 2 \cdot 1}{6 \cdot 5 \cdot 4 \cdot 3 \cdot 2 \cdot 1}$

    $= 9 \cdot 8 \cdot 7 = 504$

10. $C(8,\,4) = \dfrac{8!}{4! \cdot 4!} = \dfrac{8 \cdot 7 \cdot 6 \cdot 5 \cdot 4 \cdot 3 \cdot 2 \cdot 1}{4 \cdot 3 \cdot 2 \cdot 1 \cdot 4 \cdot 3 \cdot 2 \cdot 1}$

    $= \dfrac{8 \cdot 7 \cdot \overset{2}{\cancel{6}} \cdot 5}{\cancel{4} \cdot \cancel{3} \cdot \cancel{2} \cdot 1} = 70$

11. $0! + 3! + 4! = 1 + 3 \cdot 2 \cdot 1 + 4 \cdot 3 \cdot 2 \cdot 1 =$
    $1 + 6 + 24 = 31$

12. $\displaystyle\sum_{n=1}^{4}$ for $(2 + 2n)$

    $= [2 + 2(1)] + [2 + 2(2)] + [2 + 2(3)] + [2 + 2(4)]$
    $= 4 + 6 + 8 + 10 = 28$

13. $P^c(6,\,6) = (6-1)! = 5! = 5 \cdot 4 \cdot 3 \cdot 2 \cdot 1 = 120$

14. $4n - 1$

15. $XYZ,\ XZY,\ YXZ,\ YZX,\ ZXY,\ ZYX$

16. $C(7,\,2)x^5y^2 + C(7,\,3)x^4y^3 + C(7,\,4)x^3y^4 + C(7,\,5)x^2y^5$
    $+ C(7,\,6)xy^6 + C(7,\,7)y^7$

17. $p(EF) = \dfrac{1}{5} \cdot \dfrac{2}{3} = \dfrac{2}{15}$

18. $P(6,\,3) = \dfrac{6!}{3!} = 6 \cdot 5 \cdot 4 = 120$

19. $C(4,\,4) = \dfrac{4!}{4! \cdot 0!} = \dfrac{4 \cdot 3 \cdot 2 \cdot 1}{4 \cdot 3 \cdot 2 \cdot 1 \cdot 1} = 1$

    $C(4,\,3) = \dfrac{4!}{3! \cdot 1!} = \dfrac{4 \cdot 3 \cdot 2 \cdot 1}{3 \cdot 2 \cdot 1 \cdot 1} = 4$

    $C(4,\,2) = \dfrac{4!}{2! \cdot 2!} = \dfrac{4 \cdot 3 \cdot 2 \cdot 1}{2 \cdot 1 \cdot 2 \cdot 1} = 6$

    $C(4,\,1) = \dfrac{4!}{1! \cdot 3!} = \dfrac{4 \cdot 3 \cdot 2 \cdot 1}{1 \cdot 3 \cdot 2 \cdot 1} = 4$

    $C(4,\,0) = \dfrac{4!}{0! \cdot 4!} = \dfrac{4 \cdot 3 \cdot 2 \cdot 1}{1 \cdot 4 \cdot 3 \cdot 2 \cdot 1} = 1$

    $1 + 4 + 6 + 4 + 1 = 16$ subsets

20. $p(\text{none}) = \dfrac{11}{12} \cdot \dfrac{11}{12} \cdot \dfrac{11}{12} = \dfrac{1{,}331}{1{,}728}$

21. A series is the sum of the terms of a sequence, whose terms are merely separated by commas.

22. The order of elements is significant in a permutation but not in a combination.

23. An event consists of one or more outcomes.

MATH 1109

ALTERNATE LIFEPAC TEST

74

92

NAME _____

DATE _____

SCORE _____

Write the formula for each of the following conditions (each answer, 4 points).

1. $p(A \mid B)$ _____

2. $P(n, r)$ _____

3. $C(n, r)$ _____

Complete these items (each answer, 4 points).

4. Write an example of an arithmetic series. _____

5. Write an example of an infinite sequence. _____

6. Write an example of an infinite geometric series. _____

7. Write an example of an alternating sequence. _____

Evaluate each of the following expressions (each answer, 4 points).

8. $4! \cdot 2!$ _____

9. $P(9, 3)$ _____

10. $C(8, 4)$ _____

11. $0! + 3! + 4!$ _____

12. $\sum\limits_{n=1}^{4} (2 + 2n)$ _____

13. $P^c(6, 6)$ _____

Complete the following items (each answer, 4 points).

14. What is the general term of the sequence 3, 7, 11, 15, ... ?

_____

15. Write all the permutations of the letters *X*, *Y*, and *Z*, taking three at a time.

_____

16. Complete the expansion of the binomial $(x + y)^7$ using combination notation for the coefficients.

$(x + y)^7 = C(7, 0)x^7 + C(7, 1)x^6y +$ _____

_____

17. Suppose that event *E* has probability $\frac{1}{5}$ and event *F* has probability $\frac{2}{3}$. Also suppose that events *E* and *F* are independent. What is the probability that in a compound experiment, first *E* and then *F* results?

_____

18. Six sprinters are racing in a 100-meter dash. How many different ways can a gold, silver, and bronze medal be awarded?

_____

19. How many subsets exist of a set containing 4 elements? Include the set itself and the null set.

_____

20. Assume that the probability that a person selected at random has a December birthday is $\frac{1}{12}$. What is the probability that none of three people chosen at random have December birthdays?

_____

21. What is the difference between a sequence and a series?

_____

_____

22. What is the difference between a permutation and a combination?

_____

_____

23. What is the difference between an outcome and an event?

_____

_____

MATH 1110

Unit 10: Algebra II Review

TEACHER NOTES

MATERIALS NEEDED FOR LIFEPAC	
Required	Suggested
(none)	• compasses • straightedges

ADDITIONAL LEARNING ACTIVITIES

Section 1: Integers, Open Sentences, and Graphs

1. Discuss these questions with your class.

    a. Is a circle a relation or a function?
    b. Is an ellipse a relation or a function?
    c. Which parabolas are functions?
    d. Which hyperbolas are functions?

    Note: This activity may also be done in Section 3.

Section 2: Polynomials, Fractions, and Real Numbers

1. Direct variations and inverse variations each contain two variables. Their graphs are two-dimensional (they are graphed on the *x* and *y* axes). Discuss with the class the relationship between the number of variables in joint variations and in combined variations and the type of graph each of these two variations has.

2. Have the students graph each of the following special polynomial equations and compare the graphs. The first one is shown as an example.

    $x^2 - y^2 = 0$
    $(x + y)^2 = 0$
    $(x - y)^2 = 0$
    $x^3 - y^3 = 0$
    $x^3 + y^3 = 0$

    Example: Graph $x^2 - y^2 = 0$
    $$x^2 - y^2 + y^2 = 0 + y^2$$
    $$x^2 = y^2$$
    $$\sqrt{x^2} = \sqrt{y^2}$$
    $$x = y$$

    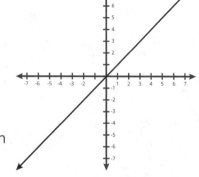

    To solve the equations for graphing, have the students set the terms equal to each other (as in the example) rather than factor the equations. This way is easier than factoring and will result in the same graph as solving by factoring.

    After each equation is graphed, have the students tell which graphs are identical and why. They may suggest other equations that have the same graphs as the ones in this activity.

    Note: This activity may also be a class activity.

3. Find the values of i, i^2, i^3, i^4, i^5, and so on until you discover the algorithm for finding any power of i.

Section 3: Quadratic Relations, Exponential Functions, and Counting Principles

1. Have the students visualize a circle, an ellipse, a parabola, and a hyperbola each being revolved and tell what figure is formed by each conic. Then have students name objects that are spheres, ellipsoids, paraboloids, and hyperboloids. Examples of these figures are shown.

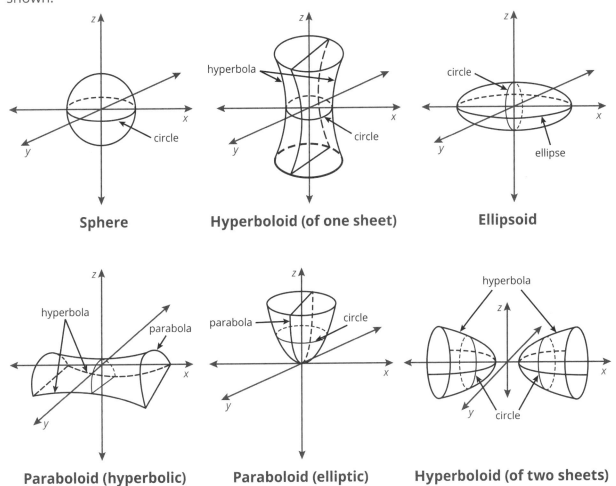

Sphere **Hyperboloid (of one sheet)** **Ellipsoid**

Paraboloid (hyperbolic) **Paraboloid (elliptic)** **Hyperboloid (of two sheets)**

2. Have the students tell where the major axis and minor axis of the two types of ellipses are located based on actual equations. If $a^2 > b^2$, then the major axis crosses the x-axis and the minor axis crosses the y-axis. If $a^2 < b^2$, then the major axis crosses the y-axis and the minor axis crosses the x-axis.

   For example, in the graph of the ellipse whose equation is $\frac{x^2}{9} + \frac{y^2}{4} = 1$, $a^2 > b^2$; therefore, the major axis crosses the x-axis and the minor axis crosses the y-axis.

3. Have the students tell which direction each of the four kinds of parabolas opens based only on their general equations. For example, the graph of a parabola whose equation is in the form $x = \frac{y^2}{4p}$ opens to the right.

4. Have the students tell how each kind of hyperbola opens (vertically, horizontally, or diagonally) based only on their general equations. For example, the graph of a hyperbola whose equation is in the form $\frac{x^2}{a^2} - \frac{y^2}{b^2} = 1$ opens horizontally.

317

ANSWER KEY

SECTION 1

1.1   h

1.2   j

1.3   s

1.4   f

1.5   a

1.6   y

1.7   m

1.8   b

1.9   w

1.10   q

1.11   c

1.12   g

1.13   e

1.14   l

1.15   t

1.16   r

1.17   u

1.18   n

1.19   z

1.20   d

1.21   {3}, {4}, {7}, {3, 4}, {3, 7}, {4, 7}, {3, 4, 7}, Ø

1.22   a. $A \cup B = \{3, 4, 7, 8, 9, 10, 11\}$
       b. $A \cap B = \{9\}$

1.23 $B \cup C = \{4, 8, 9, 10, 11, 13, 15\}$
       $A \cap (B \cup C) = \{4, 9\}$

1.24   yes

1.25   280 + 28 = 308

1.26   Distribution Property

1.27 $F = \{(3, 1), (2, 3), (1, 5)\}$

1.28   The point is 3 units to the right of the origin and 4 units below the origin.

1.29 $f(x) = 2x^2 + 3$
       $f(-3) = 2(-3)^2 + 3$
            $= 2(9) + 3 = 21$

1.30   1

1.31 $\frac{1}{6^2} = \frac{1}{36}$

1.32 $x^8 \cdot 8x^3 = 8x^{11}$

1.33 $6x^3y^5$

1.34 $r^8 \cdot \frac{1}{r^3 s^3} = \frac{r^5}{s^3}$

1.35 $p^{4 \cdot 3} y^{7 \cdot 3} = p^{12} y^{21}$

1.36 $\frac{x^3}{x^{-18}} = x^3 \cdot x^{18} = x^{21}$

1.37 $17a^2 + 12a + b + 3$

1.38 $4x - 20 + 133 - 19x = -15x + 113$

1.39 $7x^3 - 35 + 4x^3 - 28 - 3x^3 - 3y^2 = 8x^3 - 3y^2 - 63$

1.40   g

1.41   n

1.42   a

1.43   k

1.44   p

1.45   i

1.46   b

1.47   j

1.48   s

1.49   m

1.50   c

1.51   o

1.52   d

1.53   e

1.54   6

1.55 $7|8| - 3|-4| =$
       $7 \cdot 8 - 3 \cdot 4 =$
           $56 - 12 = 44$

1.56 $11 + |-11| =$
           $11 + 11 = 22$

1.57   -40

1.58 $25 \div (-5) + 7 =$
           $-5 + 7 = 2$

1.59   1,152

1.60   -1

1.61

       6.483   9.76
       8.642   8.235
       6.08   17.995
     21.205

       21.205
    − 17.995
       3.210   = 3.21

1.62 $-16 \div 4 + 38(-\frac{1}{2}) =$
           $-4 - 19 = -23$

1.63 $6|-5| - 3(\frac{2}{3}) + 7(-8) =$
         $6 \cdot 5 - 2 - 56 =$
            $30 - 58 = -28$

1.64 $|x| = 9$
       $x = 9, -9$
     Check:
       $|9| = 9$
         $9 = 9$
       $|-9| = 9$
         $9 = 9$

1.65 $|4x - 7| = 9$
$4x - 7 = 9$
$4x = 9 + 7$
$4x = 16$
$\frac{4x}{4} = \frac{16}{4}$
$x = 4$

Check:
$|16 - 7| = 9$
$|9| = 9$
$9 = 9$

$4x - 7 = -9$
$4x = -9 + 7$
$4x = -2$
$\frac{4x}{4} = \frac{-2}{4}$
$x = -\frac{1}{2}$

Check:
$|4(-\frac{1}{2}) - 7| = 9$
$|-2 - 7| = 9$
$|-9| = 9$
$9 = 9$

1.66 $6x + 5 = 29$
$6x = 29 - 5$
$6x = 24$
$\frac{6x}{6} = \frac{24}{6}$
$x = 4$

Check:
$6(4) + 5 = 29$
$24 + 5 = 29$
$29 = 29$

1.67 $2(3x + 4) = 4(x - 8)$
$6x + 8 = 4x - 32$
$6x + 8 - 4x = -32$
$2x + 8 = -32$
$2x = -32 - 8$
$2x = -40$
$\frac{2x}{2} = \frac{-40}{2}$
$x = -20$

Check:
$2[3(-20) + 4] = 4(-20 - 8)$
$2(-60 + 4) = 4(-28)$
$2(-56) = 4(-28)$
$-112 = -112$

1.68 $5x > 25$
$\frac{5x}{5} > \frac{25}{5}$
$x > 5$

1.69 $3(2x - 7) < 4x - 8$
$6x - 21 < 4x - 8$
$6x - 21 - 4x < -8$
$2x - 21 < -8$
$2x < -8 + 21$
$2x < 13$
$\frac{2x}{2} < \frac{13}{2}$
$x < \frac{13}{2}$

1.70 $6(2x + 6) + 3 = 13 - x$
$12x + 36 + 3 = 13 - x$
$12x + 39 = 13 - x$
$12x + 39 + x = 13$
$13x + 39 = 13$
$13x = 13 - 39$
$13x = -26$
$\frac{13x}{13} = \frac{-26}{13}$
$x = -2$

Check:
$6[2(-2) + 6] + 3 = 13 - (-2)$
$6(-4 + 6) + 3 = 13 + 2$
$6(2) + 3 = 15$
$12 + 3 = 15$
$15 = 15$

1.71 $-\frac{x}{8} + 7 > 8$
$-x + 56 > 64$ (multiply by 8)
$-x > 64 - 56$
$-x > 8$
$x < -8$ (multiply by -1)

1.72 $|x| < 4$
$x < 4$ and $x > -4$
$-4 < x < 4$

1.73 $|6x - 5| > 13$
$6x - 5 > 13$
$6x > 13 + 5$
$6x > 18$
$\frac{6x}{6} > \frac{18}{6}$
$x > 3$

or $6x - 5 < -13$
$6x < -13 + 5$
$6x < -8$
$\frac{6x}{6} < \frac{-8}{6}$
$x < -\frac{4}{3}$

1.74 Let x = number of half-dollars Gene saved
$x + 8$ = number of half-dollars Ernest saved
$x + 8$ = number of quarters Gene saved
   45 = number of dimes saved by each

$50x + 50(x + 8) +$
   $25(x + 8) + 45(10) + 45(10) = 20{,}000$
$50x + 50x + 400 +$
   $25x + 200 + 450 + 450 = 20{,}000$
$125x + 1{,}500 = 20{,}000$
$125x = 18{,}500$
$\frac{125x}{125} = \frac{18{,}500}{125}$
$x = 148$
$x + 8 = 148 + 8$
$= 156$

Ernest has saved 156 half-dollars and 45 dimes. Gene has saved 148 half-dollars, 156 quarters, and 45 dimes.

1.75

	r	t	d
helicopter	200	$x + 1$	$200(x + 1)$
airplane	400	x	$400x$

$200(x + 1) = 400x$
$200x + 200 = 400x$
$200 = 400x - 200x$
$200 = 200x$
$\frac{200}{200} = \frac{200x}{200}$
$x = 1$

helicopter: $200(1 + 1) = 200\,(2) = 400$
airplane: $400(1) = 400$
distance: 400 mi.

1.76

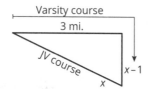

$3^2 + (x - 1)^2 = x^2$
$9 + x^2 - 2x + 1 = x^2$
$x^2 - 2x + 10 = x^2$
$-2x + 10 = 0$
$10 = 2x$
$\frac{10}{2} = \frac{2x}{2}$
$5 = x$
$3 + x - 1 = 2 + x = 2 + 5 = 7$ mi.

Varsity course is 7 miles. Junior varsity course is 5 miles.

1.76 f
1.78 g
1.79 b
1.80 n
1.81 j

1.82 d
1.83 l
1.84 i
1.85 k
1.86 c
1.87 a
1.88 $m = \frac{3 - 4}{-5 - 6} = \frac{-1}{-11} = \frac{1}{11}$
$y - 3 = \frac{1}{11}(x + 5)$
$11y - 33 = x + 5$ (multiply by 11)
$-x + 11y - 33 = 5$
$-x + 11y = 5 + 33$
$-x + 11y = 38$
$x - 11y = -38$ (multiply by -1)

1.89 $y = -\frac{1}{3}x + 6$
$3y = -x + 18$ (multiply by 3)
$x + 3y = 18$

1.90 $y + 9 = 4(x - 0)$
$y + 9 = 4x$
$-4x + y + 9 = 0$
$-4x + y = -9$
$4x - y = 9$ (multiply by -1)

1.91 Two points on given line are (0, -3) and (6, 0).
$x = 0$: $0 - 2y = 6$
$-2y = 6$
$\frac{-2y}{-2} = \frac{6}{-2}$
$y = -3$
$(0, -3)$

$y = 0$: $x - 0 = 6$
$x = 6$
$(6, 0)$

$m = \frac{0 - (-3)}{6 - 0} = \frac{0 + 3}{6 - 0} = \frac{3}{6} = \frac{1}{2}$

$m\,|| = \frac{1}{2}$
$y + 1 = \frac{1}{2}(x - 2)$
$2y + 2 = x - 2$ (multiply by 2)
$-x + 2y + 2 = -2$
$-x + 2y = -2 - 2$
$-x + 2y = -4$
$x - 2y = 4$ (multiply by -1)

1.92 $x = 6$: $2(6) - 4y = 8$
$12 - 4y = 8$
$-4y = 8 - 12$
$-4y = -4$
$\frac{-4y}{-4} = \frac{-4}{-4}$
$y = 1$
$(6, 1)$

$y - 1 = 4(x - 6)$
$y - 1 = 4x - 24$
$-4x + y - 1 = -24$
$-4x + y = -24 + 1$
$-4x + y = -23$
$4x - y = 23$ (multiply by -1)

1.93 $m = 4, b = 3$

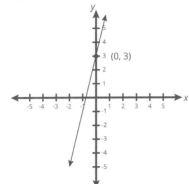

1.94 $x = 0$: $0 + 3y = -6$
$3y = -6$
$\frac{3y}{3} = \frac{-6}{3}$
$y = -2$
$(0, -2)$

$y = 0$: $2x + 0 = -6$
$2x = -6$
$\frac{2x}{2} = \frac{-6}{2}$
$x = -3$
$(-3, 0)$

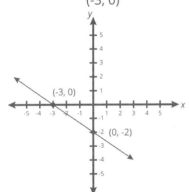

1.95 $x + y = 6$
$\underline{x - y = 2}$
$2x = 8$
$\frac{2x}{2} = \frac{8}{2}$
$x = 4$
$4 + y = 6$
$y = 6 - 4 = 2$
$(4, 2)$

1.96 $2x + 4y = 12$
$y = 3 - \frac{1}{2}x$
By substitution:
$2x + 4(3 - \frac{1}{2}x) = 12$
$2x + 12 - 2x = 12$
$12 = 12$
$y = 3 - \frac{1}{2}x$
$2y = 6 - x$ (multiply by 2)
$x + 2y = 6$
$x = 6 - 2y$
$x = -2y + 6$
$\{(x, y): x = -2y + 6 \text{ and } y = 3 - \frac{1}{2}x\}$

1.97 $3x + 7y = -4$
$2x + 5y = -3$
By opposite coefficients:
$6x + 14y = -8$ (multiply by 2)
$\underline{- (6x + 15y = -9)}$ (multiply by 3)
$-y = 1$
$y = -1$
$3x + 7(-1) = -4$
$3x - 7 = -4$
$3x = -4 + 7$
$3x = 3$
$\frac{3x}{3} = \frac{3}{3}$
$x = 1$
$(1, -1)$

1.98

$1.05 hamburger		$0.90 hamburger		$1.00 hamburger
$\boxed{}$	+	$\boxed{}$	=	$\boxed{}$
x		60		$x + 60$

$105x + 90(60) = 100(x + 60)$
$105x + 5,400 = 100x + 6,000$
$105x + 5,400 - 100x = 6,000$
$5x + 5,400 = 6,000$
$5x = 6,000 - 5,400$
$5x = 600$
$\frac{5x}{5} = \frac{600}{5}$
$x = 120$ lbs.

1.99 Let $10t + u$ = original number
$10u + t$ = new number
$t + u = 12 \longrightarrow u = 12 - t$
$10u + t = 2(10t + u) - 12$
$10u + t = 20t + 2u - 12$
$10u + t - 20t - 2u = -12$
$8u - 19t = -12$
$8(12 - t) - 19t = -12$
$96 - 8t - 19t = -12$
$96 - 27t = -12$
$-27t = -12 - 96$
$-27t = -108$
$\frac{-27t}{-27} = \frac{-108}{-27}$
$t = 4$
$u = 12 - 4 = 8$

The original number is 48; the new number is 84.

1.100 $2x + 3y \leq 10$
$x = 0$: $0 + 3y \leq 10$
$3y \leq 10$
$\frac{3y}{3} \leq \frac{10}{3}$
$y \leq \frac{10}{3}$
$(0, \frac{10}{3})$
$y = 0$: $2x + 0 \leq 10$
$2x \leq 10$
$\frac{2x}{2} \leq \frac{10}{2}$
$x \leq 5$
$(5, 0)$

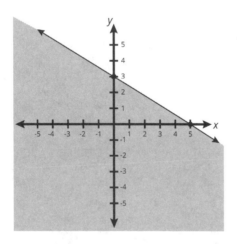

1.101 $2(x - y) > 4 - 2y$
$2x - 2y > 4 - 2y$
$2x > 4$
$\frac{2x}{2} > \frac{4}{2}$
$x > 2$

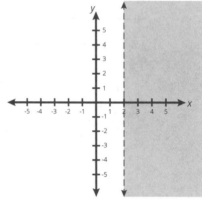

1.102 $x + y \geq 4 \longrightarrow y \geq 4 - x$
$y \leq 2x - 5$
$y \geq 4 - x$

x	0	4	2
y	4	0	2

$y \leq 2x - 5$

x	0	$\frac{5}{2}$	1
y	-5	0	-3

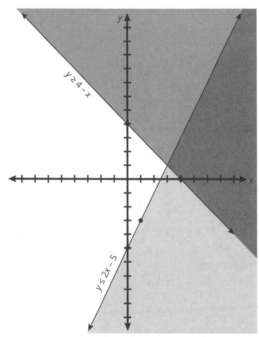

SELF TEST 1

1.01 {2}, {4}, {6}, {8}, {2, 4}, {2, 6}, {2, 8}, {4, 6}, {4, 8}, {6, 8}, {2, 4, 6}, {2, 6, 8}, {2, 4, 8}, {4, 6, 8}, {2, 4, 6, 8}, Ø

1.02 Distributive Property

1.03 $6 + 9 \div 3 + 11 = 6 + 3 + 11 = 20$

1.04 $f(x) = 3(6)^2 + 1 = 3(36) + 1 = 108 + 1 = 109$

1.05 $(3 \cdot 4)^3 = 12^3 = 1{,}728$

1.06 $\frac{1}{5^2} = \frac{1}{25}$

1.07 $|8| + |\text{-}3| - 7(\text{-}5) = 8 + 3 + 35 = 46$

1.08 $3(6) - 4|\text{-}6| \div 8 + |\text{-}8| =$
$18 - 4 \cdot 6 \div 8 + 8 =$
$18 - 24 \div 8 + 8 =$
$18 - 3 + 8 = 23$

1.09 $2a^2 - b^3 = 2(4)^2 - 3^3 = 2(16) - 27 = 32 - 27 = 5$

1.010 $8y^3$

1.011 $\frac{6x^3y^5}{2x^{\text{-}2}y^3} = \frac{6x^5y^5}{2y^3} = 3x^5y^2$

1.012 $9a$

1.013 $x(x - 3) - 4(x^2 + 7) =$
$x^2 - 3x - 4x^2 - 28 =$
$-3x^2 - 3x - 28$

1.014 $5 + 4x = 29$
$4x = 29 - 5$
$4x = 24$
$\frac{4x}{4} = \frac{24}{4}$
$x = 6$

1.015 $2(a + 7) = 5a - 13$
$2a + 14 = 5a - 13$
$2a + 14 - 5a = -13$
$-3a + 14 = -13$
$-3a = -13 - 14$
$-3a = -27$
$\frac{-3a}{-3} = \frac{-27}{-3}$
$a = 9$

1.016 $|2x - 1| = 15$
$2x - 1 = 15$
$2x = 15 + 1$
$2x = 16$
$\frac{2x}{2} = \frac{16}{2}$
$x = 8$

$2x - 1 = -15$
$2x = -15 + 1$
$2x = -14$
$\frac{2x}{2} = \frac{-14}{2}$
$x = -7$

{8, -7}

1.017 $|x - 7| > 3$
$x - 7 > 3$
$x > 3 + 7$
$x > 10$

$x - 7 < \text{-}3$
$x < \text{-}3 + 7$
$x < 4$

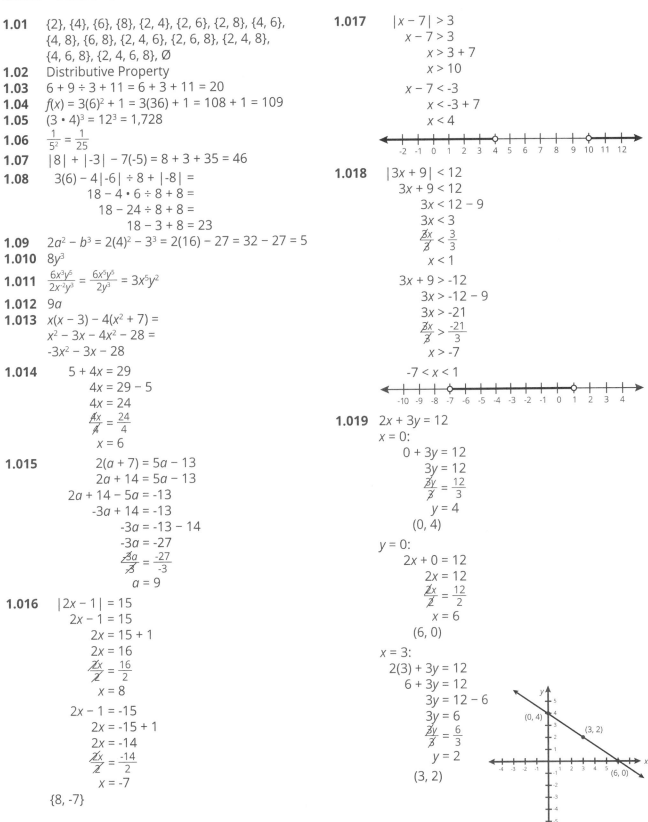

1.018 $|3x + 9| < 12$
$3x + 9 < 12$
$3x < 12 - 9$
$3x < 3$
$\frac{3x}{3} < \frac{3}{3}$
$x < 1$

$3x + 9 > \text{-}12$
$3x > \text{-}12 - 9$
$3x > \text{-}21$
$\frac{3x}{3} > \frac{\text{-}21}{3}$
$x > \text{-}7$

$\text{-}7 < x < 1$

1.019 $2x + 3y = 12$
$x = 0:$
$0 + 3y = 12$
$3y = 12$
$\frac{3y}{3} = \frac{12}{3}$
$y = 4$
$(0, 4)$

$y = 0:$
$2x + 0 = 12$
$2x = 12$
$\frac{2x}{2} = \frac{12}{2}$
$x = 6$
$(6, 0)$

$x = 3:$
$2(3) + 3y = 12$
$6 + 3y = 12$
$3y = 12 - 6$
$3y = 6$
$\frac{3y}{3} = \frac{6}{3}$
$y = 2$
$(3, 2)$

1.020 $m = 3, b = 7$

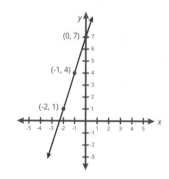

1.021 $m = \dfrac{5-7}{-3-(-5)} = \dfrac{5-7}{-3+5} = \dfrac{-2}{2} = -1$

1.022

$$y = \frac{3}{4}x + 6$$
$$4y = 3x + 24 \quad \text{(multiply by 4)}$$
$$-3x + 4y = 24$$
$$3x - 4y = -24 \quad \text{(multiply by -1)}$$

1.023

$$5x + 7y = 31$$
$$2x + 4y = 16$$

By opposite coefficients:

$$10x + 14y = 62 \quad \text{(multiply by 2)}$$
$$\underline{10x + 20y = 80} \quad \text{(multiply by 5)}$$
$$-6y = -18$$
$$\frac{\cancel{6}y}{\cancel{-6}} = \frac{-18}{-6}$$
$$y = 3$$
$$5x + 7(3) = 31$$
$$5x + 21 = 31$$
$$5x = 31 - 21$$
$$5x = 10$$
$$\frac{\cancel{5}x}{\cancel{5}} = \frac{10}{5}$$
$$x = 2$$
$$(2, 3)$$

1.024 Let x = one number
y = other number
$x = 3y - 4$
$x + y = 16$
By substitution:
$$(3y - 4) + y = 16$$
$$4y - 4 = 16$$
$$4y = 16 + 4$$
$$4y = 20$$
$$\frac{\cancel{4}y}{\cancel{4}} = \frac{20}{4}$$
$$y = 5$$
$x = 3(5) - 4 = 15 - 4 = 11$
The numbers are 11 and 5.

1.025

	r	t	d
marathon	9	$\frac{136}{45} - x$	$9(\frac{136}{45} - x)$
track	12	x	$12x$

3 hr., 1 min., 20 sec. =
$$3 + \frac{1}{60} + \frac{20}{3,600} =$$
$$\frac{10,800}{3,600} + \frac{60}{3,600} + \frac{20}{3,600} = \frac{10,880}{3,600} = \frac{136}{45} \text{ hr.}$$
$$9(\frac{136}{45} - x) + 12x = 28$$
$$\frac{136}{5} - 9x + 12x = 28$$
$$\frac{136}{5} + 3x = 28$$
$$3x = 28 - \frac{136}{5}$$
$$3x = \frac{140}{5} - \frac{136}{5}$$
$$3x = \frac{4}{5}$$
$$\frac{\cancel{3}x}{\cancel{3}} = \frac{\frac{4}{5}}{3}$$
$$x = \frac{4}{15}$$

marathon man's distance =
$$9(\frac{136}{45} - \frac{4}{15}) =$$
$$9(\frac{136}{45} - \frac{12}{45}) =$$
$$9(\frac{124}{45}) = \frac{124}{5} = 24\frac{4}{5} \text{ mi.}$$

track man's distance =
$$\overset{4}{\cancel{12}}(\frac{4}{\underset{5}{\cancel{15}}}) = \frac{16}{5} = 3\frac{1}{5} \text{ mi.}$$

SECTION 2

2.1   c
2.2   p
2.3   a
2.4   g
2.5   l
2.6   o
2.7   e
2.8   j
2.9   k
2.10   d
2.11   n
2.12   b
2.13

$$(12x^3y^2)^2 3x^2y =$$
$$(12^2x^{3\cdot2}y^{2\cdot2})3x^2y =$$
$$(144x^6y^4)3x^2y =$$
$$432x^{6+2}y^{4+1} = 432x^8y^5$$

2.14 $16a^2 - 9$
2.15

$$(2a + 7)^2 =$$
$$(2a + 7)(2a + 7) = 4a^2 + 28a + 49$$

2.16 $8a^2 + 30a + 28$
2.17

$$3ay(a + 2y)^2 =$$
$$3ay(a + 2y)(a + 2y) =$$
$$3ay(a^2 + 4ay + 4y^2) = 3a^3y + 12a^2y^2 + 12ay^3$$

2.18 $a^2 - 144$
2.19 $8x^3 - 14x^2y - 28x + 49y$
2.20

$$
\begin{array}{r}
4 \;\; - 2x \;\; + x^2 \\
2 \;\; + x \\
\hline
4x - 2x^2 + x^3 \\
8 - 4x + 2x^2 \\
\hline
8 \quad\quad\quad\quad + x^3 = 8 + x^3
\end{array}
$$

2.21

$$
\begin{array}{r}
4a^2 + \;\; 6ab \;\; + \;\; 9b^2 \\
2a \;\; - \;\; 3b \\
\hline
8a^3 + 12a^2b + 18ab^2 \\
-12a^2b - 18ab^2 - 27b^3 \\
\hline
8a^3 \quad\quad\quad\quad\quad\quad - 27b^3 = 8a^3 - 27b^3
\end{array}
$$

2.22

$$
\begin{array}{r}
m^2 - mn^2 + \;\; n^4 \\
m \;\; + \;\; n^2 \\
\hline
m^3 - m^2n^2 + mn^4 \\
m^2n^2 - mn^4 + n^6 \\
\hline
m^3 \quad\quad\quad\quad + n^6 = m^3 + n^6
\end{array}
$$

2.23 $(y + 6)^2$
2.24 $(5a^2 + 4)^2$
2.25 $2(3x^2 + 5xy - 2y^2) = 2(x + 2y)(3x - y)$
2.26 $2(10x^2 + 11xy + 3y^2) = 2(5x + 3y)(2x + y)$
2.27 $12(4x^2 + 4xy^2 + y^4) = 12(2x + y^2)^2$
2.28 $(c + 2d)(c - 2d)$
2.29 $6(16x^2 - y^2) = 6(4x + y)(4x - y)$
2.30 $(x - y)(x^2 + xy + y^2)$
2.31 $(3x^2 + 4y^4)(9x^4 - 12x^2y^4 + 16y^8)$
2.32 $(5r^2 - 2s^2)(25r^4 + 10r^2s^2 + 4s^4)$
2.33 $4x^3 - 3x^2 + x - 8$

2.34

$$
\begin{array}{r}
5a^3 \quad\quad\quad - 4a + 7 \\
6a^3 - 2a^2 \quad\quad + 4 \\
\hline
-a^3 + 2a^2 - 4a + 3
\end{array}
$$

2.35

$$
\begin{array}{r}
2x^2 - \;\; 3x + \;\; 4 + \frac{5}{3x-5} \\
3x - 5 \overline{)\;6x^3 - 19x^2 + 27x - \;\; 15} \\
\underline{6x^3 - 10x^2} \quad\quad\quad\quad\quad \\
-9x^2 + \;\; 27x \quad\quad \\
\underline{-9x^2 + \;\; 15x} \quad\quad \\
12x - \;\; 15 \\
\underline{12x - \;\; 20} \\
5
\end{array}
$$

2.36

$$
\begin{array}{r}
1 \overline{)\; 1 \quad -2 \quad 1 \quad 0} \\
1 \quad -1 \quad 0 \\
\hline
1 \quad -1 \quad 0 \quad 0
\end{array}
$$

$$a^2 - a$$

2.37

$$
\begin{array}{r}
-4 \overline{)\; 1 \quad 0 \quad -8 \quad 24 \quad 12 \quad 170} \\
-4 \quad 16 \quad -32 \quad 32 \quad -176 \\
\hline
1 \quad -4 \quad 8 \quad -8 \quad 44 \quad -6
\end{array}
$$

$$y^4 - 4y^3 + 8y^2 - 8y + 44 - \frac{6}{y+4}$$

2.38

$$\frac{x}{y} = \frac{48}{16}$$
$$\frac{x}{y} = 3$$
$$\frac{x}{5} = \frac{3}{1}$$
$$x(1) = 5(3)$$
$$x = 15$$

2.39

$$\frac{a}{bc} = 3$$
$$\frac{a}{7(9)} = 3$$
$$\frac{a}{63} = \frac{3}{1}$$
$$a(1) = 63(3)$$
$$a = 189$$

2.40 $y = 4x$

x	0	1	-1
y	0	4	-4

2.41 h

2.42 o

2.43 r

2.44 i

2.45 k

2.46 j

2.47 a

2.48 c

2.49 b

2.50 l

2.51 e

2.52 p

2.53 m

2.54 g

2.55 $\dfrac{13x^6}{51x^4} = \dfrac{13x^{6-4}}{51} = \dfrac{13x^2}{51}$

exclusions: $x \neq 0$

2.56 $\dfrac{3x^2y^2 - 6xz}{6x^2yz} = \dfrac{3x(xy^2 - 2z)}{3x(2xyz)} = \dfrac{xy^2 - 2z}{2xyz}$

exclusions: $x \neq 0, y \neq 0, z \neq 0$

2.57 $\dfrac{y^2 + y + 1}{2y - 2y^4} = \dfrac{y^2 + y + 1}{2y(1 - y^3)} = \dfrac{y^2 + y + 1}{2y(1 - y)(1 + y + y^2)} = \dfrac{1}{2y(1 - y)}$

exclusions: $1 + y + y^2 \neq 0, y \neq 0, 1 - y \neq 0$

2.58 $\dfrac{a^3 - b^3}{a^3b^3 + a^2b^4 + ab^5} = \dfrac{(a - b)(a^2 + ab + b^2)}{ab^3(a^2 + ab + b^2)} = \dfrac{a - b}{ab^3}$

exclusions: $a \neq 0, b \neq 0, a^2 + ab + b^2 \neq 0$

2.59 $\dfrac{4x^2 - 4x + 1}{8x^3 - 1} = \dfrac{(2x - 1)(2x - 1)}{(2x - 1)(4x^2 + 2x + 1)} = \dfrac{2x - 1}{4x^2 + 2x + 1}$

exclusions: $2x - 1 \neq 0, 4x^2 + 2x + 1 \neq 0$

2.60 $\dfrac{9 - y^2}{3 - y} \cdot \dfrac{12y}{9 + 3y} = \dfrac{(3 + y)(3 - y)}{3 - y} \cdot \dfrac{\overset{4}{\cancel{12}}y}{\cancel{3}(3 + y)} = 4y$

2.61 $\dfrac{2a^2 - 9a - 35}{12x^3} \cdot \dfrac{9x^2}{2a^2 - 3a - 20} =$

$\dfrac{(2a + 5)(a - 7)}{\underset{4x}{\cancel{12x^3}}} \cdot \dfrac{\overset{9}{\cancel{9}x^2}}{(2a + 5)(a - 4)} = \dfrac{3(a - 7)}{4x(a - 4)}$

2.62 $\dfrac{17a^3b^2}{15b^3c^2} \cdot \dfrac{18b^4c^3}{8a^2b^2c^2} = \dfrac{17a}{5c} \cdot \dfrac{3b^2}{4} = \dfrac{51ab^2}{20c}$

2.63 $\dfrac{xy - zy}{y} \cdot \dfrac{xw - xy}{yz - yw} = \dfrac{y(x - z)}{y} \cdot \dfrac{x(w - y)}{y(z - w)} = \dfrac{x(x - z)(w - y)}{y(z - w)}$

or $\dfrac{x^2w - xzw - x^2y + xzy}{yz - yw}$

2.64 $\dfrac{a^4}{2a^2 - 4a^4} \cdot \dfrac{8a^3 + 1}{2a + 4a^2} = \dfrac{a^4}{2a^2(1 - 2a^2)} \cdot \dfrac{(2a + 1)(4a^2 - 2a + 1)}{2a(1 + 2a)}$

$= \dfrac{a(4a^2 - 2a + 1)}{4(1 - 2a^2)}$ or $\dfrac{4a^3 - 2a^2 + a}{4 - 8a^2}$

2.65 $\dfrac{a - ab}{a^2} \div \dfrac{a - 1}{a^3} = \dfrac{a - ab}{a^2} \cdot \dfrac{a^3}{a - 1} = \dfrac{a(1 - b)}{a^2} \cdot \dfrac{a^3}{a - 1} =$

$\dfrac{a^2(1 - b)}{a - 1}$ or $\dfrac{a^2 - a^2b}{a - 1}$

2.66 $\dfrac{12xy}{z^3w} \div \dfrac{20x^2y^3}{6z^2w^4} = \dfrac{\overset{6}{\cancel{12}xy}}{\underset{z}{z^3w}} \cdot \dfrac{\overset{3}{\cancel{6}z^2}w^3}{\underset{10\,5xy^2}{\cancel{20}x^2y^3}} = \dfrac{18w^3}{5xy^2z}$

2.67 $\dfrac{9x^2 - 1}{12x^2 - 12x} \div \dfrac{9x^2 + 12x + 3}{3x^2 - 6x + 3} = \dfrac{9x^2 - 1}{12x^2 - 12x} \cdot \dfrac{3x^2 - 6x + 3}{9x^2 + 12x + 3}$

$\dfrac{(3x + 1)(3x - 1)}{12x(x - 1)} \cdot \dfrac{3(x - 1)(x - 1)}{3(3x + 1)(x + 1)} = \dfrac{(3x - 1)(x - 1)}{12x(x + 1)}$ or

$\dfrac{3x^2 - 4x + 1}{12x^2 + 12x}$

2.68 $\dfrac{81 - x^4}{3 - x} \div \dfrac{9 + x^2}{9} = \dfrac{81 - x^4}{3 - x} \cdot \dfrac{9}{9 + x^2} =$

$\dfrac{(9 + x^2)(9 - x^2)}{3 - x} \cdot \dfrac{9}{9 + x^2} = \dfrac{(3 + x)(3 - x)}{3 - x} \cdot 9 =$

$9(3 + x) = 27 + 9x$

2.69 $\dfrac{2a^2}{3b} \cdot \dfrac{15b^2}{4a^3} \div \dfrac{15b^2}{6a^3} = \dfrac{2a^2}{3b} \cdot \dfrac{15b^2}{4a^3} \cdot \dfrac{6a^3}{15b^2} = \dfrac{a^2}{b}$

2.70 $\dfrac{3a - 4}{5} + \dfrac{7a - 2}{15} - \dfrac{4a + 7}{10}$

LCD = 30

$\left[\dfrac{6}{6}\right]\left[\dfrac{3a - 4}{5}\right] + \left[\dfrac{2}{2}\right]\left[\dfrac{7a - 2}{15}\right] - \left[\dfrac{3}{3}\right]\left[\dfrac{4a + 7}{10}\right] =$

$\dfrac{18a - 24}{30} + \dfrac{14a - 4}{30} - \dfrac{12a + 21}{30} =$

$\dfrac{18a - 24 + 14a - 4 - 12a - 21}{30} = \dfrac{20a - 49}{30}$

2.71 $\dfrac{7}{xz} + \dfrac{2}{xy} + \dfrac{4}{yz}$

LCD is xyz

$\left[\dfrac{y}{y}\right]\left[\dfrac{7}{xz}\right] + \left[\dfrac{z}{z}\right]\left[\dfrac{2}{xy}\right] + \left[\dfrac{x}{x}\right]\left[\dfrac{4}{yz}\right] =$

$\dfrac{7y}{xyz} + \dfrac{2z}{xyz} + \dfrac{4x}{xyz} = \dfrac{7y + 2z + 4x}{xyz}$

2.72 $\dfrac{6}{y^2 - xy} - \dfrac{6}{x^2 - xy} = \dfrac{6}{y(y - x)} - \dfrac{6}{x(x - y)}$

LCD = $xy(x - y)$

$\left[\dfrac{-x}{-x}\right]\left[\dfrac{6}{y(y - x)}\right] - \left[\dfrac{y}{y}\right]\left[\dfrac{6}{x(x - y)}\right] =$

$\dfrac{-6x}{xy(x - y)} - \dfrac{6y}{xy(x - y)} = \dfrac{-6x - 6y}{xy(x - y)}$ or $\dfrac{6x + 6y}{xy(y - x)}$

2.73 $\dfrac{3}{a^2 - 3a + 2} - \dfrac{2}{a^2 - 1} = \dfrac{3}{(a - 2)(a - 1)} - \dfrac{2}{(a + 1)(a - 1)}$

LCD = $(a - 2)(a - 1)(a + 1)$

$\left[\dfrac{a + 1}{a + 1}\right]\left[\dfrac{3}{(a - 2)(a - 1)}\right] - \left[\dfrac{a - 2}{a - 2}\right]\left[\dfrac{2}{(a + 1)(a - 1)}\right] =$

$\dfrac{3a + 3}{(a + 1)(a - 2)(a - 1)} - \dfrac{2a - 4}{(a - 2)(a + 1)(a - 1)} =$

$\dfrac{3a + 3 - 2a + 4}{(a - 2)(a + 1)(a - 1)} = \dfrac{a + 7}{(a - 2)(a + 1)(a - 1)}$

2.74 $\dfrac{1}{x - y} - \dfrac{8}{x + y} + \dfrac{4}{y - x} - \dfrac{11x - 5y}{y^2 - x^2} =$

$\dfrac{1}{x - y} - \dfrac{8}{x + y} + \dfrac{4}{y - x} - \dfrac{11x - 5y}{(y + x)(y - x)}$

LCD = $(y + x)(y - x)$

$\left[\dfrac{-(y + x)}{-(y + x)}\right]\left[\dfrac{1}{x - y}\right] - \left[\dfrac{y - x}{y - x}\right]\left[\dfrac{8}{x + y}\right] + \left[\dfrac{y + x}{y + x}\right]\left[\dfrac{4}{y - x}\right]$

$- 1\left[\dfrac{11x - 5y}{(y + x)(y - x)}\right] =$

$\dfrac{-y - x}{(y + x)(y - x)} - \dfrac{8y - 8x}{(y + x)(y - x)} + \dfrac{4y + 4x}{(y + x)(y - x)} - \dfrac{11x - 5y}{(y + x)(y - x)}$

$= \dfrac{-y - x - 8y + 8x + 4y + 4x - 11x + 5y}{(y + x)(y - x)} = \dfrac{0}{(y + x)(y - x)} = 0$

2.75 $\dfrac{3}{a+2} + \dfrac{4}{2-a} = \dfrac{6}{a^2-4} =$

$\dfrac{3}{a+2} + \dfrac{4}{2-a} = \dfrac{6}{(a+2)(a-2)} =$

$LCD = (a+2)(a-2)$

$\left[\dfrac{(a-2)}{(a-2)}\right]\left[\dfrac{3}{a+2}\right] - \left[\dfrac{a+2}{a+2}\right]\left[\dfrac{4}{2-a}\right] - 1\left[\dfrac{6}{(a+2)(a-2)}\right] =$

$\dfrac{3a-6}{(a+2)(a-2)} - \dfrac{4a+8}{(a+2)(a-2)} - \dfrac{6}{(a+2)(a-2)} =$

$\dfrac{3a-6-4a-8-6}{(a+2)(a-2)} = \dfrac{-a-20}{(a+2)(a-2)}$ or $\dfrac{a+20}{(a+2)(2-a)}$

2.76 $xy - \dfrac{4x^5}{x^2-xy}$

$LCD = x^2 - xy$

$\left[\dfrac{x^2-xy}{x^2-xy}\right][xy] - 1\left[\dfrac{4x^5}{x^2-xy}\right] = \dfrac{x^3y - x^2y^2}{x^2-xy} - \dfrac{4x^5}{x^2-xy} =$

$\dfrac{x^3y - x^2y^2 - 4x^5}{x^2-xy} = \dfrac{\cancel{x}(x^2y - xy^2 - 4x^4)}{\cancel{x}(x-y)} = \dfrac{x^2y - xy^2 - 4x^4}{x-y}$

2.77 $\dfrac{2a-5}{3a+7} - 3$

$LCD = 3a+7$

$1\left[\dfrac{2a-5}{3a+7}\right] - \left[\dfrac{3a+7}{3a+7}\right][3] = \dfrac{2a-5}{3a+7} - \dfrac{9a+21}{3a+7} =$

$\dfrac{2a-5-9a-21}{3a+7} = \dfrac{-7a-26}{3a+7}$

2.78 $\dfrac{\dfrac{a}{b}+1}{\dfrac{a}{b}-1}$

$LCD = b$

$\dfrac{1[\frac{a}{b}] + [\frac{b}{b}][1]}{1[\frac{a}{b}] - [\frac{b}{b}][1]} = \dfrac{\frac{a}{b} + \frac{b}{b}}{\frac{a}{b} - \frac{b}{b}} = \dfrac{\frac{a+b}{\cancel{b}}}{\frac{a-b}{\cancel{b}}} = \dfrac{a+b}{a-b}$

2.79 $\dfrac{\dfrac{1}{x}+\dfrac{1}{y}}{\dfrac{1}{x}-\dfrac{1}{y}}$

$LCD = xy$

$\dfrac{[\frac{y}{y}][\frac{1}{x}] + [\frac{x}{x}][\frac{1}{y}]}{[\frac{y}{y}][\frac{1}{x}] - [\frac{x}{x}][\frac{1}{y}]} = \dfrac{\frac{y}{xy} + \frac{x}{xy}}{\frac{y}{xy} - \frac{x}{xy}} = \dfrac{\frac{y+x}{\cancel{xy}}}{\frac{y-x}{\cancel{xy}}} = \dfrac{y+x}{y-x}$

2.80 $\dfrac{x+\dfrac{x}{y}}{y-\dfrac{1}{y}}$

$LCD = y$

$\dfrac{[\frac{y}{y}][x] + 1[\frac{x}{y}]}{[\frac{y}{y}][y] - 1[\frac{1}{y}]} = \dfrac{\frac{xy}{y} + \frac{x}{y}}{\frac{y^2}{y} - \frac{1}{y}} = \dfrac{\frac{xy+x}{\cancel{y}}}{\frac{y^2-1}{\cancel{y}}} = \dfrac{xy+x}{y^2-1} =$

$\dfrac{x\cancel{(y+1)}}{\cancel{(y+1)}(y-1)} = \dfrac{x}{y-1}$

2.81 $\dfrac{6x+4}{4} = 7$

$6x + 4 = 28 \qquad$ (cross-multiply)

$6x = 28 - 4$

$6x = 24$

$\dfrac{6x}{6} = \dfrac{24}{6}$

$x = 4$

2.82 $\dfrac{3x}{8} - \dfrac{5x}{8} = -\dfrac{x}{6} - \dfrac{21}{4}$

$-\dfrac{2x}{8} = -\dfrac{x}{6} - \dfrac{21}{4}$

$LCD = 24$

$\overset{3}{\cancel{24}}\left[-\dfrac{2x}{\cancel{8}}\right] = \overset{4}{\cancel{24}}\left[-\dfrac{x}{\cancel{6}}\right] - \overset{6}{\cancel{24}}\left[\dfrac{21}{\cancel{4}}\right]$

$-6x = -4x - 126$

$-6x + 4x = -126$

$-2x = -126$

$\dfrac{\cancel{-2}x}{\cancel{-2}} = \dfrac{-126}{-2}$

$x = 63$

2.83 $\dfrac{x+3}{3} = 5 - \dfrac{x-3}{6}$

$LCD = 12$

$\overset{4}{\cancel{12}}\left[\dfrac{x+3}{\cancel{3}}\right] = 12[5] - \overset{2}{\cancel{12}}\left[\dfrac{x-3}{\cancel{6}}\right]$

$4x + 12 = 60 - 2x + 6$

$4x + 12 = 66 - 2x$

$4x + 12 + 2x = 66$

$6x + 12 = 66$

$6x = 66 - 12$

$6x = 54$

$\dfrac{\cancel{6}x}{\cancel{6}} = \dfrac{54}{6}$

$x = 9$

2.84 $\dfrac{x+1}{2x+6} - \dfrac{9}{x^2-9} = \dfrac{x-2}{2x-6}$

$\dfrac{x+1}{2(x+3)} - \dfrac{9}{(x+3)(x-3)} = \dfrac{x-2}{2(x-3)}$

$LCD = 2(x+3)(x-3)$

$\cancel{2}(x+3)(x-3)\left[\dfrac{x+1}{\cancel{2}(x+3)}\right] - 2(x+3)(x-3)\left[\dfrac{9}{(x+3)(x-3)}\right]$

$\qquad\qquad = \cancel{2}(x+3)(x-3)\left[\dfrac{x-2}{\cancel{2}(x-3)}\right]$

$x^2 - 2x - 3 - 18 = x^2 + x - 6$

$-2x - 21 = x - 6$

$-2x - 21 - x = -6$

$-3x - 21 = -6$

$-3x = -6 + 21$

$-3x = 15$

$\dfrac{\cancel{-3}x}{\cancel{-3}} = \dfrac{15}{-3}$

$x = -5$

2.85

nuts		candy		party mix
$1.10	+	$1.60	=	$1.50
x		36		$x + 36$

$$110x + 160(36) = 150(x + 36)$$
$$110x + 5{,}760 = 150x + 5{,}400$$
$$110x + 5{,}760 - 5{,}400 = 150x$$
$$110x + 360 = 150x$$
$$360 = 150x - 110x$$
$$360 = 40x$$
$$\frac{360}{40} = \frac{40x}{40}$$
$$9 = x$$
$$x = 9 \text{ lbs.}$$

2.86 Let x = time to mow lawn together

$$\frac{x}{\frac{2}{3}} + \frac{x}{1} = 1$$

$$\text{LCD} = \frac{2}{3}$$

$$\frac{2}{3}\left[\frac{x}{\frac{2}{3}}\right] + \frac{2}{3}[x] = \frac{2}{3}[1]$$

$$x + \frac{2}{3}x = \frac{2}{3}$$
$$3x + 2x = 2 \qquad \text{(multiply by 3)}$$
$$5x = 2$$
$$\frac{5x}{5} = \frac{2}{5}$$
$$x = \frac{2}{5} \text{ hr.} = \frac{2}{5}(\overset{12}{60}) = 24 \text{ min.}$$

2.87 h
2.88 k
2.89 j
2.90 f
2.91 m
2.92 d
2.93 e
2.94 g
2.95 b
2.96 a

2.97 $\frac{1}{2}\sqrt[4]{32} = \frac{1}{2}\sqrt[4]{2\cdot2\cdot2\cdot2\cdot2} = \frac{1}{2}(2)\sqrt[4]{2} = \sqrt[4]{2}$

2.98 $\sqrt[3]{10}\sqrt[3]{12} = \sqrt[3]{120} = \sqrt[3]{8\cdot15} = \sqrt[3]{2\cdot2\cdot2\cdot15} =$ $2\sqrt[3]{15}$

2.99 $\frac{\sqrt[3]{54x^5}}{\sqrt[3]{2x^2}} = \sqrt[3]{\frac{54x^5}{2x^2}} = \sqrt[3]{27x^{5-2}} = \sqrt[3]{27x^3} =$

$\sqrt[3]{3\cdot3\cdot3\cdot x\cdot x\cdot x} = 3x$

2.100 $6\sqrt[3]{-16} + \frac{2}{3}\sqrt[3]{-54} - 5\sqrt[3]{250} =$

$6\sqrt[3]{-2(-2)(-2)(2)} + \frac{2}{3}\sqrt[3]{2(-3)(-3)(-3)} - 5\sqrt[3]{5\cdot5\cdot5\cdot2} =$

$= 6(-2)\sqrt[3]{2} + \frac{2}{3}(-3)\sqrt[3]{2} - 5(5)\sqrt[3]{2}$

$= -12\sqrt[3]{2} - 2\sqrt[3]{2} - 25\sqrt[3]{2} = -39\sqrt[3]{2}$

2.101 $\frac{\sqrt{7}-5}{\sqrt{7}+\sqrt{8}} = \frac{\sqrt{7}-5}{\sqrt{7}+\sqrt{8}} \cdot \frac{\sqrt{7}-\sqrt{8}}{\sqrt{7}-\sqrt{8}} = \frac{7-5\sqrt{7}-2\sqrt{14}+5\sqrt{8}}{7-8} =$

$\frac{7-5\sqrt{7}-2\sqrt{14}+5\sqrt{8}}{-1} = -7+5\sqrt{7}+2\sqrt{14}-5\sqrt{8} =$

$-7+5\sqrt{7}+2\sqrt{14}-10\sqrt{2}$

2.102 $\sqrt{y} - 7 = 3$
$$\sqrt{y} = 3 + 7$$
$$\sqrt{y} = 10$$
$$(\sqrt{y})^2 = 10^2$$
$$y = 100$$
Check:
$$\sqrt{100} - 7 = 3$$
$$10 - 7 = 3$$
$$3 = 3$$

2.103 $4 + \sqrt{x+5} = 10$
$$\sqrt{x+5} = 10 - 4$$
$$\sqrt{x+5} = 6$$
$$(\sqrt{x+5})^2 = 6^2$$
$$x + 5 = 36$$
$$x = 36 - 5$$
$$x = 31$$
Check:
$$4 + \sqrt{31+5} = 10$$
$$4 + \sqrt{36} = 10$$
$$4 + 6 = 10$$
$$10 = 10$$

2.104 $\sqrt{x+8} = \sqrt{2x+5}$
$$(\sqrt{x+8})^2 = (\sqrt{2x+5})^2$$
$$x + 8 = 2x + 5$$
$$x = 2x + 5 - 8$$
$$x = 2x - 3$$
$$x - 2x = -3$$
$$-x = -3$$
$$x = 3$$
Check:
$$\sqrt{3+8} = \sqrt{2(3)+5}$$
$$\sqrt{11} = \sqrt{6+5}$$
$$\sqrt{11} = \sqrt{11}$$

2.105 $\sqrt{2x+7} + 1 = \sqrt{2x+14}$
$$(\sqrt{2x+7}+1)^2 = (\sqrt{2x+14})^2$$
$$2x + 7 + 2\sqrt{2x+7} + 1 = 2x + 14$$
$$2x + 8 + 2\sqrt{2x+7} = 2x + 14$$
$$2x + 8 + 2\sqrt{2x+7} - 2x = 14$$
$$8 + 2\sqrt{2x+7} = 14$$
$$2\sqrt{2x+7} = 14 - 8$$
$$2\sqrt{2x+7} = 6$$
$$\frac{2\sqrt{2x+7}}{2} = \frac{6}{2}$$
$$\sqrt{2x+7} = 3$$
$$(\sqrt{2x+7})^2 = 3^2$$
$$2x + 7 = 9$$
$$2x = 9 - 7$$
$$2x = 2$$
$$\frac{2x}{2} = \frac{2}{2}$$
$$x = 1$$

Check:
$$\sqrt{2(1) + 7} + 1 = \sqrt{2(1) + 14}$$
$$\sqrt{2 + 7} + 1 = \sqrt{2 + 14}$$
$$\sqrt{9} + 1 = \sqrt{16}$$
$$3 + 1 = 4$$
$$4 = 4$$

2.106
$$\sqrt{4x + 5} - \sqrt{x - 1} = \sqrt{x + 4}$$
$$(\sqrt{4x + 5} - \sqrt{x - 1})^2 = (\sqrt{x + 4})^2$$
$$4x + 5 - 2\sqrt{4x^2 + x - 5} + x - 1 = x + 4$$
$$5x + 4 - 2\sqrt{4x^2 + x - 5} = x + 4$$
$$-2\sqrt{4x^2 + x - 5} = x + 4 - 5x - 4$$
$$-2\sqrt{4x^2 + x - 5} = -4x$$
$$\frac{-2\sqrt{4x^2 + x - 5}}{-2} = \frac{-4x}{-2}$$
$$\sqrt{4x^2 + x - 5} = 2x$$
$$(\sqrt{4x^2 + x - 5})^2 = (2x)^2$$
$$4x^2 + x - 5 = 4x^2$$
$$4x^2 + x - 5 - 4x^2 = 0$$
$$x - 5 = 0$$
$$x = 5$$

Check:
$$\sqrt{4(5) + 5} - \sqrt{5 - 1} = \sqrt{5 + 4}$$
$$\sqrt{20 + 5} - \sqrt{4} = \sqrt{9}$$
$$\sqrt{25} - \sqrt{4} = \sqrt{9}$$
$$5 - 2 = 3$$
$$3 = 3$$

2.107
$$y^2 - 144 = 0$$
$$y^2 = 144$$
$$\sqrt{y^2} = \sqrt{144}$$
$$y = \pm 12$$

2.108
$$5y^2 = 405$$
$$\frac{5y^2}{5} = \frac{405}{5}$$
$$y^2 = 81$$
$$\sqrt{y^2} = \sqrt{81}$$
$$y = \pm 9$$

2.109
$$3(x + 5)^2 = 60$$
$$\frac{3(x + 5)^2}{3} = \frac{60}{3}$$
$$(x + 5)^2 = 20$$
$$\sqrt{(x + 5)^2} = \sqrt{20}$$
$$x + 5 = \pm 2\sqrt{5}$$
$$x = -5 \pm 2\sqrt{5}$$

2.110
$$y^2 - 5x = -4$$
$$y^2 - 5x + 4 = 0$$
$$(y - 4)(y - 1) = 0$$
$$y - 4 = 0$$
$$y = 4$$
$$y - 1 = 0$$
$$y = 1$$
$$y = 4, 1$$

2.111
$$8x = x^2 + 15$$
$$0 = x^2 - 8x + 15$$
$$x^2 - 8x + 15 = 0$$
$$(x - 5)(x - 3) = 0$$
$$x - 5 = 0$$
$$x = 5$$
$$x - 3 = 0$$
$$x = 3$$
$$x = 5, 3$$

2.112
$$3a^2 - 8a + 4 = 0$$
$$(3a - 2)(a - 2) = 0$$
$$3a - 2 = 0$$
$$3a = 2$$
$$\frac{3a}{3} = \frac{2}{3}$$
$$a = \frac{2}{3}$$
$$a - 2 = 0$$
$$a = 2$$
$$a = \frac{2}{3}, 2$$

2.113
$$\frac{x}{3} - \frac{6}{x} = 1$$
LCD $= 3x$
$$3x\frac{x}{3} - 3x\frac{6}{x} = 3x[1]$$
$$x^2 - 18 = 3x$$
$$x^2 - 3x - 18 = 0$$
$$(x - 6)(x + 3) = 0$$
$$x - 6 = 0$$
$$x = 6$$
$$x + 3 = 0$$
$$x = -3$$
$$x = 6, -3$$

2.114
$$\sqrt{3y + 10} = y + 2$$
$$(\sqrt{3y + 10})^2 = (y + 2)^2$$
$$3y + 10 = y^2 + 4y + 4$$
$$0 = y^2 + 4y + 4 - 3y - 10$$
$$0 = y^2 + y - 6$$
$$y^2 + y - 6 = 0$$
$$(y + 3)(y - 2) = 0$$
$$y + 3 = 0$$
$$y = -3$$
$$y - 2 = 0$$
$$y = 2$$

Check:
$$\sqrt{3(-3) + 10} = -3 + 2$$
$$\sqrt{-9 + 10} = -1$$
$$\sqrt{1} = -1$$
$$1 = -1; \quad y = -3 \text{ is an extraneous root}$$
$$\sqrt{3(2) + 10} = 2 + 2$$
$$\sqrt{6 + 10} = 4$$
$$\sqrt{16} = 4$$
$$4 = 4$$
$$y = 2$$

2.115 $2a^2 - 3a - 2 = 0$

$$\frac{2a^2}{2} - \frac{3a}{2} - \frac{2}{2} = \frac{0}{2}$$

$$a^2 - \frac{3}{2}a - 1 = 0$$

$$a^2 - \frac{3}{2}a = 1$$

$$\frac{1}{2} \cdot \frac{3}{2} = \frac{3}{4}$$

$$(\frac{3}{4})^2 = \frac{9}{16}$$

$$a^2 - \frac{3}{2}a + \frac{9}{16} = 1 + \frac{9}{16}$$

$$(a - \frac{3}{4})^2 = \frac{25}{16}$$

$$\sqrt{(a - \frac{3}{2})^2} = \sqrt{\frac{25}{16}}$$

$$a - \frac{3}{4} = \pm\frac{5}{4}$$

$$a = \frac{3}{4} \pm \frac{5}{4}$$

$$\frac{3}{4} + \frac{5}{4} = \frac{8}{4} = 2$$

$$\frac{3}{4} - \frac{5}{4} = \frac{-2}{4} = -\frac{1}{2}$$

$$a = 2, -\frac{1}{2}$$

2.116 $x^2 = 14 - 5x$

$$x^2 + 5x = 14$$

$$\frac{1}{2} \cdot 5 = \frac{5}{2}$$

$$(\frac{5}{2})^2 = \frac{25}{4}$$

$$x^2 + 5x + \frac{25}{4} = 14 + \frac{25}{4}$$

$$(x + \frac{5}{2})^2 = \frac{81}{4}$$

$$\sqrt{(x - \frac{5}{2})^2} = \sqrt{\frac{81}{4}}$$

$$x + \frac{5}{2} = \pm\frac{9}{2}$$

$$x = -\frac{5}{2} \pm \frac{9}{2}$$

$$-\frac{5}{2} + \frac{9}{2} = \frac{4}{2} = 2$$

$$-\frac{5}{2} - \frac{9}{2} = \frac{-14}{2} = -7$$

$$x = 2, -7$$

2.117 $8x^2 - 2x - 1 = 0$

$$a = 8, b = -2, c = -1$$

$$x = \frac{2 \pm \sqrt{(-2)^2 - 4(8)(-1)}}{2(8)}$$

$$= \frac{2 \pm \sqrt{4 + 32}}{16}$$

$$= \frac{2 \pm \sqrt{36}}{16}$$

$$= \frac{2 \pm 6}{16}$$

$$\frac{2 + 6}{16} = \frac{8}{16} = \frac{1}{2}$$

$$\frac{2 - 6}{16} = \frac{-4}{16} = -\frac{1}{4}$$

$$x = \frac{1}{2}, -\frac{1}{4}$$

2.118 $y^2 + 0.7y - 0.12 = 0$

$$a = 1, b = 0.7, c = -0.12$$

$$y = \frac{-0.7 \pm \sqrt{(0.7)^2 - 4(1)(-0.12)}}{2(1)} = \frac{-0.7 \pm \sqrt{0.49 + 0.48}}{2}$$

$$= \frac{-0.7 \pm \sqrt{0.97}}{2}$$

2.119 $2a - 5 = \frac{4}{a}$

$$LCD = a$$

$$a[2a] - a[5] = a[\frac{4}{a}]$$

$$2a^2 - 5a = 4$$

$$2a^2 - 5a - 4 = 0$$

$$a = 2, b = -5 \cdot c = -4$$

$$a = \frac{5 \pm \sqrt{(-5)^2 - 4(2)(-4)}}{2(2)} = \frac{5 \pm \sqrt{25 + 32}}{4} = \frac{5 \pm \sqrt{57}}{4}$$

2.120 $3a - 4 = a(a - 3)$

$$3a - 4 = a^2 - 3a$$

$$0 = a^2 - 3a - 3a + 4$$

$$0 = a^2 - 6a + 4$$

$$a^2 - 6a + 4 = 0$$

$$a = 1, b = -6, c = 4$$

$$a = \frac{6 \pm \sqrt{(-6)^2 - 4(1)(4)}}{2(1)} = \frac{6 \pm \sqrt{36 - 16}}{2} = \frac{6 \pm \sqrt{20}}{2}$$

$$= \frac{\overset{3}{6} + 2\sqrt{5}}{2} = 3 \pm \sqrt{5}$$

2.121 $\frac{3}{y - 2} - 2 = \frac{1}{y - 1}$

$$LCD = (y - 2)(y - 1)$$

$$(y - 2)(y - 1)[\frac{3}{y - 2}] - (y - 2)(y - 1)(2)$$
$$= (y - 2)(y - 1)[\frac{1}{y - 1}]$$

$$3y - 3 - 2y^2 + 6y - 4 = y - 2$$

$$-2y^2 + 9y - 7 = y - 2$$

$$-2y^2 + 9y - 7 - y + 2 = 0$$

$$-2y^2 + 8y - 5 = 0$$

$$2y^2 - 8y + 5 = 0 \qquad \text{(multiply by -1)}$$

$$a = 2, b = -8, c = 5$$

$$y = \frac{8 \pm \sqrt{(-8)^2 - 4(2)(5)}}{2(2)} = \frac{8 \pm \sqrt{64 - 40}}{4} = \frac{8 \pm \sqrt{24}}{4}$$

$$= \frac{\overset{4}{8} \pm 2\sqrt{6}}{\underset{2}{4}} = \frac{4 \pm \sqrt{6}}{2}$$

2.122 $\sqrt{-36} = 6i$

2.123 $10\sqrt{\frac{81}{25}} = \overset{2}{10}(\frac{9}{\underset{5}{8}}i) = 18i$

2.124 $20\sqrt{-\frac{1}{100}} - 12\sqrt{-\frac{1}{16}} = \overset{2}{20}(\frac{1}{\underset{10}{10}}i) - \overset{3}{12}(\frac{1}{\underset{4}{4}}i) = 2i - 3i = -i$

2.125 $(2\sqrt{-32})(5\sqrt{-18}) =$

$$(2 \cdot 4i\sqrt{2})(5 \cdot 3i\sqrt{2}) =$$

$$(8i\sqrt{2})(15i\sqrt{2}) =$$

$$120i^2(2) = -240$$

2.126 $\frac{-\sqrt{-36}}{-\sqrt{6}} = \frac{-6i}{-\sqrt{6}} = \frac{6i}{\sqrt{6}} \cdot \frac{\sqrt{6}}{\sqrt{6}} = \frac{6i\sqrt{6}}{6} = i\sqrt{6}$

SELF TEST 2

2.01 $\dfrac{40x^{-2}y^3 z^0}{5x^2y^{-4}z^2} = \dfrac{8\cancel{y}y z^2}{x^2 \cdot {}^2\cancel{y}^3} = \dfrac{8yz^2}{x^4}$

2.02 $\dfrac{6 - x - x^2}{x^2 - 9} = \dfrac{\cancel{(3 + x)}(2 - x)}{\cancel{(x + 3)}(x - 3)} = \dfrac{2 - x}{x - 3}$ or $-\dfrac{x - 2}{x - 3}$

2.03 $\dfrac{x^2 - 3x - 10}{x^2 - 25} \cdot \dfrac{2x + 10}{10x + 20} = \dfrac{\cancel{(x - 5)}\cancel{(x + 2)}}{\cancel{(x + 5)}\cancel{(x - 5)}} \cdot \dfrac{\cancel{2}\cancel{(x + 5)}}{\cancel{10}\cancel{(x + 2)}_5} = \dfrac{1}{5}$

2.04 $\dfrac{3y - 21}{6y^2 - 24} \div \dfrac{y - 7}{3y^2 - 8y + 4} = \dfrac{3y - 21}{6y^2 - 24} \cdot \dfrac{3y^2 - 8y + 4}{y - 7} =$

$\dfrac{3\cancel{(y - 7)}}{\cancel{6}(y + 2)\cancel{(y - 2)}_2} \cdot \dfrac{(3y - 2)\cancel{(y - 2)}}{\cancel{y - 7}} = \dfrac{3y - 2}{2(y + 2)} = \dfrac{3y - 2}{2y - 4}$

2.05 $x^2(2x^3 - 3) - 3x(x + 4) =$

$2x^5 - 3x^2 - 3x^2 - 12x =$

$2x^5 - 6x^2 - 12x$

2.06 $|2x + 5| < 4$

$2x + 5 < 4$

$2x < 4 - 5$

$2x < -1$

$\dfrac{2x}{2} < \dfrac{-1}{2}$

$x < -\dfrac{1}{2}$

$2x + 5 > -4$

$2x > -4 - 5$

$2x > -9$

$\dfrac{2x}{2} > \dfrac{-9}{2}$

$x > -\dfrac{9}{2}$

$-\dfrac{1}{2} > x > -\dfrac{9}{2}$

2.07 $6x = 4y - 7$

$0 = 4y - 7 - 6x$

$-4y = -6x - 7$

$4y = 6x + 7$ (multiply by -1)

$\dfrac{\cancel{4}y}{\cancel{4}} = \dfrac{6x + 7}{4}$

$y = \dfrac{3}{2}x + \dfrac{7}{4}$

$m = \dfrac{3}{2}$

2.08 $5x^2 + 12x + 18$

2.09 $(6x^2 + 4x - 12) - (3x^2 + 9x - 8) =$

$6x^2 + 4x - 12 - 3x^2 - 9x + 8 = 3x^2 - 5x - 4$

2.010 $2x^5y - 8x^6y^2 - 14x^2$

2.011 $4x^2 - 16y^2$

2.012 $(3x + 8)^2 = (3x + 8)(3x + 8)$

$= 9x^2 + 48x + 64$

2.013

$\begin{array}{r} a^2 - 2ab - 4b^2 \\ a + 2b \\ \hline 2a^2b - 4ab^2 - 8b^3 \\ a^3 - 2a^2b - 4ab^2 \\ \hline a^3 \qquad\quad - 8ab^2 - 8b^3 \end{array}$

2.014 $3x^2y(4xy^2 - 6x^2y^5 + 7y - 8)$

2.015 $(3x + 4y)^2$

2.016 $(4x + 5y)(4x - 5y)$

2.017 $(3x - 7y)(2x + 5y)$

2.018 $(a - b)(a^2 + ab + b^2)$

2.019 $16x^3 + 54y^6 = 2(8x^3 + 27y^6) =$

$2(2x + 3y^2)(4x^2 - 6xy^2 + 9y^4)$

2.020 $\dfrac{6}{4} = \dfrac{a}{16}$

$4(a) = 6(16)$ (cross-multiply)

$4a = 96$

$\dfrac{\cancel{4}a}{\cancel{4}} = \dfrac{96}{16}$

$a = 24$

2.021 $\dfrac{12}{2 \cdot 18} = \dfrac{16}{6y}$

$\dfrac{12}{36} = \dfrac{16}{6y}$

$\dfrac{1}{3} = \dfrac{8}{3y}$

$1(3y) = 3(8)$ (cross-multiply)

$3y = 24$

$\dfrac{3y}{3} = \dfrac{24}{3}$

$y = 8$

2.022 $\dfrac{3x}{4} + \dfrac{5x}{6} - \dfrac{2x}{3}$

$LCD = 12$

$[\tfrac{3}{3}][\tfrac{3x}{4}] + [\tfrac{2}{2}][\tfrac{5x}{6}] - [\tfrac{4}{4}][\tfrac{2x}{3}] =$

$\dfrac{9x}{12} + \dfrac{10x}{12} - \dfrac{8x}{12} = \dfrac{11x}{12}$

2.023 $\dfrac{x + y}{x^2y} - \dfrac{x - 2y}{xy^2}$

$LCD = x^2y^2$

$[\tfrac{y}{y}][\tfrac{x + y}{x^2y}] - [\tfrac{x}{x}][\tfrac{x - 2y}{xy^2}] = \dfrac{xy + y^2}{x^2y^2} - \dfrac{x^2 - 2xy}{x^2y^2} =$

$\dfrac{xy + y^2 - x^2 + 2xy}{x^2y^2} = \dfrac{y^2 + 3xy - x^2}{x^2y^2}$

2.024 $\dfrac{6}{x^2 - 4} + \dfrac{5}{x + 2} - \dfrac{5}{2 - x} = \dfrac{6}{(x + 2)(x - 2)} + \dfrac{5}{x + 2} + \dfrac{5}{x - 2}$

$LCD = (x + 2)(x - 2)$

$1[\tfrac{6}{(x + 2)(x - 2)}] + [\tfrac{x - 2}{x - 2}] \cdot [\tfrac{5}{x + 2}] + [\tfrac{x + 2}{x + 2}][\tfrac{5}{x - 2}] =$

$\dfrac{6}{(x + 2)(x - 2)} + \dfrac{5x - 10}{(x + 2)(x - 2)} + \dfrac{5x + 10}{(x + 2)(x - 2)} =$

$\dfrac{6 + 5x - \cancel{10} + 5x + \cancel{10}}{(x + 2)(x - 2)} = \dfrac{10x + 6}{x^2 - 4}$

2.025

$$\frac{7a+5}{8} - 2 = \frac{3a+15}{10}$$

LCD = 40

$$\overset{5}{\cancel{40}}[\frac{7a+5}{\cancel{8}}] - 40[2] = \overset{4}{\cancel{40}}[\frac{3a+15}{\cancel{10}}]$$

$$35a + 25 - 80 = 12a + 60$$
$$35a - 55 = 12a + 60$$
$$35a - 55 - 12a = 60$$
$$23a - 55 = 60$$
$$23a = 60 + 55$$
$$\frac{\cancel{23}a}{\cancel{23}} = \frac{115}{23}$$
$$a = 5$$

2.026

$$\frac{9}{x^2-9} - \frac{x+1}{2x+6} = \frac{2-x}{2x-6}$$

$$\frac{9}{(x+3)(x-3)} - \frac{x+1}{2(x+3)} = \frac{2-x}{2(x-3)}$$

LCD = $2(x+3)(x-3)$

$$2\cancel{(x+3)}\cancel{(x-3)}[\frac{9}{\cancel{(x+3)(x-3)}}] - $$

$$\cancel{2}\cancel{(x+3)}(x-3)[\frac{x+1}{\cancel{2(x+3)}}] = \cancel{2}(x+3)\cancel{(x-3)}[\frac{2-x}{\cancel{2(x-3)}}]$$

$$18 - (x^2 - 2x - 3) = -x^2 - x + 6$$
$$18 - x^2 + 2x + 3 = -x^2 - x + 6$$
$$-x^2 + 2x + 21 = -x^2 - x + 6$$
$$-x^2 + 2x + 21 + x^2 = -x + 6$$
$$2x + 21 = -x + 6$$
$$2x + 21 + x = 6$$
$$3x + 21 = 6$$
$$3x = 6 - 21$$
$$3x = -15$$
$$\frac{\cancel{3}x}{\cancel{3}} = \frac{-15}{3}$$
$$x = -5$$

2.027 Let x = time to complete the job

$$\frac{x}{4} + \frac{x}{6} = 1$$

LCD = 12

$$\overset{3}{\cancel{12}}[\frac{x}{\cancel{4}}] + \overset{2}{\cancel{12}}[\frac{x}{\cancel{6}}] = 12[1]$$

$$3x + 2x = 12$$
$$5x = 12$$
$$\frac{\cancel{5}x}{\cancel{5}} = \frac{12}{5}$$
$$x = \frac{12}{5} = 2\frac{2}{5} \text{ hrs.}$$

2.028 Area of original rectangle = 50(60) = 3,000 sq. ft.

$$(50+x)(60+x) = 3,000 + 1,200$$
$$3,000 + 110x + x^2 = 4,200$$
$$x^2 + 110x + 3,000 - 4,200 = 0$$
$$x^2 + 110x - 1,200 = 0$$
$$(x-10)(x+120) = 0$$
$$x - 10 = 0$$
$$x = 10$$
$$x + 120 = 0$$
$$x = -120 \text{ (reject)}$$

Dimensions of new rectangle:
$$50 + x = 50 + 10 = 60 \text{ ft.}$$
$$60 + x = 60 + 10 = 70 \text{ ft.}$$

2.029

$$\sqrt{2x+1} - 4 = 1$$
$$\sqrt{2x+1} = 1 + 4$$
$$(\sqrt{2x+1})^2 = 5^2$$
$$2x + 1 = 25$$
$$2x = 25 - 1$$
$$2x = 24$$
$$\frac{\cancel{2}x}{\cancel{2}} = \frac{24}{2}$$
$$x = 12$$

2.030

$$2x^2 - x - 10 = 0$$
$$(2x-5)(x+2) = 0$$
$$2x - 5 = 0$$
$$2x = 5$$
$$\frac{\cancel{2}x}{\cancel{2}} = \frac{5}{2}$$
$$x = \frac{5}{2}$$
$$x + 2 = 0$$
$$x = -2$$
$$x = \frac{5}{2}, -2$$

2.031

$$2x - 4 = x^2$$
$$0 = x^2 - 2x + 4$$
$$a = 1, b = -2, c = 4$$
$$x = \frac{2 \pm \sqrt{(-2)^2 - 4(1)(4)}}{2(1)}$$
$$= \frac{2 \pm \sqrt{4 - 16}}{2}$$
$$= \frac{2 \pm \sqrt{-12}}{2}$$
$$= \frac{\overset{1}{\cancel{2}} \pm \overset{1}{\cancel{2}}i\sqrt{3}}{\cancel{2}}$$
$$= 1 \pm i\sqrt{3}$$

SECTION 3

3.1 h
3.2 l
3.3 a
3.4 j
3.5 c
3.6 f
3.7 d
3.8 b
3.9 n
3.10 m
3.11 g
3.12 circle
3.13 line
3.14 hyperbola
3.15 parabola
3.16 ellipse
3.17 circle
3.18 parabola
3.19 hyperbola
3.20 hyperbola
3.21 (4, -7)
3.22 $a = \sqrt{25} = \pm 5$
(5, 0), (-5, 0)
3.23 $y = \dfrac{x^2}{32}$
$y = \dfrac{x^2}{4(-8)}$
directrix: $y = -8$
3.24 $x = 0, y = 0$
3.25 $\dfrac{x^2}{36} - \dfrac{y^2}{5} = 1$
$a = \sqrt{36} = 6$
$b = \sqrt{5}$
$y = \dfrac{b}{a}x$
$y = \dfrac{\sqrt{5}}{6}x$
$y = -\dfrac{b}{a}x$
$y = -\dfrac{\sqrt{5}}{6}x$
3.26 $y = \dfrac{x^2}{8}$
$y = \dfrac{x^2}{4(2)}$
$F = (0, 2)$
directrix: $y = -2$

x	±2	±4
y	$\dfrac{1}{2}$	2

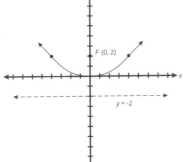

3.27 $\dfrac{x^2}{16} - \dfrac{y^2}{9} = 1$
$a = \sqrt{16} = \pm 4$
vertices: (-4, 0), (4, 0)
$b = \sqrt{9} = 3$
asymptotes: $y = \pm\dfrac{b}{a}x$
$y = \pm\dfrac{3}{4}x$

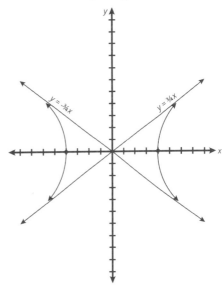

3.28 $x^2 + y^2 - 8y - 4 = -16$
$x^2 + y^2 - 8y = -16 + 4$
$x^2 + y^2 - 8y = -12$
$x^2 + y^2 - 8y + 16 = -12 + 16$
$(x - 0)^2 + (y - 4)^2 = 4$
center = (0, 4)
$r = \sqrt{4} = 2$

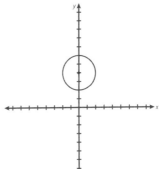

3.29 $y = x^2 + 4$
vertex: (0, 4); opens upward

x	±1	±2	±3
y	5	8	13

$y - 4x = 1$

x	0	$-\frac{1}{4}$	2
y	1	0	9

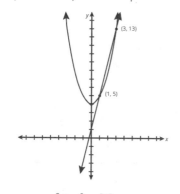

3.30
$$x^2 + y^2 = 36$$
$$x + y = 6$$
$$x = 6 - y$$
By substitution:
$$(6 - y)^2 + y^2 = 36$$
$$36 - 12y + y^2 + y^2 = 36$$
$$36 - 12y + 2y^2 = 36$$
$$-12y + 2y^2 = 36 - 36$$
$$2y^2 - 12y = 0$$
$$y^2 - 6y = 0 \quad \text{(divide by 2)}$$
$$y(y - 6) = 0$$
$$y = 0$$
$$y - 6 = 0$$
$$y = 6$$
$$x + 0 = 6$$
$$x = 6$$
$$(6, 0)$$
$$x + 6 = 6$$
$$x = 6 - 6$$
$$x = 0$$
$$(0, 6)$$

3.31
$$6x^2 - 4y^2 = 25$$
$$4x^2 + 4y^2 = 65$$
By substitution:
$$4y^2 = 65 - 4x^2$$
$$6x^2 - (65 - 4x^2) = 25$$
$$6x^2 - 65 + 4x^2 = 25$$
$$10x^2 - 65 = 25$$
$$10x^2 = 25 + 65$$

$$10x^2 = 90$$
$$\frac{10x^2}{10} = \frac{90}{10}$$
$$x^2 = 9$$
$$\sqrt{x^2} = \sqrt{9}$$
$$x = \pm 3$$
$$6(\pm 3)^2 - 4y^2 = 25$$
$$6(9) - 4y^2 = 25$$
$$54 - 4y^2 = 25$$
$$-4y^2 = 25 - 54$$
$$-4y^2 = -29$$
$$\frac{-4y^2}{-4} = \frac{-29}{-4}$$
$$y^2 = \frac{29}{4}$$
$$\sqrt{y^2} = \sqrt{\frac{29}{4}} = \frac{\sqrt{29}}{\sqrt{4}}$$
$$y = \pm\frac{\sqrt{29}}{2}$$
$$(3, \frac{\sqrt{29}}{2}), (3, -\frac{\sqrt{29}}{2}), (-3, \frac{\sqrt{29}}{2}), (-3, -\frac{\sqrt{29}}{2})$$

3.32
$$x^2 + y^2 - 10y = 0$$
$$3y^2 - 16x - 30y = -75$$
By opposite coefficients:
$$3x^2 + 3y^2 - 30y = 0$$
$$\underline{-16x + 3y^2 - 30y = -75}$$
$$16x + 3x^2 \quad\quad = 75$$

$$3x^2 + 16x - 75 = 0$$
$$(3x + 25)(x - 3) = 0$$
$$3x + 25 = 0$$
$$3x = -25$$
$$\frac{3x}{3} = \frac{-25}{3}$$
$$x = -\frac{25}{3}$$
$$x - 3 = 0$$
$$x = 3$$
$$(\frac{-25}{3})^2 + y^2 - 10y = 0$$
$$\frac{625}{9} + y^2 - 10y = 0$$
$$625 + 9y^2 - 90y = 0$$
$$9y^2 - 90y + 625 = 0; \text{ leads to imaginary roots}$$
$$3^2 + y^2 - 10y = 0$$
$$9 + y^2 - 10y = 0$$
$$y^2 - 10y + 9 = 0$$
$$(y - 1)(y - 9) = 0$$
$$y - 1 = 0$$
$$y = 1$$
$$y - 9 = 0$$
$$y = 9$$
The real roots are (3, 1) and (3, 9).

3.33 $y > x^2$

x	0	±1	±2	±3
y	0	1	4	9

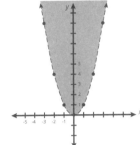

3.34 g

3.35 d

3.36 a

3.37 e

3.38 j

3.39 b

3.40 k

3.41 l

$$\begin{bmatrix} 2 & 4 \\ 7 & 3 \end{bmatrix} + \begin{bmatrix} 3 & 6 \\ 5 & 2 \end{bmatrix} = \begin{bmatrix} 2+3 & 4+6 \\ 7+5 & 3+2 \end{bmatrix} = \begin{bmatrix} 5 & 10 \\ 12 & 5 \end{bmatrix}$$

3.42 f

$$\begin{bmatrix} 2 & 4 \\ 7 & 3 \end{bmatrix} \cdot \begin{bmatrix} 3 & 6 \\ 5 & 2 \end{bmatrix} = \begin{bmatrix} 2\cdot3+4\cdot5 & 2\cdot6+4\cdot2 \\ 7\cdot3+3\cdot5 & 7\cdot6+3\cdot2 \end{bmatrix}$$

$$= \begin{bmatrix} 26 & 20 \\ 36 & 48 \end{bmatrix}$$

3.43 h

$$\begin{bmatrix} 6 & 9 \\ 2 & 1 \end{bmatrix} = \begin{bmatrix} 0 & 3 \\ 2 & 1 \end{bmatrix} \text{ (subtract 6 from row 1)}$$

$$= \begin{bmatrix} 0 & 3 \\ 1 & 0 \end{bmatrix} \text{ (subract 1 from row 2)}$$

3.44 1

3.45 $2^{-1} + 5^{-1} = \frac{1}{2} + \frac{1}{5} = \frac{5}{10} + \frac{2}{10} = \frac{7}{10}$

3.46 $(\frac{3}{4})^{-2} = (\frac{4}{3})^2 = \frac{16}{9}$

3.47 $81^{\frac{5}{4}} = (\sqrt[4]{81})^5 = (\sqrt[4]{3\cdot3\cdot3\cdot3})^5 = 3^5 = 243$

3.48 $16^{-\frac{1}{2}} = (\frac{1}{16})^{\frac{1}{2}} = \sqrt{\frac{1}{16}} = \frac{\sqrt{1}}{\sqrt{16}} = \frac{1}{4}$

3.49 $y = 4^x$
$y = 4^{-2} = \frac{1}{4^2} = \frac{1}{16}$

3.50 $y = 4^x$
$y = 4^{-1} = \frac{1}{4}$

3.51 $y = 4^x$
$y = 4^0 = 1$

3.52 $y = 4^x$
$y = 4^1 = 4$

3.53 $y = 4^x$
$y = 4^2 = 16$

3.54

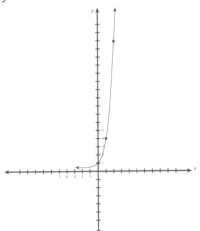

3.55 $\log_{12} 144 = 2$

3.56 $\log_a y = x$

3.57 $4^3 = 64$

3.58 $10^3 = 1{,}000$

3.59 $\log_2 16 = x$
$2^x = 16$
$2^x = 2^4$
$x = 4$
$\log_2 16 = 4$

3.60 $\log_{10} 10 = x$
$10^x = 10^1$
$x = 1$
$\log_{10} 10 = 1$

3.61 $\log_4 2 = x$
$4^x = 2$
$4^x = 4^{\frac{1}{2}}$
$x = \frac{1}{2}$
$\log_4 2 = \frac{1}{2}$

3.62 2.1732

3.63 0.2788

3.64 7.0792 − 10

3.65 1,450

3.66 0.106

3.67 c

3.68 d

3.69 b

3.70 $\begin{bmatrix} 3 & 8 \\ 4 & 9 \end{bmatrix} + \begin{bmatrix} 12 & 6 \\ 1 & 2 \end{bmatrix} = \begin{bmatrix} 3+12 & 8+6 \\ 4+1 & 9+2 \end{bmatrix} = \begin{bmatrix} 15 & 14 \\ 5 & 11 \end{bmatrix}$

3.71 $\begin{bmatrix} 29 & 7 \\ 312 & 41 \end{bmatrix} - \begin{bmatrix} 72 & 3 \\ 58 & 60 \end{bmatrix} = \begin{bmatrix} 29-72 & 7-3 \\ 312-58 & 41-60 \end{bmatrix} =$

$\begin{bmatrix} -43 & 4 \\ 254 & -19 \end{bmatrix}$

3.72 $\begin{bmatrix} 24 & 32 \\ 60 & 10 \end{bmatrix} \cdot \begin{bmatrix} 1 & 2 & 0 \\ 0 & 3 & 1 \end{bmatrix}$

$a_{11} = (24 \quad 32)(1 \quad 0) =$
$\quad 24 \cdot 1 + 32 \cdot 0 = 24 + 0 = 24$
$a_{12} = (24 \quad 32)(2 \quad 3)$
$\quad 24 \cdot 2 + 32 \cdot 3 = 48 + 96 = 144$
$a_{13} = (24 \quad 32)(0 \quad 1)$
$\quad 24 \cdot 0 + 32 \cdot 1 = 0 + 32 = 32$
$a_{21} = (60 \quad 10)(1 \quad 0)$
$\quad 60 \cdot 1 + 10 \cdot 0 = 60 + 0 = 60$
$a_{22} = (60 \quad 10)(2 \quad 3)$
$\quad 60 \cdot 2 + 10 \cdot 3 = 120 + 30 = 150$
$a_{23} = (60 \quad 10)(0 \quad 1)$
$\quad 60 \cdot 0 + 10 \cdot 1 = 0 + 10 = 10$

matrix is $\begin{bmatrix} 24 & 144 & 32 \\ 60 & 150 & 10 \end{bmatrix}$

3.73 $\begin{matrix} 2x + 7y = 48 \\ 3x - 12y = 27 \end{matrix} =$

$\begin{bmatrix} 2 & 7 & 48 \\ 3 & -12 & 27 \end{bmatrix} =$

$\begin{bmatrix} 2 & 7 & 48 \\ 1 & -4 & 9 \end{bmatrix}$ (divide row 2 by 3) =

$\begin{bmatrix} 0 & 15 & 30 \\ 1 & -4 & 9 \end{bmatrix}$ (multiply row 2 by 2 and subtract from row 1) =

$\begin{bmatrix} 0 & 1 & 2 \\ 1 & -4 & 9 \end{bmatrix}$ (divide row 1 by 15) =

$\begin{bmatrix} 0 & 1 & 2 \\ 1 & 0 & 17 \end{bmatrix}$ (multiply row 1 by 4 and add to row 2)

$x = 17, y = 2$

3.74 k
3.75 f
3.76 l
3.77 a
3.78 h
3.79 i
3.80 n
3.81 d
3.82 b
3.83 e
3.84 g
3.85 $1 + 7(n - 1)$
3.86 $10(2)^{n-1}$
3.87 $2(-2)^{n-1}$
3.88 $a + 4(n - 1)$

3.89 $6a(\frac{a^{-1}}{3})^{n-1}$
3.90 arithmetic; finite
3.91 arithmetic; infinite
3.92 geometric; finte
3.93 arithmetic; infinite
3.94 geometric; infinite

3.95 $\displaystyle\sum_{n=1}^{10} -1 + (n - 1) = \sum_{n=1}^{10} n - 2$

3.96 $\displaystyle\sum_{n=1}^{\infty} -5 + (n - 1)(-5) = \sum_{n=1}^{\infty} -5 - 5n + 5 = \sum_{n=1}^{\infty} -5n$

3.97 $\displaystyle\sum_{n=1}^{7} 5(2)^{n-1}$

3.98 $\displaystyle\sum_{n=1}^{\infty} 1.05 + (n - 1)(0.05) = \sum_{n=1}^{\infty} 1.05 + 0.05n - 0.05$

$= \displaystyle\sum_{n=1}^{\infty} 1.00 + 0.05n = \sum_{n=1}^{\infty} 0.05n + 1$

3.99 $\displaystyle\sum_{n=1}^{\infty} \frac{1}{5}(\frac{1}{2})^{n-1}$

3.100 d
3.101 c
3.102 b
3.103 a
3.104 b
3.105 $P(5, 3) = \dfrac{5!}{(5-3)!} = \dfrac{5!}{2!} = \dfrac{5 \cdot 4 \cdot 3 \cdot 2!}{2!} = 60$
3.106 $P(4, 4) = 4! = 4 \cdot 3 \cdot 2 \cdot 1 = 24$
3.107 $P(20, 5) = \dfrac{20!}{(20-5)!} = \dfrac{20!}{15!} = \dfrac{20 \cdot 19 \cdot 18 \cdot 17 \cdot 16 \cdot 15!}{15!}$
$\quad = 1,860,480$
3.108 $C(5, 3) = \dfrac{5!}{3! \, 2!} = \dfrac{5 \cdot \overset{2}{4} \cdot 3!}{3! \cdot 2 \cdot 1} = 10$
3.109 $C(15, 5) = \dfrac{15!}{5! \, 10!} = \dfrac{\overset{3}{15} \cdot \overset{7}{14} \cdot 13 \cdot \overset{}{12} \cdot 11 \cdot 10!}{5 \cdot 4 \cdot 3 \cdot 2 \cdot 1 \cdot 10!}$
$\quad = 3 \cdot 7 \cdot 13 \cdot 11 = 3,003$
3.110 $p(H) = \dfrac{1}{2}$
$\dfrac{1}{2} \cdot \dfrac{1}{2} \cdot \dfrac{1}{2} \cdot \dfrac{1}{2} = \dfrac{1}{16}$
3.111 $p(\text{not butterscotch})$
$1 - p(\text{butterscotch})$
$1 - \dfrac{2}{10} = \dfrac{8}{10} = \dfrac{4}{5}$
3.112 $p(\text{white}) = \dfrac{1}{57}$
$p(\text{yellow}) = \dfrac{14}{57}$
$p(\text{white or yellow}) = \dfrac{1}{57} + \dfrac{14}{57} = \dfrac{15}{57}$
3.113 $\dfrac{14}{57} \cdot \dfrac{13}{56} \cdot \dfrac{12}{55} = \dfrac{2,184}{175,560} = \dfrac{91}{7,315} = \dfrac{13}{1,045}$

SELF TEST 3

3.01 $3^5 x^5 y^5 = 243 x^5 y^5$

3.02 $\dfrac{18a^3b^4c^2}{6a^5bc^{-3}} = \dfrac{\overset{3}{\cancel{18}}a^{\cancel{5}}\overset{b^3}{\cancel{b^4}}c^{2+3}}{\underset{a^2}{\cancel{6a^5}\cancel{b}}} = \dfrac{3b^3c^5}{a^2}$

3.03 $|6(-7) - 4| - |-4| \cdot |7| + 8(-3) =$
$|-42 - 4| - 4 \cdot 7 + (-24) =$
$|-46| - 28 - 24 =$
$46 - 52 = -6$

3.04 $12x - 8y + 7 = 9$
$12x - 8y = 9 - 7$
$12x - 8y = 2$
$-8y = 2 - 12x$
$\dfrac{-8y}{-8} = \dfrac{2 - 12x}{-8}$
$y = -\dfrac{1}{4} + \dfrac{3}{3}x$
$y = \dfrac{3}{2}x - \dfrac{1}{4}$
$m = \dfrac{3}{2}$

3.05 $2x - 4y = 10$ ←
$7x - 9y = 12$ ←
By opposite coefficients:
$14x - 28y = 70$ ←
$\underline{14x - 18y = 24}$ ←
$-10y = 46$
$\dfrac{-10y}{-10} = \dfrac{46}{-10}$
$y = -\dfrac{23}{5}$ or $-4\dfrac{3}{5}$
$2x - 4(-\dfrac{23}{5}) = 10$
$2x + \dfrac{92}{5} = 10$
$2x = \dfrac{50}{5} - \dfrac{92}{5}$
$2x = -\dfrac{42}{5}$
$\dfrac{2x}{2} = \dfrac{-\frac{42}{5}}{2}$
$x = -\dfrac{21}{5}$ or $-4\dfrac{1}{5}$
$(-4\dfrac{1}{5}, -4\dfrac{3}{5})$

3.06 Let x = one number
y = another number
$x = 2y + 3$
$x + y = 21$
By substitution:
$(2y + 3) + y = 21$
$3y + 3 = 21$
$3y = 21 - 3$
$3y = 18$
$\dfrac{3y}{3} = \dfrac{18}{3}$
$y = 6$
$x = 2(6) + 3 = 12 + 3 = 15$
The numbers are 6 and 15.

3.07 $(a - 3)(a^2 + 3a + 9)(a^2 - 2b)$
$\quad a^3 \quad - 27$
$\quad\quad \underline{a^2 \quad - 2b}$
$\quad\quad -2a^3b + 54b$
$\underline{a^5 - 27a^2}$
$a^5 - 27a^2 - 2a^3b + 54b$

3.08 $24x^2 - 6xy - 63y^2 =$
$3(8x^2 - 2xy - 21y^2) =$
$3(4x - 7y)(2x + 3y)$

3.09 $\dfrac{3x^3 \cdot y^{-2}}{5x^{-2} \cdot y^3} = \dfrac{3x^5}{5y^5} = \dfrac{3(2)^5}{5(3)^5} = \dfrac{\cancel{3}(32)}{\underset{81}{5\cancel{(243)}}} = \dfrac{32}{405}$

3.010 $\dfrac{31}{3x + 3} = \dfrac{1}{6} - \dfrac{2}{x + 1}$
$\dfrac{31}{3(x + 1)} = \dfrac{1}{6} - \dfrac{2}{x + 1}$
LCD = $6(x + 1)$
$\overset{2}{\cancel{6}}(x + \cancel{1})[\dfrac{31}{3\cancel{(x+1)}}] = \cancel{6}(x + 1)[\dfrac{1}{\cancel{6}}] - 6(x + \cancel{1})[\dfrac{2}{\cancel{x+1}}]$
$62 = x + 1 - 12$
$62 = x - 11$
$62 + 11 = x$
$73 = x$

3.011 $\sqrt[3]{2x} + 6 = -8$
$\sqrt[3]{2x} = -8 - 6$
$\sqrt[3]{2x} = -14$
$(\sqrt[3]{2x})^3 = (-14)^3$
$2x = -2,744$
$\dfrac{2x}{2} = \dfrac{-2,744}{2}$
$x = -1,372$

3.012 $x^{\frac{2}{3}}y^{\frac{4}{3}}$

3.013 $7x^2 - 3x = 2$
$7x^2 - 3x - 2 = 0$
$a = 7, b = -3, c = -2$
$x = \dfrac{3 \pm \sqrt{(-3)^2 - 4(7)(-2)}}{2(7)}$
$= \dfrac{3 \pm \sqrt{9 + 56}}{14}$
$= \dfrac{3 \pm \sqrt{65}}{14}$

3.014 $a = \sqrt{49} = 7$
$b = \sqrt{12} = 2\sqrt{3}$
$y = \dfrac{b}{a}x$ and $y = -\dfrac{b}{a}x$
$y = \dfrac{2\sqrt{3}}{7}x$ and $y = -\dfrac{2\sqrt{3}}{7}x$

3.015 Center: $(8, -2)$
Radius = $\sqrt{64} = 8$

3.016 $\quad |2x - 9| < 7$

$\qquad 2x - 9 < 7$

$\qquad 2x < 7 + 9$

$\qquad 2x < 16$

$\qquad \dfrac{\cancel{2}x}{\cancel{2}} < \dfrac{16}{2}$

$\qquad x < 8$

$\qquad 2x - 9 > -7$

$\qquad 2x > -7 + 9$

$\qquad 2x > 2$

$\qquad \dfrac{\cancel{2}x}{\cancel{2}} > \dfrac{2}{2}$

$\qquad x > 1$

$\qquad 1 < x < 8$

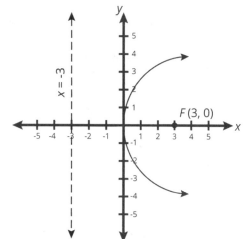

3.017 $\quad x = \dfrac{y^2}{12} = \dfrac{y^2}{4(3)}$

$\quad F = (3, 0)$

$\quad$ directrix: $x = -3$

3.018 $\quad 4xy + 2y^2 = 80$

$\qquad 6xy + 4y^2 = 136$

$\qquad$ By opposite coefficients:

$\qquad 8xy + 4y^2 = 160$

$\qquad \underline{6xy + 4y^2 = 136}$

$\qquad 2xy \qquad\quad = 24$

$\qquad\quad \dfrac{\cancel{2}xy}{\cancel{2}} = \dfrac{24}{2}$

$\qquad\quad xy = 12$

$\qquad 4(12) + 2y^2 = 80$

$\qquad 48 + 2y^2 = 80$

$\qquad 2y^2 = 80 - 48$

$\qquad 2y^2 = 32$

$\qquad \dfrac{\cancel{2}y^2}{\cancel{2}} = \dfrac{32}{2}$

$\qquad y^2 = 16$

$\qquad \sqrt{y^2} = \sqrt{16}$

$\qquad y = \pm 4$

$6x(\pm 4) + 4(\pm 4)^2 = 136$

$\pm 24x + 64 = 136$

$\pm 24x = 136 - 64$

$\pm 24x = 72$

$\dfrac{\cancel{\pm 24}x}{\cancel{\pm 24}} = \dfrac{72}{\pm 24}$

$x = \pm 3$

$(3, 4), (3, -4), (-3, 4), (-3, -4)$

3.019 $\quad \log_4 16 = x$

$\qquad 4^x = 16$

$\qquad 4^x = 4^2$

$\qquad x = 2$

$\qquad \log_4 16 = 2$

3.020 $\quad (\frac{7}{16})^{-2} = (\frac{16}{7})^2 = \frac{256}{49}$

3.021 $\quad \begin{bmatrix} 2 & 7 \\ 3 & 8 \end{bmatrix} \cdot \begin{bmatrix} 2 & 3 & 5 & 0 \\ 1 & 6 & 2 & 8 \end{bmatrix}$

$a_{11} = (2 \quad 7) \cdot (2 \quad 1)$

$\quad = 2 \cdot 2 + 7 \cdot 1 = 4 + 7 = 11$

$a_{12} = (2 \quad 7) \cdot (3 \quad 6)$

$\quad = 2 \cdot 3 + 7 \cdot 6 = 6 + 42 = 48$

$a_{13} = (2 \quad 7) \cdot (5 \quad 2)$

$\quad = 2 \cdot 5 + 7 \cdot 2 = 10 + 14 = 24$

$a_{14} = (2 \quad 7) \cdot (0 \quad 8)$

$\quad = 2 \cdot 0 + 7 \cdot 8 = 0 + 56 = 56$

$a_{21} = (3 \quad 8) \cdot (2 \quad 1)$

$\quad = 3 \cdot 2 + 8 \cdot 1 = 6 + 8 = 14$

$a_{22} = (3 \quad 8) \cdot (3 \quad 6)$

$\quad = 3 \cdot 3 + 8 \cdot 6 = 9 + 48 = 57$

$a_{23} = (3 \quad 8) \cdot (5 \quad 2)$

$\quad = 3 \cdot 5 + 8 \cdot 2 = 15 + 16 = 31$

$a_{24} = (3 \quad 8) \cdot (0 \quad 8)$

$\quad = 3 \cdot 0 + 8 \cdot 8 = 0 + 64 = 64$

Matrix is $\begin{bmatrix} 11 & 48 & 24 & 56 \\ 14 & 57 & 41 & 64 \end{bmatrix}$

3.022 $x + 2y = 8$
$-2x + 4y = -8$

$\begin{bmatrix} 1 & 2 & 8 \\ -2 & 4 & -8 \end{bmatrix} =$

$\begin{bmatrix} 1 & 2 & 8 \\ 0 & 8 & 8 \end{bmatrix}$ (multiply row 1 by 2 and add to row 2) =

$\begin{bmatrix} 1 & 2 & 8 \\ 0 & 1 & 1 \end{bmatrix}$ (divide row 2 by 8) =

$\begin{bmatrix} 1 & 0 & 6 \\ 0 & 1 & 1 \end{bmatrix}$ (multiply row 2 by 2 and subtract from row 1) =

$x = 6, y = 1$

3.023 $3 + 23(5) = 3 + 115 = 118$

3.024   geometric

3.025 $P(8, 4) = \dfrac{8!}{4!} = \dfrac{8 \cdot 7 \cdot 6 \cdot 5 \cdot \cancel{4!}}{\cancel{4!}} = 1{,}680$

3.026 $C(8, 4) = \dfrac{8!}{4!\,4!} = \dfrac{\cancel{8} \cdot 7 \cdot \overset{2}{\cancel{6}} \cdot 5 \cdot \cancel{4!}}{\cancel{4} \cdot \cancel{3} \cdot \cancel{2} \cdot \cancel{1} \cdot \cancel{4!}} = 70$

3.027 $p = \dfrac{\text{number of outcomes favorable to } E}{\text{total number of outcomes}}$

$p = \dfrac{5}{13}$

3.028   h

3.029   j

3.030   m

3.031   e

3.032   b

3.033   k

3.034   f

3.035   d

3.036   g

3.037   a

LIFEPAC TEST

1. c

2. a. d

b. a

c. c

3. b

4. {2}, {7}, {8}, {12}, {2, 7}, {2, 8}, {2, 12}, {7, 8}, {7, 12}, {8, 12}, {2, 7, 8}, {2, 7, 12}, {2, 8, 12}, {7, 8, 12}, {2, 7, 8, 12}, ∅

5. $12x^2y^{-1} = \dfrac{12x^2}{y} = \dfrac{12(3)^2}{4} = \dfrac{\overset{3}{\cancel{12}}(9)}{\cancel{4}} = 27$

6. $3x - 4y = 7$

$-4y = 7 - 3x$

$\dfrac{\cancel{-4}y}{\cancel{-4}} = \dfrac{7 - 3x}{-4}$

$y = -\dfrac{7}{4} + \dfrac{3}{4}x$

$y = \dfrac{3}{4}x - \dfrac{7}{4}$

$m = \dfrac{3}{4}$

x	0	$\frac{7}{3}$
y	$-\frac{7}{4}$	0

7. $2x + 7y = -38$

$-5x - 8y = 38$

By opposite coefficients:

$10x + 35y = -190$

$\underline{-10x - 16y = 76}$

$19y = -114$

$\dfrac{\cancel{19}y}{\cancel{19}} = \dfrac{-114}{19}$

$y = -6$

$2x + 7(-6) = -38$

$2x - 42 = -38$

$2x = -38 + 42$

$2x = 4$

$\dfrac{\cancel{2}x}{\cancel{2}} = \dfrac{4}{2}$

$x = 2$

$2x + 7y = -38$

x	0	-19
y	$-\frac{38}{7}$	0

$-5x - 8y = 38$

x	0	$-\frac{38}{5}$
y	$\frac{19}{4}$	0

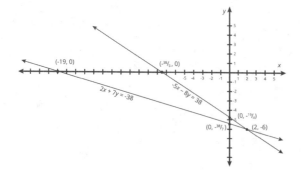

8. Let x = one number

y = other number

Use opposite coefficients:

$x + y = 14$

$\underline{x - y = 6}$

$2x = 20$

$\dfrac{\cancel{2}x}{\cancel{2}} = \dfrac{20}{2}$

$x = 10$

$10 + y = 14$

$y = 14 - 10 = 4$

The numbers are 10 and 4.

9. $x^2 - 5x - 8$

$\underline{2x^2 - 4x - 3}$

$-x^2 - x - 5$

10.

$$3x + 8 \overline{\smash{\big)}\,6x^4 - 2x^3 - 13x - 7}$$

$$2x^3 - 6x^2 + 16x - 47 + \dfrac{369}{3x + 8}$$

$\underline{6x^4 + 16x^3}$

$-18x^3$

$\underline{-18x^3 - 48x^2}$

$48x^2 - 13x$

$\underline{48x^2 + 128x}$

$-141x - 7$

$\underline{-141x - 376}$

369

11. $8x^2 + 72x + 112 = 8(x^2 + 9x + 14) =$

$8(x + 7)(x + 2)$

12. $\dfrac{3x + 9}{2x + 6} + \dfrac{8x + 12}{x^2 + 6x + 9} = \dfrac{3x + 9}{2(x + 3)} + \dfrac{8x + 12}{(x + 3)(x + 3)}$

LCD $= 2(x + 3)(x + 3)$

$= 2(x + 3)^2$

$\left[\dfrac{x + 3}{x + 3}\right]\left[\dfrac{3x + 9}{2(x + 3)}\right] + \left[\dfrac{2}{2}\right]\left[\dfrac{8x + 12}{(x + 3)(x + 3)}\right] =$

$\dfrac{3x^2 + 18x + 27}{2(x + 3)(x + 3)} + \dfrac{16x + 24}{2(x + 3)(x + 3)} =$

$\dfrac{3x^2 + 18x + 27 + 16x + 24}{2(x + 3)(x + 3)} = \dfrac{3x^2 + 34x + 51}{2(x + 3)(x + 3)} =$

$\dfrac{3x^2 + 34x + 51}{2x^2 + 12x + 18}$

13. $\dfrac{y + 4}{2y} + \dfrac{y - 2}{3} = \dfrac{3y^2 + 10}{x + 3}$

LCD $= 6y$

$[\cancel{6y}]\left[\dfrac{y + 4}{\cancel{2y}}\right]^3 + [\cancel{6y}]\left[\dfrac{y - 2}{\cancel{3}}\right]^{2y} = \cancel{6y}\left[\dfrac{3y^2 + 10}{\cancel{6y}}\right]$

$3y + 12 + 2y^2 - 4y = 3y^2 + 10$

$2y^2 - y + 12 = 3y^2 + 10$

$2y^2 - y + 12 - 3y^2 - 10 = 0$

$-y^2 - y + 2 = 0$

$y^2 + y - 2 = 0$ (multiply by -1)

$(y + 2)(y - 1) = 0$

$y + 2 = 0$

$y = -2$

$y - 1 = 0$

$y = 1$

$y = 1, -2$

14.
$$\sqrt{x + 1} = 5$$
$$(\sqrt{x + 1})^2 = 5^2$$
$$x + 1 = 25$$
$$x = 25 - 1 = 24$$

15.
$$3x^2 + 9x + 5 = 17$$
$$3x^2 + 9x + 5 - 17 = 0$$
$$3x^2 + 9x - 12 = 0$$
$$a = 3, b = 9, c = -12$$
$$x = \frac{-9 \pm \sqrt{9^2 - 4(3)(-12)}}{2(3)} = \frac{-9 \pm \sqrt{81 + 144}}{6} = \frac{-9 \pm \sqrt{225}}{6}$$
$$= \frac{-9 \pm 15}{6}$$
$$\frac{-9 + 15}{6} = \frac{6}{6} = 1$$
$$\frac{-9 - 15}{6} = \frac{-24}{6} = -4$$
$$x = 1, -4$$

16.
$$d = \sqrt{(-3 - 8)^2 + [(4 - (-7)]^2}$$
$$= \sqrt{(-11)^2 + 121} = \sqrt{121 + 121} = \sqrt{2 \cdot 121}$$
$$= 11\sqrt{2}$$

17.
$$7i^4 - 12i^2 =$$
$$7(1) - 12(-1) = 7 + 12 = 19$$

18.
$$4^x = 256$$
$$4^x = 4^4$$
$$x = 4$$

19.
$$\log(1{,}789 \cdot 387) =$$
$$\log 1{,}789 + \log 387 =$$
$$3.253 + 2.58 = 5.833$$

20.
$$\begin{bmatrix} 2 & 8 \\ 7 & -4 \end{bmatrix} + \begin{bmatrix} 6 & -14 \\ 9 & 3 \end{bmatrix} = \begin{bmatrix} 2 + 6 & 8 - 14 \\ 7 + 9 & -4 + 3 \end{bmatrix} = \begin{bmatrix} 8 & -6 \\ 16 & -1 \end{bmatrix}$$

21.
$$5x - 3y = 18$$
$$2x + 7y = -1$$
$$\begin{bmatrix} 5 & -3 & 18 \\ 2 & 7 & -1 \end{bmatrix} =$$
$$\begin{bmatrix} 10 & -6 & 36 \\ 10 & 35 & -5 \end{bmatrix}$$ (multiply row 1 by 2, row 2 by 5)
$$\begin{bmatrix} 10 & -6 & 36 \\ 0 & 41 & -41 \end{bmatrix}$$ (subtract row 1 from row 2)
$$\begin{bmatrix} 10 & -6 & 36 \\ 0 & 1 & -1 \end{bmatrix}$$ (divide row 2 by 41)
$$\begin{bmatrix} 10 & 0 & 30 \\ 0 & 1 & -1 \end{bmatrix}$$ (multiply row 2 by 6 and add to row 1)
$$\begin{bmatrix} 1 & 0 & 3 \\ 0 & 1 & -1 \end{bmatrix}$$ (divide row 1 by 10)
$$x = 3, y = -1$$

22. $2 + 36(3) = 2 + 108 = 110$

23. $2 + 5 + 8 + 11 + 14 + \dots$; arithmetic

24. $P(10, 7) = \frac{10!}{3!} = \frac{10 \cdot 9 \cdot 8 \cdot 7 \cdot 6 \cdot 5 \cdot 4 \cdot \cancel{3!}}{\cancel{3!}} = 604{,}800$

25.
$$p(\text{yellow}) = \frac{12}{43}$$
$$p(\text{red}) = \frac{16}{43}$$
$$p(\text{yellow or red}) = \frac{12}{43} + \frac{16}{43} = \frac{28}{43}$$

26.
$$9x^2 + 4y^2 - 36 = 0$$
$$9x^2 + 4y^2 = 36$$
$$\frac{9x^2}{36} + \frac{4y^2}{36} = \frac{36}{36}$$
$$\frac{x^2}{4} + \frac{y^2}{9} = 1$$

$$a = \sqrt{4} = 2$$
$$b = \sqrt{2} = 3$$

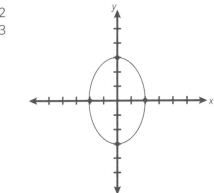

27.
$$16x^2 - 300 - 25y^2 = 100$$
$$16x^2 - 25y^2 = 100 + 300$$
$$16x^2 - 25y^2 = 400$$
$$\frac{16x^2}{400} - \frac{25y^2}{400} = \frac{400}{400}$$
$$\frac{x^2}{25} - \frac{y^2}{16} = 1$$

$$a = \sqrt{25} = 5$$
$$b = \sqrt{16} = 4$$
Foci: $(\pm\sqrt{41}, 0)$
Asymptotes: $y = \pm\frac{4}{5}x$

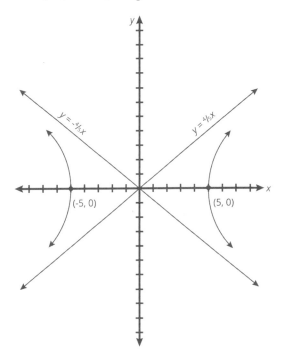

28. $4x^2 + 4(y^2 - 4) = 0$
$4x^2 + 4y^2 - 16 = 0$
$x^2 + y^2 - 4 = 0$ (divide by 4)
$x^2 + y^2 = 4$
center = (0, 0)
$r = \sqrt{4} = 2$

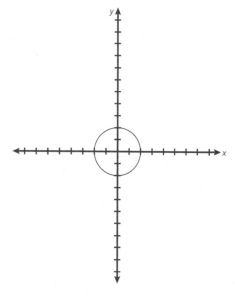

29. $5x^2 - y = 12$
$5x^2 = 12 + y$
$5x^2 - 12 = y$
$y = 5x^2 - 12$
Vertex: (0, -12)
Parabola opens upward.

x	±1	±2
y	-7	8

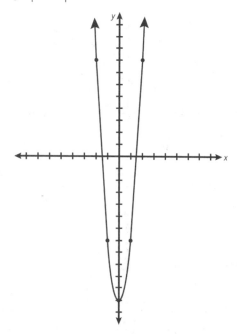

ALTERNATE LIFEPAC TEST

1. a

2. a. b
   b. c
   c. a

3. d

4. {e}, {f}, {g}, {e, f}, {e, g}, {f, g}, {e, f, g}, Ø

5. $18x^4y^{-2} = \dfrac{18x^4}{y^2} = \dfrac{18(4)^4}{(-3)^2} = \dfrac{\overset{2}{18}(256)}{\cancel{9}} = 512$

6. $2x - 5y = 12$
   $2x - 2x - 5y = 12 - 2x$
   $-5y = -2x + 12$
   $-\frac{1}{5}(-5y) = -\frac{1}{5}(-2x + 12)$
   $y = \frac{2}{5}x - \frac{12}{5}$

   $m = \frac{2}{5}$

7. $\begin{array}{l} 3x - 4y = 33 \\ 5x + 4y = 29 \end{array} \longrightarrow \begin{array}{l} 3x - 4y = 33 \\ 10x + 4y = 58 \\ \hline 13x \quad\quad = 91 \end{array}$

   $\frac{1}{13}(13x) = \frac{1}{13}(91)$
   $x = 7$

   $3x - 4y = 33$
   $3(7) - 4y = 33$
   $21 - 4y = 33$
   $21 - 21 - 4y = 33 - 21$
   $-4y = 12$
   $-\frac{1}{4}(-4y) = -\frac{1}{4}(12)$
   $y = -3$
   The solution is (7, -3).

8. Let x = first number
   y = second number
   $\begin{array}{r} x + y = 78 \\ x - y = 24 \\ \hline 2x \quad = 102 \end{array}$

   $\frac{1}{2}(2x) = \frac{1}{2}(102)$
   $x = 51$
   $x + y = 78$
   $51 + y = 78$
   $51 - 51 + y = 78 - 51$
   $y = 27$
   The numbers are 51 and 27.

9. $\begin{array}{r} 2x^3 \quad\quad - 7x + 12 \\ 6x^2 + 11x - 18 \\ \hline 2x^3 + 6x^2 + 4x - 6 \end{array}$

10. $$3x - 6 \overline{\smash{)}\begin{array}{l} 3x^3 + \quad 6x^2 + \quad 11x + \quad 16 + \frac{105}{3x-6} \\ 9x^4 \quad\quad\quad - \quad 3x^2 - 18x + \quad 9 \\ \underline{9x^4 - \quad 18x^3} \\ 18x^3 - \quad 3x^2 \\ \underline{18x^3 - \quad 36x^2} \\ 33x^2 - \quad 18x \\ \underline{33x^2 - \quad 66x} \\ 48x + \quad 9 \\ \underline{48x - \quad 96} \\ 105 \end{array}}$$

11. $16x^2 - 92x + 90 = 2(8x^2 - 46x + 45) =$
    $2(4x - 5)(2x - 9)$

12. $\dfrac{4x + 12}{x^2 - 6x + 9} + \dfrac{-4x + 5}{2x - 6} = \dfrac{4x + 12}{(x-3)(x-3)} + \dfrac{-4x + 5}{2(x-3)}$
    The LCD is $2(x - 3)(x - 3)$.
    $\dfrac{2[4x + 12]}{2[(x-3)(x-3)]} + \dfrac{(x-3)[-4x+5]}{(x-3)[2(x-3)]} =$
    $\dfrac{8x + 24}{2(x-3)^2} + \dfrac{-4x^2 + 17x - 15}{2(x-3)^2} = \dfrac{8x + 24 - 4x^2 + 17x - 15}{2(x-3)^2} =$
    $\dfrac{-4x^2 + 25x + 9}{2(x-3)^2}$ or $\dfrac{-4x^2 + 25x + 9}{2x^2 - 12x + 18}$

13. $\dfrac{2x - 5}{2x} = \dfrac{x + 5}{x} - \dfrac{17 + 2x}{3x}$
    The LCD is $6x$.
    $\overset{3}{\cancel{6x}}\left[\dfrac{2x-5}{\cancel{2x}}\right] = 6x\left[\dfrac{x+5}{\cancel{x}}\right] - \overset{2}{\cancel{6x}}\left[\dfrac{17+2x}{\cancel{3x}}\right]$
    $6x - 15 = 6x + 30 - 34 - 4x$
    $-15 = -4 - 4x$
    $-15 + 4 = -4 + 4 - 4x$
    $-11 = -4x$
    $-4x = -11$
    $-\frac{1}{4}(-4x) = -\frac{1}{4}(-11)$
    $x = \frac{11}{4}$

14. $\sqrt{x - 1} = 7$
    $(\sqrt{x - 1})^2 = 7^2$
    $x - 1 = 49$
    $x - 1 + 1 = 49 + 1$
    $x = 50$

15. $2x^2 - 11x + 12 = 7$
    $2x^2 - 11x + 12 - 7 = 7 - 7$
    $2x^2 - 11x + 5 = 0$
    $x = \dfrac{-b \pm \sqrt{b^2 - 4ac}}{2a}$
    $a = 2, b = -11, c = 5$
    $x = \dfrac{11 \pm \sqrt{(-11)^2 - 4(2)(5)}}{2(2)} = \dfrac{11 \pm \sqrt{121 - 40}}{4} = \dfrac{11 \pm \sqrt{81}}{4}$
    $= \dfrac{11 \pm 9}{4}$
    $x = \dfrac{11 + 9}{4} = \dfrac{20}{4} = 5$
    $x = \dfrac{11 - 9}{4} = \dfrac{2}{4} = \dfrac{1}{2}$
    The solution is $\{5, \frac{1}{2}\}$.

16. $16i^6 + 9i^4 = 16(-1) + 9(1) = -16 + 9 = -7$

17. $d = \sqrt{[6 - (-7)]^2 + (-3 - 6)^2}$
$= \sqrt{250} = 5\sqrt{10}$

18. $3^x = 729$
$3^x = 3^6$
$x = 6$

19. $\log\frac{1,384}{256} = \log 1,384 - \log 256 =$
$3.141 - 2.408 = 0.733$

20. $\begin{bmatrix} -7 & -11 \\ -9 & 15 \end{bmatrix} - \begin{bmatrix} -6 & 8 \\ 11 & -17 \end{bmatrix} = \begin{bmatrix} -7 - (-6) & -11 - 8 \\ -9 - 11 & 15 - (-17) \end{bmatrix} = \begin{bmatrix} -1 & -19 \\ -20 & 32 \end{bmatrix}$

21. $\begin{bmatrix} 2 & 11 & -29 \\ 6 & -13 & 51 \end{bmatrix} =$

$\begin{bmatrix} 2 & 11 & -29 \\ 0 & -46 & 138 \end{bmatrix}$ (multiply each number in first row by -3 and add to second row)

$\begin{bmatrix} 2 & 11 & -29 \\ 0 & 1 & -3 \end{bmatrix}$ (divide second row by -46)

$\begin{bmatrix} 2 & 0 & 4 \\ 0 & 1 & -3 \end{bmatrix}$ (multiply second row by -11 and add to first row)

$\begin{bmatrix} 1 & 0 & 2 \\ 0 & 1 & -3 \end{bmatrix}$ (divide first row by 2)

$x = 2, y = -3$

22. $5 + 30(4) = 5 + 120 = 125$

23. $5 + 9 + 13 + 17 + \ldots$; arithmetic

24. $C(9, 5) = \frac{9!}{5!4!} = \frac{9 \cdot 8 \cdot 7 \cdot 6 \cdot 5!}{4 \cdot 3 \cdot 2 \cdot 1 \cdot 5!} = \frac{9 \cdot \cancel{8} \cdot 7 \cdot \cancel{6}^{2}}{\cancel{4} \cdot \cancel{3} \cdot \cancel{2} \cdot 1} = 126$

25. The bag contains 30 marbles.
$p(\text{red or blue}) = p(\text{red}) + p(\text{blue}) =$
$\frac{6}{30} + \frac{14}{30} = \frac{20}{30} = \frac{2}{3}$

26. $x^2 + y^2 - 25 = 0$
$x^2 + y^2 - 25 + 25 = 0 + 25$
$x^2 + y^2 = 25$
center $= (0, 0)$
$r = 5$

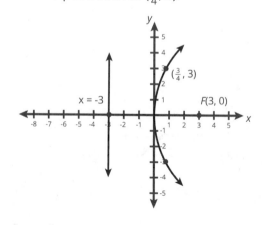

27. $9x^2 - 36y^2 - 300 = 24$
$9x^2 - 36y^2 - 300 + 300 = 24 + 300$
$9x^2 - 36y^2 = 324$
$\frac{9x^2}{324} - \frac{36y^2}{324} = \frac{324}{324}$
$\frac{x^2}{36} - \frac{y^2}{9} = 1$
To find the vertices, let $y = 0$.
$\frac{x^2}{36} = 1$
$x^2 = 36$
$\sqrt{x^2} = \sqrt{36}$
$x = \pm 6$
The vertices are (-6, 0) and (6, 0).

The asymptotes are $y = \frac{b}{a}x$ and $y = -\frac{b}{a}x$.
$a = \sqrt{36} = 6$
$b = \sqrt{9} = 3$
The asymptotes are $y = \frac{3}{6}x$ and $y = -\frac{3}{6}x$ or
$y = \frac{1}{2}x$ and $y = -\frac{1}{2}x$.

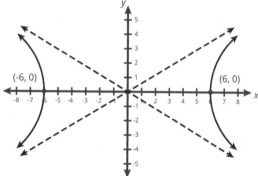

28. $4x^2 + y^2 = 4$
$\frac{4x^2}{4} + \frac{y^2}{4} = \frac{4}{4}$
$\frac{x^2}{1} + \frac{y^2}{4} = 1$
$a = \sqrt{1} = 1$
$b = \sqrt{4} = 2$

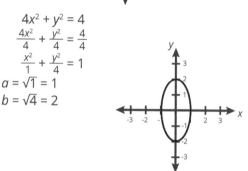

29. $x = \frac{1}{12}y^2$
$x = \frac{1}{4(3)}y^2$
$p = 3$
Focus is $(p, 0) = (3, 0)$.
Directrix is $x = -p$, which is $x = -3$.

To graph the parabola more precisely, graph an extra point such as $(\frac{3}{4}, 3)$.

MATH 1110

ALTERNATE LIFEPAC TEST

NAME _____

DATE _____

SCORE _____

$\frac{91}{114}$

Write the letter of the correct choice (each answer, 2 points).

1. Which one of the following equations illustrates the associative property? _____
    a. $(2 + 5) + 7 = 2 + (5 + 7)$
    b. If $3 + 4 = b$, then $b = 3 + 4$.
    c. $2 + 3 = 3 + 2$
    d. $8(6 + 4) = 48 + 32$

2. Which one of the following numbers is
    a. a rational number? _____
    b. an irrational number? _____
    c. an imaginary number? _____

    a. $3i$ b. 0.8621 c. $0.898641...$ d. $a + 0 = a$

3. The graph of the parabola $x = \frac{y^2}{12}$ opens _____ .
    a. upward   b. downward   c. to the left   d. to the right   e. none of these

Answer each item as directed (each answer, 4 points).

4. List all the subsets of the set {e, f, g}.

5. Evaluate $18x^4y^{-2}$ for $x = 4$ and $y = -3$.

6. Give the slope of $2x - 5y = 12$.

7. Solve $3x - 4y = 33$ and $5x + 2y = 29$ for x and y.

8. The difference of two numbers is 24. Their sum is 78. Find the two numbers, using two variables.

9. Add $2x^3 - 7x + 12$ and $6x^2 + 11x - 18$.

10. Divide $9x^4 - 3x^2 - 18x + 9$ by $3x - 6$.

11. Factor $16x^2 - 92x + 90$ completely.

12. Add $\dfrac{4x + 12}{x^2 - 6x + 9} + \dfrac{-4x + 5}{2x - 6}$.

13. Solve $\dfrac{2x - 5}{2x} = \dfrac{x + 5}{x} - \dfrac{17 + 2x}{3x}$ for x.

14. Solve $\sqrt{x - 1} = 7$ for x.

15. Solve $2x^2 - 11x + 12 = 7$ with the quadratic formula.

16. Evaluate $16i^6 + 9i^4$.

17. Find the distance on the coordinate system from the point (6, -3) to the point (-7, 6).

18. Solve $3^x = 729$.

19. If the log of 256 is 2.408, and the log of 1,384 is 3.141, find the log of $\frac{1,384}{256}$.

20. Subtract $\begin{bmatrix} -7 & -11 \\ -9 & 15 \end{bmatrix} - \begin{bmatrix} -6 & 8 \\ 11 & -17 \end{bmatrix}$.

21. Solve $2x + 11y = -29$ and $6x - 13y = 51$ with matrices.

22. Find the 31st term of the sequence 5, 9, 13, 17, ...

23. Make a series of the sequence in Item 22 and identify it as *geometric* or *arithmetic*.

_____ ; _____

24. Find the number of combinations of 9 things taken 5 at a time.

25. What is the probability of drawing a red marble or a blue marble from a bag containing 10 black marbles, 6 red marbles, and 14 blue marbles?

Graph the following conics (each graph, 5 points).

26. $x^2 + y^2 - 25 = 0$

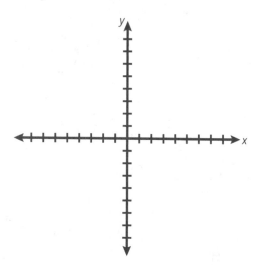

27. $9x^2 - 36y^2 - 300 = 24$

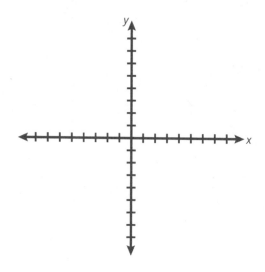

28. $4x^2 + y^2 = 4$

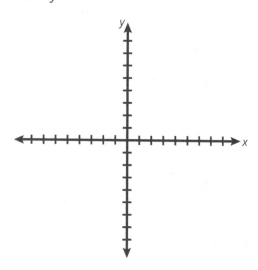

29. $x = \frac{1}{12}y^2$

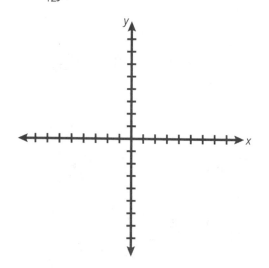